1996

YEARBOOK OF SCIENCE AND THE FUTURE

1996

Encyclopædia
Britannica, Inc.

Chicago
Auckland
London
Madrid
Manila
Paris
Rome
Seoul
Sydney
Tokyo
Toronto

1996
Yearbook of Science and the Future

foreword

The collision of Comet Shoemaker-Levy 9 with Jupiter, the discovery of a cave rich in Stone Age art, and the detection, after years of effort, of the top quark are among the many significant developments in science and technology that are discussed by expert authors in this 1996 edition of Encyclopædia Britannica's *Yearbook of Science and the Future*. Fourteen feature articles, lavishly illustrated in full color, range in subject matter from science and the Internet to asteroids to the science of wine making, and a pictorial essay displays the work of outstanding entomologist and photographer Thomas Eisner. In the Year in Review section, 44 articles deal with the year's events in the various disciplines of science and technology. Along with those already mentioned, they include the completion of the Channel Tunnel (Eurotunnel) connecting France and Britain, the discovery of a mammal previously unknown to science, and the isolation of the gene responsible for inherited breast cancer.

The year also had its share of conflict and controversy, and the yearbook addresses these issues. In the Overview essay, author Robert Crease discusses the book *The Bell Curve: Intelligence and Class Structure in American Life,* which argues that intelligence is largely inherited and varies on average between races. Also described in the Overview are two Smithsonian Institution exhibits—"Science in American Life" and "The Last Act: The Atomic Bomb and the End of World War II"—and the disputes that each of them caused. The flawed Pentium microprocessor chip and the manufacturer's offer to replace it are discussed in ELECTRONICS AND INFORMATION SCIENCES, and the MATHEMATICS article relates the continuing efforts of Andrew Wiles to prove Fermat's Last Theorem after a gap was found in his first proof. Finally, the feature article A STAR WARS LEGACY discusses the technological advances produced by the controversial Strategic Defense Initiative and the ways in which they might have valuable peacetime applications.

We are also pleased to present this year a completely redesigned book. New page layouts have allowed a more innovative and flexible use of illustrations and other graphic material. The results, we think, are both pleasing to the eye and useful to the reader because of the closer coordination of illustrations and text.

I hope that you find the yearbook informative and enjoyable. If you have any suggestions as to how to improve it, please write to us and let us know.

—David R. Calhoun, Editor

contents

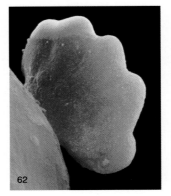

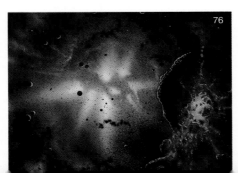

301

240

252

For most of the two billion years that life has existed on the Earth, the seas were home to all living things. Long before they existed on the continents, the plant communities of the ancient oceans produced the oxygen-rich atmosphere that the later land creatures would need to breathe. Clearly, however, we take the seas for granted. Many thousands of times more of humankind's resources are spent on learning about the land, the atmosphere, and the distant planets and stars than on the ocean. Only recently have we awakened to the fact that our activities on land, on the shores, and even on the high seas are placing at risk the great diversity of life in the oceans of the world.

LIFE IN THE OCEANS: A WORLD OF DIVERSITY AT RISK

by Leighton Taylor and Norbert Wu

Leighton Taylor, a marine biologist and former director of the Waikiki Aquarium in Hawaii, is president of Leighton Taylor & Associates, St. Helena, California. Norbert Wu has worked as a chief still photographer for Jacques Cousteau's Calypso in New Zealand and as research diver for the Smithsonian Tropical Research Institute.

Goose barnacles attached to an abandoned fisherman's float in the northern Pacific Ocean feed by using their fine-haired legs to filter out food particles from the water.

Look to the sea: it is the source of life.
It sends the rain and it receives the rivers
While the sea lives, we will live.

—Herbert Sartorius

A brittle star (right) rests on a vase sponge in the Caribbean Sea off the coast of Honduras. Far right, a green turtle hatchling makes its way to the sea in Borneo.

BIODIVERSITY

More than just a term denoting the rich variety or number of species in a place or time, biodiversity—a contraction of "biological diversity"—embraces three different but interrelated aspects: species diversity, ecosystem diversity, and genetic diversity.

Anemone fish often nip at their host anemone, possibly to cause the anemone to spread its tentacles to cover the fish's nests.

(Opposite page and this page)
© Norbert Wu

Species Diversity

When ecologists speak of the numbers and kinds of creatures in an ecosystem, they use the term species richness. One can quantitatively express diversity in an ecosystem by comparing species richness with the total number of individuals in the ecosystem. Relative numbers of species vary from area to area and within taxonomic groups. For example, there

are about 40,000 species of vertebrates, of which more than half are fish. In tropical rain forests, however, insect species may number in the hundreds of thousands. Species richness also can differ from place to place. More species are found in an Asian tropical rain forest than in those in the Western Hemisphere.

A brittle star climbs to the top of a rope sponge to catch plankton at night.

Ecosystem Diversity

Distinctly different physical areas may contain very different aggregations of plants and animals. Diversity differences can also be found within similar kinds of ecosystems; for example, the bottom-living communities found beneath polar ice show marked contrasts to those found on temperate coasts.

Genetic Diversity

Genetic diversity, which is important to the vigor and viability of a species, is less apparent than species or ecosystem diversity. In any sexually interbreeding population, genetic diversity becomes greater as the numbers of individuals increase; when the population declines, so does diversity. Such a loss in genetic diversity may place a population at great risk.

The humpback whale has been protected throughout the world since the mid-1960s.

Biologists are concerned, for example, that genetic diversity in North Atlantic right whales may have been reduced drastically because their numbers have dropped to a few dozen. Even if the population rises again, it will have low genetic diversity.

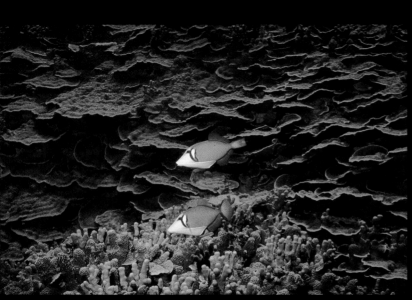

Two lei triggerfish swim past a coral reef. A large spine on its dorsal fin allows this fish to lock itself into a coral crevice if threatened.

In the intertidal (littoral) zone many marine animals are fixed to subtidal rocks and so are subject to any and all changes in the composition and temperature of the water.

Conserving biological diversity in the sea has been even more neglected than on land, yet the sea is rich in genetic, species, and ecosystem diversity. Recent research suggests that the diversity in the marine realm, as with that on land, has been greatly underestimated. . . . In fact, the sea is far richer in major groupings of animals than on land; nearly half of animal phyla occur only in the sea.

—Elliott Norse, Center for Marine Conservation

TERRESTRIAL VERSUS MARINE BIODIVERSITY

An examination of the land-atmosphere environment and that of the sea reveals significant differences in their biodiversity.

Terrestrial Biodiversity

Cowries (top) live in coastal waters of the Pacific and Indian oceans. Biodiversity also includes a Costa Rican rain forest (above left) and mangroves in Borneo (left).

Land-atmosphere biodiversity is almost completely limited to a narrow stratum along the surface or near-surface areas. The thin atmosphere supports very little life far from the surface.

Air holds heat inefficiently, so the temperature range is greater on land than in the sea.

Compared to the sea, the land is relatively unaccommodating in providing habitats. Accordingly, there is a relatively limited number of habitat types.

Unlike the sea, the land is host to an abundance of large, complex plants and, in turn, many large, plant-eating animals.

Kelp (above), an unusually large and complex marine plant, has its food-producing blades at the sea's surface to gather energy from sunlight. Gas-filled bulbs keep the blades afloat. Purple sea urchins (left) feed on kelp plants at their base and can uproot and kill 30-meter (100-foot)-tall plants.

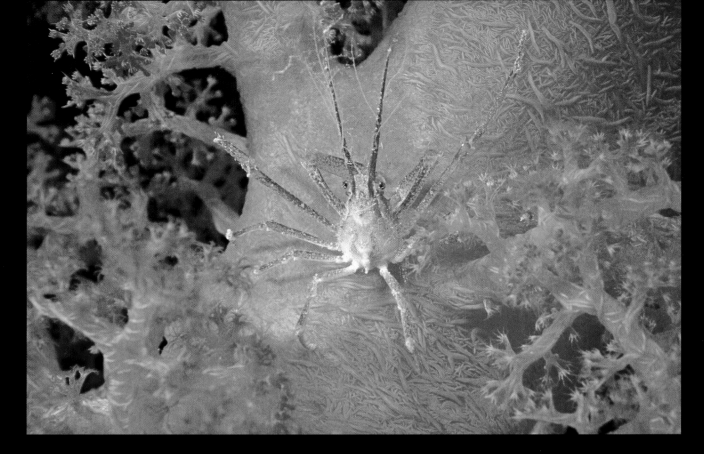

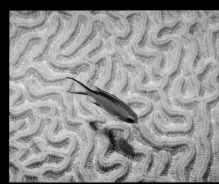

Marine Biodiversity

Although many life forms live near the ocean surface, marine biodiversity is more three-dimensional than on land; life forms are distributed across all levels of the sea.

The characteristics of the marine medium (water) promote life. Its density (830 times that of air) allows widespread distribution of animal life, and it transmits a richness of food organisms.

The sea offers a great diversity of habitat types—for example, the rich continental shelves and coastlines, mangrove forests, coral reefs, sandy beaches, and ice-floe communities.

Remarkably, the sea supports a relative lack of large, complex plants. Kelp forests are an exception, but most marine plants are single-celled and microscopic. This means that there is also a rarity of large plant-eating marine animals.

16

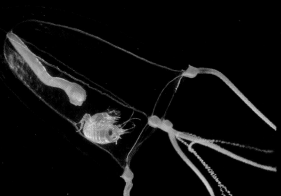

Opposite page, animals of coral reefs include the spider crab (top), coral grouper (bottom left), porcelain crabs (bottom center), and blue chromis, a member of the damselfish family (bottom right). Creatures of the open ocean include the siphonophore (above left), isopod, seen riding in the bell of a jellyfish (left), and ctenophore, feeding on a krill (above right).

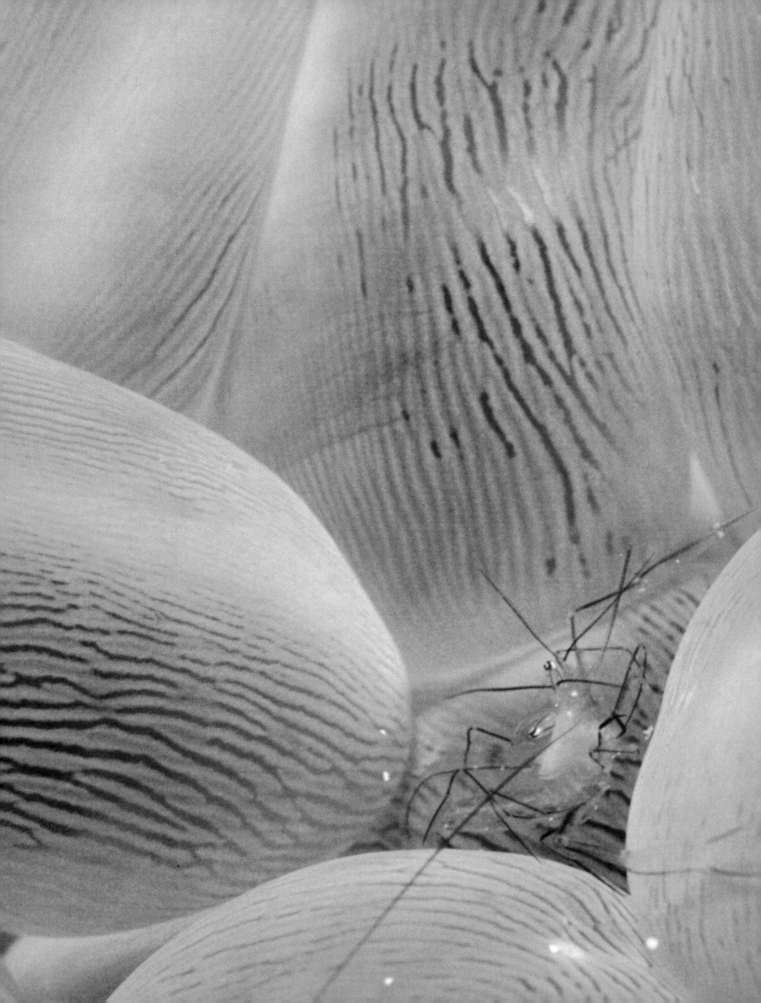

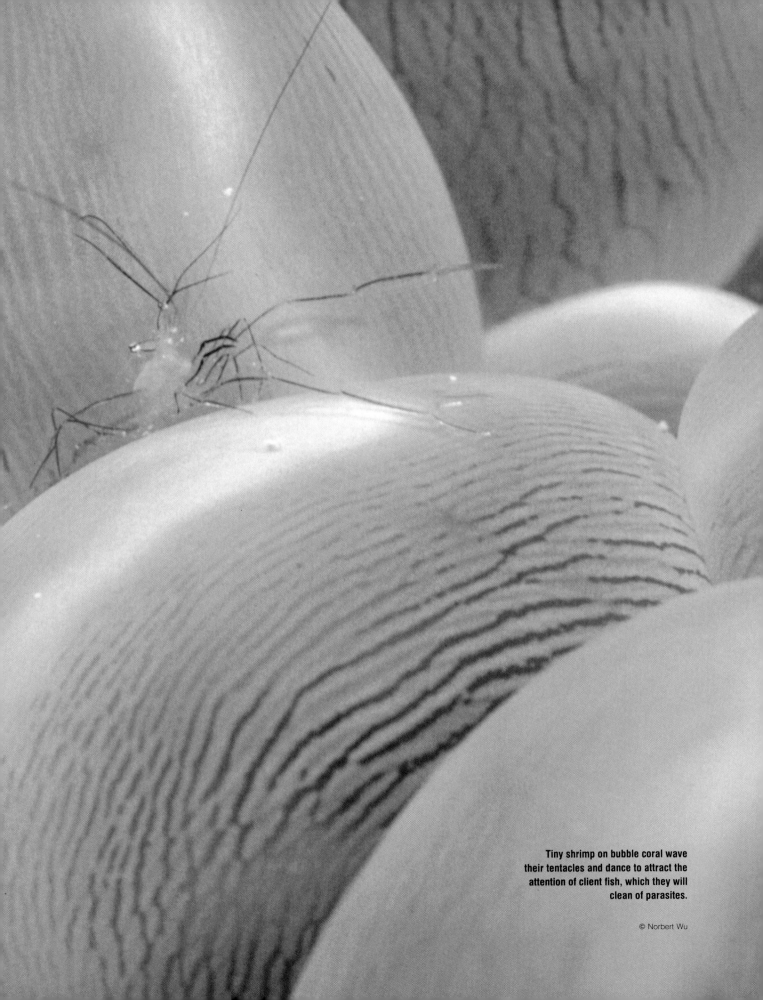

Tiny shrimp on bubble coral wave
their tentacles and dance to attract the
attention of client fish, which they will
clean of parasites.

© Norbert Wu

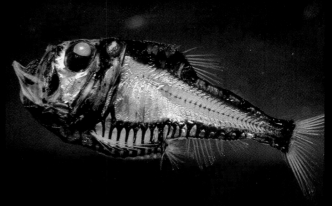

Below, of the 33 animal phyla only one, the wormlike Onychophora, is exclusively nonmarine. Fifteen are exclusively marine, and 17 are both.

Animals in the deep scattering layer include the Atlantic long-fin squid (above left) and the hatchetfish (above), whose coloring makes it invisible when viewed from above.

Deep Scattering Layer

FRONTIERS OF MARINE BIODIVERSITY STUDIES

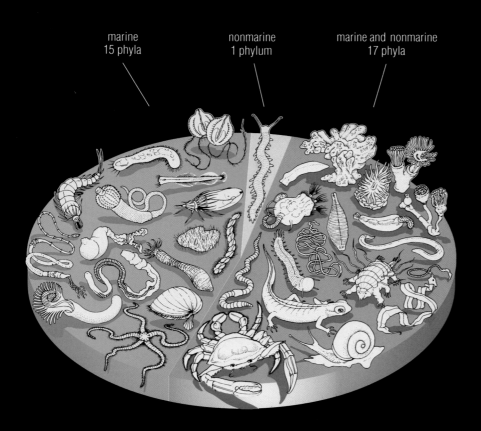

marine
15 phyla

nonmarine
1 phylum

marine and nonmarine
17 phyla

A marine ecosystem unrecognized by scientists until the mid-1900s is called the deep scattering layer (DSL) community of animals. In the 1950s U.S. oceanographers working in the deep ocean with sonar noticed that their sound signals were being scattered by an unknown layer, which was detected at varying depths at different times of day but which was always located well above the seafloor. Deepwater trawls conducted through the layer found that it comprised a variety of tiny fish and crustaceans, including lantern fish and jellyfish-like creatures called siphonophores. The DSL community lives in the upper layers of deep ocean water throughout the oceans of the world. These animals seek low light levels, swimming near the surface on dark moonless nights and migrating to waters as deep as 600 meters (2,000 feet) at noon on sunny days.

Megamouth Sharks

A new variety of shark, called "megamouth," was first discovered in 1976. Since then, six males 4.3–4.6 meters (14–15 feet) in length have been taken, and the first female washed ashore in Japan in late November 1994. In 1990 one megamouth was collected alive and tagged with a sonic transmitter. It was tracked for almost 48 hours, during which time it followed a regular up-and-down pattern, swimming near the surface on dark nights and then plunging to depths of more than 300 meters (1,000 feet) during the day. The shark was apparently following the DSL. Megamouth sharks strain small creatures from water taken in through their mouths and passed over gills that have long, comblike structures to trap the food.

Mark Dell'Aquila

A megamouth shark was captured, tagged with a sonic transmitter, and returned to the ocean, where its swimming pattern seemed to place it in the deep scattering layer. This type of shark was first discovered in 1976.

Recently discovered nudibranches include (top to bottom, by genus) *Chromodoris, Halgerda, Nembrotha,* and *Halgerda.*

Nudibranches Even relatively accessible coral reefs
provide reminders
of how little is known of the
sea's creatures. In 1988–
93 biologist Pauline Fiene-
Severns found more than
80 new species of nudi-
branches on the reefs off

the province of Sulawesi Utara in Indonesia. (A nudibranch is a type of snail that lacks a shell and bears unprotected gills on its back.) Previous explorations of the reefs had failed to detect the presence of these animals.

Nudibranches recently found on reefs in Indonesia include, by genus, *Flabellina* (above) and *Chromodoris* (right).

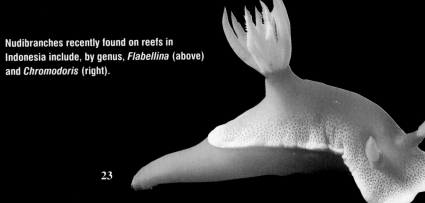

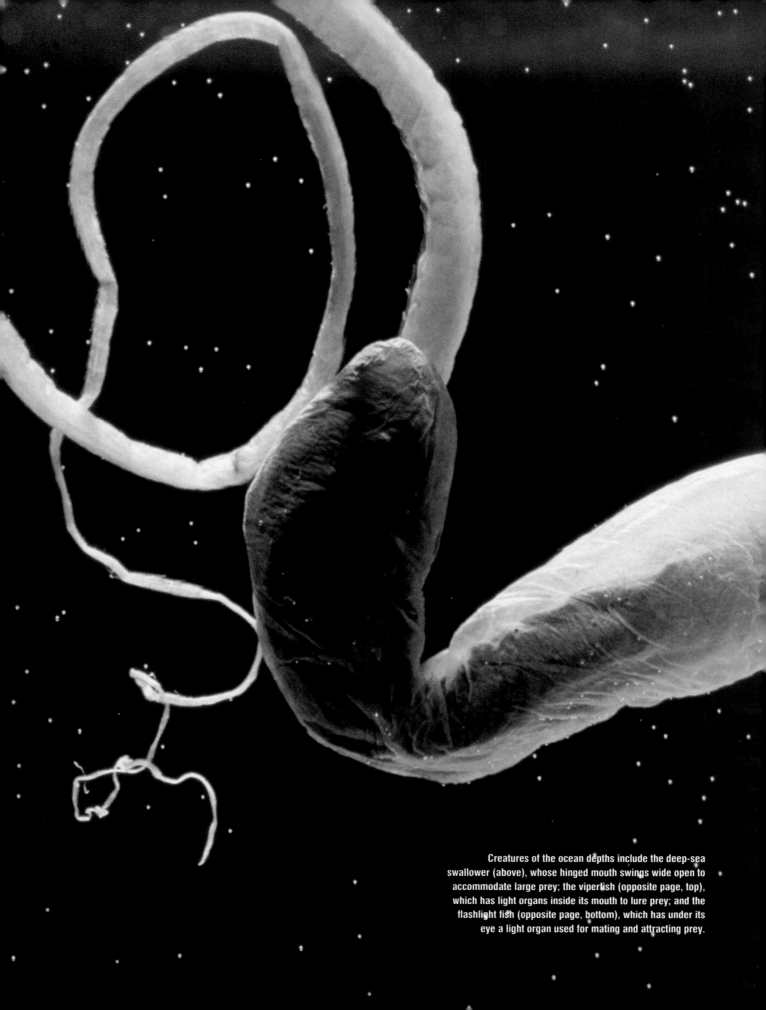

Creatures of the ocean depths include the deep-sea
swallower (above), whose hinged mouth swings wide open to
accommodate large prey; the viperfish (opposite page, top),
which has light organs inside its mouth to lure prey; and the
flashlight fish (opposite page, bottom), which has under its
eye a light organ used for mating and attracting prey.

Photos, © Norbert Wu

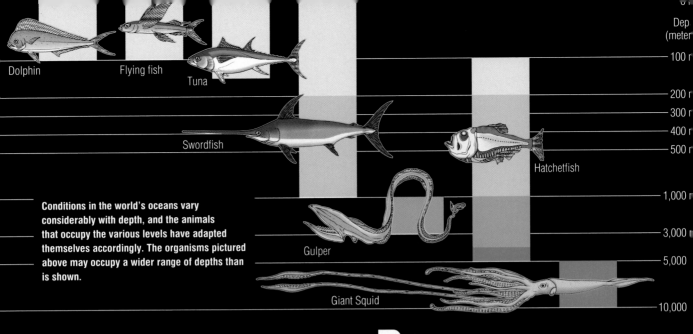

Dolphin

Flying fish

Tuna

Swordfish

Hatchetfish

Gulper

Giant Squid

Dep (meter)

— 100 r
— 200 r
— 300 r
— 400 r
— 500 r
— 1,000 r
— 3,000 r
— 5,000
— 10,000

Conditions in the world's oceans vary considerably with depth, and the animals that occupy the various levels have adapted themselves accordingly. The organisms pictured above may occupy a wider range of depths than is shown.

Deep-Sea Research

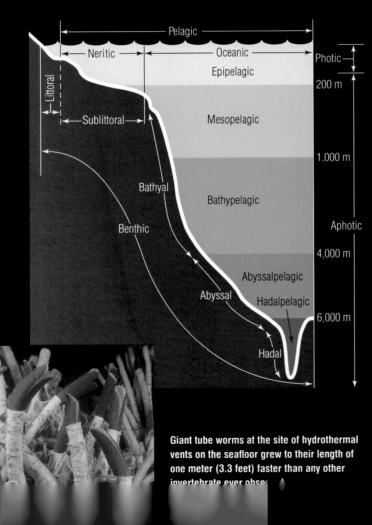

Pelagic

Neritic — Oceanic

Photic

Littoral

Epipelagic

200 m

Sublittoral

Mesopelagic

1,000 m

Bathyal

Bathypelagic

Benthic

Aphotic

4,000 m

Abyssalpelagic

Abyssal

Hadalpelagic

6,000 m

Hadal

Giant tube worms at the site of hydrothermal vents on the seafloor grew to their length of one meter (3.3 feet) faster than any other invertebrate ever obs...

Perhaps the most exciting new frontier for biodiversity research has been the seafloor. During 1994, using disinfected core drilling tools, scientists found evidence of thriving communities of previously unknown bacterial life in the sediments of the floors of the Pacific Ocean and the Sea of Japan. In 1977 new complex communities of animals were discovered living at depths of 2,500–3,000 meters (8,000–10,000 feet) around volcanic vents in the eastern Pacific that emit mineral-rich hot water. Other communities were later found at similar depths around vents on both sides of the Pacific basin and on the Mid-Atlantic Ridge. Hydrothermal vent creatures live in deep darkness, and because there is no light, there is no photosynthesis. Scientists were puzzled as to how the food chain could work without

the primary productivity c plants. They found that th source of energy for thes food webs comes from ba teria that synthesize ca bon compounds by usin energy from sulfur com pounds in the hot wate streaming from the deep sea fissures. In 1993 bio ogists in the submersibl *Alvin* found giant tub worms growing on a patc of seafloor almost 2,50 meters deep. The mete long worms had not bee noticed on earlier visi by *Alvin* two years earlie soon after the area ha been formed by a volcan flow. Biologists conclude that the tube worms ha colonized and grown t this size in the interin They remarked that th was the fastest growth any invertebrate that the had ever seen.

Female deep-sea anglerfish, equipped with a luminous lure between its eyes to attract prey, was found at depths below 300 meters (1,000 feet)

The oceans envelop almost three quarters of the Earth, dwarfing the land surface occupied by humans. Yet, in just the last 50 years we have so persistently overused global ocean resources that many individual species have declined to a position poised literally at the brink of ecological extinction. A long list of fisheries have been depleted with remarkable efficiency, and coastal zones and reefs show ever worsening impacts from human activities.

—Paul Boyle, Wildlife Conservation Society

Corals and sponges inhabit a healthy reef. Such reefs can be destroyed when the population of plant-eating fish is not sufficient to control the growth of algae.

MARINE BIODIVERSITY AT RISK

"Ecological Extinction"

Extinction—the complete elimination of a species from the Earth—is the extreme measure of damage that humans can inflict on a plant or animal. If the individuals of a species are reduced in number so that they can no longer function in an ecosystem, however, they face a fate almost as dire—"ecological extinction." This we see happening repeatedly in ocean environments.

(Top) © 1995 Stephen Frink—Waterhouse; (opposite page and below) © Norbert Wu

Coral is bleached when single-celled algae vital to its survival die off. Bleaching is spreading, but the causes of the algae die-offs are unknown.

Example I: Georges Bank

Once among the richest and most-diverse fisheries, Georges Bank, off the coast of New England, has experienced an enormous decline during the past 30 years. Haddock, once the most-abundant species in the fishery, accounted for less than 2% of the total catch in 1994. Cod landing plummeted by more than 95%. The Atlantic bluefin tuna, the largest of its species, has suffered an adult population loss of more than 90% in the Eastern Atlantic since 1975, and bluefin larvae have shown a similar decline in the Gulf of Mexico.

Example II: Coral Reefs

The coral reefs of Jamaica are an example of the interrelation of various species and the danger of concentrating attention exclusively on a single species. Until the 1970s the reefs were rich in a variety of corals, but many areas are now dull expanses where a few dominant algae grow in thick layers over a "basement" of coral skeletons originally formed by the diverse coral community. A typical sequence of events in the cycle of a reef might begin with a storm surge that rips living coral polyps off the surfaces of their calcareous bases, exposing fresh, nonliving surfaces. Algae spores settle on these new surfaces and expand their colonies. These algae "pastures" are grazed down by fish, and the corals gradually grow back and regain their space. When the number of plant-eating fish is reduced by overfishing, however, there may not be enough individual fish to crop back the expanding algae. Corals then cannot regain their lost area, and the encrusting algae expand with each storm. The result is a less-diverse reef, far fewer corals, and fewer kinds of animals that depend on corals for food and shelter.

Coral reef off the Hawaiian island of Maui is overgrown with a mat of algae, which prevents new coral from forming.

CONTINUING CONCERNS

Many alarming signs point to the continuing deterioration of the marine environment.

© Norbert Wu

A California sea lion entangled in a fisherman's gill net is strangling to death. Many sea mammals and fish are inadvertently killed by such means.

Biologist Elliott Norse lists ways in which humans are reducing the biodiversity of the sea:

* *overexploiting living things*
* *altering the physical environment*
* *polluting the sea*
* *introducing alien species*
* *adding substances to the atmosphere that increase ultraviolet radiation and alter the climate*

Salinity is increasing in the Bay of Florida because of a redirection of freshwater runoff.

Baltic Sea seals show a high respiratory disease rate, possibly because of chemical pollution.

The plant cells that live within the coral are dying off and threatening the survival of the coral.

Whales, officially protected by international agreement, are still being hunted for food.

The Bering Sea ecosys-

parently because of the overfishing of crab and haddock.

Divers throughout the tropical waters from Baja California to Indonesia have observed that large fish such as groupers and sharks are disappearing, probably as a result of overfishing.

The ozone level in the upper atmosphere is decreasing, with a concomitant increase in ultraviolet radiation. This, in turn, has a harmful effect on phytoplankton, the basis of

POSITIVE DEVELOPMENTS

Still, there are a number of reasons for hope.

© Bill Curtsinger

Public awareness is increasing, in part because of the actions of groups such as the Center for Marine Conservation, which monitor ocean affairs and publicize their findings.

There is a growing tendency to think of the world in terms of ecosystems and their connectedness.

There is a growing public interest in the ocean and its life, as reflected in the popularity of aquariums and books and films about the ocean.

Individual governments, groups of states, and international bodies have taken action to protect the maritime environment:

• The reauthorization by the U.S. Congress of the Marine Mammal Protection Act and its debate in 1995 about reauthorizing the Fisheries Management Act.

• Convention on Biodiversity—an international agreement supported by the UN to help all nations recognize and protect the species and ecosystems within their borders, in international trade, and in the seas.

• Law of the Sea, a UN-mediated treaty on the management of the oceans. Since 1958 delegates have convened international summits three times to establish what is essentially a constitution of the oceans. So far, more attention has been given to exploitation of marine resources than to marine conservation, but the Law of the Sea sets forth a compact within which global initiatives can take place. One example is a treaty regulating pollution from ships. It is hoped this agreement soon will be extended by ratification of member nations to control pollution by raw sewage from ships.

• The International Maritime Organization, established 30 years ago, could succeed in raising safety standards for oil shippers and help reduce ecological damage from tanker wrecks.

Scientists have developed new capabilities for locating and measuring minute substances and microscopic organisms.

Remote-operated submersibles and seafloor vehicles are expanding our knowledge of deep-sea and other ecological systems difficult to access in traditional ways.

Remote sensing permits the monitoring, for example, of individual blue whales throughout the Atlantic and of schools of economically important fish such as tuna.

Satellite oceanography provides valuable new ways to study the ocean's productivity, temperature, and salinity and other economic and physical attributes.

FOR ADDITIONAL READING

■ *Abandoned Seas: Reversing the Decline of the Oceans,* Peter Weber (Worldwatch Institute, 1993).

■ *The Diversity of Life,* E.O. Wilson (Harvard University Press, 1992).

■ *Global Biodiversity: Status of the Earth's Living Resources,* Brian Groombridge (ed.) (Chapman & Hall, 1992).

■ *Global Marine Biological Diversity: A Strategy for Building Conservation into Decision Making,* Elliott A. Norse (ed.) (Island Press, 1993).

■ *Marine Biology: An Ecological Approach,* James W. Nybakken (Harper Collins, 1993).

■ *Sea Change,* Sylvia Earle (Putnam, 1995).

■ *Splendors of the Seas,* Norbert Wu (Hugh Lauter Levins Associates, 1994).

Visitors at the National Aquarium in Baltimore, Maryland, watch a bottlenose dolphin (top right). The growing public interest in the ocean and its life is encouraging to marine scientists. Below, a female sea otter has had its nose rubbed raw by the male during mating. In 1994 the U.S. Congress reauthorized the Marine Mammal Protection Act.

© Norbert Wu

Science and the Internet

by Wm. A. Wulf

Already comprising more than two million interconnected computers and growing rapidly every month, the Internet is a technological and social phenomenon that is revolutionizing the ways in which scientists do their work.

A Morning on the Internet

Some people are night people; I'm not. I like to get up at 5 or so and get my "thinking work" done before the hubbub of the day begins. After making my coffee, I log on to my computer and thence to the Internet. That's where a good part of my day's work will be done. Most of my graduate students are night people, so invariably there are some messages from them—elation, depression, or just a knotty technical question. I can usually send an answer that gets them unstuck; if not, a note to my secretary will have an appointment for them set up before they are awake. My current research is on a new memory system for high-performance computers and involves building a fairly complex integrated circuit. We design the chip locally and then submit it electronically over the Internet to a service called MOSIS. Six to 10 weeks later they mail us the chips. This service gives us access to the most modern chip fabrication available; without it, academics would be unable to participate in this kind of research. The National Science Foundation still sends me paper copies of proposals to review, but at least I can send back my evaluation by E-mail. Several journals now send the papers out for reviewing electronically and require the reviews to come back that way. I don't lug paper back and forth anymore—for that, at least. If I really need a paper copy, I print it at home. On a recent morning I exchanged E-mail with my funding agency officer, who was inquiring about when a particular report was to be published; I sent an E-mail message to my secretary asking her to mail him a half dozen copies. I was in Washington that day for a meeting not very far from the funding officer and a hundred miles from my secretary; distance does not matter on the Internet. This fall a visiting professor and I are coteaching a seminar on science policy, an activity that has reaquainted me with our library. Frankly, I like the slightly musty smell of the stacks, and I have spent several wholly happy days puttering around them this summer—but it's awfully convenient to browse the catalog from my home, submit a request for a book electronically at 6 AM, and have the book on my office desk by noon.

Wm. A. Wulf is AT&T Professor of Engineering and Applied Science at the University of Virginia, Charlottesville.

Illustrations by Horacio Cardo

This article is about science on the Internet, but it is important to keep in mind that information technology—the union of computing and telecommunications—has become a crucial part of the infrastructure that supports all of a researcher's activities. Researchers are not one-dimensional; they do not just do research. They teach, review proposals and papers, interact with students, serve on committees, try to keep up with related research, etc. Science is an immensely complex social structure, and the Internet has become an essential part of the fabric of it.

WHAT IS THE INTERNET?

An apparently simple question—What is the Internet?—does not have such a simple answer. It is, of course, the mechanism that allows people, via their computers, to access the sorts of information and services mentioned above—and many more. To really understand it, though, one needs to understand a bit about the technology, the history, the organization, and even the ethics of the Internet.

The basic technology of computer networking is "packet switching," which con-trasts with the "circuit switch-ing" of traditional telephone technology. When one places a voice phone call, a process that is known as "call setup" finds and then allocates a path between the caller and the re-cipient. This path is then ded-icated for the duration of the call.

Packet switching, by con-trast, more closely resem-bles a decentralized postal system. Messages are placed inside electronic "envelopes" called packets; the address of the recipient is written on the outside; and the packet is launched into the system. When a computer on the network receives messages, it keeps those that are ad-dressed to it but passes along the rest—specifically, it passes them to a computer that it thinks is closer to the destina-tion.

The relative advantages of circuit and packet switching are easy to understand. Cir-cuit switching takes several seconds to set up the call, but once this has been done there is no additional expense for the rest of the conversation. For telephone communica-tion, where conversations last many minutes, this is the right choice. Packet switching has no setup cost, but each packet involves some processing by each of the several computers along its route. For computer interactions that may last only a few milliseconds, this is the right choice.

The first practical packet-switched network was de-ployed in the late 1960s by the Advanced Research Pro-jects Agency (ARPA) of the U.S. Department of Defense; it was called, appropriately, ARPAnet. While the basic idea underlying all computer networking is packet switch-ing, a great variety of differing and incompatible technolo-gies emerged in the decades following the first ARPAnet. They differed in everything from the media being used to protocols. ("Protocols" are the standards imposed on the form and meaning of mes-sages and are what allow one computer to understand the messages from another.)

Each of the technologies had its advantages, but their incompatibility prevented the interconnection of computers on different networks. Con-sequently, in the late 1970s ARPA funded the develop-ment of a suite of protocols called TCP/IP. Rather than imposing a universal standard, the idea was to permit rel-atively easy translation be-tween each of the differing network schemes and a "back-bone" network using the TCP/IP protocols. At least in prin-ciple, local media and pro-tocols would be used locally and would be translated by a "gateway" computer if the message was to be sent to an-other network—in which case it was first translated to TCP/IP and then, if necessary, into the local protocols of the re-cipient.

The scheme worked excep-tionally well; the TCP/IP pro-tocols enabled and sustain the Internet. They are the "glue" that holds it together. They allow local organizations run-ning their own distinctive net-works to connect to the global infrastructure. This explains the first part of the answer to "What is the Internet?" It is a "network of networks," with TCP/IP as the common language.

Indeed, the Internet is a network of networks in both a technological sense and an organizational one. A com-panion question to "What is the Internet?" is "Who owns it?"—and the answer to that is everyone and no one. There is no legal entity that "owns" the Internet. The individual com-ponent networks are owned and managed by companies or universities. National govern-ments have realized the value of providing interconnections both within their boundaries and internationally, but con-trary to some popular misconceptions, these represent a relatively small fraction of both the capital and the operating costs of the Internet. For the most part, governance of the Internet has been a cooperative endeavor of visionary volunteers.

Given that no one runs the Internet, there are relatively few hard and fast rules about its use. Instead, an informal code of behavior has evolved. It is at the same time collegial and institutional, enormous yet personal, structured yet chaotic. It is the lightning rod for concerns over individual privacy, free speech, and intellectual property in this new environment.

Growing from 200 interconnected computers in 1983 to two million a decade later, and with traffic rates continuing to grow at 10–15% per month, the Internet is an unprecedented social phenomenon. It is a phenomenon that is bound to change as economic interests transmute it into a global "information infrastructure," but in what way it will do so is unclear.

CURRENT USE IN SCIENCE

Most people are by now familiar with electronic mail (E-mail). Fewer, but a rapidly growing number, are famil-

iar with the other tools for finding and accessing information on the Internet— "bulletin boards" for topical discussions, File Transfer Protocol for moving datasets, "gopher" and "archie" for searching for information, and the "world wide web" and its wonderful interface, Mosaic, for browsing. These are general services that have become just as indispensable to scientists as they are to others. During the first few months after the announcement of the first high-temperature superconductors, for example, E-mail and bulletin boards were the most effective ways for physicists to keep up with the rapidly breaking developments.

These communications mechanisms have become a major part of the fabric of science. They may, in fact, be the most important current use of the Internet in the conduct of science. However, there are other, scientific uses of the Internet that may not be as familiar as E-mail or bulletin boards but are growing in importance. They are described in the following discussion.

Computation has become an indispensable tool of modern research. Because the fastest supercomputers are too expensive for most universities, the U.S. has pooled re-

sources at five national centers. These machines are useless, however, unless scholars can not only access them but also easily move massive datasets to and from them. This need was the immediate rationale for the creation of the NSFnet in 1986, which became the backbone of the U.S. Internet and enabled its subsequent explosive growth.

The computation provided by these five supercomputer centers, allowing scientists to "experiment" with systems that previously they could only observe, has led to remarkable breakthroughs—from understanding the dynamics of thunderstorms and the collision of galaxies to understanding the complex folding of proteins. Even more important than the specific science itself is the networked access to these powerful computers. It has helped create a new approach to resolving scientific questions—sometimes called the third modality of scientific investigation—on a par with theory and experimentation.

Although the supercomputer centers provide one form of computational resource on the network, it is not the only one. For example, a team of some 600 volunteers from 20 countries recently contributed the idle time of their workstations—

equivalent to some 10^{17} individual arithmetic operations in all—to find the prime factors of a 129-digit number called RSA-129. Factoring this number had been an outstanding challenge for almost two decades.

Supercomputers are still accessed via the Internet, but they are no longer the prime rationale for its existence. However, the idea that one can pool expensive, scarce instruments and make them accessible by the net remains and, indeed, has been extended. The San Diego (California) Supercomputer Center has made an electron microscope accessible via the net, for example.

In addition to making scarce resources available, the Internet is being used to eliminate the need for the physical presence of an investigator at inaccessible instruments. Connecting the network to such instruments can provide researchers access to them from their homes—or at least from their home institutions. For example, because the ground-based observatory for space physics at Søndre Strømfjord in Greenland is "on the net," real-time viewing of data from the observatory allows those not present to respond to rarely occurring geophysical phenomena such as solar pro-

ton events. Remote access is also permitting large groups of scientists to be involved in these interactions simultaneously, thus improving decision making and productivity.

Databases are among the first things that many people think about when Internet support of science is discussed. Certainly there are many such databases now: MedLine, at the U.S. National Library of Medicine (NLM), permits on-line searches of medical abstracts and bibliographic citations; GenBank, also at NLM, is the national repository for nucleic acid sequence data; NASA Earth Observing System data, dubbed EOSDIS, will contain information for the study of the Earth. Increasingly, however, the distinction between the data, the literature about them, and the methods of accessing both are blending. A good example is the "worm community" system. Genetic research has centered on a number of model organisms, one of which is the nematode worm *Caenorhabditi elegans*. The worm community system, WCS, is a digital library that contains a significant fraction of the information about the worm: gene descriptions, genetic maps, physical maps, DNA sequences, journal literature, informal newsletters,

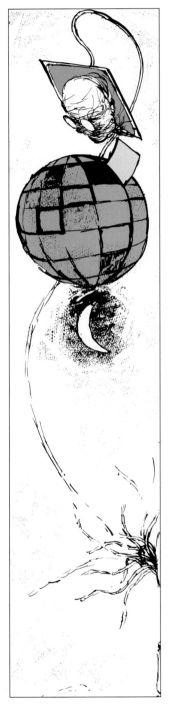

and other informal information. Much of this material is linked through hypertext so that a user can browse through the information, moving back and forth between related materials by simply "clicking."

An increasing number of services are becoming available on the Internet. MOSIS permits researchers in the U.S. to submit designs for complex integrated circuits electronically and have them fabricated on modern semiconductor production lines. The fabrication facilities necessary to support MOSIS are too expensive for a university, but the Internet allows them to be shared by many institutions.

A similar service, called MUMPS, was recently inaugurated to give researchers access to fabrication of microelectromechanical systems (MEMS). Using semiconductor fabrication techniques, MEMS combines traditional integrated circuits with such mechanical components as motors, gears, pumps, and sensors that have micrometer (millionths of a meter) dimensions. Because of their very small size and integrated electronics, MEMS devices can become intelligent sensors and actuators in previously wholly inaccessible places. Just as with MOSIS, since the fabrication facilities can be shared via the Internet, this technology will become both a topic of research and a part of the infrastructure of science. Also like MOSIS, the MUMPS facility will teach a new generation of students to exploit this technology.

A particularly interesting service to identify integer sequences was announced recently by AT&T Bell Laboratories. Sequences such as the familiar factorial

$$\mathrm{factorial}(n) = n \cdot \mathrm{factorial}(n-1) = (1,2,6,24,\ldots)$$

arise in a wide variety of scientific problems. If one knows the first few terms but does not recognize the pattern, those terms can be E-mailed to Bell Labs, where a program will compare them with the beginning of some 5,000 known sequences. Failing a direct match, the program will try a collection of techniques to see whether the sequences can be transformed into a known one.

FUTURE USES OF NETWORKING

The ultimate objective of scientific investigation is understanding. Information is the "raw stuff" of understanding, and so it is not especially surprising that a technology that revolutionizes the storage, communication, and manipulation of information might affect the conduct of science as well. In fact, it seems pretty safe to predict changes at least as dramatic as those seen in the last three decades. As Donald Langenberg, chancellor of the University of Maryland and chair of a U.S. National Academy study on information technology and the conduct of research said, "That there is a revolution occurring in the creation and dissemination of information, knowledge and, ultimately, understanding is clear to me." But knowing that there will be a revolution and understanding just what it will produce are not the same. There has never before been a comparably rapid and sustained improvement in a technology; by comparison, even the industrial revolution seems limited in scope and leisurely in pace. For more than three decades computers have doubled in speed and halved their size and power consumption every 18–30 months. Capacities of networks have increased a thousandfold in the past decade, and usage of them increases 15% per month. These trends are expected to continue at least for another decade.

It seems beyond human ability to predict the ways in which the power of this technology will be used. In the face of such rapid development, as Alan Kay of Apple Computer remarked, it is easier to invent the future than to predict it. Kay, who in the early 1970s was working to understand the implications of what are now called laptop computers, is one of the most insightful futurists, but even he is reluctant to make predictions.

Surely, some things will continue to be done in the same way, only faster, cheaper, and more accurately. Examples include more accurate models of physical systems, increasingly remote and autonomous instruments, and more nearly complete and accessible databases and libraries, to name a few. Some other things will change more dramatically, however. The following discussion considers a few possibilities.

Modern science is heavily dependent on sophisticated instruments, and that dependence will only increase. Two trends seem fairly obvious in the context of information technology. First, there will be an increasing number of instruments designed to be "on the net" and accessed remotely. Second, there will be increasingly smaller, more intelligent instruments made possible by MEMS.

Telescopes are an obvious example of the first of these trends. There is relatively little reason for an investigator to be physically present at a modern telescope. Other examples include exploration of the deep sea, the polar regions, and other such inhospitable environments. One can imagine that special communications facilities might be used for such remote instrumentation, but increasingly the various media will operate together as part of a single "information infrastructure." The ability (and need) to measure, compute, publish, study, and teach from the same information base will be a powerful force to make that information accessible in a common medium.

The MEMS technology is too new for its impact to be predicted, but it has sparked a great deal of excitement in the medical and biological communities for measurement within a living organism, for example. Indeed, the concept of a tiny injected or implanted device that can measure, compute a strategy, and then act (to deliver a drug, for example) is especially exciting.

The worm community system described above provides an inkling of what have been termed *collaboratories*— a word created by fusion

37

of *collaboration* and *laboratory* and intended to connote an electronic environment to support a group of researchers who are not necessarily located near one another. The concept, according to a recent report, is that of "a center without walls, in which the nation's researchers can perform their research without regard to physical location—interacting with colleagues, accessing instrumentation, sharing data and computational resources, [and] accessing information in digital libraries."

A report by the Computer Science and Telecommunications Board of the National Research Council studied collaboratories in three disciplines: molecular biology, physical oceanography, and space physics. In each case the report concluded that while the current Internet is somewhat of a crude tool, it provides an opportunity to enhance traditional modes of collaboration as well as provide new ones that would enable new scientific questions to be addressed.

The computing environment that most people are now using will probably evolve to a "network transparent" one. While Internet users are now acutely conscious of the boundary between their own machines and the rest of the

network, that boundary will blur and possibly disappear. There are several reasons for this.

First, although the computing power of the desktop computer will increase nearly a hundredfold in the next decade, if the past is any guide, that will not be enough to deal with many future tasks. The ability to pose computational challenges to tickle out nature's secrets far outstrips the advances in technology. However, the technology to use the idle cycles on other computers more easily and safely, as was done to factor RSA-129, is advancing rapidly. With more than two million computers now connected to networks, this untapped resource is too tempting to ignore.

Second, as has been demonstrated by the explosive growth in the use of the worldwide web and Mosaic, the desire to browse and access information independently from its location is compelling. In fact, the notion of the "location" of information is somewhat out of date; when information was always associated with a container such as a book, perhaps the notion of location made sense, but in a networked world information is everywhere.

Third, the current practice of "bringing data to the com-

putation" is both conceptually and technically inefficient. In many cases it would be far better to move the computation to where the data are stored. The basis for an intelligent decision between these options may depend on a variety of factors that the user cannot determine—current network load, for example—but there is no strong reason why the user should know or care as long as the computation is done correctly, quickly, and cost-effectively.

Finally, the kind of collaboratory discussed above requires a "network transparent" environment. Therefore, in the future the network will be subtly interwoven with scientists' everyday use of information technology in ways they will not be consciously aware of.

Another major change in the future concerns the communication of information. One often hears today, "I don't know anyone who prefers to read from a computer screen, and besides, you can't take a computer to the beach." There are two fallacies in this complaint. The first is the assumption that "electronic books" will contain only text and thus be the essentially the same as paper books but presented differently. In reality, it will not be possible to

reproduce electronic books on paper. They will contain animation and sound. They will let one "see the data" behind a graph by clicking on it. They will let one annotate and augment the documents for use by later readers, thereby making it a "living document."

The second fallacy is the assumption that technology will remain the same. On the contrary, one should remember that future electronic books will not be read from today's computer screen. Screens already exist in the laboratory with a resolution about the same as that of a laser printer. Why then would anyone lug around several heavy books when something the size, clarity, and weight of a single one contains them all?—I mean them *all*—all the ones in the Library of Congress. You *will* take your computer to the beach!

In addition, one should note that books are passive; they sit on shelves waiting to be read and interpreted. While the intellectual thrill of discovery and interpretation is heady, passivity of the text is not required for that. One of the profound changes in store for libraries, and for science, is that parts of their collection will be active—software organizing and summarizing information on behalf

of their human authors. Texts will "spontaneously" become richer and more useful.

PERSONAL ISSUES, AGAIN

The Internet has raised a lengthy list of social issues whose resolution will strongly affect the way that the future information infrastructure will be used. These issues include individual privacy, free speech, intellectual property rights, and universal access. Even the deepest foundations of law, such as the notion of jurisdiction, are challenged by the Internet. If a user in England accesses a database in Germany via fiber in Norway and uses the information to scoop a researcher in Russia, which countries' laws apply? Is a person's constitutionally guaranteed freedom of speech in the U.S. applicable to E-mail to China?

These questions are not technical, and answers cannot always be found through simply extension of existing law. Nonetheless, the incredible explosion in the use of the Internet makes it essential that answers be found. This is especially true in the pursuit of science, where the tradition of free exchange of information has been fundamental to progress.

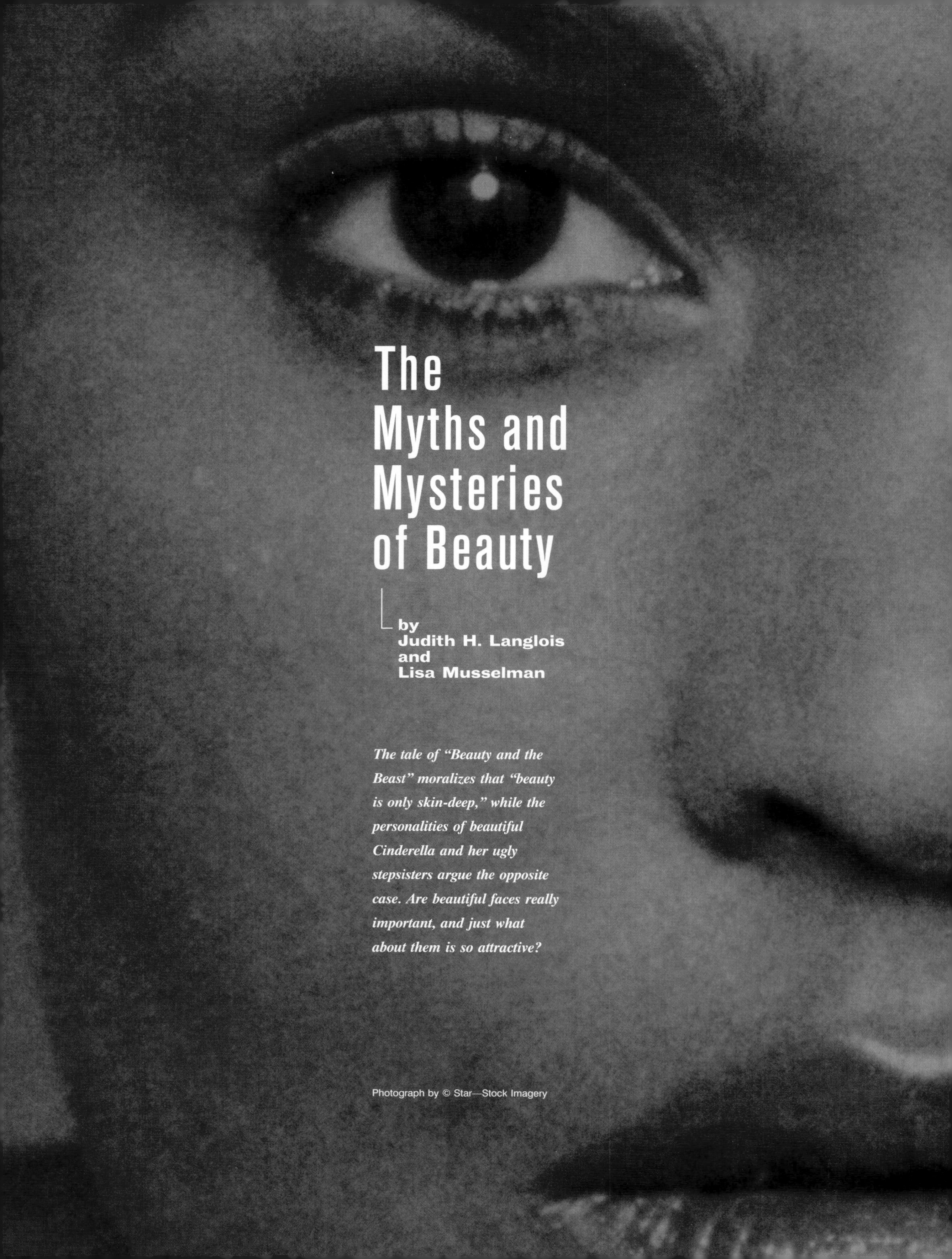

The Myths and Mysteries of Beauty

by
Judith H. Langlois
and
Lisa Musselman

The tale of "Beauty and the Beast" moralizes that "beauty is only skin-deep," while the personalities of beautiful Cinderella and her ugly stepsisters argue the opposite case. Are beautiful faces really important, and just what about them is so attractive?

Photograph by © Star—Stock Imagery

What makes a face beautiful? The question is one that scientists and philosophers have tried to answer for centuries. Even the ancient Greeks struggled to define the exact nature of beauty, as the following observation of Socrates, quoted from Plato's *Phaedo*, reveals:

> If I am told that anything is beautiful because it has a rich color, or a goodly form, or the like I pay no attention, for such language only confuses me: and in a simple and plain, and perhaps foolish way, I hold to the doctrine that the thing is only made beautiful by the presence or communication, or whatever you please to call it, of absolute beauty—I do not wish to insist on the nature of the communication, but what I am sure of is, that

Judith H. Langlois is Charles and Sarah Seay Regents Professor and Lisa Musselman is a Research Assistant in the Department of Psychology, University of Texas at Austin.

it is absolute beauty which makes all beautiful things beautiful.

The dictionary definition—for example, from *Merriam-Webster's Collegiate Dictionary,* 10th edition—is no more help:

BEAUTY:

the quality or aggregate of qualities in a person or thing that gives pleasure to the senses or pleasurably exalts the mind or spirit.

Even if Socrates and Webster cannot define it, all of us know a beautiful face when we see it. Nevertheless, from childhood we are taught aphorisms such as "Never judge a book by its cover" and "Beauty is in the eye of the beholder." As a result, most of us believe in a set of assumptions about attractiveness that deny its importance. Still, although we may not be aware of it, attractiveness influences many aspects of our daily lives. Recent research supports this assertion by showing that many of our commonly held beliefs denying the importance of facial attractiveness are not true. It thus seems reasonable to take a hard look at some of these myths and misconceptions and to explore the questions of what facial attractiveness is and why attractive faces are so preferred.

An exotic tropical blossom (above), a flowing sculpture by Constantin Brancusi (right), a spiral of stars in deep space (opposite page)—we know beauty when we see it in its various manifestations. Yet we are hard put to define its exact nature. From at least the time of Plato, philosophers and scientists have struggled, mostly with unsatisfying results, to discover what it is that makes a thing beautiful.

Daniel J. Cox—Tony Stone Images

Bird in Space, bronze (unique cast) by Constantin Brancusi, 1928, 137.2 x 21.6 x 16.5 cm; The Museum of Modern Art, New York. Given anonymously. Photo © 1995 The Museum of Modern Art, New York

Courtesy, Anglo-Australian Observatory; photo, David Malin

MYTH 1

"Beauty is in the eye of the beholder." This myth exists in two commonly expressed forms. One form asserts that we all have different standards of beauty and therefore do not agree about who is attractive and who is not.

How can we determine whether people, in fact, do disagree about who is and is not attractive? If judgments about facial beauty vary from person to person, they should show little consistency among people who are asked to rate attractiveness. Hence,

judgments about attractiveness would have very low reliability coefficients if beauty is in the eye of the beholder. A reliability coefficient is a statistic that shows how well sets of data—in this case, people's ratings—agree with each other. It can range from 0, which indicates complete lack of agreement between people, to 1, which indicates perfect agreement.

Contrary to the myth, research has shown that reliability coefficients for group judgments of attractiveness are consistently very high; most are in the 0.90s, indicating al-

most perfect agreement. For example, in 1960 the English psychologist A.H. Iliffe published a study in which attractiveness judgments were collected from more than 4,000 raters. The raters were both male and female and ranged in age from 15 to 55 and older. The reliability coefficients were in the very high 0.90s for raters of the same age and sex and in the high 0.80s and low 0.90s for dissimilar raters (15-year-old girls compared with men 55 years old and older, for example). In another study even the attractiveness of babies was reli-

ably rated by college students who initially complained that all babies look alike and that they could not possibly rate the attractiveness of infants. Despite their protestations, the reliability coefficients for these students were also in the high 0.90s.

It is certainly true that a specific pair of people judging a particular face may disagree about the person's attractiveness. Someone passing you at the shopping mall may remind you of your mean, wicked Aunt Hilda, while your partner, who has never met Hilda and who does not associate

Owen Franken—Stock, Boston

Lawrence Migdale—Stock, Boston

© Julie Habel—Westlight

(Above) Bob Daemmrich—Stock, Boston; (below) © Jeffrey Dunn—Stock, Boston; (opposite page) © Donald Johnston—Tony Stone Images

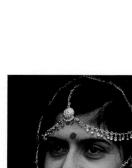

© Robert Frerck—Tony Stone Images

her looks with meanness, may very well rate both Hilda and the person walking past you as quite attractive. Nevertheless, the research data clearly show that the "eye of the beholder" myth is simply not true for groups larger than specific pairs of raters. Populations of raters are quite consistent in rating attractiveness in populations of faces.

It is also true that familiarity can make a difference in ratings of attractiveness, especially in rating individuals who are neither extremely attractive nor extremely unattractive. Numerous studies have shown that knowing and liking someone can increase one's attractiveness rating of that person. In most cases, however, the increase is quite trivial; knowing someone does not change the attractiveness evaluation of the person from unattractive to beautiful or handsome. Such familiar people are still seen as relatively unattractive, but if they are well-known and liked, they are simply placed higher in the category of unattractive persons than if the rater did not know and like them.

The other form of the "eye of the beholder" myth suggests that standards of at-

tractiveness vary dramatically across different ethnic and cultural groups. In examining this interpretation, many studies in the U.S. have analyzed the attractiveness judgments of African-American, Hispanic, and Caucasian adults and children in their ratings of adults, children, and infants from these same groups. The studies find surprisingly high levels of agreement among the three groups, whether the raters are judging people from their own group or from the other groups. Thus, Caucasian raters agree with African-Americans about which African-American infants are attractive and which are not and vice versa. However, because all of the raters in these ethnic groups live in the same culture, it is possible that they may have assimilated a single standard of beauty and applied it when making all their attractiveness ratings.

True cross-cultural studies, in which the individuals mak-

ing the judgments live in a different culture from that of the individuals they are judging, are not likely to reflect assimilated standards of beauty and thus may be a more accurate reflection of the level of cross-cultural agreement about beauty. Several recent studies have addressed this issue. Among the numerous combinations of raters and

The elusive quality of beauty shines from faces around the world, irrespective of age, ethnicity, or adornment (this page and opposite page).

44

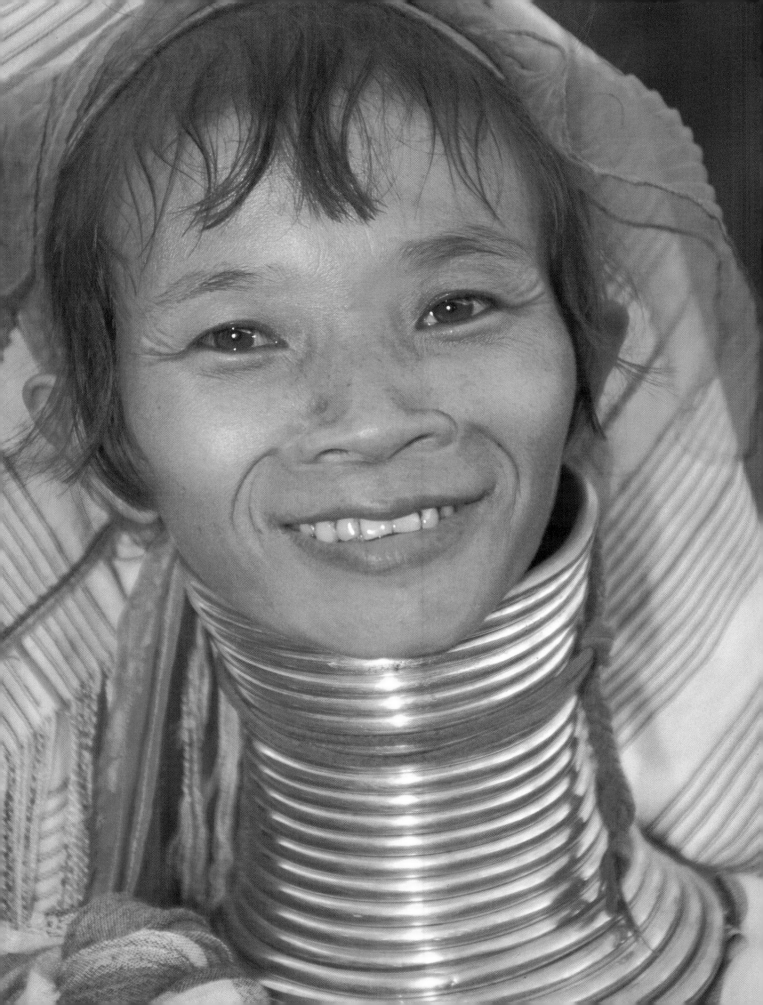

faces rated, Asians and Caucasians have rated each other for attractiveness; Chinese, Indian, and English females have judged Greek males; and South African and American males and females have rated each other. Although agreement among raters is not quite as high as that obtained from studies within a single culture, it is still surprisingly high and statistically significant (0.66–0.93).

This high level of agreement both within and across cultures suggests that although ethnically diverse faces possess some distinct facial features, they are also structurally similar. These similarities seem to be extracted and evaluated as attractive by people, regardless of their own ethnic heritage. Thus, the old "eye of the beholder" adage does not seem to be true.

MYTH 2

"Standards of attractiveness change greatly over time." Unlike the first myth, the data by which this common assumption can be evaluated are much less abundant. No known studies have had faces from centuries ago rated by people alive at that time and by people alive today. Therefore, the claim that this assumption is a myth should be regarded as a hypothesis for further thought and investigation. However, what people really seem to mean when they assert that standards of beauty change with time is not that standards for facial beauty have changed but rather that preferences for different body types have changed.

When making this assertion, people frequently turn to the art world, citing the paintings of plump women by Renaissance and Baroque artists as evidence. They assume that the paintings, such as those of the Flemish artist Peter Paul Rubens, reflect the standards and ideals of the time and culture. A comparison of these paintings with the thin

models popular in late 20th-century advertisements and fashion magazines—Twiggy in the '60s or Kate Moss in the '90s, for example—suggests that there indeed have been changes in preferred body type over time. Nevertheless, variation in preferences for body type does not necessarily imply variation in preferences for facial characteristics. The former may well have more to do with changes in those qual-ities that a culture perceives to be indicators of its health, because body weight is strongly associated with the ability of a society to feed its members. In earlier societies, in which getting enough to eat was a daily concern of the masses, plumpness was probably preferred because weight served as a sign of wealth, health, and social status. Today, given our comparatively wealthy society, thinness rather than heaviness signals health, wealth, and social status. Working out at the local health club for a fee or paying the prices for lean meats, fresh produce, and pre-pared health foods are more likely to be activities of the wealthiest in society than of the poorest.

Thus, contrary to what we commonly assume, there is just no convincing evidence currently available to suggest that changes in preferences for body types imply or require changes in preferences for fa-cial attractiveness. Changes in preferred body type do not preclude the possibility that standards of facial attractive-ness are universal and stable over time.

George Rose—Gamma Liaison

MYTH 3

"Attractiveness matters only for first impressions and su-perficial interactions." Natu-rally, appearance is one of the first things we notice about a person whom we meet for the first time. Ap-pearance is immediately evi-dent to us, whereas person-ality characteristics are not. Hundreds of studies have re-vealed that in first-impression situations—for example, job interviews, jury deliberations, performance evaluations, or first dates—a person's appear-ance can be extremely impor-tant. In general, according to these first-impression studies, we often assume that attrac-tive people possess other pos-itive characteristics, such as friendliness, honesty, and in-telligence; in contrast, we of-ten assume that unattractive individuals possess negative characteristics, such as aggres-siveness, social awkwardness, and weakness. Still, we all believe that once we get to know more about a person, the individual's interests, val-ues, and other personal qual-ities become more important to us than appearance.

In fact, however, research shows that attractiveness in-fluences our perceptions and treatment of people we know, even those we know very well. For example, many studies have shown that facial attrac-tiveness is a significant deter-minant of children's popular-ity in the classroom, where the children are among famil-iar peers. One study showed

Beauty contestants from many nations pose during a Miss Universe pageant. One interpretation of the "eye of the beholder" aphorism holds that standards of attractiveness vary dramatically across ethnic and cultural groups. In fact, however, several single-culture and cross-cultural studies in which people were asked to rate facial beauty found significant agreement about who is and is not attractive.

that attractiveness was significantly related to social acceptance and popularity for girls throughout the entire school year. For boys, low attractiveness was associated with rejection by peers. Moreover, the likelihood that unattractive boys would be rejected increased, not decreased, as the year went on and as the boys became friends. These studies on children's popularity directly contradict the notion that attractiveness becomes less important as people get to know each other.

Perhaps the most powerful way to test the effects of familiarity on the importance of attractiveness is to study the relationships between parents and their children. At the University of Texas at Austin one of us, Judith Langlois, together with Jean Ritter, Rita Casey, and Douglas Sawin, conducted a study of 150 mothers from a variety of ethnic backgrounds and their healthy, full-term, firstborn infants. Right after the infants' birth and again several months later, we recorded the behavior of each mother and baby during feeding and play times. We also had photographs of the infants rated for attractiveness by groups of college students.

We found that, in general, infant attractiveness was not related to the mothers' routine feeding and play behaviors; *i.e.,* all mothers fed and played with their infants. On the other hand, attractiveness was associated with the mothers' level of interest in their babies and the amount of positive emotion that the mothers showed toward their babies. The more attractive the babies, the more the mothers directed their attention to and interacted with their babies. Also, the more attractive the babies, the more the mothers expressed positive emotion toward them by kissing, cooing, and smiling while holding them close and cuddling them.

This is not to say that the mothers of unattractive babies in the study treated their babies badly. All the mothers were observed to be relatively positive about their infants. The more attractive infants, however, seemed to be "first among equals" in the eyes of their own mothers. The mothers in the study were not even aware of their own behavior. Mothers of both attractive and unattractive infants reported that they believed they were giving about the same amount of attention to their infants, indicating that the tendency to prefer attractive individuals and to treat them preferentially is not something most

The ample bodies of Peter Paul Rubens' "The Three Graces" (opposite page) contrast with the leanness of model Kate Moss (right). Variation in body-type preferences over time does not necessarily imply the same for facial characteristics.

© Kate Garner—Visages

49

of us recognize in our own behavior.

Other studies with infants have found almost identical results to those described above, while studies with adolescent children have found that attractiveness influences parenting behavior and attitudes, particularly toward girls. Still, one cannot infer from these results that attractiveness is the only or even the most important factor in liking or loving someone. It is not. But, like it or not, facial attractiveness makes a significant and meaningful contribution in childhood and adulthood to our social acceptance of others and to our ascription of personality traits and other characteristics to those we know.

MYTH 4

"Beauty is only skin-deep." This old adage just has to be true. After all, we have learned from the fairy tale "Beauty and the Beast" that the Beast is a kind, sensitive, intelligent guy—the kind that many women would want to marry. Yet the messages from our favorite tales and fables are confusing, because they also tell us that beautiful Cinderella is good and kind, while her ugly stepsisters are mean and selfish. Which fairy

A horrific but kindly Beast contemplates Beauty in Jean Cocteau's film *Beauty and the Beast* (opposite page), while in Walt Disney's *Cinderella* the beautiful and good title character is accosted by her ugly stepsister Drizella (above). Which fairy-tale message is true: beauty is only skin-deep, or the soul mirrors the surface?

tales are we to believe—those that claim that beauty (or the lack of it) is only skin-deep or those that claim that the interior of the person mirrors the exterior? The limited data that are available on this topic suggest that there indeed may be a relationship between appearance and at least some types of behavior.

In one study of the relationship between behavior and attractiveness in children, Langlois and A. Chris Downs recorded the play behaviors of three- and five-year-old children and found that attractive and unattractive children—again, as judged by independent raters—differed from each other in a number of ways. The most important difference was in aggressive behavior. While all the three-year-olds showed low levels of aggression regardless of their attractiveness, five-year-old unattractive children were much more aggressive, exemplified by such behaviors as hitting, biting, kicking, and pushing, than their attractive counterparts. This correlation was true for both boys and girls.

These behavioral differences are present in older children as well. While at the University of Toronto, psychologist Karen Dion investigated behavioral differ-

ences between attractive and unattractive children of elementary-school age. Attractive and unattractive fifth and sixth graders were asked to try to persuade peers from another class to eat some bad-tasting "health" crackers. The interactions between children were tape-recorded, and the ways in which the children tried to influence each other were analyzed. Dion found that unattractive girls were much more forceful, persistent, and assertive in their influence strategies than were their attractive female peers. Nevertheless, the attractive girls, who were the least forceful and persistent of all the children, were more successful in persuading boys to eat the bad-tasting crackers. Unattractive boys paired with other boys were the most successful cracker sellers; they used commands and threats of bodily harm to "persuade" their male peers to eat the crackers. Thus, in this study, as

in the one involving preschoolers, unattractive children were found to be more aggressive and assertive than attractive children.

Several other studies have shown that adult criminals and juvenile delinquents are rated as less attractive than nondelinquent children and adults who were matched with the delinquent individuals with regard to economic background, IQ, and education. In fact, in one study plastic surgery to ameliorate facial anomalies or scars was found to be more successful than social and vocational rehabilitative services in reducing the rate of return to prison and in increasing social adjustment in adult male criminals.

Thus, although only a few studies have looked at behavioral differences between attractive and unattractive children and adults, they contain strong hints that behavioral differences do exist. Furthermore, the differences are re-

flected in behaviors, such as aggression, that are important in our society.

MYTH 5

"Standards of and preferences for beauty are gradually learned through exposure to the media." Researchers and laypeople alike have long believed that standards of and preferences for facial beauty are shaped by such agents as television, motion pictures, newspapers, and magazines and thus are learned gradually through experience. For example, today's beer advertisements portray attractive people having fun at the beach, whereas medicine advertisements portray unattractive, unfortunate individuals suffering from symptoms of the cold or flu. Similarly, movie and TV villains such as Frankenstein's monster and Batman's arch nemesis, the Joker, are often unattractive, while heroes such as Robin Hood, Won-

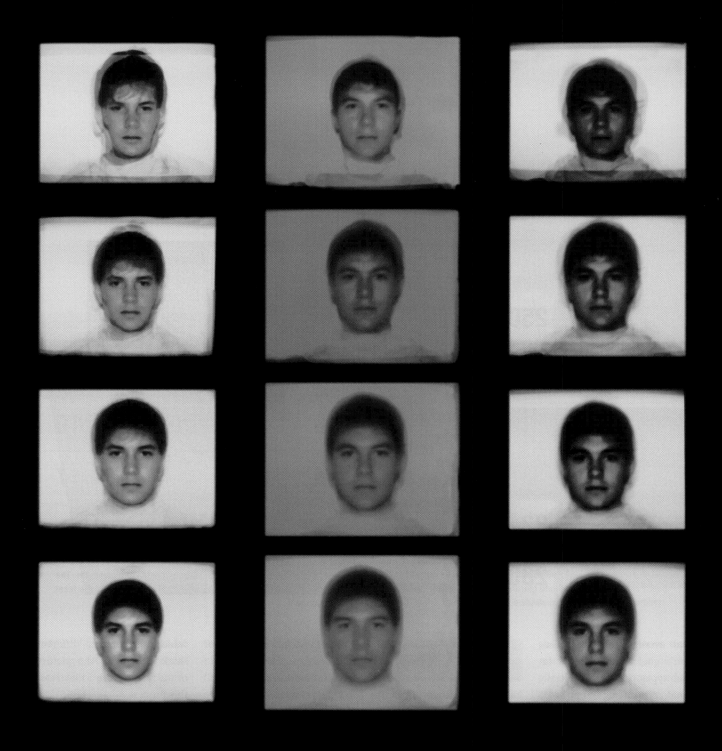

Figure 3 (this page and opposite page): Faces from left to right represent six different composite sets made from randomly selected individual faces. Faces from top to bottom represent composite levels of 4, 8, 16, and 32 faces averaged together.

The good and wicked witches (above and left, respectively) from Hollywood's *The Wizard of Oz*—have they influenced our preferences for attractiveness?

der Woman, and James Bond are usually pleasing to the eye. Because it was assumed that standards of facial beauty are learned through the media, it was also assumed that these preferences are not evident until considerable media exposure has taken place, certainly not until preschool age or later. This assumption was so strongly held that no one bothered to question it until recently.

Langlois, Casey, Ritter, Lori A. Roggman, Loretta Rieser-Danner, and Vivian Jenkins examined this assumption directly in a series of studies. In the first one we showed color

The media have been thought to shape standards of facial beauty. Actors playing villains like the Joker (top) and Frankenstein's monster (center right) are uglified, while those playing heroes like Fletcher Christian (center left), Star Wars' Lando Calrissian (bottom left), *The Untouchables'* Eliot Ness (bottom right), and Robin Hood (far right) are pleasing to the eye.

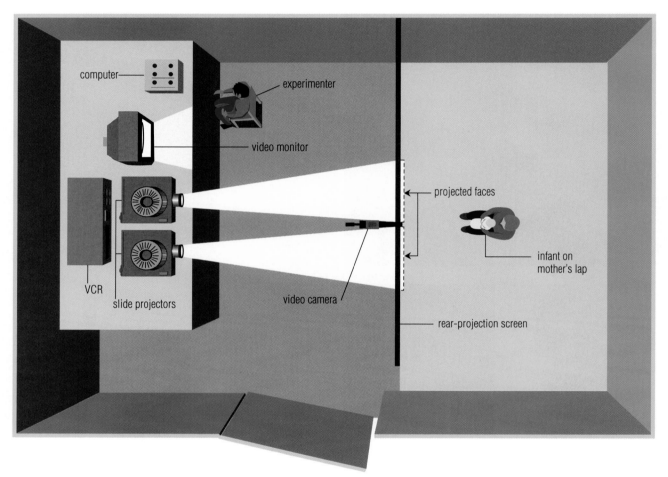

The preferences of infants for attractive and unattractive faces have been investigated within the laboratory setup depicted above. The infant, sitting on the mother's lap, faces a screen onto which pairs of faces are projected. On the other side of the screen, the experimenter uses a camera and video monitor to watch the infant's eye movements and a computer to record the amount of time the infant looks at each face.

slides of women's faces that had been reliably rated for attractiveness by adult raters to three- and six-month-old infants. Eight attractive and eight unattractive faces that could be matched closely for hair length, hair color, and facial expression were chosen from a large group of

faces. Pairs of these faces were projected side-by-side so that each image was about the size of a real face. Because the appearance of the infant's mother might influence the infant's preferences (because of familiarity), attractiveness ratings of the mothers also were obtained. The amount of time

that the infants looked at each face was recorded. The results were straightforward and unequivocal: both three- and six-month-old infants looked significantly longer at attractive female faces than unattractive ones. The attractiveness of the infants' mothers did not influence their preferences.

Langlois, Roggman, Ritter, and Leslie Vaughn repeated the study three more times with six-month-old babies, using faces of adult males, African-American females, and other infants as the stimuli. In all three cases the babies looked longer at attractive than unattractive faces, and the mothers' attractiveness was not associated with the infants' preferences. Thus, our tendency to use information about attractiveness is present even in infancy, contrary to the myth that we learn to use such information only gradually and from the media.

We also wondered whether the visual preferences displayed by infants extended to other infant behaviors. To answer this question Langlois, Roggman, and Rieser-Danner asked a professional mask maker to design and construct attractive and unattractive masks for a woman who would later interact with infants as a "stranger." The masks were very lifelike and thin enough to move with the stranger's face, allowing her to smile, blink her eyes, and so on. The stranger played with 60 one-year-old infants, one at a time, using a strict, rehearsed script so that her behavior would be consistent for all infants. The interactions between the stranger and the babies were recorded by observers who could not see the stranger's face and who, therefore, could not be biased by the mask she wore.

The results showed that infants' preferences for attractive females extend beyond visual preferences to include actual behavioral differences displayed toward an adult female based on her attractiveness. The infants more frequently avoided the stranger when she was unattractive than when she was attractive, and they showed more negative emotion and distress in the unattractive than in the attractive condition. Furthermore, boys (but not girls) approached the female stranger more often in the attractive than in the unattractive condition—perhaps a foreshadowing of the types of interactions that will occur later in social situations, when the boys are older.

Thus, it appears that something that is often presented as true—that we learn standards of attractiveness through exposure to the media—is actually wrong. Standards of and preferences for attractive faces are either innate or acquired much earlier than previously supposed.

WHAT IS BEAUTY, AND WHY IS IT PREFERRED?

If it is not true that beauty is in the eye of the beholder but rather considerable agreement exists about who is and is not attractive both within and across cultures, if appearance influences our behavior and attitudes even toward those we know, and if standards of and preferences for attractiveness are innate or acquired very early in life, then what indeed is facial beauty, and why should it be so preferred by infants, children, and adults alike?

As was mentioned above, defining facial beauty is a task that has challenged humans since ancient times. The lack of a conceptual definition, however, has not prevented researchers from carrying out empirical investigations into the effects of facial attractiveness. Researchers have merely defined attractive faces as those that raters agree are attractive.

Unlike previous attempts to define what an attractive face is, we and our research colleagues have defined facial beauty in short, parsimonious terms—attractive faces are those faces that are close to the average of the population of faces. Our definition is based on principles from cognitive and evolutionary psychology and on hints from previous research.

Cognitive psychology, in attempting to understand how human beings process information, places special emphasis on the role of prototypes. As used in this setting, a prototype is an abstract cognitive representation that re-flects the best example of a category of objects or events; as such, it reflects the central tendency or the averaged members of the class of examples. For example, you have a prototype of *dog* that no doubt includes four legs, fur, a wagging tail, and a certain size. Although you or your neighbor may own a Chihuahua or a Great Dane, neither is likely to resemble your prototype for dog. Rather, an average-sized dog, neither very large nor very small, is usually represented as the prototypical dog. Thus, just as a dog that represents the average of all dogs would be the prototypical dog, a face that represents the average of all faces in the population would be the prototypical face.

Many studies have revealed that after people are shown several examples of a category, for instance, schematic animals or schematic faces, they respond to an averaged representation of those category members as if it were special or familiar even if they have never seen it before. Studies have demonstrated that even young infants can average incoming stimuli to form a prototype. Perhaps this is why the infants in the studies discussed above preferred attractive faces; if attractive faces are prototypical of the cate-

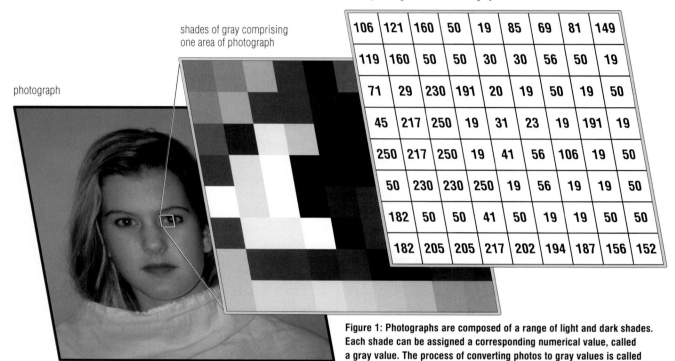

numerical values (gray values)
corresponding to each shade of gray

shades of gray comprising
one area of photograph

photograph

106	121	160	50	19	85	69	81	149
119	160	50	50	30	30	56	50	19
71	29	230	191	20	19	50	19	50
45	217	250	19	31	23	19	191	19
250	217	250	19	41	56	106	19	50
50	230	230	250	19	56	19	19	50
182	50	50	41	50	19	19	50	50
182	205	205	217	202	194	187	156	152

Figure 1: Photographs are composed of a range of light and dark shades. Each shade can be assigned a corresponding numerical value, called a gray value. The process of converting photos to gray values is called digitizing. In the figure the lighter a shade is, the higher is its number.

gory of faces, they would be preferred because they seem more facelike, or more familiar, to the infants.

As an alternative to the theories of cognitive psychology, the field of evolutionary biology suggests that there are innate, built-in mechanisms that account for the preferences for attractive faces. In the most common form of natural selection, called normalizing or stabilizing selection, evolutionary pressures operate against the extremes of

the population and in favor of characteristics representing the average or central tendency of the population. Thus, average values of characteristics shaped by normalizing selection would be preferred in the population. Indeed, according to this view, individuals with average population characteristics should be less likely to carry harmful genetic mutations than individuals with extreme population characteristics. In fact, Donald Symons, a sociobiologist

at the University of California, Santa Barbara, has proposed an innate mechanism of perception that detects the population mean of anatomic features. For faces, Symons has referred to this mechanism as a "beauty detector." The beauty detector averages observed faces and, because of stabilizing selection pressures, prefers these "average" faces over faces that are more distant from the mean.

Thus, both cognitive and evolutionary psychology sug-

gested to us that faces representing the average of the population will be perceived as attractive. Furthermore, two very old studies gave us a hint that "average" faces would be attractive. In the 1800s both the English anthropologist Francis Galton and the American psychologist John T. Stoddard created composite photographic portraits by superimposing exposures of individual faces, one on top of the other. In so doing they created imprecise mathemat-

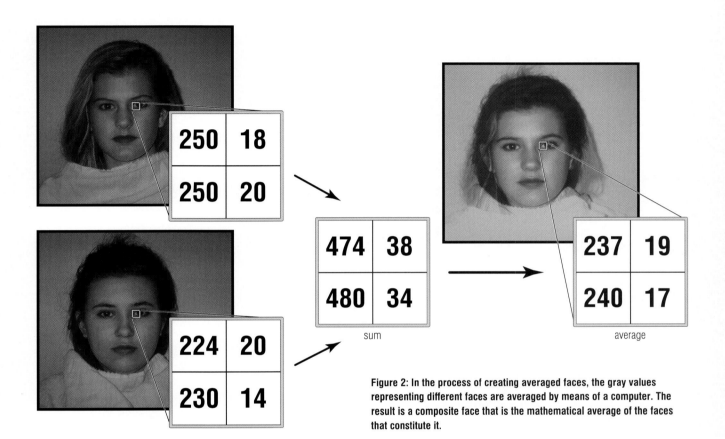

Figure 2: In the process of creating averaged faces, the gray values representing different faces are averaged by means of a computer. The result is a composite face that is the mathematical average of the faces that constitute it.

ical averages of faces. Galton's goal was to create facial types; he was especially fond of making composites of criminals and vegetarians. Stoddard made composites of members of the U.S. National Academy of Sciences and of the 1883 and 1884 graduating classes of Smith College, Northampton, Massachusetts. Both Galton and Stoddard noticed and remarked that the composites were "better looking" than their individual components.

ARE "AVERAGE" FACES ATTRACTIVE?

Langlois and Roggman examined the hypothesis that averaged faces would be attractive by means of a high-tech version of Galton's technique. Using a standard background, lighting, and distance, we took photographs of a large number of male and female undergraduates at the University of Texas. We then randomly selected 96 male faces and 96 female faces and randomly

sorted them into three sets of 32 faces for each sex, with no face in more than one set. We then created three 32-face composite, or averaged, faces for each sex on a computer in a two-step process.

In the first step we digitized the individual faces by converting the light and dark shades that each face comprises to an array of numbers, or gray values, that represent each face and that can be manipulated just like any other set of numbers. Each gray

value represents a different shade present in the picture of the face. Figure 1 illustrates this process.

In the second step we mathematically averaged the numbers representing the different individual faces in each of the six sets. (*See* Figure 2.) We created composite faces of 2, 4, 8, 16, and 32 different faces averaged together for each set of randomly selected individual faces. These averaged faces were then photographed and rated for attractiveness

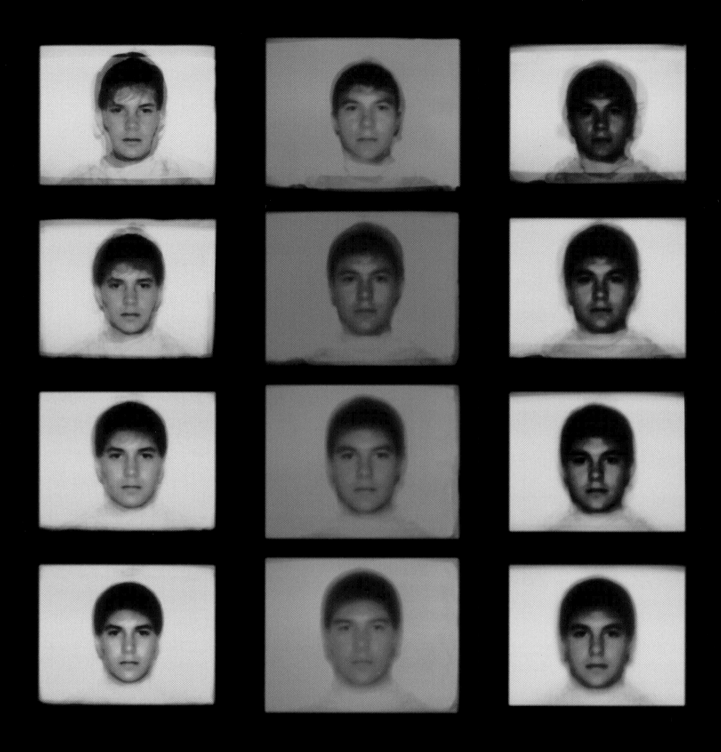

Figure 3 (this page and opposite page): Faces from left to right represent six different composite sets made from randomly selected individual faces. Faces from top to bottom represent composite levels of 4, 8, 16, and 32 faces averaged together.

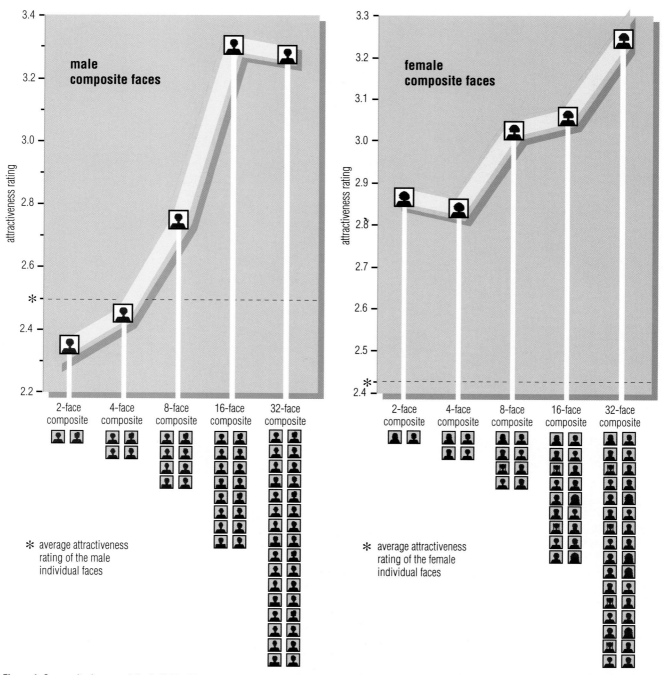

Figure 4: Composite faces and the individual faces used to make them were rated for attractiveness by 300 judges. The judges perceived the composites, particularly the 16- and 32-face composites, to be more attractive than their individual constituents.

by 300 judges along with the photographically equivalent—*i.e.,* slightly blurred—slides of the individual faces that went into them.

We found that the judges rated averaged faces made of 16 and 32 faces as significantly more attractive than the average attractiveness level of all the individual faces. (*See* Figure 3.) Additional analyses indicated that of the 96 individual male faces, only three were judged to be significantly more attractive than the 32-face composite in which they were included—about what is expected by chance. Of the female faces, only four were rated as significantly more attractive than the composites—again only that expected by chance. (*See* Figure 4.)

Thus, by using modern computer technology, we demonstrated that averaged faces are perceived as attractive. We replicated this finding in two populations, male and female, and in three samples from each population. Although we do not think that "averageness" is the only aspect of facial beauty (for example, expression and age are also important), we do believe that it is a necessary and critical element of attractiveness. Without averageness even the most youthful, smiling face will not be judged as attractive.

Although evolutionary theory and cognitive theory are generally considered quite different approaches to accounting for human behavior, they both posit similar mechanisms in the case of preferences for attractive faces by suggesting that prototypical or averaged faces underlie the tendency of infants and adults from diverse cultures to notice and prefer attractive faces. At this stage of research it is not possible to choose between evolutionary theory, which suggests that preferences for attractive faces are innate, and cognitive theory, which suggests that such preferences are acquired very early in life through exposure to category members. Nevertheless, both the evolutionary and cognitive perspectives bring theoretical coherence to the cross-cultural and infant data on preferences for attractive faces.

A NOTE OF CAUTION

One may wonder if the above discussion about the myths of attractiveness and our research into the nature of facial beauty is in some way an advocacy of the importance of beauty, an approval of the emphasis on beauty in the media, or an assertion that because preferences for attractiveness are evident so early in life,

they are an immutable aspect of human nature. The answer to all three questions is "no"; such views could not be more incorrect in summarizing our own position.

It is true that we fall victim to the "beauty-is-good" bias automatically and that we are often not aware that we have such biases in favor of attractive individuals. As humans, however, we are capable of controlling many aspects of our thoughts and behavior, an ability that distinguishes us from other animals and allows us to change undesirable aspects of our behavior. Studying and examining unconscious influences, such as our biases toward facial beauty, help us become aware of how and when they operate and thus allow us to learn to deal with them. The very research that identifies these hidden influences can rob them of their mystique and power and lead us to behave more consciously and humanely.

FOR ADDITIONAL READING

■ "Attractive Faces Are Only Average," J.H. Langlois and L.A. Roggman, *Psychological Science* (vol. 1, 1990, pp. 115–121).

■ "The Categorical Representation of Visual Pattern Information

by Young Infants," P.C. Quinn, *Cognition* (vol. 27, 1987, pp. 145–179).

■ *The Evolution of Human Sexuality,* D. Symons (Oxford, 1979).

■ "Facial Diversity and Infant Preferences for Attractive Faces," J.H. Langlois *et al., Developmental Psychology* (vol. 27, 1991, pp. 79–84).

■ "Importance of Physical Attractiveness in Dating Behavior," E. Walster *et al., Journal of Personality and Social Psychology* (vol. 4, 1966, pp. 508–516).

■ *Inquiries into Human Faculty and Its Development,* Francis Galton (Macmillan, 1883).

■ "Physical Attractiveness and Interpersonal Influence," K.K. Dion and S. Stein, *Journal of Experimental Social Psychology* (vol. 14, 1978, pp. 97–108).

■ "Principles of Categorization," E. Rosch, in E. Rosch and B.B. Lloyd, eds., *Cognition and Categorization* (Erlbaum, 1978).

■ "A Study of Preferences in Feminine Beauty," A.H. Iliffe, *The British Journal of Psychology* (vol. 51, 1960, pp. 267–273).

■ "What Is Average and What Is Not Average About Attractive Faces?," J.H. Langlois, L.A. Roggman, and L. Musselman, *Psychological Science* (vol. 5, 1994, pp. 214–220).

A Time to Die

by Michael Hengartner

The hand of a developing human fetus is a simple paddle at 5 weeks (above) but has separate fingers by 42 weeks (right). In the interval the cells between the fingers are eliminated by programmed cell death.

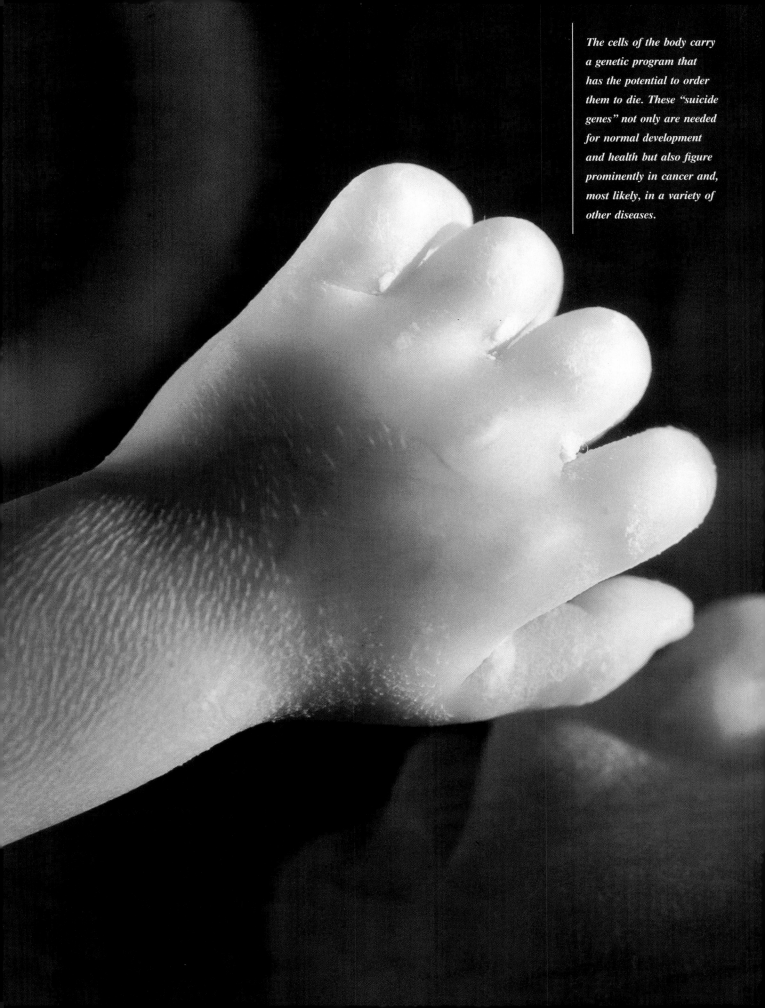

The cells of the body carry a genetic program that has the potential to order them to die. These "suicide genes" not only are needed for normal development and health but also figure prominently in cancer and, most likely, in a variety of other diseases.

Death is a natural part of life. While we sometimes have a hard time accepting the statement, we know it to be true. Humans, other animals, plants, individuals of all species—with very few exceptions—eventually die. This is as it should be, people often say, for death is necessary for the order of life. It turns out that the naturalness of death holds not only for the organism but also for the cells that make up the organism, including the cells of the human body. Beginning in the mid-1980s, and to the surprise of many, biologists have been finding that just as there are instructions that allow cells to multiply, there are also instructions that cause cells to die—to commit suicide, in fact—and that their deaths are necessary to maintain order within the body. Because this type of death results from the activation of a suicide program in the condemned cells, it has been called programmed cell death.

Why do cells commit suicide? How do they do it? What

Michael Hengartner, a Staff Investigator at Cold Spring Harbor (N.Y.) Laboratory, conducts research into the phenomenon of programmed cell death.

Death, it is said, is necessary for the order of life. To their surprise scientists have discovered that the naturalness of death holds not only for the organism but also for the cells that make up the organism.

justifies such apparently extravagant, not to mention potentially dangerous, behavior from the organism? Does the process sometimes go awry, resulting in harm to the organism? Can a detailed knowledge of the suicide program aid in the understanding, and perhaps even the cure, of certain diseases? Scientists now have some of the answers, but many questions remain.

EARLY OBSERVATIONS

The idea that most, if not all, of the body's cells are capable of committing suicide at a moment's notice has crystallized only in recent years. Nevertheless, biologists have known about the existence of programmed cell death for a long time. Indeed, the first observations suggesting that

cells can actively end their lives in an organized and reproducible fashion were made more than a century ago. The earliest studies of the phenomenon were done by developmental biologists, and for a good reason: normal development provides some of the most dramatic examples of the importance and uses of programmed cell death.

The frog, for example, begins its life in the water as a tadpole but lives on land as an adult. During its metamorphosis to the adult form, the animal gains limbs, lungs, and other structures important for life on land, but it also loses organs, such as fins and gills, that had been necessary during its aquatic stage. One of the most dramatic changes of metamorphosis is the loss of the tadpole's tail. Over a few weeks, this structure gradually regresses and then completely disappears. The biochemical mechanism is simple. Certain cells of the frog secrete a chemical message in the form of a special protein, the hormone thyroxine, that is received by the cells in the tail. As levels of thyroxine rise, more and more tail cells shrivel and die until the tail is completely gone. Amazingly, the increase in thyroxine levels is all that is required. If the tail cells are exposed to

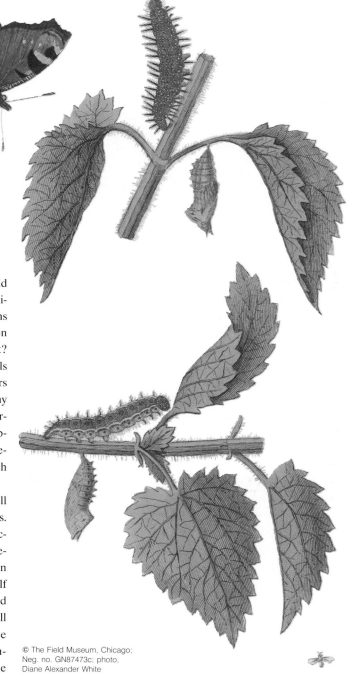

In the process of metamorphosis, most of a caterpillar's cells die to make room for the cells that will make up the butterfly. The occurrence of such massive cell deaths in nature caught the attention of early developmental biologists.

thyroxine administered experimentally in the laboratory, they immediately die even if their time is not yet up. Conversely, if the normal rise in the tadpole's thyroxine levels is experimentally prevented, the tail remains whole and functional.

A similar, equally vivid change can be observed during pupation, the transformation that insect larvae undergo to become adults. For a caterpillar to become a butterfly, most of its cells must die to make room for the cells that will compose the butterfly. Such widespread cell deaths did not escape the attention of developmental biologists, who dutifully described what they observed in the scientific journals of the 19th and early 20th centuries.

INITIAL SKEPTICISM

The rest of the scientific community largely dismissed these early observations, and most biologists remained skeptical that cells would—let alone could—commit suicide. Several factors made it hard for scientists of the time to accept that cell death is a normal part of development.

First, developmental biologists claimed to see massive die-offs of cells during embryonic development, a period of life associated with rapid growth and extensive cell division. Why would cell deaths occur when cell proliferation is necessarily at its highest? What would cause some cells to die while their neighbors were left unaffected? And why would an organism deliberately get rid of cells, in an apparently extravagantly wasteful act, after spending so much effort to make them?

Second, programmed cell death is a very rapid process. Dying cells are quickly recognized in the body and removed. Consequently, even in tissues in which more than half of the cells that are generated eventually die, only a small number of dying cells can be observed at any one time, usually much less than 1% of the

Programmed cell death is not easily observed, but the consequences can be dramatic. Photographs compare abdominal cross sections from moths of the same species before emergence of the adult from its pupal case (top) and 36-hours after emergence (bottom). In that time the intersegmental muscles, the large vertical fibers, disappear.

Photos, Lawrence M. Schwartz, University of Massachusetts, Amherst

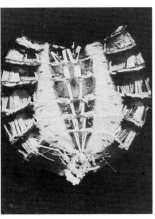

total cells present. Most biologists could not imagine how a process that seemed to affect only such a small proportion of cells could play any significant role in development.

Finally, and perhaps most important, it was hard to believe that cells could die as part of a normal, healthy physiological process. The cell deaths with which biologists were familiar, both in vivo (in the living body) and in vitro (in culture flasks), were almost always the result of "unnatural," that is, pathological, causes. These cell deaths, which had been termed necrotic, occurred when cells were exposed to drastic conditions under which they could not survive, such as temperature extremes (as happens in burns or frostbite) or lack of oxygen (as happens following a stroke or heart attack). Necrotic cell deaths are quite disruptive to the organism; they significantly damage the surrounding tissue and usually provoke a strong inflammatory response. This inflammation, a particularly aggressive form of immune response, does even further damage.

By contrast, the cell deaths that can be seen during development appear to be physiological; the body does not consider the loss of these cells to be abnormal in any way. No in-

flammation or tissue damage is observed, even when more than half of the cells are being eliminated. Furthermore, the dying cells are quickly recognized by macrophages—specialized cells of the immune system that act as the body's garbage collectors—which literally consume the dying cells to ensure their rapid removal. It is as if the naturally occurring cell deaths are the result of a contract between the organism and the dying cells wherein the cells agree not to induce an inflammatory response but rather to allow the organism to rapidly dispose of them.

To distinguish between "normal" and "abnormal" cell deaths, Andrew Wyllie and his colleagues of the University of Edinburgh suggested in 1972 that they be called by different names. While the process of pathological death would re-

main known as necrosis, Wyllie proposed that the process of physiological, programmed cell death be named apoptosis, from the Greek word meaning "to fall off" or "to wither away," as leaves fall off tree branches in the autumn. His suggestion was well received and quickly took hold; consequently, the terms *programmed cell death* and *apoptosis* are now usually used interchangeably.

Apoptosis and necrosis can be distinguished not only by the types of response they elicit from the organism but also by the structural changes that can be observed in the dying cells and by the molecular mechanisms that underlie the two processes. Apoptotic cells shrink, becoming denser, and then break into small, neatly packed bundles of cell material that can readily be taken up by macrophages. By contrast, necrotic cells usually swell and eventually burst (lyse), spilling their contents into the surrounding tissue; it is this spilling that subsequently provokes the inflammatory response.

What is programmed cell death good for? As it happens, scientists have uncovered an almost bewildering array of specific purposes. In general, the primary reasons for which cells are eliminated

are that they are in the way of further development, they are no longer useful, or they are potentially dangerous. A number of examples can serve to explore these reasons.

BODY SCULPTING

Shaping the body is a use for apoptosis that occurs during development. Building a new living organism is a little like making a statue from clay. The sculptor needs not only to build a mound of clay to the right size and mold it to the right shape but also to remove clay carefully where it is in excess. In the same way, many of the body's elaborate shapes are created not only through cell divisions and cell migrations (addition and molding) but also through programmed cell death (precise and selective removal).

A good example of the process can be found during the formation of the human hand. In its early stages of development, the hand is a simple, tiny, relatively flat paddle; the individual fingers are not yet apparent. To carve distinct fingers from the paddle, the organism "tells" those cells that will become the fingers to continue dividing, whereas those cells in the tissue between the fingers are ordered to undergo programmed cell death. Were

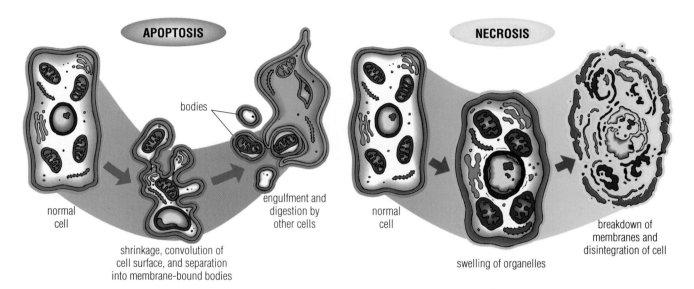

APOPTOSIS

NECROSIS

bodies

normal
cell

engulfment and
digestion by
other cells

shrinkage, convolution of
cell surface, and separation
into membrane-bound bodies

normal
cell

swelling of organelles

breakdown of
membranes and
disintegration of cell

Programmed cell death, or apoptosis, and pathological cell death, or necrosis, are distinguishable by the structural changes that take place in the dying cells. Apoptotic cells shrink and then separate into membrane-bound packages of cell material that can be readily engulfed and digested by other cells. Necrotic cells, by contrast, usually swell. Eventually their membranes break down, and they disintegrate, or lyse, spilling their contents into the surrounding tissue. The lysing of necrotic cells usually provokes a strong inflammatory response in the surrounding tissue; the "tidy" deaths of apoptotic cells do not.

this cell death not to occur, the human hand would be webbed. This, in fact, is what happens as a normal process in ducks and other waterfowl; cell deaths between the digits of the feet (but not the wings) are greatly reduced, which results in the webbed feet characteristic of the animals. Thus, a fairly small change in the proportion of cells dying in a given tissue can result in fairly major changes in the shape of the animal. This underscores the importance of apoptosis in morphogenesis, a term in biology that literally means "the generation of form."

SAFETY IN NUMBERS

How is it that developing organisms always end up with the correct number of cells in all tissues and with all those cells in contact with the right set of neighbors? The task, arduous at first sight, is actually even more formidable considering that no two individuals are the same. Scientists know, for example, that despite the protective environment of the womb, developing human babies are exposed to widely varying conditions. Owing in part to these differing environments and in part to dis-

tinct genetic backgrounds, the development of a given human being proceeds in a way that is subtly, or sometimes not so subtly, different from that of every other human. Hence, human development cannot be a rigid process; rather, it must be flexible if it is to result in a coherent and functional baby.

As an example, consider the situation faced by the group of developing nerve cells that will innervate the muscles of the feet; that is, connect those muscles with the spinal cord so that the brain can control the feet. Because of the in-

dividual differences in human development, the number of foot muscle cells present will vary slightly from one fetus to the next, so it is reasonable to expect that the exact number of nerve cells needed to innervate them also will vary. The problem is compounded by the fact that each of these nerve cells, which are located in the lower end of the spinal cord, must send a long, slim projection, called an axon, to the precise location of the muscle cells in the foot. Once there, the axon must establish a proper connection with the muscle cells so that the two kinds of cells can communicate with each other. On the scale of a cell, it is a long way from the spinal cord to the foot; not all of the spinal cord axons will make it. Some will stop growing before they reach their target, and others will take a wrong turn and end up somewhere else in the leg. Clearly these stray axons will never help connect the foot muscles with the brain. Like the exact number of muscle cells present in the foot, the exact number of nerve cells that will be lost in this way is somewhat variable.

The approach that the body uses in coming up with the correct number of cells during development is to make too many cells, accomplish the task at hand, and then get rid of the excess cells. If the organism needs 10 million nerve cells to innervate all the foot muscles, it may generate 20 million to be on the safe side. It then lets the nerve cells find their way to the foot and connect with the muscle cells. Subsequently, all the unneeded cells—those in excess and those that either failed to reach the foot or connected to the wrong cells—are eliminated through programmed cell death. Thus, during development, cells that are perfectly normal are discarded, not because they were defective but because they were not the right kind or in the right place or because they had accomplished their function.

MAINTAINING THE MACHINE

Elimination of nondefective cells continues in the adult, but with a slight twist. Once the process of development is done, all the structures that had to be built exist, and the body's main job is to keep the "machine" running smoothly. For living organisms this maintenance of constant (and presumably optimal) conditions has been termed homeostasis. Part of homeostasis consists in regularly replacing components that have a finite life span, just as people service cars and other machines by replacing parts that are nearing the end of their useful life. Obviously, the body cannot directly replace an old, "used" organ such as a liver with a new one. Rather, it "rejuvenates" the liver by replacing old liver cells with new ones. The new cells are generated through the divisions of progenitor cells, while the old cells are eliminated by apoptosis. This steady turnover, which happens in many tissues, ensures that even as the body ages, its machinery keeps in shape. (Obviously, humans still age, in part because the replacement of old cells and the generation of new cells slow down with age and because some cells, such as the nerve cells in the brain, are never replaced.)

In those tissues in which cell replacement occurs, a problem exists that at first sight may not be evident. If the body is to maintain homeostasis, it must ensure that the rate of generation of new cells and the rate of elimination of old cells are the same so that the total number of cells in the tissue does not change. Were a mismatch in the rates to occur, the tissue would then either shrink or enlarge. Such a situation can sometimes occur and is quite dangerous to the organism.

BETTER SAFE THAN SORRY

Programmed cell death is also useful for removing cells that are potentially harmful to the body. Because most cells are dispensible and can be replaced fairly easily, it makes sense to get rid of individual cells early rather than risk having a major crisis later. It is reasonable to ask how a single cell could cause trouble for a whole organism. The answer, as it turns out, is "in many ways."

One clear example is found in the maturation process of a particular set of immune-system cells known as T and B cells. These cells participate in the body's defense system against foreign invaders, their function being to recognize alien material such as viruses or bacteria and attack them. Because of the way they are generated, a certain subset of B cells and T cells will invariably recognize not foreign material but rather the body's own components (and are therefore called self-reactive cells). Self-reactive cells are rapidly identified and forced to commit suicide before they become functional. If they were to survive, they would attack the body's healthy cells. Such a situation occasionally arises and results in a condition termed an autoimmune disease. Why autoimmune diseases occur at all is not clear, but one leading hypothesis is that the mechanism that causes self-reactive cells to die goes awry.

LOOKING AT THE MOLECULAR LEVEL

Understanding the molecular basis of apoptosis requires some background knowledge of genes and mutations. Genes are units of information, present in the cell in the form of DNA molecules, that determine the exact nature of the various components that make up living organisms. The information contained in the genes is used to build other molecules, usually proteins, that perform specific functions useful to the organism. When a gene manifests its effects, for example, when its protein product is made in the cell, the gene is said to be expressed. One of the functions of genes is to regulate expression; that is, to make sure that the right proteins are made in the right cells at the right time in the right amounts.

Sometimes the sequence of the molecular building blocks of the DNA becomes altered. The change is called a mutation, and the gene, cell, or organism carrying the mutation is known as a mutant. Usually a mutation is deleterious; in changing the information that the gene carries coded in its sequence, it cripples the gene's normal function. A mutation also can be deleterious if the altered gene works too well. In either case the mutant cell or organism is expected to behave differently and, therefore, can be identified as being different from its peers. (Two other kinds of mutations exist: those that are neutral—neither deleterious nor beneficial—and the rare mutation that improves on the original. Both are important on the evolutionary scale but have little direct effect on individual organisms.) It is the existence of mutations that makes genetic analysis possible. In practice, geneticists study genes and their functions by finding mutants in which the genes are missing, defective, or otherwise altered. Of course, a given mutant can have mutations in any number of different genes. On the other hand, two mutants that look the same might have mutations in different genes. By means of laboratory tests, geneticists can determine whether two mutants have a mutation in the same gene.

By studying the effect that the absence or aberrant expression of a particular gene has on the organism, the geneticist tries to understand the normal function of the gene. The process of genetic analysis can be likened to learning how a car works by removing or making changes in its various components—say, pulling out the brake pedal or cutting a wire to a headlight—and then observing what happens to the car. The strength of this strategy is that the investigator need know nothing about the function of the brake pedal, headlight, or gene before starting to study it. Furthermore, almost any cellular process can be studied via genetic analysis, since almost everything that a cell does requires, either directly or indirectly, the products of genes.

Thus, by means of genetic analysis, investigators should be able to identify genes that are important for programmed cell death. A mutation in such a gene that renders the gene nonfunctional should result in a mutant organism showing abnormal programmed cell death. The particular kind of abnormality would depend on the normal role played by the gene's protein product. For example, if the protein is required for killing cells, elimination of the gene would result in a mutant with little or no programmed cell death.

APOPTOSIS AND CANCER

The cancer cell's great danger lies in its lack of response to the normal chemical signals used by the organism to maintain the right number of cells in each tissue—in particular, to the signals that tell cells to stop proliferating when enough are present. A single cancer cell will continue dividing, eventually giving rise to a large group of cells; i.e., a tumor. In the case of a benign tumor, the cancer cells stay together as a single mass, which can be surgically removed. The tumor may become malignant, however, whereupon the cancer cells invade other tissues, often forming secondary centers of cancerous growth, called metastases, throughout the body. This behavior, in which the cancer cell's multiplication proceeds at the expense of the whole organism, eventually leads to the death of the organism and the resulting demise of both normal and cancer cells.

What can an organism do to prevent this scenario? The best solution is to avoid getting cancerous cells. One of the great medical advances in understanding the causes of cancer has been the realization that cancer is the result of genetic changes—mutations—in the DNA of a cell. While some mutations are spontaneous, many are the result of attacks on the cell's DNA by chemicals (for example, certain pesticides or components of cigarette smoke) or physical agents such as high-energy radiation (for example, exposure to the ultraviolet radiation in sunlight or to radioactive radon gas that has been found at high levels in some homes).

Michael O. Hengartner and
H. Robert Horvitz

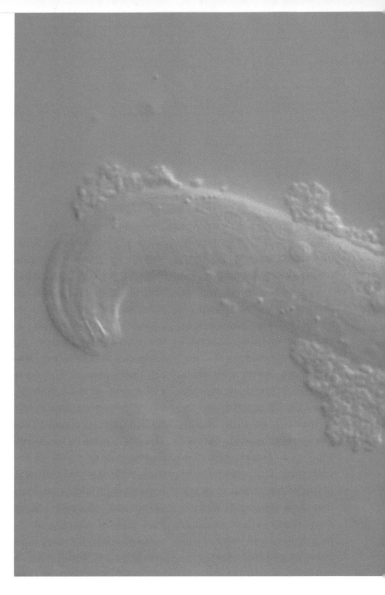

hinges on the realization that most tumor cells have mutations in several distinct oncogenes that cooperate in causing cancer. In fact, mutations in a single oncogene rarely are able to transform a normal cell into a full-fledged cancer cell. For example, researchers have observed that although mutations in any of a number of individual oncogenes cause cells to divide rapidly, they also make the cells more likely to undergo apoptosis. (Why this should be is still a matter of debate.) Mutations in these genes alone are not very efficient at causing tumors, as the cells die almost as fast as they are generated. However, if a mutation of this type is combined in the same cell with a mutation that results in overexpression of *bcl-2,* the coupling of rapid cell division and protection against programmed cell death leads to aggressive tumor growth.

Not only does overexpression of *bcl-2* increase the potential for cancer in cells that have a mutation in another oncogene, but it also makes such a mutation more likely to occur. Overexpression of *bcl-2* allows extra cells to survive, thereby increasing the number of cells that can be targeted for another random mutational "hit." This increase in "target size" might be one rea-

son (another might be to save energy) why organisms have evolved mechanisms for getting rid of superfluous cells.

Given that *bcl-2* has the makings of a potent cancer-causing gene, it is surprising that it is only rarely found altered in tumors other than follicular lymphomas. Nevertheless, programmed cell death clearly plays a fundamental role in the body's fight against cancer.

THE DEATH PROGRAM

Understanding why cells should commit suicide is only part of the task facing researchers. They also want to know how such death occurs. As the name *programmed cell death* implies, the cell is believed to have a specific built-in suicide program. Like a computer utility program, it is always there, inactive but ready to run at the stroke of a key. The genes involved in this program are collectively termed cell-death genes, and scientists' best guess is that there are many of them. A mechanism as important, complex, and deadly as cell suicide must have several levels of regulation to ensure that only the correct cells die and that potentially harmful cells are efficiently removed.

It must also be flexible enough to be able to kill all the different cell types that make up organisms as sophisticated as human beings.

What is the evidence for the existence of a cellular suicide program? As mentioned above, all cells dying by apoptosis share common characteristic morphological features, which suggests that they follow a specific route to death. Also mentioned was *bcl-2,* a gene that presumably acts as a brake on the cell-death program. The best evidence for the existence of a suicide program, however, comes from studies of the wormlike nema-

tode *Caenorhabditis elegans,* a microscopic soil animal.

C. elegans is extensively used by researchers as a model organism for studying basic biological questions such as how muscles contract or how nerve cells function. The nematode's popularity as an experimental system is due to several factors. First, although its fundamental cellular processes are similar to those of humans, it is much simpler and thus allows difficult questions to be more easily addressed. The animal has only about 1,000 cells in its body, compared with the billions that a human being comprises. It is

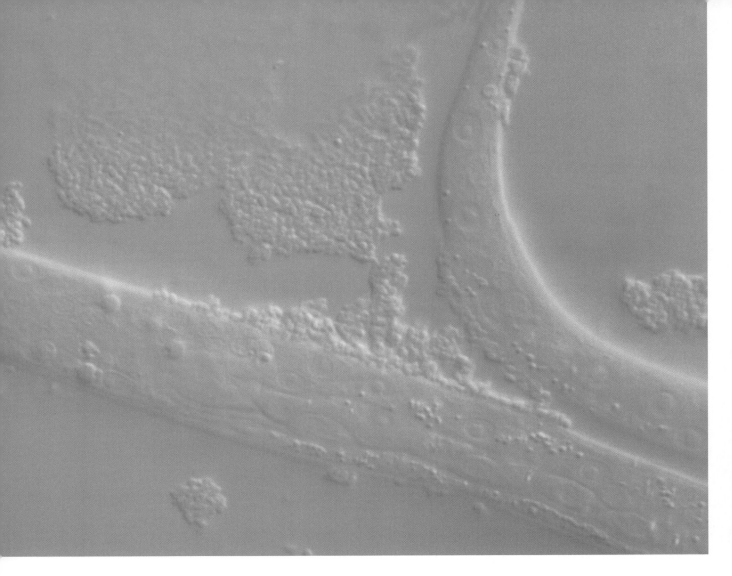

A micrograph of a nematode with a mutation in a gene, *ced-5*, for programmed cell death shows several cell "corpses" (small disks) in the animal. Although these cells died normally during the nematode's development, they were not recognized and engulfed by other cells.

also highly stereotyped; all individuals look the same and even have the same number and types of cells. Every adult comprises exactly 959 somatic (non-sex) cells, of which exactly 302 are nerve cells. Importantly, many of the kinds of cells that are found in humans are also found in the nematode, but they occur in

tiny, easily studied quantities. For example, the animal's 302 nerve cells come in 186 distinct types—fewer than two cells of each type on average.

A second reason for the popularity of *C. elegans* is that it is easy to grow and maintain in the laboratory. It eats bacteria, is not dangerous to the scientists studying it, and develops very rapidly. Embryos become fertile adults in less than four days.

Perhaps the most important advantage of the nematode is that it is highly amenable to genetic analysis. For practical reasons genetic studies are more easily done on smaller,

simpler animals. The genetic study of apoptosis in *C. elegans* has been particularly successful and has given insight as to the way the process occurs in humans.

In addition to the 959 cells found in the adult nematode, another 131 cells are formed during its development, only to be discarded via cellular suicide. As with the rest of development in *C. elegans,* programmed cell death follows a very predictable pattern. From one animal to the next the same cells die, and each cell always dies at the same point in development. This makes looking for abnor-

mal patterns of programmed cell death, *i.e.,* cell-death mutants, straightforward.

Searches for cell-death mutants of *C. elegans,* first pioneered by Edward Hedgecock at the MRC Laboratory for Molecular Biology, Cambridge, England, and subsequently expanded by Robert Horvitz and his colleagues at MIT, have led to the identification of more than a dozen genes that are important for programmed cell death in the animal. The genes can be divided into four classes, the first three of which are involved in the death of all cells. Mutations in genes of the first

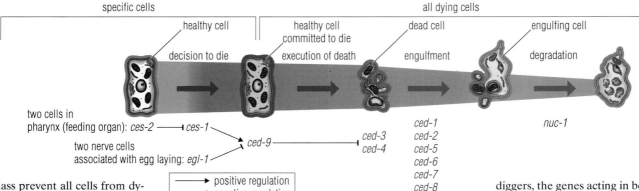

specific cells | all dying cells

healthy cell — decision to die → healthy cell committed to die — execution of death → dead cell — engulfment → engulfing cell — degradation

two cells in pharynx (feeding organ): *ces-2* ⊣ *ces-1*

two nerve cells associated with egg laying: *egl-1* ⊣ *ced-9* → *ced-3* ⊣ *ced-4*

ced-1
ced-2
ced-5
ced-6
ced-7
ced-8
ced-10

nuc-1

→ positive regulation
⊣ negative regulation

Steps in the genetic pathway for programmed cell death as it is understood in *Caenorhabditis elegans* are outlined above; those genes whose mutations are known to affect programmed cell death are listed with the steps affected. Genes that participate in the last three steps are common to all cells that die by cell suicide, whereas genes that act in the first step affect only a few cells. In the micrographs below the tail of a normal male nematode (top) is compared with that of a nematode with a mutation in its *ced-9* gene (bottom). *Ced-9* is expressed normally in many or most cells that are not fated to die by programmed cell death. In those cells it blocks the killing power of the suicide genes *ced-3* and *ced-4*. In the mutant animal *ced-9* failed to protect some of the cells that normally give rise to the tail rays (18 in normal males), resulting in missing or deformed rays.

Michael O. Hengartner, Ronald E. Ellis, and H. Robert Horvitz

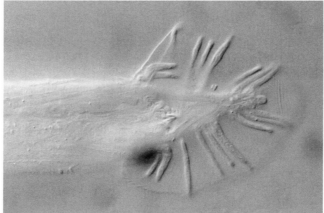

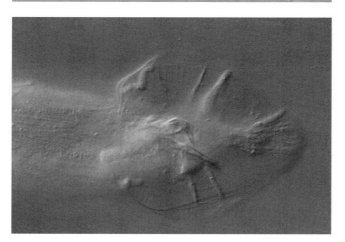

class prevent all cells from dying. The second class of genes is involved in the removal of dying cells. Like mammalian cells, *C. elegans* cells that undergo programmed cell death are rapidly recognized and engulfed by other cells. At least six genes participate in this process, and if any one of them is defective, the cells die as usual, but their "corpses" are not removed and eventually lyse. One additional gene, which makes up the third class, is required for complete digestion of the consumed cells. If that gene fails, the dying cells are recognized and engulfed by other cells, but parts of them remain undegraded inside the engulfing cell. Finally, one class of genes affects only small subsets of the cell deaths that occur in the nematode. These genes could be involved in deciding whether specific cell types live or die.

TWO TO DIE, ONE TO LIVE

Mutations in genes of the first class are perhaps the most interesting, as they involve genes that play a fundamental role in the actual killing of the cell. Whereas genes acting prior to this step can be likened to judges passing a death sentence and those acting afterward can be likened to grave diggers, the genes acting in between are the hooded executioners. Extensive studies have identified two genes, called *ced-3* and *ced-4* (ced stands for cell death abnormal), that are absolutely required for *C. elegans* cells to commit suicide. If either gene fails to function, all 131 cells that usually die will survive. These "undead" cells appear quite normal and healthy, which indicates that *ced-3* and *ced-4* act on live, functional cells and that both of them are required if any harm is to be done to the cell.

How does the nematode control the suicide program such that only the right cells die? At least part of the answer comes from the discovery that the animal has a gene that can oppose and prevent the killing power of the two suicide genes. This cell-survival gene, called *ced-9,* appears to be expressed normally in many or most cells that are not fated to die by apoptosis, presumably to protect them from *ced-3* and *ced-4*. Indeed, in mutant nematodes that have no *ced-9,* many cells that normally would survive now also die by apoptosis. Moreover, in mutants that overexpress *ced-9,* even the cells that normally would die survive, which confirms that *ced-9* can block the killing activity of *ced-3* and *ced-4*.

FROM NEMATODES TO HUMANS

Is programmed cell death in *C. elegans* the same as in humans? If it is, then what has been learned about cell death in the simpler animal can be applied to the much more complex one. Even though all cells undergoing programmed cell death look very similar, regardless of cell type or species of origin, a stricter requirement must be met; namely, that the genes involved in the process are also the same. Evidence from several sources suggest that this is indeed so.

It is not difficult to see that the functions of the nematode *ced-9* gene and the human *bcl-2* gene are very similar; both genes protect cells that should live from programmed cell death. Furthermore, overexpression of *ced-9,* like overexpression of *bcl-2,* can prevent the death of cells that should die. In addition, analysis of the DNA sequence of the *ced-9* and *bcl-2* genes has shown that they are evolutionarily closely related; in other words, both genes evolved from a common ancestor gene and have not changed much since their evolution went separate ways hundreds of millions of years ago. Genes that are similar even though they come from organisms that may

be quite distantly related are said to be conserved.

This last finding is not a trivial one. If one pair of corresponding genes involved in apoptosis has been evolutionarily conserved, it is likely that the others also have been. This prediction, in fact, has been proved true for the *ced-3* gene. Scientists have discovered that humans possess a large family of genes that are similar to the nematode *ced-3* gene. At least one member of this family—and possibly several—has been implicated in causing all cell suicide in mammals.

It is really no surprise that a process as fundamental as programmed cell death functions the same way in organisms as different as soil nematodes and humans. The program probably evolved very early in the history of life on Earth and turned out to be so useful that it has been retained with little modification ever since.

In fact, apoptosis is so useful and important that even viruses have learned to modulate it. One use for programmed cell death not discussed above is the elimination of cells that are infected by a virus. Viruses can multiply only in living cells, and this replication takes time, usually several hours. Therefore, it makes sense for an infected cell to sacrifice itself quickly

before the virus can replicate and so prevent infection of its neighbors. While rather crude, this defense mechanism has been shown to be very effective in limiting the spread of viral infections.

The existence of cellular defense mechanisms should put an evolutionary pressure on viruses to devise ways to get around them. Consistent with this hypothesis, scientists have found that many viruses carry genes that usurp the cell's normal control on the death machinery and prevent activation of the death program in the infected cell. Interestingly, some the viral genes resemble the *ced-9* and *bcl-2* genes, which suggests that the viruses have taken a cue from the cell as to the kind of molecules that are effective in preventing cell death.

THE FUTURE

The combination of work on cancer cells and *C. elegans* is gradually elucidating the mechanism by which cells commit suicide, but much remains to be done. Biologists still understand very little about how *ced-3* and *ced-4* work to kill cells or how *ced-9* can prevent cell death. Are they the only genes involved in this dance of death, or are there more to be found?

As researchers identify all the genes involved in apoptosis and begin to understand how they work, they can address questions that pertain to human health. For example, how do cell-death genes work to help prevent cancer? Could they be manipulated into helping the body get rid of cancer that has already developed? Are mutations in cell-death genes responsible for the gradual death of nerve cells that is observed in people with such neurodegenerative disorders as Alzheimer's disease, Huntington's disease, and amyotrophic lateral sclerosis (ALS, or Lou Gehrig's disease)? Research has found intriguing hints that this may be the case. Is apoptosis responsible for the widespread cell death observed following stroke or for the reduced numbers of a certain type of T cell seen in persons with AIDS? Ultimately, how can the knowledge being gathered about apoptosis be applied to curing disease and increasing the quality of life?

As scientists' understanding of programmed cell death increases, its macabre attraction gives way to an appreciation of its essential role in our lives. In the context of the whole organism, cell suicide makes sense. Yes, death is indeed a natural part of life.

Asteroids: Secrets Locked in Stone

by Clark R. Chapman

Illustration by William K. Hartmann

What do asteroids look like? What are they made of? What would happen if one hit the Earth? Unprecedented images from the Galileo spacecraft, new ground-based techniques, and a spectacular crash of a comet into Jupiter are providing some of the answers.

A

steroids are the countless small planets that revolve around the Sun, mostly between the orbits of Mars and Jupiter. In the mid-1990s there were about 6,000 officially numbered asteroids

Clark R. Chapman *is a Senior Research Scientist, Planetary Science Institute (a division of the San Juan Capistrano Research Institute), Tucson, Arizona.*

(those with particularly well-defined orbits), with about 400 being added each year. By astronomical standards they are tiny, ranging from Ceres, nearly 1,000 kilometers in diameter, down to house-sized objects (a kilometer is about 0.62 mile). Because of their size and distance from Earth, they look like slowly moving stars, even in the largest telescopes. The name *asteroid,* which literally means "like a star," reflects that perception. The last few years, however, have seen the greatest advance in knowledge about asteroids since the first ones were discovered nearly two centuries ago—partly because scientists finally had the chance to view a pair of asteroids up close.

In 1991 and 1993 the Galileo spacecraft, en route to the planet Jupiter, flew past the asteroids Gaspra and Ida and took their portraits. Suddenly these two specks of light in the sky became real worlds, with craters and other geologic features and, in the case of Ida, a moonlet of its own. Moreover, dramatic improvements in ground-based astronomical techniques, such as radar and charge-coupled-device (CCD) spectroscopy, have resulted in new information about the nature of other asteroids. Several, for example, seem to be double bodies.

Planetary scientists have long been interested in asteroids—and in their outer-solar-system siblings, the comets—because of the clues they are thought to hold about the origin of the solar system. It is now widely believed that the major planets grew by the gathering together, or accretion, of countless small asteroid-like bodies, called planetesimals, that had condensed from the original nebular disk of gas and dust from which the solar system formed. Asteroids and comets are the leftover planetesimals that never became part of a planet. Comets are remnants of the population of icy planetesimals from the outer solar system—between the orbits of the outer planets and beyond the orbits of Neptune and Pluto. Asteroids are remnants of the more rocky planetesimals left over in the inner solar system, chiefly residing in the so-called main asteroid belt between the orbits of Mars and Jupiter, where a potential planet failed to form.

The processes that affected asteroids and comets during their first tens of mil-

In an artist's conception of the early solar system, asteroid-like planetesimals collide, chipping off smaller pieces that may one day fall to Earth as meteorites.

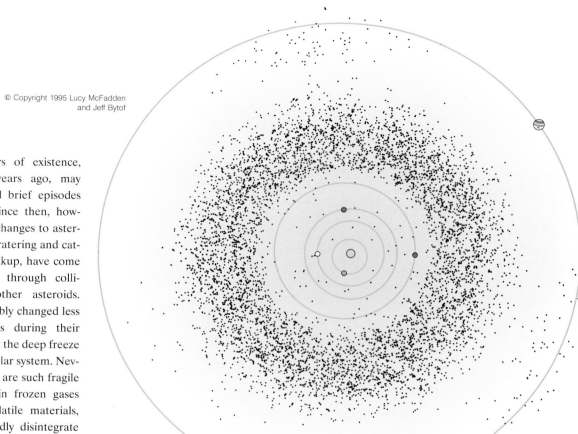

lions of years of existence, 4½ billion years ago, may have included brief episodes of heating. Since then, however, further changes to asteroids, mainly cratering and catastrophic breakup, have come about chiefly through collisions with other asteroids. Comets probably changed less than asteroids during their long storage in the deep freeze of the outer solar system. Nevertheless, they are such fragile objects, rich in frozen gases and other volatile materials, that they rapidly disintegrate once their orbital paths move them into the inner solar system. In just tens of thousands of years in the heat of the Sun, they lose their icy surface layers, and many simply break into pieces, as Comet Shoemaker-Levy 9 did two years before it plunged into the atmosphere of the planet Jupiter in July 1994.

Debris from the reservoirs of comets and asteroids occasionally rains down on the planets, including Earth. The smallest fragments that make it through Earth's atmosphere to the ground are called meteorites. They are thought to be small pieces of asteroids since cometary debris burns up during atmospheric flight. Most meteorites show little of the extensive high-temperature processing that affected

LARGEST MAIN-BELT ASTEROIDS AND INTERESTING EARTH-APPROACHING OBJECTS

name	diameter (km)	mean distance from Sun (AU)	composition
1 Ceres	933	2.77	carbonaceous
2 Pallas	523	2.77	uncertain
4 Vesta	505	2.36	basaltic
10 Hygiea	415	3.14	carbonaceous
511 Davida	337	3.18	carbonaceous
433 Eros	22	1.46	siliceous
1620 Geographos	5.1 X 1.8	1.24	siliceous
2062 Aten	1.1	0.97	siliceous
3361 Orpheus	0.8	1.21	basaltic
1915 Quetzalcoatl	0.5	2.54	siliceous

A computer-generated map (top) plots the positions of 5,856 known asteroids and the planets from Mercury to Jupiter on January 1, 2000. The main belt, between Mars and Jupiter, is prominent, as are the Trojan groups that lie in Jupiter's orbit about 60° on either side of the planet. Some asteroids are seen to make deep incursions into the inner solar system. The table (left) describes the largest known asteroids and some whose orbits approach that of Earth. (Opposite page) Once-frozen gases and dust boil from Halley's Comet in an image taken during the Giotto spacecraft's 1986 flyby mission. The fragile comets, rich in volatile materials, rapidly disintegrate once their orbital paths bring them into the inner solar system.

rocks on Earth, the Moon, and other larger worlds. Evidently, because of the small size of their asteroidal parent bodies, these rocks were never subjected to the high temperatures and crushing pressures that are developed within a planet or large moon. They were either melted very early in the history of the solar system or never melted at all. Thus, they provide a window through which to view the accretionary epoch of the solar system that is unequaled by any other material that can be analyzed in the laboratory. Scientists who study meteorites would dearly love to know from which asteroids their samples have come and to peer back through the billions of years of collisional changes that asteroidal material has undergone in order to read the record of planetary formation.

In the past decade and a half, attention has focused on the biggest projectiles that occasionally strike Earth. The hypothesis that the collision of an asteroid or comet with Earth 65 million years ago was responsible for ushering out the Cretaceous Period of geologic history has gained widespread acceptance in recent years since the discovery of a huge impact crater in the Yucatán Peninsula and the

dating of its formation to that time. The boundary between the Cretaceous and subsequent Tertiary periods marks an environmental calamity beyond all comprehension; most species of life were rendered extinct. Researchers now wonder if life on Earth faces a serious continuing threat from impacts.

The stunning collision of Comet Shoemaker-Levy 9 with Jupiter raised concerns that a similar impact on Earth might be even more devastating than had been thought. There was renewed international interest in mounting a telescopic survey to find most of the asteroids and comets that approach Earth and could cause a global catastrophe. Against this backdrop the U.S. space agency NASA officially embarked on the first-ever dedicated spacecraft mission to an asteroid. In 1996 the Near Earth Asteroid Rendezvous (NEAR) spacecraft is scheduled to be launched toward an encounter three years later with one of the largest of the Earth-approaching asteroids, Eros. It will stay in orbit around Eros for a

year, permitting much more comprehensive studies than Galileo could accomplish during its brief, single-pass flybys of Gaspra and Ida.

CHIPS OFF THE BLOCK

Astronomers for a quarter century have tried to use reflectance spectroscopy to determine the composition of asteroids. The idea is that the spectrum of sunlight reflected from an asteroid's sur-

face shows deficits in certain wavelengths, called absorption bands, due to absorption of those wavelengths by the asteroid's component minerals. Some of the absorption bands are the same as those observed in the laboratory for various minerals. Such assays, combined with studies that compare asteroid spectra with the spectra of meteorites in the laboratory, should provide links between asteroids and meteorites. Success has been a long time coming, however.

Ordinary chondrites, like the example at right, are the most abundant type of meteorite found on Earth, but identifying asteroids that represent the parent bodies of this type has proved difficult.

In the early 1970s it was shown that the larger main-belt asteroids have the same variety of reflectance spectra as meteorites. Some are very black, with featureless spectra, like the type of carbon-bearing meteorites called carbonaceous chondrites. Other asteroids show the spectral absorption bands of silicate minerals, such as olivine and pyroxene, that make up the bulk of other kinds of meteorites. One of the largest asteroids, Vesta, was found to be a dead ringer for the basaltic achondrites—meteorites that seem to be pieces of basalt, much like lava flows on Earth.

Some of the spectral data were ambiguous, however. The second most abundant type of asteroid, called the S class, evidently contains large amounts of olivine and pyroxene. The problem is that two very dissimilar types of meteorites are rich in those minerals, the ordinary chondrites and the stony-iron meteorites. Ordinary chondrites, like their darker carbonaceous-chondrite siblings, are thought to be nearly unadulterated samples of the solid material that originally condensed from the solar nebula. They have been linchpins in many theories for the origin of the planets. Stony-irons, however, are the product of

The stony-iron meteorite at top (in cross section) appears to be a composite of rock and metal derived from a differentiated parent body. By contrast, an ordinary chondrite seems to be nearly pristine material that condensed from the original solar nebula. Spectroscopically the two types are hard to tell apart. The iron meteorite above (in cross section) is thought to have come from the metallic core of a differentiated parent body.

melting and geochemical differentiation of a chondritelike precursor body. Such a parent body melted (the source of the heating is uncertain), metal elements sank to its center to form a core, and lighter silicates such as basalt floated upward to erupt onto its surface. Stony-iron meteorites seem to be a composite of such differentiated rocks and metals. Yet the spectral differences between the undifferentiated ordinary chondrites and the differentiated stony-irons are very subtle and difficult to measure.

The S-class asteroids show a slightly reddish spectrum, characteristic of about 50% nickel-iron metal. Ordinary chondrites also contain metal, but comparatively little. Consequently, most asteroid spectroscopists in the 1970s were of the opinion that S-class asteroids were stony-irons and that ordinary chondrite meteorites had to come from another asteroidal source. On the other hand, ordinary chondrites are the most abundant meteorites in the world's museums, and it was difficult to understand why large source bodies for them were not being identified. A couple of small Earth-approaching asteroids showed spectra resembling those of ordinary chondrites, but Earth-approaching asteroids are comparatively recent, transient visitors to near-Earth space and must themselves have originated from larger parent bodies in the main asteroid belt.

Later, two schools of thought developed. One retained the stony-iron interpretation for the S-class asteroids and reasoned that ordinary chondrites must have derived from asteroids no more than a few kilometers in diameter, which were too small and faint to be included in spectral surveys. The other school held that the reddish trait seen in the spectra of S-class asteroids was due not to metal but to some form of "space weathering"—a hypothetical process that somehow slightly modifies spectra. Thus, perhaps the S-class asteroids were really spectrally modified ordinary chondrites.

Finally, in the early 1990s the superior light-gathering ability of CCDs was applied to measuring spectra of fainter, and hence smaller, asteroids than could be studied before the technique had matured. Richard P. Binzel of the Massachusetts Institute of Technology (MIT) began a survey and soon collected spectra of dozens of fainter asteroids. A main-belt object spectrally like ordinary chondrites was found. Named Boznemcova, it was expected to be the first of a group of small asteroids that would prove to be the long-sought parent bodies of the ordinary chondrites. By late 1994, however, after surveying 316 asteroids, Binzel had found few, if any, that resembled Boznemcova. Instead, most looked like pieces of the larger ones already known.

The one surprise was Binzel's discovery of dozens of small asteroids having spectra of basaltic minerals, just like

A false-color image of Gaspra, produced from data gathered during Galileo's 1991 flyby, shows the asteroid to be an irregular, cratered body. Bluish regions are thought to correspond to areas of more freshly exposed rock, and reddish regions to accumulations of unconsolidated rubble.

Vesta. It is thought that early in the history of the solar system only a very large asteroid could generate enough internal heat to partially melt and exude basalts onto its surface. How could the small "Vestoids," only a few kilometers in size, be basaltic? The answer seems to be that they all are pieces chipped off Vesta's surface. Rather than being distributed throughout the asteroid belt, the small Vestoids lie in orbits that are rather close to the orbit of Vesta itself. Evidently Vesta was struck by another asteroid, and pieces of its basaltic crust were ejected into neighboring orbits, forming a "family" of fragments.

Some Vestoids are located much closer than is Vesta itself to the so-called three-to-one resonance gap in the as-

teroid belt. This is a region, somewhat closer to the Sun than the middle of the main belt, where asteroids revolve about the Sun exactly three times for every 11.9-year revolution of Jupiter. The repetitious effects of Jupiter's gravity tend to induce chaotic motion in any asteroid near the resonance, making its orbit more elongated (elliptical, or eccentric). Through such chaotic motion, the orbits of asteroidal fragments that enter the three-to-one resonance can actually reach into the inner solar system to cross the orbit of Earth.

Binzel's survey thus solved a long-standing problem— how basaltic meteorites get to Earth when the only large source known, Vesta, seemed to be too far away from the three-to-one resonance for its fragments to reach the gap. The survey showed that small members of the Vesta family clearly had reached it, which allowed them to serve as the intermediate source bodies for these meteorites. The question now has shifted to how Vesta's fragments, kilometers in size, could have been launched from the asteroid all the way to the gap. Why did the enormous accelerations that presumably were needed fail to tear them apart?

Since ordinary chondrites that land on Earth greatly outnumber basaltic meteorites, the inability to find small asteroids with ordinary-chondrite spectra near the three-to-one resonance, where fragments of them could then be redirected toward Earth, became all the more embarrassing. Although the problem has not been resolved, the Galileo flybys of Gaspra and Ida, which are both S-class asteroids, have provided important new clues.

TALES FROM TWO ASTEROIDS

Galileo was designed to be not an asteroid mission but a probe for studying Jupiter and its moons. It was to have been carried into space by a U.S. space shuttle in the early 1980s, but problems with the shuttle launch schedule, including the catastrophic *Challenger* accident in 1986, forced a launch delay until 1989. During that time Jupiter moved away from the favorable position that it had occupied, so it was required that Galileo be given gravity assists, accomplished by close passages to Venus and Earth, in order to gain enough energy to make it out to Jupiter. Thus, engineers steered Galileo through the asteroid belt twice on its

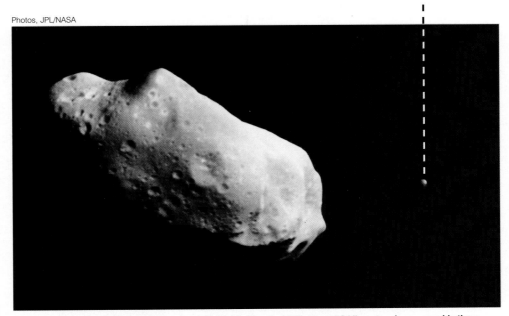

Photos, JPL/NASA

Ida (above) was the second asteroid to be visited by Galileo, in 1993. About 56 kilometers long—roughly three times the length of Gaspra—Ida surprised scientists with its highly irregular shape and its own tiny moon. Named Dactyl, the moon (top) has a crater chain and an intriguing central peak in one of its larger craters.

six-year journey to Jupiter, providing opportunities for asteroid flybys. Meanwhile, ambitious plans for asteroid missions by the European Space Agency and the Soviet Union in the 1980s failed to materialize, and NASA's Comet Rendezvous Asteroid Flyby (CRAF) mission was canceled in 1991 owing to budgetary pressures. Therefore, when Galileo flew past Gaspra in October 1991, it was the first-ever near encounter with an asteroid.

From spectra obtained by ground-based telescopes, Gaspra was known to be an S-class body. It is, however, an extreme variety of S class, far richer in olivine than any ordinary chondrite, so Galileo's flyby was not expected to resolve the spectral debate. Pictures taken of the object, which measures about 18 × 10 kilometers, did reveal for the first time what an asteroid actually looks like. Similar-sized bodies, the two small moons of Mars, had been photographed by space probes before, but Gaspra was the first true asteroid to be so examined.

The initial impression of Gaspra from its images is of a very angular, irregularly shaped body. This is not surprising since planetary scientists have long understood that planets and the larger satellites and asteroids are spherical because their own gravity molded them into that shape during formation. On the other hand, a body as small as Gaspra has little gravity (an object needs to be traveling only about 10 meters per second [22 miles per hour] to escape it), so its shape should reflect its origin and subsequent collisional history. Asteroids the size of Gaspra are struck from time to time by other asteroids large enough to shatter them. Thus, Gaspra was expected to be a comparatively recent fragment (less than a billion years old) of a larger precursor. Its angular shape may reflect the collision that created it, or perhaps subsequent collisions have chipped off additional pieces.

Galileo's pictures show many craters, hundreds of meters to a few kilometers across. The craters, however, in particular the multikilometer-sized ones, are not as numerous as on the Moon, where craters of such sizes are packed to the maximum density that saturated bombardment can produce. Evidently Gaspra is comparatively youthful for an object its size, perhaps only a couple of hundred million years old. Alternatively, Gaspra just possibly may be made substantially of metal, in which case the same impacting asteroids would make much smaller craters and those that are visible would reflect a longer exposure to bombardment—which means that Gaspra may be as old as the solar system itself. The question of whether Gaspra is mostly rock or metal remains unsolved for two reasons. First, the spectral signature of metal is ambiguous, as was discussed above. Second, Galileo flew by Gaspra too rapidly and at too great a distance to measure its mass.

(A flyby distance of 1,600 kilometers was required so it could avoid hitting any rocks that might be in orbit around Gaspra.) Consequently, the bulk density of Gaspra, which may have helped to identify its composition, could not be determined.

Gaspra showed other intriguing features on its surface, including mysterious grooves. But it was Ida that stunned Galileo scientists in late 1993 and 1994 as data from the August 1993 flyby were slowly played back to Earth from Galileo's tape recorder. Ida is even more irregular in shape than Gaspra—indeed, it is the most irregularly shaped body yet seen in the solar system. The higher-resolution pictures of this larger asteroid, 56 kilometers long with a "waist" only 15 kilometers thick, show a wealth of geologic features, including large overlapping craters, grooves, boulders, and landslides.

Most significantly, Ida was found to have a moonlet, only about a kilometer and a half across, orbiting around it. Named Dactyl, the object proved to be a bonanza for scientists. First, it surprised them by having its own crater chain and an inexplicable central peak in one of its largest craters—features nor-

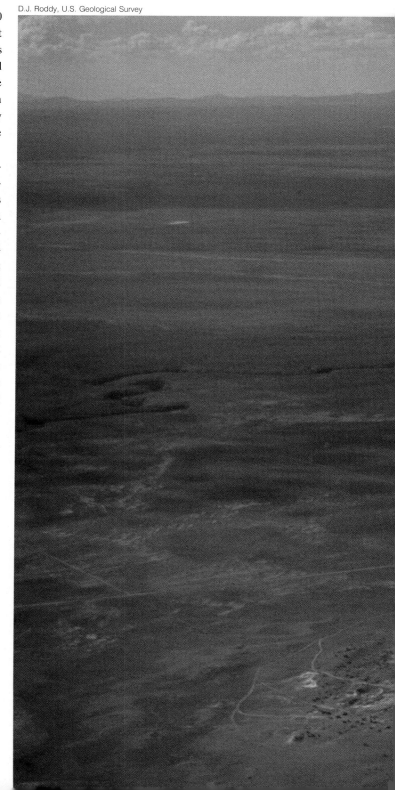

Arizona's Meteor Crater, 1,200 meters (three-fourths of a mile) across, was proved in the late 1950s to have been caused by an impacting body from space. Nevertheless, the idea that Earth's history might be changed swiftly and sometimes catastrophically by extraterrestrial forces remained generally unpopular with scientists for the next three decades.

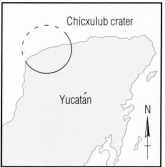

Chicxulub crater

Yucatán

N

A three-dimensional image of the Chicxulub crater (below), synthesized from gravity data, shows a multiringed structure as large as 300 kilometers across. Buried under the Yucatán coastline (left), the crater is strong support for the theory that an extraterrestrial impact brought about the mass extinction of species 65 million years ago.

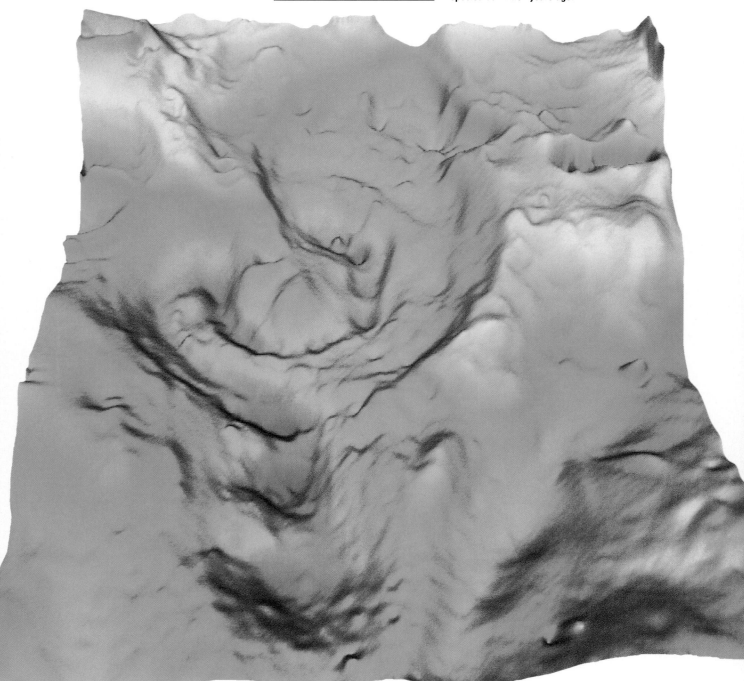

mally expected only on much larger bodies. Moreover, by employing Kepler's third law of planetary motion, scientists were able to use the moonlet's orbital period to estimate the mass of Ida itself. Unfortunately, Dactyl's period has not proved easy to determine from Galileo's data, but measurements of the moonlet's changing position during the six-hour flyby have helped scientists home in on the mass. Were the mass too low, Dactyl would have escaped from Ida into solar orbit. Were it too high, Dactyl would have been pulled toward Ida and either have hit the asteroid or been knocked into a different, unstable orbit.

According to Michael J.S. Belton, leader of Galileo's imaging team, the best estimate for Ida's mass, combined with its volume, yields a bulk density of only about 2½ grams per cubic centimeter. This is a surprisingly low value, and a disappointing one for advocates of the idea that Ida might be a stony-iron body. Stony-iron meteorites, which are about half metal, typically have densities of about five grams per cubic centimeter. The density estimated for Ida is even a little low for ordinary chondrites or other kinds of rocks. It has been theorized that some asteroids, fol-

lowing a collision that breaks them into pieces, may reaccrete into collections of fragments and boulders. Ida may be such "rubble pile," made of ordinary chondritic or rocky material with density-lowering spaces between the chunks.

Unlike Gaspra, Ida's spectrum indicates that it has the right proportions of olivine and pyroxene to be an ordinary chondrite. But, like some other S-class asteroids, its spectrum is too red. An important discovery of Galileo is that colors vary somewhat on Ida and that the very freshest, most recently formed craters are less red than most of Ida. Evidently a space-weathering process does operate on Ida to gradually redden it, although whether the effect is due to micrometeorites striking the surface, electrostatic suspension and sorting of surface grains, or something else is not known. Perhaps Ida's underlying rock is ordinary chondritic material, and it is the weathering process, rather than high metal content, that causes Ida and some other S-class asteroids to look different from ordinary chondrite meteorites in the laboratory.

The next stage of spacecraft studies of asteroids will address the S-class conundrum in even greater detail. The NEAR spacecraft is expected

to orbit the 30-kilometer-long asteroid Eros for a year beginning in January 1999. It will carry not only a camera and infrared spectral instrument, like Galileo, but also X-ray and gamma-ray analyzers. The latter instruments can perform chemical assays of Eros that scientists are sure will settle the debate about composition once and for all. They require many days and weeks to acquire a satisfactory signal, however, which explains why NEAR must be an asteroid-orbiting mission. Eros, like Ida, is another potential candidate for an ordinary chondrite even though the current wisdom is that it is a stony-iron. As the clues pile up, NEAR is being readied for its role as master detective at the Johns Hopkins University Applied Physics Laboratory, Laurel, Maryland, in time for a scheduled launch in February 1996.

TARGET EARTH?

Although a few Earth-approaching asteroids, such as 38-kilometer-long Eros, were discovered in the 19th century, not until 1932 was one found—Apollo—that actually crosses the orbit of Earth. Several prescient scientists, including Harvard University's Fletcher Watson, Amer-

ican astrophysicist-industrialist Ralph Baldwin, and Estonian-turned-Northern-Irish astronomer Ernst Opik, warned of the potential for such asteroids to strike Earth with terrifying consequences. Yet geologists were not open to interpreting Earth's history in terms of swiftly acting extraterrestrial forces, even after Eugene Shoemaker of the U.S. Geological Survey proved in the late 1950s that Arizona's Meteor Crater indeed was caused by an extraterrestrial impact.

By the late 1960s, when an MIT engineering class considered hypothetically how society might deal with an imminent collision of an asteroid with Earth, only a handful of true Earth-crossing asteroids were known. A few years later Shoemaker and Eleanor F. Helin of the California Institute of Technology mounted a modest project to search for these objects. By the early 1980s three separate observing programs—two using a small wide-field telescope on Mount Palomar in California and one using a small telescope equipped with CCD technology on Kitt Peak in Arizona—were responsible for most of the discoveries.

As the observing techniques improved, the discovery rate went up, and the chances of

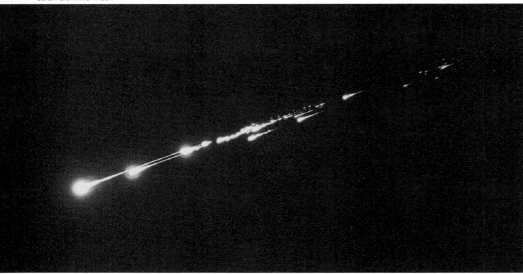

The spectacular breakup of a body dubbed the Peekskill meteorite was photographed on October 9, 1992, as it lit up the skies of the northeastern U.S. Estimates placed its original diameter at 1.5 meters (five feet).

witnessing "near misses" with Earth increased. In March 1989 one of these small objects came close enough to Earth (though still farther away than the Moon) that NASA put out a press release that received media coverage around the world. Not long afterward, geologic studies in the Caribbean and Mexico led to the discovery of the Chicxulub crater, a buried structure at least 180 kilometers in diameter (and perhaps as large as 300 kilometers) on the northwestern coast of the Yucatán Peninsula, and the conclusion that the impact that created it was the likely cause of the extraordinary changes in the fossil record 65 million years ago. This provided the "smoking gun" required for widespread acceptance in the scientific community of a hypothesis, proposed by Nobel laureate Luis Alvarez a decade earlier, that the impact of an asteroid or comet caused severe environmental changes on Earth that led to the mass extinction of species at the end of the Cretaceous.

In the early 1990s interest in Earth-approaching asteroids and the potential effects of their impacts, both past and future, continued to develop throughout the scientific community and in the news media. The first International Conference on Near Earth Asteroids, held in California in 1991, was soon followed by meetings on the same topic in Russia, Italy, and Arizona and at UN headquarters in New York City.

The chief concern is not about impacts from small meteorites, which are not known

to have killed anyone in modern times, or even from house-sized objects, which, unless they are one of the rare metallic bodies, explode too high in Earth's atmosphere to cause harm. Larger objects can do severe local damage, as happened in the Tunguska region of Siberia in 1908 when an explosion equivalent to that of a 15-megaton bomb leveled a forest for many kilometers in every direction. To put such an impact into perspective, however, Tunguska-scale devastation is produced a hundred times more often by natural earthquakes, floods, and volcanoes than by extraterrestrial bodies. Still larger bodies, hundreds of meters in diameter, could create enormously destructive sea waves (tsunamis) if they struck in oceans with heavily populated coastlines.

The most devastating impacts of all are those from comets or asteroids larger than one or two kilometers in diameter. There are estimated to be about 2,000 Earth-crossing asteroids of such sizes, of which fewer than 200 have been found so far, and an un-

Although this 12.4-kilogram (27-pound) piece of the Peekskill meteorite hit a parked car, impacts from such small bodies offer little threat. They are not known to have killed anyone in modern times.

known number of comets. The impact of any one of them could eject so much material into Earth's stratosphere that sunlight would be blocked for several months; this would threaten agricultural production worldwide and possibly lead to global famine.

In early 1994 David Morrison of NASA's Ames Research Center, Moffett Field, California, and I published calculations of the probabilities of impacts by comets and asteroids of various sizes. We estimated that impacts large enough to threaten civilization

occur, on average, about once every several hundred thousand years. Although such an impact is very unlikely to occur in the foreseeable future, the consequences are so enormous as to approach the statistically averaged killing rate of natural disasters. The difference is that a disaster on

the scale of the January 1995 earthquake that struck near Kobe, Japan, will kill many thousands of people every few years, whereas a large impact would kill billions of people once in a few hundred thousand years.

A proposal to mount a Spaceguard Survey was offered to the U.S. Congress in 1992 (although as of early 1995 its fate remained undecided). Its task would be to search for asteroids that might actually be headed toward Earth. If one was found, then nuclear weapons conceivably

could be used to "nudge" it aside. Of course, it is unlikely that any such body would be discovered, and if it was, we would probably have decades before action would be required. Thus, there would be no need to build a defense

system until a threatening object was actually found.

It probably would be unwise to design a nuclear blast to shatter the object into a spray of fragments, which could still remain on course for Earth and might do more damage than a single projectile. Alternatively,

rather than shatter, the targeted asteroid might turn out to be stronger, and the pieces larger and more damaging, than expected. An examination of asteroids by radar, carried out by Steven J. Ostro of the Jet Propulsion Labora-

Burnt, leveled trunks (left) and a vast treeless plain (right) are legacies of the explosion of an extraterrestrial object over the Siberian forest on June 30, 1908. Called the Tunguska event, the blast released the energy of a 15-megaton bomb. Such a scale of devastation, however, is produced a hundred times more often on Earth by earthquakes, floods, and volcanoes.

Twin water-filled craters at Clearwater Lakes in northern Quebec were photographed during a U.S. space shuttle mission. Measuring 36 and 26 kilometers across (left and right, respectively), the craters were created 290 million years ago by the impacts of a pair of asteroids.

An asteroid passes ominously close to a modern-day Earth in an artist's conception that offers a perspective from the surface of the asteroid itself. There are perhaps 2,000 Earth-crossing asteroids whose impacts could be sufficiently devastating to threaten civilization. Fewer than 200 have been found to date.

93

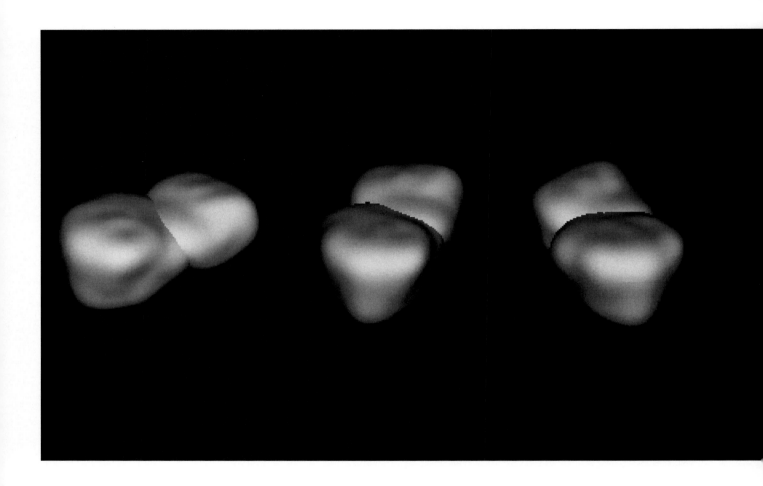

tory, Pasadena, California, has shown a few of them to be made of solid metal. Ostro's recent analyses of radar images of Castalia and Toutatis raise another concern. Both of these Earth-approaching asteroids look like compound objects. Castalia has a dumbbell shape and may consist of two chunks loosely resting together. Toutatis may be a rubble pile of several large chunks. Even an indirect nuclear blast designed to nudge such an object off course might cause it to break apart in dangerous, unpredictable ways.

These findings highlight the need to study the physical nature of any object before taking action against it. Advance reconnaissance by well-instrumented spacecraft would be required. On the other hand, there is every reason to expect that a Spaceguard Survey would find no objects capable of doing global damage to Earth for the foreseeable future. Even the much more frequent impacts capable of local damage are unlikely over the next century. Nevertheless, the threat is not negligible, as was shown in Comet Shoemaker-Levy 9's dramatic meeting with Jupiter.

A FATAL ENCOUNTER

In July 1994 scientists were given an extraordinary opportunity to observe what happens when kilometer-scale objects strike a planet. Shoemaker-Levy 9 was probably a typical comet from the outer solar system that, like a few other comets seen in the past, became captured temporarily

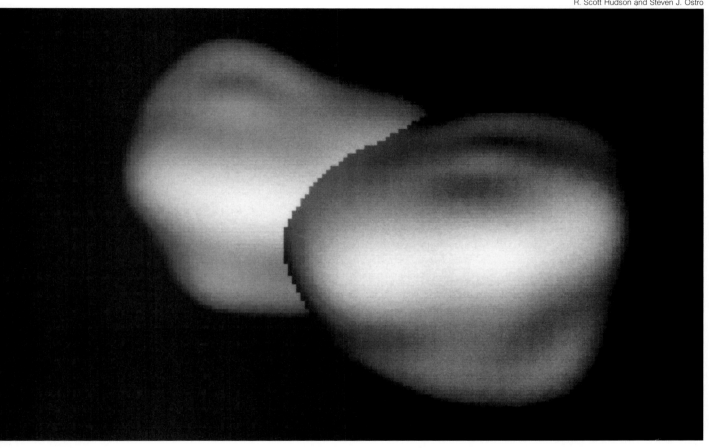

into a very large, loose orbit around Jupiter. On the other hand, it may have been more rocky than icy—possibly an asteroid that escaped from one of the so-called Trojan groups that orbit the Sun in Jupiter's orbit, about 60° ahead of the planet and 60° behind. Whatever it was, it came very close to Jupiter in mid-1992 and, because it was so weakly held together, the giant planet's dif-

ferential gravitational tug on the near and far sides of the object was sufficient to pull it apart into about 20 pieces or, perhaps, 20 swarms of smaller pieces.

Comets have been seen to break up before, sometimes during a close passage to the Sun or Jupiter but sometimes for no apparent reason. The few comets that are temporarily captured by Jupiter nor-

mally escape back out into solar orbit before they can crash into the planet. Comet Shoemaker-Levy 9, however, on the very first orbit following its breakup, was perturbed slightly by the Sun onto a path that carried all 20 pieces directly into Jupiter—at a velocity of 60 kilometers per second (130,000 miles per hour). This was an extraordinarily rare combination of events.

A computer model of the Earth-approaching asteroid Castalia (opposite page and above), constructed from radar data, shows the compound nature of the object as it is rotated counterclockwise through 120°. Castalia, about 1.8 kilometers at its widest, may consist of two loose chunks resting together. Were a nuclear weapon directed at such an object to "nudge" it from a collision course with Earth, the blast could cause it to break up in dangerous, unpredictable ways.

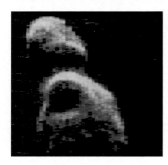

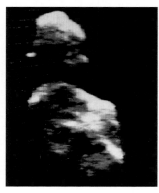

had begun two decades earlier.) Calculations soon predicted that the comet was on a fatal encounter with Jupiter. At that stage astronomers had more than a year to plan for the impacts and arrange for use of the most sophisticated ground-based equipment available as well as Earth-orbiting observatories such as the Hubble Space Telescope. Because the impacts would occur on the nightside of Jupiter, the side facing away from Earth, the best-situated observatory was the Galileo spacecraft, nearly a year past its encounter with Ida and approaching Jupiter from the side.

Each of the larger comet fragments that plunged explosively into Jupiter's atmosphere unleashed an energy approaching a million megatons of TNT—approximately the same energy that would be liberated by a two-kilometer-sized asteroid striking Earth and causing a global catastrophe. Despite early concerns that the comet impacts might turn out to be duds, the events were spectacular indeed. Although the explosions took place on Jupiter's nightside, they lofted debris thousands of kilometers into space, where they reached sunlight and could be photographed directly from Earth. The ma-

After the comet broke up, it became bright enough to be discovered in March 1993 by Eugene Shoemaker, his wife, Carolyn, and a collaborator, amateur comet hunter David H. Levy. (Fittingly, Eugene Shoemaker at the time was engaged in the very same photographic patrol for Earth-approaching asteroids that he

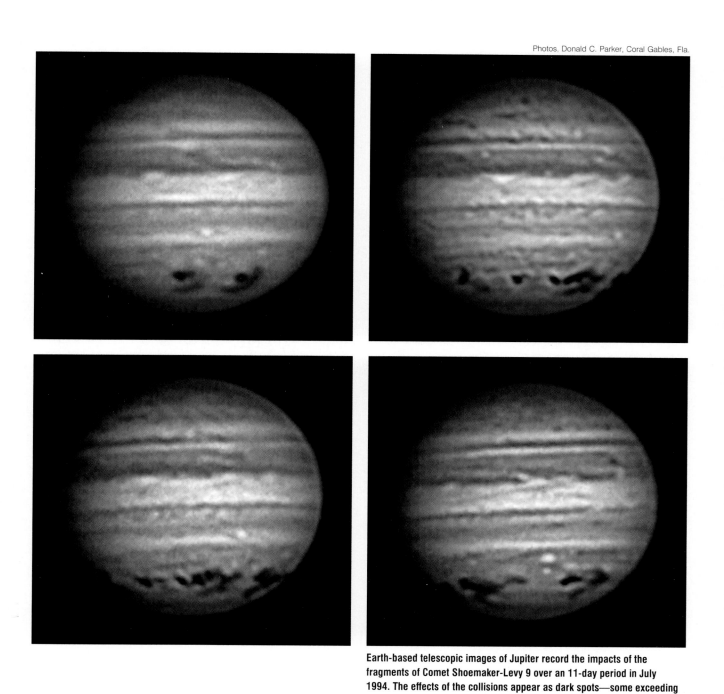

Photos, Donald C. Parker, Coral Gables, Fla.

Earth-based telescopic images of Jupiter record the impacts of the fragments of Comet Shoemaker-Levy 9 over an 11-day period in July 1994. The effects of the collisions appear as dark spots—some exceeding the size of Earth—near the south pole. Each of the larger impacts released roughly the same amount of energy that would be liberated by a two-kilometer asteroid striking Earth and causing a global catastrophe.

A sequence of images by the Hubble Space Telescope follows a plume of debris from an impacting fragment of Comet Shoemaker-Levy 9 as it expands into space above Jupiter's shadow and then sinks back into the atmosphere.

terial then rained back down across expanses of Jupiter's stratosphere that exceeded the total area of Earth. These secondary impacts raised the temperature of those regions to nearly 1,000 kelvins (1,300° F).

During ensuing days even nonprofessional observers using small telescopes could see enormous black spots on Jupiter at the impact sites. Some spots exceeded the size of Earth and were among the largest ever seen on Jupiter since the invention of the telescope. Moreover, the spots, which comprised dark-colored aerosols (suspended particles of matter), lingered in the atmosphere. Although upper winds soon stretched the discrete spots into a black belt encircling Jupiter, the belt persisted into 1995.

The implications of an impact hazard for Earth were clear for all to see. The impact of an ordinary comet was capable of creating a dark atmospheric pall the size of Earth. What if a similar pall

remained in Earth's stratosphere for as long as the black belt lasted on Jupiter? Worldwide climate effects from impacts had been calculated on the assumption that silicate dust derived from crustal rocks crushed and thrown up by the impact would spread out in Earth's stratosphere and block sunlight—part of Alvarez' original mass-extinction hypothesis. The Shoemaker-Levy 9 crash raises the

possibility that highly absorbing black aerosols may form that are more efficient than silicate dust at soaking up sunlight. If such aerosols can be created from materials de-

rived from the impacting body during an atmospheric explosion, the same could happen on Earth, and the effects on climate and agriculture could be worse than thought.

THE FUTURE

Asteroids and comets long have held a fascination because of the clues they are thought to carry about the early history of the solar system. Recently astronomers have begun to identify numbers of small objects located beyond the orbit of Neptune. More than 20 of these trans-Neptunian bodies were discovered in just the first two and a half years after the first was found in 1992. Having formed so far from the Sun, these bodies probably have the icy composition of

comets, and scientists suspect that they are part of a storehouse of comets, called the Kuiper Belt, that is postulated to lie beyond Neptune. Some of the Earth-approaching as-

98

Photos, H. Hammel, MIT/STScI/NASA

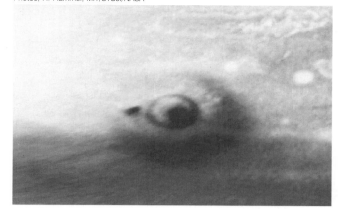

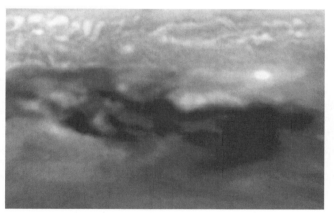

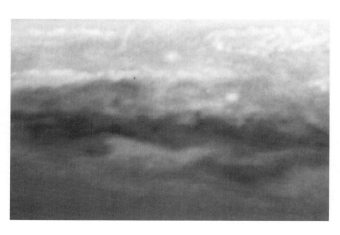

teroids probably originated in this region as comets, which later lost all their volatile materials through repeated swings past the Sun and are now "dead." Although during the era of planetary formation there were too few Kuiper Belt objects to form a 10th planet, there nevertheless may be 30,000 or more that are larger than 100 kilometers in diameter. Even if only a tiny fraction of that material has ventured into near-Earth space, it could have been a major component of what has rained down since the Earth's formation.

The ongoing impacts of asteroids and comets have shaped the geology of all solid-surfaced planets and moons, with the exception of those that are extremely volcanically active, such as Jupiter's moon Io. Scientists are now beginning to appreciate the very significant role that asteroidal and cometary impacts have

Dark particles of suspended matter generated in Jupiter's atmosphere from one of the cometary impacts are drawn into a streak by upper winds in a sequence of Hubble Space Telescope images covering about a five-week period. The black aerosols created by the impacts eventually formed a belt around the planet that persisted into 1995.

had on the Earth's fragile ecosphere. Paleontologist David Raup of the University of Chicago has gone so far as to suggest that impacts may be chiefly responsible for shaping the broad pattern of biological evolution on Earth—by creating the occasional global environmental crises that have driven mass extinctions and the consequent emergence of new species.

It is now apparent that there will be more impacts in the future, although the chance of one's happening in a given human lifetime is very small. Of more immediate interest is the fact that the near-Earth asteroids include some of the easiest targets for robotic or piloted space missions and that they represent a diverse array of raw materials of potential use for exploring and living in space. Whether it is we who first visit asteroids on research or mining missions or asteroids that come calling on us, our consciousness has been raised about these tiny worlds left over from the ancient birth of the solar system.

See also *1986 Yearbook of Science and the Future* Feature Article: PERIODIC COMET SHOWERS: THE MAINSPRING OF EVOLUTION?; *1993 Yearbook of Science and the Future* Feature Article: THE SEARCH FOR THE KT CRATER.

A Star Wars Legacy

by Edward A. Heighway

The subjects of intense research during the Strategic Defense Initiative, particle accelerators are now poised to play a potential role in destroying plutonium and other nuclear waste. They may even be able to help produce a source of safe nuclear electric energy that would generate almost no nuclear waste.

Illustration by Greg Spalenka

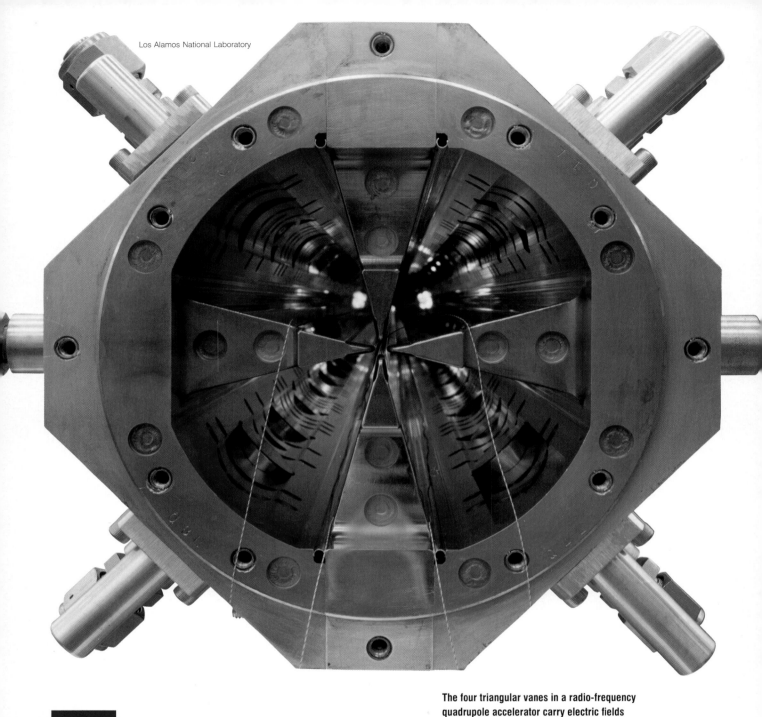

The four triangular vanes in a radio-frequency quadrupole accelerator carry electric fields that accelerate, bunch, and focus a beam of particles. The beam passes through the narrow channel between the four vanes.

The Strategic Defense Initiative (SDI), inaugurated in the United States in 1983, was an ambitious program designed to protect the U.S. from nuclear attack. Its investment in advanced technology—high-power lasers, particle beams, high-resolution space-based sensors, and advanced missile interceptors—though never more than 2% of the national defense budget, was nonetheless unprecedented. Though SDI was never completed, it produced many advances in technology.

One of the project's most important goals was to deploy in high-Earth orbit a number of highly maneuverable satellites on which would be mounted particle accelerators that could, with great rapidity, fire intense beams of particles against very large numbers of incoming missiles. The expected source of those missiles was, of course, the Soviet Union. It is not surprising

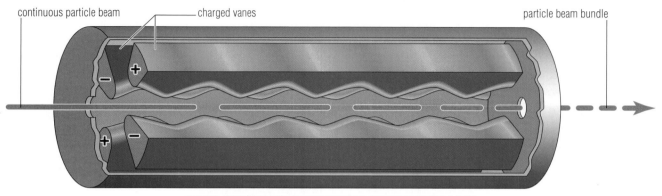

RADIO-FREQUENCY QUADRUPOLE ACCELERATOR (RFQ)

The Russian-invented radio-frequency quadrupole revolutionized particle accelerators. Compact and efficient, it converts a continuous stream of particles into bunches (like droplets) that are ideal for acceleration to high energy.

that these devices, together with space-based high-power chemical lasers, gave rise to the popular name for SDI, "Star Wars." It is of some irony that an invention by Soviet scientists enabled the U.S. to even imagine orbiting such technology. Thus, it is a source of some gratification that after the end of the Cold War it is this technology that is the basis for a close collaboration between Russia and the U.S. on civilian applications with far-reaching potential benefits to society.

Edward A. Heighway is a project leader at Los Alamos National Laboratory. For 25 years in Canada and the U.S., he has been an active researcher and developer of particle accelerators for applications in medicine, fundamental science, defense, and energy.

THE SDI MISSION

The mission envisioned for particle beams was primarily one of inspection or discrimination rather than destruction. The concept was simple. If there were a barrage of incoming missiles deliberately mixed in with additional objects that were largely visually indistinguishable from the real missiles, there would be no alternative for the defenses but to assume the worst and launch enough interceptors to destroy everything. If there were enough of these decoys, the defenses would then become saturated, and missiles would leak through.

For such decoys to be effective, there must be many of them, and for many of them to be launched, they must be lightweight. On the

other hand, the missiles themselves, because they necessarily contain high-density metals needed in a warhead, have to be heavy. The role of the particle beams was to inspect the missiles and decoys and "weigh" them. They could do this by simply shining the particle beam on the objects and watching for resulting reaction radiations. By choosing to look at the radiations that depended strongly on whether the object contained heavy metals, scientists could use particle beams to discriminate those objects that were missiles from those that were simply decoys or dummies.

If this discrimination could be done fast enough, then the missiles within a large group of mixed objects could be identified and the interceptors directed only at them,

thereby neutralizing the value of using decoys. To be able to have the beam "see" inside the missile and at the same time get a return signal strong enough to make the analysis very quickly, the incident particle beam must be both highly penetrating and of high intensity—thus, the need for high-energy, high-current, particle-beam accelerators.

THE PARTICLE ACCELERATOR

One of the simplest particles that accelerators deliver is the ionized hydrogen atom. A hydrogen atom consists of a proton around which a single electron orbits. Ions can be formed either by addition of an extra electron to form a negative hydrogen ion, the so-called H − particle, or by the stripping away of the single electron to leave the positively charged proton, or H+ ion. In most accelerators electric forces are used to push, or accelerate, these ions to higher and higher energies. H+ ions are used in the largest accelerators for high-energy physics, but H− particles were chosen for use by SDI. They were selected because at the last instant before the beam leaves the satellite, the extra electron can be easily stripped off, and the neutral beam begins its path through space. Because it has no electric charge, the beam is undisturbed by the Earth's magnetic field and travels in a straight line through space.

There are two forms of electric acceleration, electrostatic and radio frequency (rf). The first, in its simplest form, is based on the principle of using a constant voltage between two plates to create an electric field to accelerate the ions. In the latter the electric field is not static and can be manipulated so that the particles in some sense "surf" along on it and thus gain higher and higher energy. This rf acceleration is an essential component of the biggest accelerators and is described below.

One of the most difficult tasks of accelerators is starting the beam. Until the mid-1980s all proton linear accelerators employed a large high-

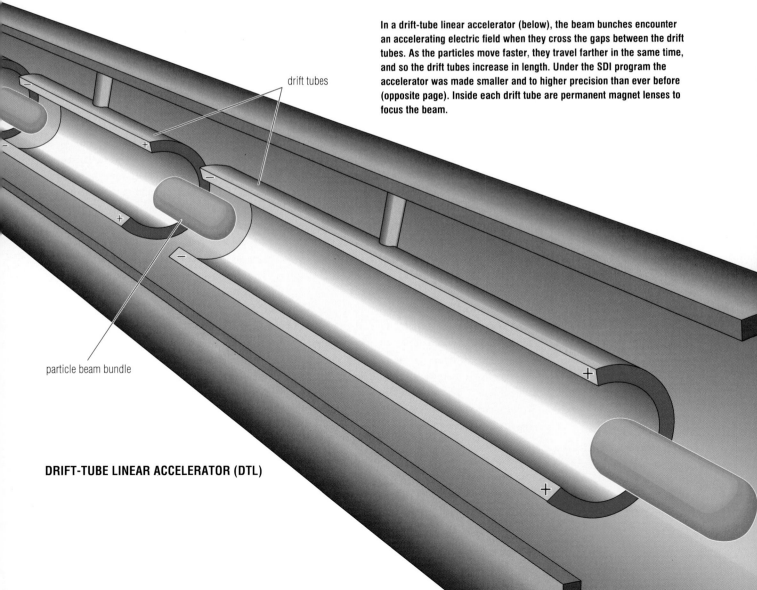

In a drift-tube linear accelerator (below), the beam bunches encounter an accelerating electric field when they cross the gaps between the drift tubes. As the particles move faster, they travel farther in the same time, and so the drift tubes increase in length. Under the SDI program the accelerator was made smaller and to higher precision than ever before (opposite page). Inside each drift tube are permanent magnet lenses to focus the beam.

drift tubes

particle beam bundle

DRIFT-TUBE LINEAR ACCELERATOR (DTL)

voltage, electrostatic injector for the first several hundred thousand volts of acceleration. Such devices required a very large enclosure (many meters [one meter is about 3.3 feet] across) to reduce the chance of high-voltage sparking (disruptive electrical discharging) and were powered by large Cockcroft-Walton generators to provide the high voltage. Because of their size they were not practical for use in orbiting devices.

This problem was addressed and solved in the 1970s by two Soviet scientists, Iliya M. Kapchinsky and Vladimir A. Tyeplakov. They did so by inventing the radio-frequency quadrupole (RFQ) accelerator, a structure that formed an rf electric field that would simultaneously accelerate and focus the particle beam over a sustained distance. The RFQ consists of four vanes (long plates laid parallel to the beam such that their section forms a cross but with the center left open for the beam) at modest rf voltage (tens of kilovolts) and of alternating polarity—plus, minus, plus, minus. This results in an electric field that focuses the beam in one plane while simultaneously defocusing it in the perpendicular plane. As the electric field changes over time, the net effect is to alternately focus and defocus the particles. As is true for the simple Galilean telescope, such a combination results in net focusing and, consequently, confinement of the beam. The key trick in the RFQ was to add modulations or ripples along the length of the vanes so that there would also be a component of electric field along the beam axis. By careful design of those modulations, scientists can accelerate the beam smoothly and in a short length to energies much higher than those of the big electrostatic injectors without losing particles or high beam quality.

Soviet, U.S., and other scientists have produced many applications of the RFQ, but it was researchers at the Los Alamos (New Mexico) National Laboratory who first built such a device in the U.S. and aggressively developed systems of smaller size and higher precision. Thus, the high-voltage electrostatic injector (occupying a volume of many meters on a side) was replaced with a device measuring less than one meter long and only 20 centimeters (8 inches) across. Such an RFQ was the subject of a successful space demonstration. That experiment proved that accelerators could be built to survive the violence of a rocket launch, be started up and operated in space, and still perform to meet stringent design specifications.

THE RF ACCELERATOR

Taking the particle beam beyond the low energies produced by the RFQ requires two other accelerator types that employ similar principles of rf acceleration but that operate quite differently. The first of these is called the drift-tube linear accelerator (DTL). It consists of a long cylindrical cavity through which the beam passes. An external radio-frequency power source provides an oscillating electric field directed along the axis of the cavity. The cavity is long enough so that during the time it takes for a particle to travel along its length, the electric field goes through several cycles and sometimes is in a direction to accelerate the particle and sometimes in one to decelerate the particle. To prevent the deceleration, tubes are installed inside the cavity that act as so-called Faraday shields to "hide" the particles from the electric field when it is in the wrong direction. The particles are accelerated only when they are

Scientists first envisioned large orbiting space platforms that could destroy missiles with particle beams. However, much smaller spacecraft equipped to determine which missiles were actually carrying warheads were found to be more effective.

in the gaps between the tubes and simply coast or drift when they are inside the tubes—thus the name drift tube.

Unlike the RFQ, the DTL provides no electric confining or focusing fields, and so these must be provided in another way. Making the drift tubes do double duty by containing small permanent magnets that act as lenses to keep the beam tightly confined along its axis accomplishes this. Without such focusing, the beam would gradually get larger and larger until it started to hit the walls of the accelerator and become lost.

At higher energies the acceleration mechanism changes from the DTL to the so-called coupled-cavity linear accelerator (CCL). The geometry of the CCL is different from that of the DTL in that, instead of single long cavities that require drift tubes to shield the beam from reverse fields during traversal, this accelerator consists of a string of short cavities, each of which is arranged to give the particle an accelerating kick while it is in the cavity field. The CCL is the workhorse of high-energy linear accelerators. In the CCL structure the focusing to confine the beam is no longer contained inside drift tubes but can instead be located between cavities.

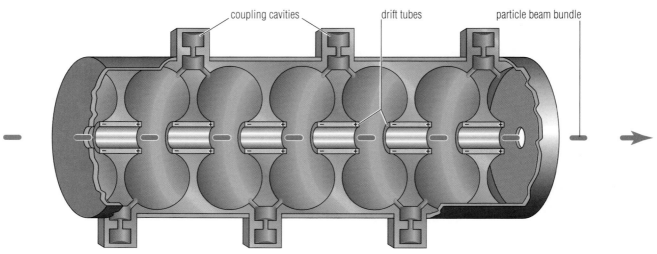

coupling cavities   drift tubes   particle beam bundle

COUPLED-CAVITY LINEAR ACCELERATOR (CCL)

The coupled-cavity linear accelerator (CCL; opposite page, top) consists of a string of short cavities where particles are continuously accelerated. The focusing to confine the particle beam is located between groups of cavities. Below, the CCL at the Fermi National Accelerator Laboratory, Batavia, Illinois, is used for high-energy research.

Fermi National Accelerator Laboratory

SDI'S CONTRIBUTIONS TO THE TECHNOLOGY

Although the development of accelerators for the SDI application ended before a fully integrated system could be demonstrated either on the ground or in space, considerable technological progress was made. By concentrating on the technology of accelerating high-intensity beams and designing and building the hardware to do so, scientists gained a broad understanding of the physics and engineering of these devices. As a result, they were able to extend considerably the range of energies and currents over which high-intensity accelerators can be built and operated.

In addition, an infrastructure was developed that enabled the construction of such accelerating devices to much higher precision than had previously been possible. This applied not only to the mechanical parameters of the accelerators, which were built to higher frequency and therefore smaller dimensions and tighter tolerances, but also to the electrical parameters of the rf field, which were controlled to a very tight electrical amplitude and phase. To add to this, the understanding of the transport of the particles once they leave the accelerator cavities was greatly increased. This latter advance is important in delivering the high-energy particle beam to illuminate any target that might be envisioned.

Because the beams produced were of such high precision, an additional and separate infrastructure of diagnostic tools had to be built so that the quality of the beams could be determined accurately and so that operation could be compared with design prediction. These diagnostic tools were often quite exotic in themselves, using lasers, for example, to probe into the particle beam in order to measure the detailed distribution of particles in the core. These improved diagnostic techniques are now available to be applied to all major accelerator systems.

Furthermore, because these systems were intended for remote operation in space, a big investment was made in the development of computer control systems. In this area the payoff has been remarkable, and control systems that are direct descendants or close cousins of those pioneered for the particle-beam devices are now in use and in continued development at about 30 institutes and industries throughout the world.

BENEFITS OF HIGH-INTENSITY ACCELERATORS

It is well known that atoms colliding at high energies produce showers of reaction particles. At modestly high energies, around 1,000 MeV, proton or H− collisions with heavy target atoms, such as lead, result in a process called spallation, in which about 20–30 neutrons are generated by each collision of an incoming beam particle with the target. The 1,000-MeV energy is about one-tenth to one-one hundredth of the energies of those accelerators typical of the world's major particle physics laboratories. Nonetheless, a 1,000-MeV accelerator is a substantial device, several hundred meters or so in length. Since the number of neutrons produced depends on the intensity of the incoming beam, particle accelerators that can deliver very intense beams will in turn produce very intense fluxes of neutrons. (Neutron flux is the intensity of neutron radiation expressed as the number of neutrons passing through a unit area per unit time.)

The recent advances in technology have increased the confidence of scientists that they can design, build, and operate accelerators to pro-

The accelerator at Los Alamos (New Mexico) National Laboratory was designed to accelerate high-intensity beams of particles.

Los Alamos National Laboratory

duce the required stable, high-quality, intense beams; deliver them in a controlled way to a target; and, consequently, produce intense fluxes of neutrons. It is these intense fluxes that enable the most significant applications and that are spawning research within and beyond the accelerator community worldwide. These applications have the potential to contribute to the solution of many of the problems facing today's society.

Researchers have begun to examine three major areas where this accelerator technology might be beneficial. The first is the destruction of plutonium in warheads being taken out of the nuclear weapons stockpiles in Russia and the U.S. Second is the possibility of burning the plutonium remaining in spent fuel from commercial power reactors and with it to burn much of the other nuclear waste in that spent fuel. Third, in the longer term, systems are being considered that would use this technology as a component of an energy system that burns thorium rather than uranium. Such a system could be efficient in that it would burn virtually all of its fuel and produce minimal nuclear waste.

This is a tall order, but the potential is indeed real, and researchers are actively examining all aspects of these applications to identify and remove possible obstacles from the technical path to their realization.

Each of these payoff applications succeeds by uniting an accelerator with a target assembly that uses fission reactor technology but that by

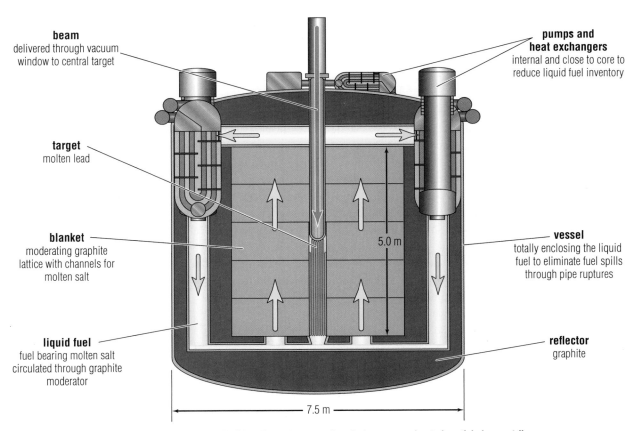

beam
delivered through vacuum window to central target

pumps and heat exchangers
internal and close to core to reduce liquid fuel inventory

target
molten lead

blanket
moderating graphite lattice with channels for molten salt

liquid fuel
fuel bearing molten salt circulated through graphite moderator

5.0 m

vessel
totally enclosing the liquid fuel to eliminate fuel spills through pipe ruptures

reflector
graphite

7.5 m

Target-blanket assembly, designed to generate power, is driven by neutrons produced when an accelerated particle beam strikes the molten lead target. Slowed by the moderating graphite lattice, the neutrons react with a fissionable fuel material to produce more neutrons and, ultimately, power.

itself is not a reactor. It is well understood that the catalysts that make fission reactors work are neutrons. These neutrons trigger a steady-state fission process—a stable chain reaction—within the reactor core. Neutrons are a precious commodity in reactors, so much so that the term neutron economy is used to describe the careful balance between neutrons available to create fissions (and hence power) and those lost to other nonfission reactions such as capture in other materials in the reactor. Much of the effort in the design of a modern reactor is expended in the selection of materials and the laying out of a geometry that results in a system that is neutron-efficient. It is then not difficult to understand that if many neutrons are supplied from an external source, such as from an accelerator-driven spallation, the neutron economy becomes much improved.

The geometry of these accelerator-driven systems is such that an external accelerator delivers its beam to a heavy, and probably liquid, metal target, such as lead, which is placed at the center of an assembly referred to as a blanket. This blanket assembly has many of the attributes of a reactor in that it contains a moderating material to slow down the spallation-produced neutrons from the target in order to make them more efficient in the fission process. It must also, of course, contain fissionable fuel material that is burned when it absorbs the moderated neutrons and then fissions to produce yet more neutrons and, ultimately, power. It is different from a reactor in that it cannot sustain a chain reaction.

DESTROYING PLUTONIUM IN WEAPONS

With the end of the Cold War and the resulting arms-reduction treaties, there was much effort to secure the plutonium from dismantled warheads, primarily to prevent possible proliferation. Beyond achieving simple physical security, there was considerable investigation of means to convert the plutonium to forms that would allow it to be disposed of safely and in a way that would be very resistant to proliferation. Such disposition could be either to retrievable storage or to geologic repositories, the latter intended to make it inaccessible forever.

Research was also under way to discover how best to "burn" the plutonium. The plutonium can be used as the fuel, or as a component of the fuel, in existing reactors of several types. Each reactor can burn the plutonium taken from weapons with differing degrees of efficiency, but in large measure the end product is spent fuel similar to that from existing power reactors. Such a solution for plutonium disposal, realizable as it is, therefore transfers the burden to that of dealing with the spent fuel, for which the solution on the table is storage in geologic repositories.

There is yet a third option, and that is to develop systems that can burn the plutonium virtually completely. In this case the combination of an accelerator with a reactor-like blanket is effective. Different types of blankets have been proposed for this burning, most notably a molten salt-fueled system and a modular gas-cooled graphite system. Each has demonstrated that it can provide a complete burn of the plutonium, thereby destroying all of it.

BURNING SPENT COMMERCIAL FUEL

Although a great deal of energy is produced from the fuel in reactors, much potential energy remains in the fuel when it has to be taken from the reactor as spent. The fuel becomes spent because the fission products (atoms resulting from the fissioning process) and other so-called poisons in it have built up to a level where they start to absorb too many of the valuable neutrons. Eventually too many neutrons are lost to keep the reactor critical (criticality is the condition in which each fission results in exactly one more fission). When that many neutrons are lost, the power production from the fuel can no longer be maintained. New fuel is needed to replace the old in order to allow the system to continue to produce power.

If, however, there is a supply of additional neutrons, such as those produced by spallation in an accelerator, it can be used to extend the life of the fuel by creating enough of an extra margin to overcome the losses of neutrons in the fission products. There is also another benefit that these additional neutrons can provide. Several of the fission products and other nuclei produced in the reactor are long-lived radioactive materials. Normally these remain in the fuel when it is spent and removed from the reactor. These long-lived radioactive wastes have driven the need for geologic deposition. However, if they can be kept in the reactor long enough, these materials actually absorb neutrons and undergo chemical changes. These new materials are either nonradioactive or much shorter-lived. This change in the nuclear identity is called transmutation. If this burning can be done effectively, the volume and half-life of the radioactive waste can be reduced and the burden on waste-disposal facilities greatly reduced.

PRODUCTION OF ENERGY

In the longer term there is yet another potential benefit of this technology, and that is to fuel the accelerator-driven blanket systems with thorium rather than uranium. Thorium is nonfissile but is converted to a fissile uranium fuel by the neutrons in the blanket. Such systems produce less radioactive waste than conventional uranium systems, and if use can be made of the higher burn fraction of the fuel and the burn of the fission products provided by the accelerator-driven systems, it may be possible to build a cleaner nuclear energy producer that could significantly extend energy resources.

However, even with the extra neutrons supplied by the accelerator, it is technically challenging to build a system that is capable of achieving the simultaneous goals of a complete burn of the fuel and the total destruction of the long-lived fission products. For the maximum burn to be attained, there must be some way to

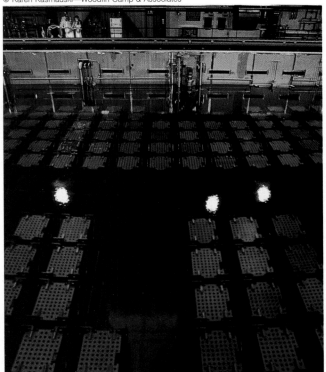

Blue containers of decaying radioactive fuel float in a pond at a nuclear plant in France. Such wastes might be destroyed or greatly reduced by accelerator-based systems.

clean the fuel of the neutron-poisoning fission products and then return it for additional burning. For maximum transmutation of the long-lived fission products to be gained, they must be separated from the extracted total spectrum of fission products and also returned for more burning. This then requires additional research and the development of the necessary separations technology.

FUTURE PROSPECTS

While much work must be done to develop these technologies fully and to bring them to commercial realization, there are no fundamental obstacles to their feasibility. As with all new technology approaches, there will be a period of intense study and experimentation required for overcoming the detailed technical issues and making such systems operate effectively and to their full potential. With the effort of scientists of several Western nations and Russia, however, there is much cause for optimism. It is to be hoped that these applications, enabled in large part by the attention of SDI to advanced accelerator technology, may effectively address important global issues.

FOR ADDITIONAL READING

■ "Accelerators Address Nuclear Waste Problems," Francesco Venneri, Charles Bowman, and Robert Jameson, *Physics World* (August 1993, p. 40).

■ *Controlling the Atom in the 21st Century*, David P. O'Very, Christopher E. Paine, and Dan W. Reicher, eds. (Westview Press, 1994).

■ "Nuclear Energy Generation and Waste Transmutation Using an Accelerator-Driven Intense Thermal Neutron Source," C.D. Bowman et al., *Nuclear Instruments and Methods in Physics Research* (vol. A320, 1992, pp. 336–367).

■ "The RFQ Is Alive and Well," John T. Ahearne, *The Atom* (vol. 17, no. 4, July–August 1980).

The Elusive Neutrino: A Window on the Universe

by Francis Halzen

Astronomers believe that neutrinos can be used as powerful research tools to shed new light on the universe. First, though, they must detect and capture these elusive particles.

During the past year the world witnessed the first attempts to commission a strange, novel type of telescope. It has no mirrors, does not use light, and, with few exceptions, is not operated by astronomers. Its purpose is to exploit the neutrino, a common but elusive subatomic particle, to probe cosmic mysteries. Environmentalists, geologists, glaciologists, particle physicists, and even some astronomers are going to this instrument from universities throughout the world with such diverse agendas as study-

ing supermassive black holes in the hearts of distant galaxies, monitoring the skies for exploding stars, studying the physics of elementary particles, and studying deep ocean water and old Antarctic ice. Most of all, they hope to be surprised. Historically, new ways of looking at the sky have led to unexpected discoveries.

The origins of the neutrino can be traced back to the discovery of radioactivity by Henri Becquerel, who around 1896 accidentally discovered that photographic plates (as well as his skin!) were blackened by invisible radiation emanating from uranium salts. In such radioactive decays the nuclei of atoms transform into different nuclei when neutrons are transformed into slightly

Francis Halzen is a Professor of Physics at the University of Wisconsin, Madison.

lighter protons with the emission of electrons:

**neutron →
proton + electron.**

The principle of conservation of energy implies that all the electrons in this reaction should have the same energy, which would be determined by the small mass difference between the neutron and proton. However, by the late 1920s experiments had produced unquestionable evidence that the energy spectrum of the electrons is continuous instead. Consequently, Niels Bohr heralded the demise of one of the most fundamental laws of physics, the conservation of energy. In 1930 the more cautious Austrian physicist Wolfgang Pauli proposed instead that the emitted electron shares its energy with an invisible new particle, the neutrino. In a shared arrangement with the neutrino, the electron can acquire the full complement of observed energies while conspiring to conserve energy in all cases. The postulated particle has no mass and no electric charge; it just serves as an agent to balance the observed spectrum of electron energies. Pauli announced, "I have done a terrible thing, I have postulated a particle that cannot be detected." Clyde Cowan

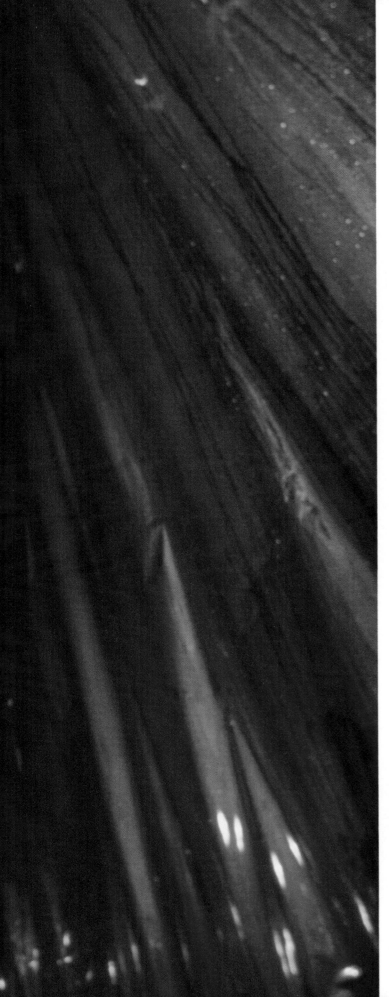

and Fred Reines proved him wrong 23 years later.

Observing neutrinos is straightforward in principle. In the presence of protons they should occasionally initiate the inverse reaction of radioactive decay:

**neutrino + proton →
neutron + electron.**

Experimentally, one simply looks for the coincident appearance of an electron and a neutron. There is, however, a problem. Four years after Pauli's suggestion, physicist Enrico Fermi developed a theory of weak interactions, which, except for some updating, is part of the present so-called standard model of weak and electromagnetic interactions. Hans Bethe and Rudolf Peierls promptly calculated the probability that a neutrino is captured by a proton or a nucleus and found a number that, by the standards of their time, must have looked so small that it precluded any possibility of performing the experiment. This handicap can, of course, be overcome by a source that produces abundant amounts of neutrinos. Cowan and Reines contributed to its construction: the atom bomb! The experiment they eventually designed was, however, operated in the vicinity of a more friendly source, the Savannah River nuclear reactor. There, in 1953, researchers were able to definitely demonstrate

When a supernova exploded in the Large Magellanic Cloud (right), billions of neutrinos streamed through the Earth for 10 seconds. Only 19 stopped in detectors in Kamioka, Japan (left), and near Cleveland, Ohio.

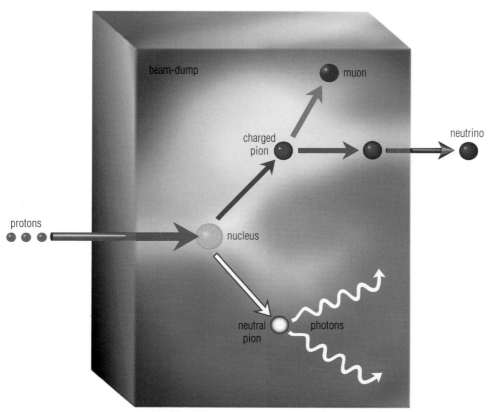

To form a beam of neutrinos, scientists shoot a stream of accelerated protons into a beam-dump, made of earth or stainless steel. The protons interact with nuclei in the dump to produce charged and neutral pions. A neutral pion decays into two photons, and a charged pion decays into a muon and a neutrino. The material in the dump absorbs the photons and muons so that only neutrinos exit at the opposite end.

the existence of the neutrino.

More than anything else, its feeble interaction with ordinary matter is what makes the neutrino so special. The weak force, through which it interacts with matter, is a hundred million times weaker than the familiar electromagnetic force. Neutrinos, which outnumber the nuclei of ordinary matter by a billion to one, are almost as ubiquitous

in the universe as particles of light (photons). The nuclear furnace burning at the center of the Sun is the source of a hundred thousand billion neutrinos passing through each person's body every second, yet it takes detectors weighing a thousand tons to catch one a day. On Feb. 24, 1987, billions upon billions of neutrinos streamed through the Earth for 10 seconds when

a supernova exploded in the Large Magellanic Cloud. Only 19 stopped in detectors in Kamioka, Japan, and near Cleveland, Ohio.

Scientists are now taking the first steps in the design of kilometer-scale neutrino detectors, consisting of a thousand billion liters (a teraliter; a liter is slightly more than a quart) of instrumented natural water or ice. These instru-

ments should be able to facilitate the study of the universe far beyond the Sun and observe cosmic cataclysms without having to wait for a one-in-a-century miracle like a nearby supernova. In order to design their detectors, physicists dream up potential sources of cosmic neutrinos. They use detailed computer simulations of their future instruments to optimize size and design and thereby guarantee detection. Such computer experiments range from the detection of neutrinos from bright, faraway galaxies to those produced by the annihilation of cold dark matter particles inside our own Galaxy's halo. Fortunately, the answer is the same whatever the job contemplated—instruments with volumes of one kilometer on a side are required. There is one notable exception; researchers have not been able to figure out how to detect the few hundred neutrinos per cubic centimeter (about 0.06 inch) that originated in the big bang and fill all of space. That task has been left for future scientists.

NEUTRINO BEAMS: HEAVEN AND EARTH

The penetrating power of the neutrino did not escape the attention of particle physicists,

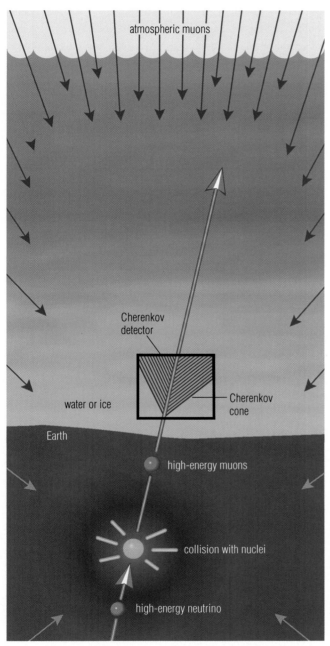

atmospheric muons

Cherenkov
detector

Cherenkov
cone

water or ice

Earth

high-energy muons

collision with nuclei

high-energy neutrino

In a neutrino telescope high-energy neutrinos collide with nuclei of matter and spawn high-energy muons. As the muons pass through a Cherenkov detector, they radiate photons in the form of a "Cherenkov cone" of light, which indicates the presence and direction of the high-energy neutrinos.

who readily understood that by illuminating matter with an intense neutrino beam, one can glean information on the structure deep inside protons. Thus, one could say that neutrinos are a diagnostic tool to "X-ray" protons or nuclei. During the 1960s neutrino beams passed from a futuristic dream to one of the most important tools of particle physics. They contributed in important ways to the discovery of quarks, the constituents of protons and neutrons. The technique is conceptually simple but technologically challenging. An intense beam of accelerated protons is shot into a "beam-dump," which typically consists of a kilometer (0.62-mile)-long mound of earth or a 100-meter (328-foot)-long block of stainless steel. Particle physics does the rest. Protons interact with nuclei in the dump and produce tens of pions in each collision. A neutral pion decays into two photons, while a charged pion decays into a muon and a neutrino. The material in the dump will eventually absorb the photons and muons so that only neutrinos exit at the opposite end, forming an intense and controlled beam ready to perform neutrino microscopy of matter.

We meet here for the first time one of the important

players in neutrino astronomy: the muon. It is no more than a fat electron, and its discovery more than half a century ago raised for the first time one of the outstanding riddles in particle physics. All matter, its chemistry, and nuclear physics can be understood in terms of electrons, neutrinos, protons, and neutrons or, in more up-to-date nomenclature, up and down quarks. Two almost identical copies of each of these particles exist. Thus, besides the electron there is a muon and tauon, differing only by their heavier masses. There are also three neutrinos labeled, after their companions, the electron-, muon-, and tau-neutrino. Thus, nature has also made a copy of the process Reines studied in his discovery experiment:

muon-neutrino + proton → muon + neutron.

High-energy muons are marvelous particles. Unlike electrons, they can travel through kilometers of water and ice, thus making high-energy neutrino astronomy possible.

Can neutrinos be used to X-ray the universe just like particle physicists X-rayed the proton? Are there neutrino beam-dumps producing neutrinos in space? All that is needed for such production is a proton beam energetic enough to produce pions and target material to act as the dump. The answer is definitively positive; cosmic-ray experiments have detected cosmic protons with energies in excess of 10^{20} eV—the energy, carried by a single proton, of a solidly hit tennis ball. When such particles interact with the Earth's atmosphere, the collision energy exceeds by more than a thousand times those achievable with the largest man-made accelerators. Such a cosmic-ray beam will produce neutrinos in any target material. The target may be as ordinary as the Earth's atmosphere or as exotic as the cosmic photons that fill outer space.

Incredibly, scientists have no clue as to where these cosmic rays come from and how they are accelerated to such energies. Those of highest energy are, almost certainly, of extragalactic origin, and when one searches the sky beyond our Galaxy, powerful quasars stand out as the most likely sites from which particles can be hurled at Earth with such high energy. This idea is rather compelling, as bright quasars are also the dominant source of high-energy protons. Quasars are the brightest sources in the universe; some are so far away that they are messengers from the earliest of times. They emit photons with energies never matched by particle accelerators. The sources of these emissions must be black holes, small in area but a billion times more massive than the Sun.

Neutrino astronomers believe that the high-energy sky as revealed by neutrinos will shine uniformly, revealing galaxies far brighter than the Milky Way, but the results may be even more spectacular. As is the case in man-made beam-dumps, photons from celestial accelerators may be absorbed in matter near the source. The neutrino sky may reveal sources with no counterpart in any wavelength of light. It is also likely to reveal the sources of the high-energy cosmic rays, thus resolving one of the longest-lingering puzzles in astronomy.

Some mixture of elementary particle physics and astrophysics allows scientists to compute that quasars will emit

Bruce Koci, Polar Ice Coring Office, University of Alaska, Fairbanks

Left, the Antarctic Muon and Neutrino Detector Array (AMANDA) is located about one kilometer (0.62 mile) from the geographic South Pole. The drilling tower is used to place the optical modules in the Antarctic ice sheet at depths between one and two kilometers, and the tent houses electronic equipment. A close-up of the AMANDA drill (right) reveals the caliper (with the four arms), which monitors the width of the hole that is melted through the ice, and the optical module (the sphere at the top).

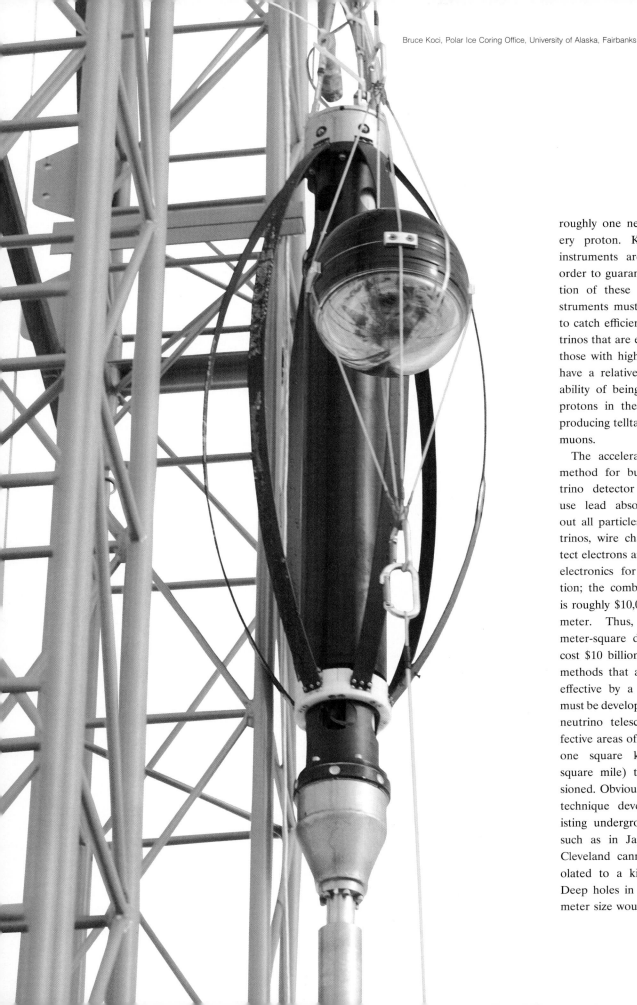

Bruce Koci, Polar Ice Coring Office, University of Alaska, Fairbanks

roughly one neutrino for every proton. Kilometer-sized instruments are required in order to guarantee the detection of these neutrinos. Instruments must be optimized to catch efficiently those neutrinos that are easy to catch—those with high energies that have a relatively large probability of being absorbed on protons in the detector and producing telltale electrons or muons.

The accelerator physicist's method for building a neutrino detector will typically use lead absorber to filter out all particles but the neutrinos, wire chambers to detect electrons and muons, and electronics for data acquisition; the combined price tag is roughly $10,000 per square meter. Thus, a one-kilometer-square detector would cost $10 billion. Realistically, methods that are more cost-effective by a factor of 100 must be developed in order for neutrino telescopes with effective areas of approximately one square kilometer (0.4 square mile) to be commissioned. Obviously, the proven technique developed by existing underground detectors such as in Japan and near Cleveland cannot be extrapolated to a kilometer scale. Deep holes in mines of kilometer size would be unstable.

Thick glass spheres (center) are the pressure-resistant housing for the photomultiplier tubes deployed more than 4 kilometers (2½ miles) deep in the Mediterranean Sea off the coast of Greece as part of the Neutrinos from Supernovae and TeV Sources Ocean Range (NESTOR) project.

Leo Resvanis, Athens University, Greece

(ICE) FISHING FOR NEUTRINOS

As described above, the interaction of neutrinos with matter is so weak that the neutrinos will have to penetrate the full thickness of the Earth in order to have some chance of being captured. Detectors of astrophysical neutrinos must, therefore, be orders of magnitude larger than familiar astronomical instruments. Large volumes of water or ice are needed to trap a few unlucky neutrinos. When these collide with nuclei of matter, they will spawn muons, which will act as observable tracers of the presence and direction of neutrinos.

A high-energy neutrino telescope detects muons made by neutrinos in the water or ice inside or in the vicinity of the detector. High-energy muons travel over distances of one kilometer or more, allowing the reach of the detector to be extended well beyond the actual instrumented volume. Also, high-energy muons are nicely aligned with the direction of their parent neutrinos, making astronomy possible. The muons point back to the neutrino sources with an accuracy of better than 1°, a deviation that decreases further with increasing neutrino energy.

In a Cherenkov detector, the direction of the neutrino is inferred from the muon track. Physicists measure the track by mapping the cone of Cherenkov light radiated by the muon as it travels through the detector. The bluish Cherenkov light surrounding the muon is of the same origin as the ghostly blue glow emanating from the water that covers a nuclear reactor. Just like a boat exceeding the speed of the bow waves in its wake, a high-energy muon, traveling faster than the speed of light in water or ice, will radiate photons in the form of a "Cherenkov cone" of light. The arrival times of the Cherenkov photons at a grid of optical detectors are used to reconstruct the direction of the radiating muon. The photons can be detected with commercial photomultiplier tubes (PMTs). A PMT performs the reverse function of a lightbulb—light is transformed into an electric signal. The faint signals are amplified by a factor of up to 100 million.

All this sounds relatively straightforward until one faces the fact that the detector is constantly bombarded with muons produced by cosmic rays in the Earth's atmosphere. These are the decay products of pions and are totally unrelated to neutrinos. Near the Earth's surface these muons are more than 10 billion times more numerous than those signaling the arrival of cosmic neutrinos. In a detector shielded by a kilometer-thick layer of water or ice, that number is reduced to one million. The trick is to use the Earth as a filter; muons traveling upward through the detector must be spawned by neutrinos because the Earth will shield out atmospheric muons. Neutrino telescopes point into the ground, with the South Pole telescope studying the northern skies.

The experimental challenge thus becomes well-defined—record the muon direction with sufficient precision (sufficient to reject the much more numerous down-going cosmic-ray muons from the upcoming muons of neutrino origin) with a minimum number of PMTs in order to limit cost. Critical considerations are detector depth, which determines the level of the cosmic-ray muon background, and the noise rates in the PMTs, which will sprinkle a muon timing pattern with false timing signals. Sources of such noise include radioactive potassium in seawater, bioluminescent deep-sea organisms, and, inevitably, the background counts in the photomultiplier tube it-

Photos, Robert Morse, University of Wisconsin, Madison

The ice on Lake Baikal in Siberia is used as a platform for deploying the neutrino detector (top). Through the hole, electronics for data acquisition are lowered in pressure-resistant glass spheres. A former station on the Trans-Siberian Railroad (above) houses laboratories and equipment for the Lake Baikal project.

self. For Cherenkov light to be collected efficiently, only the clearest water and ice can be instrumented.

Although many kinds of detectors have been proposed, as of late 1994 three were under construction and one more had received funding. The experimental advantages and challenges are different for each experiment, and in this sense they nicely complement one another as engineering projects for constructing the ultimate large detector. Each has its own method of achieving neutrino detection with a minimum number of PMTs: (1) The Antarctic

Muon and Neutrino Detector Array (AMANDA) uses sterile ice, free of radioactivity; (2) the Lake Baikal detector in Siberia requires simultaneous signals in adjacent pairs of PMTs in order to suppress the large background noise in each individual PMT; and (3) the Deep Underwater Muon and Neutrino Detector (DU-MAND) and Neutrinos from Supernovae and TeV Sources Ocean Range (NESTOR) collaborations shield their arrays with more than four kilometers of ocean water.

Detectors under construction will have a nominal effective area of several times 10,000 meters squared for high-energy neutrinos. The optical modules are deployed like beads on strings separated by 20–50 meters. (An optical module consists of a pressure vessel containing a PMT and, sometimes, electronics.) There are typically 20 per string, separated from one another by roughly 10 meters. The Lake Baikal detector in 1994 was operating 36 optical modules, 18 pointing up and 18 down, and the South Pole AMANDA experiment started operating 4 strings with a total of 80 optical modules in January 1994. When completed, the first-generation telescopes will consist of approximately 200 modules.

ICE TELESCOPES

AMANDA freezes optical modules in the Antarctic ice sheet at depths between one and two kilometers. The strings are deployed by means of a hot-water drilling technique pioneered by glaciologists. The drill has been compared to a rather heavy bathroom showerhead. Gushing out hot water, it melts its way down the ice, steered only by gravity. During its free fall it is designed to deviate by less than one meter from vertical when reaching the one-kilometer mark. The melted ice is not removed from the hole; the hot water is continuously recirculated in order to keep the hole from refreezing. This task is not too difficult, as the surrounding solid ice is a great insulator. After the stream of hot water is interrupted, the water will not refreeze for several days, which allows plenty of time for deployment of the equipment. The polar environment turned out to be surprisingly friendly thanks to the excellent support provided by the U.S. South Pole research program. The technology was satisfactorily demonstrated with the deployment of the first four strings in Antarctic summer 1993–94. It is now clear that the hot-water drilling technique can

A module for the Deep Underwater Muon and Neutrino Detector (DUMAND) houses a photomultiplier tube and electronic equipment for processing data. DUMAND operates under 4.5 kilometers (2.8 miles) of ocean water off the coast of the island of Hawaii.

University of Hawaii, Honolulu

be used to deploy optical modules larger than the 20-centimeter (8-inch) photomultiplier tubes now used to any depth in the three-kilometer-deep ice cover.

AMANDA was designed to operate in deep, clear ice with an absorption length in excess of 200 meters, larger than that of the clearest triple-distilled water used in the underground tanks that observed Supernova 1987A. (The absorption length represents a measure of how far light can travel in a medium before fading away.) The ice provides a convenient mechanical support for the detector as well as a platform for its deployment. The immediate advantage is that all electronics can be positioned at the surface. Only the optical modules are deployed into the deep ice.

Polar ice is a sterile medium with a concentration of radioactive elements that is low compared with sea or lake water. This low radioactive background results in an improved sensitivity, which allows high-energy muons to be detected with very simple data acquisition schemes that are implemented by means of off-the-shelf electronics. Being positioned under only one kilometer of ice, it is operating in a cosmic-ray muon flux that is more than 100 times larger than deep-ocean detectors such as DUMAND.

Although residential bubbles were found in South Pole ice at depths of one kilometer, their density decreases rapidly with depth. Ice at the South Pole should be bubble-free below 1,100–1,400 meters as it is in similar polar regions. AMANDA was scheduled to deploy six more strings in 1995 at a depth of 1,500 meters.

Below left, two string controllers contain electronics for gathering data from the 24 optical modules on a DUMAND string. They will be deployed in pressurized metal housing called a "porcupine" unit (right).

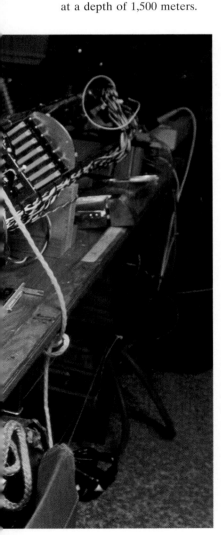

WATER TELESCOPES

The detector in Lake Baikal is deployed during winter, with the thick ice cover of the lake used as a deployment platform. Half its optical modules are pointing up so that it can achieve a uniform acceptance over upper and lower hemispheres. Because the depth of the lake is 1.6 kilometers, the experiment cannot expand downward and will have to grow horizontally.

The original expectations that this deep lake would be very clear and free of radioactive substances were not totally fulfilled. Its background rate of several times 10,000 counts per second from bioluminescence and radioactive decays is similar to that in deep ocean waters. Pairing optical modules in the trigger suppresses this high rate to a manageable 50 per second.

In the face of adversity created by political events in the former Soviet Union, the physicists succeeded in deploying the first small underwater telescope. The Baikal group has been operating an array of 36 Quasar photomultiplier units deployed in April 1994. The Quasar is a 38-cm (15-in) photomultiplier tube. The Lake Baikal experiment set a record up/down rejection ratio of about one in 10,000 and will, according to computer simulations, reach the goal of one in one million required for detecting neutrinos as soon as the full complement of 200 optical modules has been deployed.

DUMAND is positioned under 4,5 kilometers of ocean water, below most biological activity and well shielded from cosmic-ray muon backgrounds. The deep ocean water off the coast of the island of Hawaii is very clear, with an absorption length of about 40 meters for the bluish light detected by the photomulti-

pliers. The DUMAND group successfully analyzed data on cosmic-ray muons obtained from a test string. They installed the 25-kilometer-long power and signal cables from detector to shore as well as the junction box for deploying the strings. The strings are deployed from a ship and attached to the junction box by a remote-control robotic submarine. The group planned to deploy three more strings in 1995.

The NESTOR detector, being placed in the deep Mediterranean Sea off the coast of Greece, is similar to DUMAND except for one critical difference. Like the detector in Lake Baikal, half of its optical modules point up and half down. The angular response of the detector is being tuned to be much more isotropic (having uniform detection efficiency for all directions in the sky) than either AMANDA or DU-

MAND, which will give it advantages in, for instance, the study of neutrino mass effects in the atmospheric neutrino beam.

Other detectors have been proposed for lakes or ponds, but as of late 1994 none was being constructed. These detectors would have the great advantage of accessibility and ability for dual use as extensive air shower detectors of cosmic rays but would suffer from the 10 billion down-to-up ratio of muons. They face great civil engineering costs for water systems and light-tight containers. Even if any of these are built, it would seem that the costs may be too large for a full kilometer-scale detector to be contemplated.

FUTURE PROSPECTS

In summary, four major experiments are under way, each of which has different strengths and faces different challenges. For the construction of a kilometer-scale detector, one can imagine any of the above detectors being the basic building block for the ultimate telescope. A worldwide effort is under way to agree on a technology to realize the dream of building this instrument. It is possible, however, that the most exciting and unexpected discoveries may be those made

by these small prototype detectors.

Although nothing can be guaranteed, history is on our side. The lensmakers in Flanders developed the telescope to make an early inventory of the goods on ships crossing the English Channel. Little did they know that Galileo would use the same instrument to discover the moons of Jupiter. The first X-ray telescope was built to study the Sun and Moon; its successors discovered all kinds of wonderful objects such as neutron stars and accreting binaries. The gamma-ray instruments developed by the U.S. to search for thermonuclear explosions in the Soviet Union discovered the still enigmatic gamma-ray bursts. Each wavelength of light has a story like this to tell. It is hoped that in a not-too-distant future, short-wavelength neutrinos will contribute their own tale.

FOR ADDITIONAL READING

■ "Ice Fishing for Neutrinos," Leif J. Robinson, *Sky and Telescope* (July 1994, pp. 44–48).

■ *Spaceship Neutrino*, Christine Sutton (Cambridge University Press, 1992).

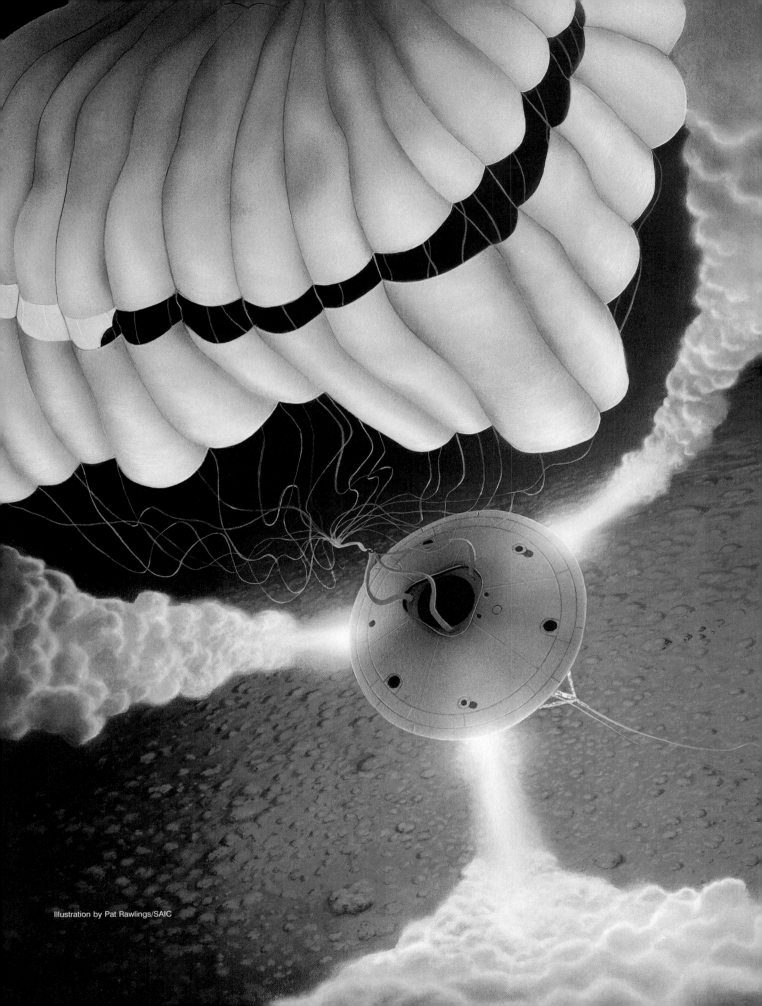

Illustration by Pat Rawlings/SAIC

Discovery: A New Journey into Space

by Dave Dooling

Designed to explore the nearby planets and asteroids, a new series of low-cost space probes will collect information that will be essential for the planning of more complex and expensive missions.

One of the prices of success in the exploration of space has been that each discovery has led to more questions in order for new puzzles to be understood. At first, a few close-up pictures of a planet could tell far more about it than had been gleaned in decades of obser-

Mars Pathfinder will descend by parachute (opposite page) to the Martian surface. Just before the landing, a cluster of air bags (left) will inflate to cover the craft and cushion the impact.

vations by ground-based telescopes. In order to make new discoveries, however, the next probes had to carry more sophisticated, and more expensive, instruments. In time, this increase in cost reduced the number of missions that could be flown.

Today, changes in technology and (more important) in management attitudes are enabling the United States to reverse that trend. In 1993 the U.S. National Aeronautics and Space Administration (NASA) initiated the Discovery program. Its goal was to start and launch one new low-cost mission each year. To do this, NASA stepped outside traditional practices and vested greater authority in smaller teams of scientists and engineers. By 1994 two missions had been scheduled, and a third was to be selected in 1995. If successful, Discovery will become a series of probes collecting basic information that will enable scientists to direct the work of more complex, expensive missions.

ORIGINS AND ORGANIZATION

The Discovery program originated from concerns about the "data gap" that could arise after the Galileo probe completed its primary data collection at Jupiter in 1997 and the arrival of Cassini at Saturn in 2004. Such a gap first occurred between Pioneer Venus (launched in 1978) and Magellan (launched in 1989). (The Discovery program's name should not be confused with the space shuttle orbiter *Discovery*.)

The U.S. Senate in 1991 directed NASA to plan for smaller missions and projects. On Nov. 16–20, 1992, at the San Juan Capistrano (California) Research Institute, NASA held its first Discovery program workshop. Participants evaluated 73 concepts such as Sample of Comet Coma Earth Return (SOCCER), Pluto Fast Flyby, and a Mercury Polar Flyby. They selected 11 for initial study, including two missions to Mercury, two to Venus, one to Mars, four to small bodies (asteroids or comets), one to sample the solar wind, and one to monitor Jupiter with a telescope in Earth orbit. Missions to the Moon and outer planets were excluded because the former is covered by a separate program and the latter would take too long and require the use of expensive nuclear power sources. Other missions that would have strained the resources of the program also were left out. Participants set four primary considerations to guide the program: scientific quality, program balance, risk, and mission duration.

To hold down launch costs, NASA selected the Delta II and the Pegasus XL rockets as Discovery's launchers. Each actually is a family of rockets that can be optimized for the customer's needs. The Delta II is descended from the Thor ballistic missile developed in the 1950s. It comprises 3.8-meter (12.5-foot)-diameter liquid-propellant first and second stages, three or nine strap-on solid-fuel rocket motors as a booster stage, and a spin-stabilized solid-fuel rocket as a third stage. The Delta II is launched from the Cape Canaveral (Florida) Air Force Station. The Pegasus XL is a more innovative winged vehicle consisting of three solid-fuel rocket stages. It is carried to an altitude of about 10 kilometers (6.2 miles) by a B-52 bomber or L-1011 cargo jet and released. A few seconds later its rockets ignite to carry the payload into space. Launch costs range from $16 million for a Pegasus XL to $60 million for a Delta 7925S.

A key element of the program, decided in April 1992, was that NASA wanted the science community and universities to take the lead roles in developing Discovery missions and report directly to NASA headquarters rather than through the field centers. NASA also decided to forgo much of the paperwork and reporting usually required in a project. The projects were to operate like the legendary "Skunk Works," where Kelly Johnson's design teams created innovative, often secret aircraft such as the SR-71 Blackbird. In return, NASA expected greater responsibility from the Discovery teams than from previous programs. "We are imposing on our mission teams the expectation that they perform as they propose," said Mark P. Saunders, the Discovery program manager at NASA headquarters.

In addition, Wesley T. Huntress, Jr., NASA associate administrator for space science, warned in a "Dear Colleague" letter to scientists on June 1, 1994, that proposals must fall within the prescribed $150 million (in 1992 U.S. dollars) budget for the design and development of each mission and stay within a 36-month development cycle. NASA even planned to encourage missions costing less than $100 million, and "the

Dave Dooling *is an Aerospace Consultant and Science Writer in Huntsville, Alabama.*

Data returns from U.S. planetary probes reveal gaps that have occurred between missions. With its frequent low-cost flights, the Discovery program is designed to prevent such gaps in the future.

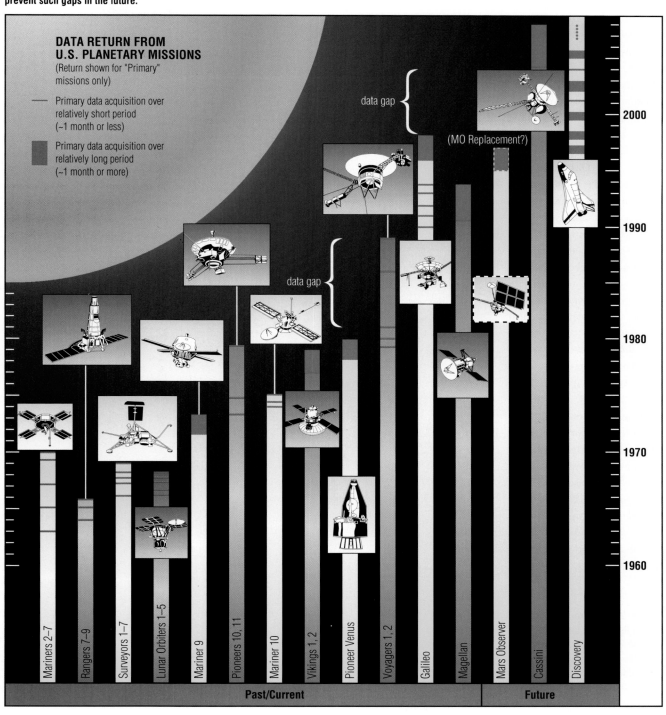

DATA RETURN FROM U.S. PLANETARY MISSIONS
(Return shown for "Primary" missions only)

— Primary data acquisition over relatively short period (~1 month or less)

▌ Primary data acquisition over relatively long period (~1 month or more)

data gap

data gap

(MO Replacement?)

2000

1990

1980

1970

1960

Mariners 2–7
Rangers 7–9
Surveyors 1–7
Lunar Orbiters 1–5
Mariner 9
Pioneers 10, 11
Mariner 10
Vikings 1, 2
Pioneer Venus
Voyagers 1, 2
Galileo
Magellan
Mars Observer
Cassini
Discovery

Past/Current

Future

proposal with the most science will not necessarily win."

Another major change will be full public access to the data that are returned by each mission. Previously, each science team had exclusive use of the data for a year.

NASA also warned scientists that Discovery's fate depended on their support. "The planetary community has an excellent chance of getting a Discovery program that will ultimately address a broad range of science goals, provide a needed robustness to a very lean program, and enable a near continuous stream of planetary data," wrote William Piotrowski, acting director of solar system exploration, on Aug. 26, 1993. "A divided planetary community and/or lackluster support will surely result in no Discovery program at all," however.

Finally, a Discovery Management Workshop in 1993 selected two missions already under way, the Mars Pathfinder and the Near Earth Asteroid Rendezvous

A Delta II booster rocket launches a Global Positioning Satellite for the U.S. Air Force in 1992. Descended from the Thor ballistic missile, the Delta II was chosen as one of the launch vehicles for the Discovery program.

(NEAR), to be the first in the new program. Pathfinder is managed by the Jet Propulsion Laboratory (JPL) in Pasadena, California. Although the public often sees it as a NASA center, JPL is actually part of the California Institute of Technology. It has been the heart of NASA's planetary missions since the 1960s. NEAR is managed by the Applied Physics Laboratory outside Laurel, Maryland, a division of Johns Hopkins University. It was selected because "we have a legacy of doing quick missions within budget," said NEAR project scientist Andrew F. Cheng. The laboratory has a history of building small, successful satellites for the military and NASA on short schedules and tight budgets.

REASONS FOR DISCOVERY

The need for a new approach to planetary exploration was highlighted by a NASA failure in 1993 and a U.S. Department of Defense success in 1994. In August 1993 NASA was forced to declare its Mars Observer spacecraft (launched September 1992) missing and presumed lost just before it was to go into orbit around Mars. Mars Observer had grown out of a recom-

Orbital Sciences Corporation

mendation to develop a low-cost series of planetary observers by purchasing "production line" spacecraft and modifying them, as needed, for planetary missions. Satellites are not mass-produced like cars; each is optimized for its primary mission. However, these modifications use parts with well-known designs and performance records, often in "buses," complete assemblies that vary little from one spacecraft to the next. Manufacturers could build planetary observers cheaply, it was reasoned, by buying "one more" bus and then adding science instruments. Some officials worried that this would require more discipline than managers had in order to avoid increasing the capabilities and cost of the probe.

Pegasus XL, chosen as a launch vehicle for the Discovery program, is a winged craft with three solid-fuel rocket stages. It is carried by plane to an altitude of 10 kilometers (6 miles) and then released, after which its rockets ignite to send the payload into space.

Indeed, that was the case, and Mars Observer eventually cost twice as much as had been anticipated. Ironically, as an investigation board later concluded, leaving the attitude-control system unchanged from its design for satellite use probably led to the mission's downfall. The spacecraft was built by Martin Marietta Corp., a manufacturer of Satcom communications satellites. Such a satellite normally reaches its orbit, 35,-725 kilometers (19,290 miles)

in attitude, in a few hours. Mars Observer was launched on Sept. 25, 1992, and was to orbit Mars on Aug. 21, 1993. During the last nine months before entering Mars orbit, a period of "coasting" for which the attitude-control system was not designed, nitrogen tetroxide slowly leaked from it through valves and accumulated inside the fuel manifold. When the hydrazine (fuel) valves were opened to pressurize the fuel lines, the two chemicals came into contact with each other, ignited, and ripped the lines open. Gas vented through the sides of Mars Observer, causing it to tumble out of control. The loss of Mars Observer highlighted the risk of having a single spacecraft carry too large a portion of the plane-

The Mars Observer, shown below in an artist's conception, was lost when an explosion in its fuel lines caused it to tumble out of control just before it was scheduled to go into orbit around Mars. The loss of the craft underlined the risk of having a single mission undertake a large portion of the planetary-exploration program. On the opposite page, the Earth is revealed rising over the Moon's north pole in an image obtained by the probe Clementine. The angular separation between the Earth and the lunar horizon has been reduced for illustration purposes.

tary-exploration program and strengthened the position of the then-new Discovery program.

Five months later (January 1994) the U.S. Ballistic Missile Defense Organization (BMDO) launched its Clementine probe to the Moon to test an array of its ultra-small missile defense sensors and other advanced technologies. To save the cost of launching a target vehicle, BMDO decided to use the Moon as the observation target. They named the probe Clementine because, like the Old West song, she would be "lost and gone forever" on the prospecting mission.

Clementine was launched on Jan. 25, 1994, orbited the Moon from February 19 to May 3, 1994, and returned 1.8 million pictures of the Moon and Earth. Although it failed to fly past an asteroid, it proved the design of its sensors and that planetary missions could be conducted by small, highly focused development teams given broad authority and responsibility.

The success of Clementine was, however, slightly deceptive. Its advanced sensors emerged from several development programs whose costs were not charged against Clementine. Furthermore, BMDO managers were

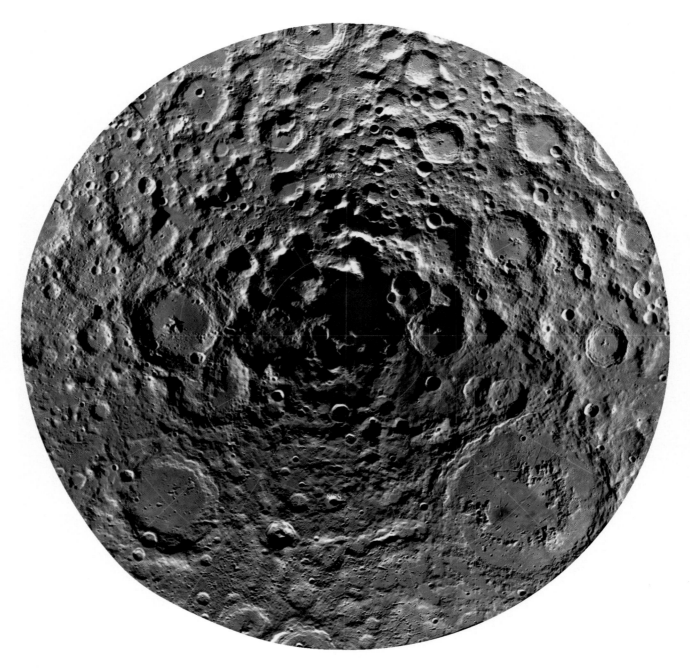

A mosaic of 1,500 images obtained by Clementine reveals the south polar region of the Moon.

Naval Research Laboratory

Left, an image from Clementine reveals the Sun rising over the Moon, with Venus in the background. Below, Clementine is attached to its launch vehicle, a Titan IIG.

given authority to conduct research in promising areas, to take risks, and to buy equipment without following the usual rules of competition.

MARS PATHFINDER

The Discovery program's first mission is based on the Mars Environmental Survey (MESUR, or "measure") Pathfinder. Known as Mars Pathfinder, it is designed to demonstrate how a series of 16 landers would be scattered around Mars to measure its environment, starting in 1999.

Mars has long been of great interest to scientists and the public because it may harbor life or signs of previous life. Even though the Mariners and Viking showed Mars to be far more barren than the most forbidding desert on Earth, they also yielded tantalizing evidence that Mars had once had running water. Life may have existed there eons ago. Although manned missions to Mars do not seem likely in the near future, NASA began planning a series of robotic missions to explore the planet's surface.

Mars Pathfinder is to be launched by a Delta II rocket during a window extending from Dec. 5, 1996, to Jan. 3, 1997. (A launch window is a period of a few days or weeks

when the energy needed to get to a planet is less than what the rocket will provide; therefore, more power is available than the trip requires.) The journey to Mars will take six months, with arrival set for July 4, 1997. Unlike the Viking spacecraft, Mars Pathfinder will not go into orbit before landing; when the spacecraft is 24 hours away from the planet, its cruise portion will be jettisoned and the lander will dive into the Martian atmosphere at 7.6 kilometers (4.7 miles) per second (1.7 times faster than Viking). Peak deceleration will be 25 times Earth's gravity at an altitude of 32 kilometers (20 miles). At 10 kilometers (6.2 miles), just 100 seconds after entry, the aerodynamic shell will be jettisoned and an 11-meter (36-foot)-wide parachute deployed. Just 90 meters (295 feet) above the surface, small rockets attached to the parachute will fire to slow Pathfinder 1.5 seconds before impact. Air bags will inflate to cushion the touchdown at 3:14 AM, local Mars time, in Ares Vallis, a valley about 19.5° north of the planet's equator. The space-

An artist's rendition shows the Mars Pathfinder entering the Martian atmosphere and descending by parachute to the planet's surface.

craft is to operate for a 30-day primary surface mission. If it continues to function well, it will be operated until September 1998.

The Viking landers were extremely lucky in that each just missed large rocks that could have toppled the spacecraft. Rather than rely on that kind of luck, Pathfinder is designed as a tetrahedron that will survive hitting a 50-centimeter (20-inch)-wide rock and tumbling across the surface. About 90 minutes after landing, and as the Earth rises above the Martian horizon, the tetrahedron will open, like petals on a flower, and set the spacecraft upright regardless of its position. Each petal contains solar cells that will power the spacecraft. Total mass on the surface will be 250 kilograms (551 pounds).

Mars Pathfinder actually comprises two spacecraft, the Pathfinder and a small rover that will operate in the immediate vicinity. This is an example of the way in which the Discovery program maintains flexibility. Originally, Mars Pathfinder included just the lander. NASA's Office of Advanced Concepts and Technology offered to provide a small rover, at no extra charge to the program, as an early demonstration of small robotics technology. Fi-

After landing on Mars and opening its protective shell like petals on a flower, the Pathfinder will transmit to the Earth data collected during its descent to the planet's surface.

nally, the Max Planck Institute and the University of Chicago agreed to provide an alpha particle/proton/X-ray spectrometer (APX), originally developed for Russia's Mars '94 mission.

Pathfinder's two color stereo cameras will rotate to scan the terrain and send to Earth an image of the ground near the rover. Ten hours and 31 minutes after touchdown, the rover is to roll off the petal and start returning images from its own fore-and-aft cameras. Half an hour later it will place the APX instrument against a rock selected by scientists on Earth. By measuring the "backscattered" radiation from the rock, scientists can determine the chemical composition of rocks and soil.

The rover itself is an exercise in miniaturization, weighing just 10 kilograms (22 pounds). It will communicate with the lander by means of an ultrahigh-frequency computer modem and will carry a solar panel and rechargeable battery.

Because the "more for less" approach is a new challenge, JPL established several criteria to define mission success. Just reaching the surface of Mars and transmitting entry and landing data will represent a 50% successful mission. Transmitting panoramic pictures from the surface and deploying the rover will each add another 20%. The final 10% will be the most interesting to the public: 30 days and nights of images plus scientific data including soil analyses as the rover places the APX in different locations.

To build Pathfinder, JPL will draw on proven designs, such as star scanners used by Magellan's attitude-control system, the charge-coupled device (CCD) camera planned for Cassini's Huygens probe imaging system, the heat shield and parachutes designed for Viking, and tractor rockets and altimeters designed for military missions. At the same time, Pathfinder will live up to its name by using several new technologies: a solid-state X-band power amplifier, a radiation-hardened Loral RS 6000 32-bit computer, air bags, and data-compression software. To keep the project on its fast track, JPL adopted a "soft projectized mode" in which workers remain tied to certain JPL divisions but work for Pathfinder and are responsible for specific products that will eventually be part of the mission.

If Mars Pathfinder succeeds, NASA envisions following it with a Mars Global Surveyor in November 1996 and an orbiter and lander in 1998. One launch might also carry two stations plus an orbiter to collect and relay data more efficiently. NASA and the European Space Agency were also considering Europe's future participation in the program, possibly by using the Ariane 5 launcher or by supplying spacecraft and instruments.

NEAR EARTH ASTEROID RENDEZVOUS

The second Discovery probe will investigate asteroids, the smallest bodies in the solar system. The first asteroid was discovered in 1801. Most are first seen as streaks of light across time exposures of star fields and thus were given their name meaning "little stars" (other names are minor planets, planetoids, and plantesimals). Because they spoiled star pictures and were just materials left over from the creation of the solar system, they were long regarded as "vermin of the skies." Now, however, they are of great interest precisely because they may represent original solar system materials virtually unchanged for the last four and a half billion years.

Asteroids also stir interest because they may be the engines of mass extinctions throughout Earth's history. Although the total mass of the largest known asteroid is only 0.1% that of Earth, a collision with one would release a tremendous amount of energy into the environment because of the relative speeds of the two bodies. While other programs have been developed to locate and track nearby asteroids—at least 200 large near-Earth asteroids are known, and there may be another 2,000 that are less than one kilometer (0.62 mile) in diameter—no one knows whether an asteroid threatening the Earth with collision could be diverted or fractured.

Only four asteroids have been seen close-up by space probes. On its way to Jupiter the Galileo probe flew as

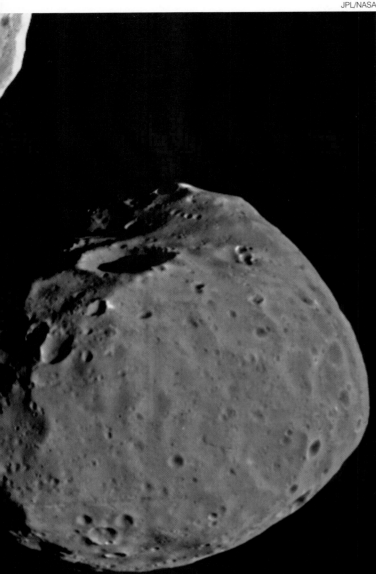

Asteroid 951 Gaspra (opposite page, top) is seen to be comparable in size to the two moons of Mars, Deimos (opposite page, bottom) and Phobos (above). The second Discovery probe will investigate asteroids, only four of which have been viewed close-up by space probes.

close as 1,601 kilometers (994 miles) to 951 Gaspra in October 1991 and 2,400 kilometers (1,490 miles) to 243 Ida in August 1993. The Viking orbiters passed near Mars's two moons, Phobos and Deimos, which are believed to be cap-

tured asteroids. (The only other small body studied in great detail was Comet Halley in 1986.) NEAR will study 433 Eros, a small Class S (silicate rock) asteroid that orbits from 1.13 to 1.78 AU from the Sun (1 AU, or astronomical unit, is the average distance from the Sun to the Earth [149 million kilometers, or 92.5 million miles]). The launch window and curiosity about its composition were factors in its selection. Its orbital period is 1.76 years, and every seven years its orbit passes within

22.5 million kilometers (13.7 million miles) of Earth. Rendezvous will occur at about the 100th anniversary of its Aug. 13, 1898, discovery.

Getting to Eros will require a gravitational-assist trajectory similar to those used by spacecraft exploring the outer solar system. NEAR is to be launched by a Delta II rocket on Feb. 17, 1996 (dates and speeds may change as the mission is refined). On Jan. 29, 1997, NEAR will fire its thrusters to return it to the Earth on Jan. 24, 1998, in order to use the planet's gravitational field to swing it about 19.9° out of the Earth's orbit so that it can catch Eros in its orbit, which is inclined 10.8° to that of the Earth. Such maneuvers require a great deal of propellant if done by rocket engine; using the Earth as the slingshot will achieve the same effect without needing much propellant.

On Feb. 6, 1999, NEAR will arrive at Eros, fire its onboard thrusters to increase speed by 961 meters (3,150 feet) per second, and thereby go into orbit around the asteroid. Eros' irregular shape—about twice the length and width of Manhattan Island—may have been caused by many collisions after it cooled from the primordial swirl of solar system material. Because Eros

rotates end-over-end every 5 hours 16 minutes, NEAR's initial orbit will be at an altitude of 500 kilometers (310 miles). As scientists observe the asteroid during the next year, they will use observations about its gravitational field and size to move NEAR ever closer to it. Ultimately, they hope to settle into an orbit that comes within 24 kilometers (15 miles) of the asteriod. The mission is expected to end around Dec. 31, 1999, as the propellants are used up.

The 805-kilogram (1,770-pound) spacecraft will not appear to be as exotic as Voyager or Galileo. Its bus (main body) will be a 1.7-meter (5.6-foot)-diameter box with a single 1.5-meter (5-foot)-diameter dish antenna on the top and four solar panels deployed from the sides. Most of the systems within the spacecraft will be derived from designs proved in the many small spacecraft built by the Applied Physics Laboratory for the military and NASA during the past 30 years.

NEAR's instrument suite is larger than that of Mars Pathfinder. It includes an X-ray/gamma-ray spectrometer that will assay the asteroid's elements by measuring how it reflects solar and cosmic radiation, a magnetometer that will measure the in-

Applied Physics Laboratory, Johns Hopkins University

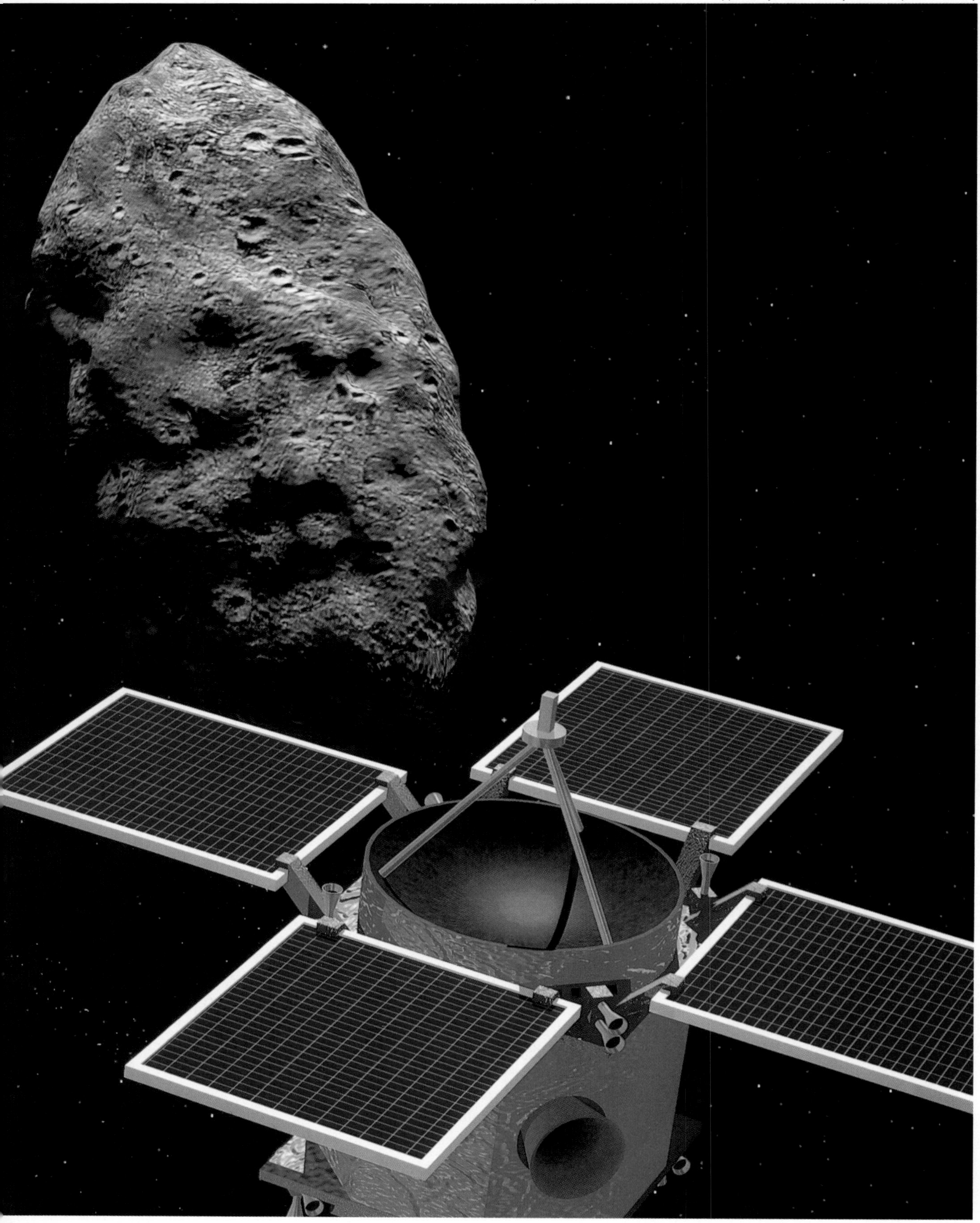

tensity and direction of Eros' magnetic field if it has any, a near-infrared imaging spectrograph that will assay its chemistry, and a CCD camera that will produce images in visible light with resolutions down to one meter (3.3 feet).

Finally, a laser altimeter will be included as part of the navigational system so that engineers can measure NEAR's distance as it orbits Eros. It also can produce precise topographic profiles with a resolution down to 6 meters (19.7 feet). This will be important since under the harsh lighting of space, a crater can just as easily look like a bump. The altimeter will also scan inside openings to determine whether they are really craters or instead are deep vents, which would reveal Eros to be the spent core of a comet. And NEAR's radio transmissions themselves will become part of the science effort as scientists translate radio frequency shifts into measurements of Eros' gravitational pull on NEAR.

The NEAR team hopes to develop three follow-up missions. The first, Rendezvous with a Comet Nucleus (RE-

An artist's conception shows the Near Earth Asteroid Rendezvous (NEAR), scheduled for launch to the asteroid Eros in 1996.

CON), would be launched in 1999, fly past two asteroids, and rendezvous with a comet by 2005. The second would be the Comet Nucleus Tour (Contour) of three comets during 1999–2005, and the third would be the Near Earth Asteroid Returned Sample (NEARS) mission to be launched in 2000.

FUTURE DISCOVERY MISSIONS

On Aug. 4, 1994, NASA issued a formal Announcement of Opportunity (AO) soliciting Discovery mission proposals from the science community. Missions chosen for study by the San Juan Capistrano workshop will be in a more competitive position but are not necessarily assured of winning. "The formal selection process is open to all interested parties," announced Richard Vorder Bruegge, a member of the Discovery Advanced Study Review Group. "These [AO] proposals will have to be more extensive than the studies and include science rationale, spacecraft design, observations, data systems—a start-to-finish proposal for a new mission."

Proposals were due at NASA on Oct. 21, 1994. On Feb. 28, 1995, NASA announced that it had selected

one proposal for immediate development for flight and three more for advanced study leading to a selection of one in late 1995. The $59 million Lunar Prospector will be launched in June 1997 and go into lunar polar orbit to "map the chemical composition of the lunar surface and the Moon's global magnetic and gravity fields at a level of detail greater than that achieved by previous missions," according to NASA. One resource it will seek is evidence of water ice trapped in shadowed craters around the lunar poles.

The three additional missions to be studied are: Stardust, to fly through the extended coma of the active comet P/Wild 2, obtaining images and returning a sample of cometary dust to Earth laboratories; Venus Multiprobe Mission, to drop 16 small probes into the thick Venusian atmosphere in order to study its unusual atmospheric circulation; and Suess-Urey, to collect samples of solar particle matter streaming outward from the Sun and return them to the Earth for laboratory study.

All of the missions will have to meet four major goals NASA established for the Discovery program: (1) perform high-quality scientific investigations that will maintain

U.S. leadership in planetary science and that will ensure continuity in the U.S. solar system exploration program; (2) pursue innovative ways of doing business; (3) encourage the use and transfer of new technologies in achieving program objectives; and (4) enhance appreciation for solar system exploration and support the nation's educational initiatives.

In a broader sense, however, the justification for the Discovery program is much that same as the earliest reasons given for exploring the solar system. "The study of the planets provides other planetary examples against which to compare our own Earth, in order to understand better how planet Earth works and how it behaves" said Huntress. "The study of the solar system, and the planetary bodies within it, also will help us to understand how our solar system formed, how other solar systems might form around other stars, and therefore lead us to answer whether or not there are other Earths and other life in the universe." The Discovery program should provide a steady stream of clues that will help researchers find features in the solar system that are worth detailed exploration by more expensive probes, or perhaps by humans.

Aerogels: The Lightest Solids

by Arlon Hunt

Solid materials that weigh only one ounce while covering a surface area equivalent to six football fields are proving valuable as transparent, energy-efficient insulators and can also substantially speed the operation of microelectronic circuits.

When seeing aerogel for the first time, people often do a double take. Its ghostly appearance has been described as resembling "a pet cloud" or "frozen smoke." Almost disappearing against a white background and having a ghostly bluish color when viewed against a dark object, aerogel appears to be insubstantial, but it can be cut, drilled, or crushed between the fingers. Silica aerogel is a transparent, thermally insulating solid useful in a variety of applications.

As the name implies, aerogel is mostly air and is the lightest existing solid material; its density can be as low as five milligrams per cubic centimeter, about three times that of air. Because of its extremely fine-scale structure, aerogel has a host of unusual properties. It can be formed into slabs, cylinders, or almost any desired shape. It is the best solid known for providing thermal insulation. Sound propagates more slowly through aerogel than through air. While it betrays its presence by a slight bluish haze, it is quite transparent, and distant objects can be viewed clearly through aerogel that is many centimeters thick. It is one of the very few materials that are both transparent and porous. It has a very high surface area—typically as much as 1,000 square meters per gram, the equivalent of six football fields per ounce of material. Aerogels can be clear or colored, be stiff or flexible, land on a hard surface with a clang or a thud, and dissolve in or float on water. Silica (pure glass) aerogel

Arlon Hunt is a Group Leader/ Staff Scientist at Lawrence Berkeley Laboratory, Berkeley, California.

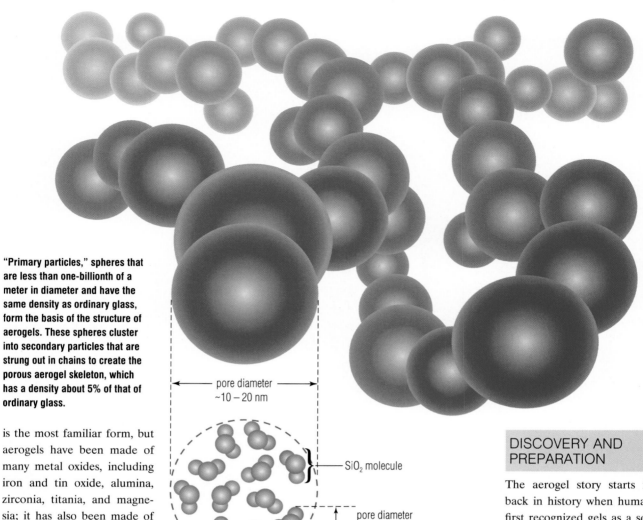

"Primary particles," spheres that are less than one-billionth of a meter in diameter and have the same density as ordinary glass, form the basis of the structure of aerogels. These spheres cluster into secondary particles that are strung out in chains to create the porous aerogel skeleton, which has a density about 5% of that of ordinary glass.

pore diameter ~10 – 20 nm

SiO₂ molecule

pore diameter ~2 – 4 nm

is the most familiar form, but aerogels have been made of many metal oxides, including iron and tin oxide, alumina, zirconia, titania, and magnesia; it has also been made of gelatin, organic polymers, natural gels, and carbon.

Although discovered more than 60 years ago, aerogels are just now becoming widely known. Within the last decade a variety of applications for them have been proposed: as superinsulating windows, as solar collector covers, and as insulation for refrigerators, water heaters, and pipes. Aerogels might also be used as catalysts for gas-phase reactions and as ultrafilters, battery electrodes, acoustic devices, and even safe insecticides. However, as with most newly available materials, incorporating aerogel into a commercial product is proving to be a slow and difficult process.

PROPERTIES OF SILICA AEROGELS

Characteristics	Collapses upon contact with water Does not burn One-inch slab provides the same insulation as 30 panes of glass
Color	Near transparent with bluish tinge
Composition	90 – 99.8% air 10 – 0.20% SiO₂
Density	5 mg/cm³
Pore sizes	2 – 4 nanometers (small) 10 – 20 nanometers (medium) >300 nanometers (large)
Sound velocity	~100 m/sec
Structural temperature	up to 750° C (1,380° F)
Surface area	400 – 1,000 m²/g
Thermal conductivity	0.02 watts/meter-kelvin (20° C) 0.008 watts/meter-kelvin (vacuum)

DISCOVERY AND PREPARATION

The aerogel story starts far back in history when humans first recognized gels as a separate state of matter. Gels occur in nature and are common as food products. They may also be prepared by simple reactions of metal oxides in the presence of water. While gels have been known for many centuries, it was only in the 1930s that their nature was determined. Steven Kistler at what is now the University of the Pacific in Stockton, California, speculated that gels consist of an open solid network of cells permeated by a liquid. It is a common observation that when a food gelatin is left uncovered, it slowly shrinks to a volume considerably smaller than the original. Kistler postulated, correctly, that surface tension within the fine pores of the gel forced them to collapse as the liquid they held slowly evaporated. To prove this was the case, he eliminated the surface tension and removed the liquid from the gel. He recognized that when a liquid is heated to a supercritical condition, a pressure and temperature above its critical point, there is no longer a distinction between liquid and gas. (The critical point is the temperature and pressure at which two phases of a substance in equilibrium with each other become identical, forming one phase.) When this distinction is gone, surface tension forces vanish, and the fluid can escape the gel network without causing it to collapse. This process is called supercritical drying or supercritical extraction.

Kistler experimented with silica gels made with a technique known as "the waterglass process." When he tried to remove the water from an aquagel (a gel containing water) under supercritical conditions, he found that the water dissolved the silica. To avoid this, he substituted alcohol for water in the gel by soaking the aquagels in an alcohol bath. He then heated the alcohol and gel in a closed container to above its critical point (more than 80 atmospheres of pressure and 240° C [460° F]) and slowly de-

Lawrence Berkeley Laboratory

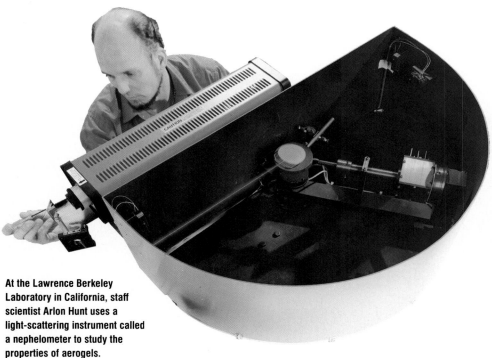

At the Lawrence Berkeley Laboratory in California, staff scientist Arlon Hunt uses a light-scattering instrument called a nephelometer to study the properties of aerogels.

pressurized the vessel, allowing the alcohol, now in vapor form, to escape. An extremely light solid remained. Kistler had discovered aerogel. He went on to make aerogels that had a variety of compositions and reported on many of their unusual properties in the following years. However, the work on solid aerogels never found practical application and was mostly forgotten until the 1970s.

A difficulty in preparing silica aerogel with the water-glass process involved the removal of salt and acids generated by the chemical reaction that formed the gel. This removal involved a long and tedious soaking of the gel. An improved method of preparing gels for drying to obtain aerogels was discovered by Stanislas Teichner at

the University Claude Bernard near Lyon, France. He found that silica gels could be prepared directly with alcohol and without salt through the use of a relatively new class of compounds called metal alkoxides. These compounds are composed of one or more metal atoms surrounded by alcohol groups. The two most common alkoxides for silica preparation are tetraethylorthosilicate (TEOS) and tetramethylorthosilicate (TMOS). The alkoxide reacts with water (hydrolysis) to form metal oxides and release alcohol. If the reaction conditions are carefully controlled, fine particles of the oxide are created, interact with one another, and form into a gel. This technique, called "sol-gel processing," is a rapidly growing field in materials science.

Much of sol-gel materials science is based on the hydrolysis of metal alkoxide compounds.

Today scientists prepare many metal oxide aerogels by reacting a metal alkoxide with water to form an alcosol, a colloidal suspension of metal oxide particles in alcohol that link together to make an alcogel (gel permeated by alcohol). The alcogel is then supercritically dried to produce aerogel. A development at Lawrence Berkeley Laboratory in Berkeley, California, permits reduction of the temperature and pressure required for supercritical drying by substituting, under pressure, liquid carbon dioxide for the alcohol in the gel and then supercritically drying the aerogel with carbon dioxide. The process results in a reduction of the temperature

and pressure required for drying aerogels to about 33° C (91° F) and 70 atmospheres of pressure. The reduced temperature allows the equipment to be cycled more rapidly and considerably reduces the risk of explosion and fire that is associated with the use of supercritical alcohol.

The carbon-dioxide substitution technique is also useful in drying an important new class of aerogels based on organic polymers. These aerogels, first synthesized at Lawrence Livermore National Laboratory in Livermore, California, are made with the use of organic molecules that polymerize (combine to form larger molecules that contain repeating structural units) with a high degree of cross-linking. Cross-linking, the connection of parallel chains in a molecule, provides the strength necessary for the material to survive the drying process. The carbon-dioxide drying method avoids the high temperatures associated with alcohol processing and provides conditions that do not destroy the polymer gel network. Carbon aerogels can be made from organic polymer aerogels by being heated to high temperatures in a nonreacting gas (argon or nitrogen) or vacuum. The oxygen and hydrogen that are released as

Organic aerogels, a new family of these materials, were developed at Lawrence Livermore National Laboratory in California. Below and at the bottom left are samples of melamine-formaldehyde, and at the left is resorcinol-formaldehyde. Inside the glass vials at the far left and bottom right are the gels before their liquid has been extracted to produce the aerogel.

the polymer breaks down are driven off, and the result is a pure carbon aerogel.

A greater range of densities can be achieved through variation of the type of solvent used. Researchers at Lawrence Livermore National Laboratory prepared silica aerogels with densities as low as 0.001 of bulk silica by using solvents other than alcohols. These low-density aerogels are very transparent but have higher thermal conductivity and are quite weak.

Multicomponent aerogels and new composite materials based on aerogels have opened an exciting new field. Sol-gel processing can be used to make gels of multiple metal oxides or to prepare gels that are a combination of organic

and inorganic components. At Lawrence Berkeley Laboratory composite aerogel materials have been prepared by means of chemical vapor infiltration. In this approach gas or vapor compounds are introduced into an aerogel at elevated temperatures. The aerogel decomposes the gaseous compound by means of catalysis, and the products of the decomposition are deposited as solids within the aerogel. The deposits are of very fine scale and result in materials with new and unusual properties.

With aerogel as a host for the deposition of gas decomposition products, there is a nearly unlimited range of possibilities for new nanocomposite materials (nanometer [one billionth of a meter]-

scaled materials) because both the composition of the aerogel and the type of decomposing gas can be varied. To date, researchers at Lawrence Berkeley Laboratory have incorporated nanometer-sized deposits of carbon, metallic iron, iron oxides, and elemental silicon into the aerogel structure.

SCIENTIFIC APPLICATIONS

What are the uses for materials with such unique properties? The first modern applications involved using silica aerogel in detectors called Cherenkov counters that measure the velocity of elementary particles and cosmic rays. The modern surge in interest started with the preparation of some 1,700 liters (1,796 quarts) of silica aerogel for a Cherenkov counter at the Deutsches Elektronen-Synchrotron (DESY) particle accelerator in Hamburg, Germany, in the late 1970s.

Other scientific applications of aerogel include its use in laser fusion targets and as a cushion to catch micrometeorites in space. A host of related research into sol-gel chemistry was focusing on preparing new ceramic materials, providing a transparent matrix for sites for photoactive materials, and preparing optical fibers.

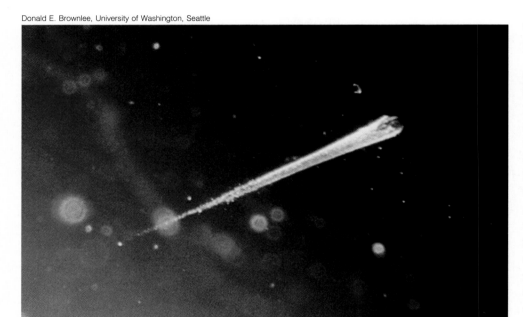

In this magnified image a micrometeorite impact onto silica aerogel that has a density of 0.05 gram per cubic centimeter is revealed by a track that is about one millimeter long and tapers to a point where the particle is preserved.

WINDOWS

Today the primary application for aerogel is generally considered to be as a transparent or high-performance insulator. The excellent thermal performance and transparent nature of aerogel make it an obvious choice for superinsulating windows, skylights, solar collector covers, and specialty windows.

Aerogel is transparent because its microstructure is very small compared with the wavelength of light. However, all but the clearest aerogels scatter some light at the blue end of the spectrum, giv-ing them a slightly hazy appearance. Transmission electron microscopy (TEM) and angle-dependent light scattering were used to determine the origin of light scattering in aerogels and to reduce the scattering so that aerogels would be acceptable for standard windows. TEM showed that aerogels made by the catalysis of a base, such as an alkoxide, are composed of cross-linked chains of primary particles with diameters of two to four nanometers. (One nanometer equals one one-billionth of a meter.) Other measurements indicated an average pore size of 10 to 20 nanometers. However, light-scattering measurements and calculations revealed that neither the average-sized particles nor pores were the major cause for the observed scattering. The TEM studies revealed that the structure occasionally contains larger pores or low-density regions. These are thought to be the primary cause of the scattering. The scattering can be thought of as arising from the large holes or pores that have a lower index of refraction than the average of the aerogel. Thus, research on aerogel preparation to improve its clarity is focused on minimizing the number and size of the large pores in the material.

INSULATION

Kistler very early recognized aerogel's extraordinary thermal insulating properties. Standard silica aerogel has a higher thermal resistance than the polyurethane foams that are widely used in refrigerators, water heaters, and roof insulation. While aerogels are excellent thermal insulators in normal settings, they really excel when enough of the air within them is evacuated to create a mild vacuum. The reason for this is that half to two-thirds of the thermal conductivity arises from the air within the aerogel. Evacuated silica aerogel has a thermal conductivity of approximately 0.007 milliwatts per meter per degree Kelvin. An evacuated aerogel window that is 2.5 centimeters (one inch) thick has about the same thermal resistance as a window made of 10 successive double panes of glass. Even better news is that this thermal performance is reached after only 90% of the air has been removed.

The key to this high performance at a modest vacuum is again related to the small pore size of aerogels. Their fine microstructure impedes conductivity because at

SEAgel (Safe Emulsion Agar gel)
floats on top of soap bubbles. Made
from agarose, a product
extracted from kelp, SEAgel is 10%
lighter than silica aerogel.

Windows on the lower levels
of a new research building for the BASF manufacturing firm in Ludwigshafen, Germany, are insulated
with aerogel pellets. Such insulation is notably energy-efficient.

a pressure of one-tenth of an atmosphere, the collisions of air molecules with the silica lattice are more frequent than with other molecules, thus limiting the ability of heat to traverse the medium via gas. Because aerogel requires such a modest vacuum to achieve high insulating performance, minor vacuum leaks or outgassing have little effect on the performance, resulting in a long, useful life—an important consideration in its use in commercial products. Other insulations typically require a more nearly complete vacuum, making a long-lived seal much more difficult to achieve.

Evacuated aerogel insulation can provide an energy-efficient alternative to polyurethane-foam insulation and result in significant energy savings. To improve energy conservation in the U.S., Congress mandated the Appliance Efficiency Standards Act of 1987. This law required that efficiency standards be set for most appliances, including refrigerators, freezers, and water heaters. The standards require substantial increases in the energy efficiency of those appliances in 1996. Meeting the new standards with existing foamed insulation will be difficult if not impossible. The new stan-

Aerogel pellets provide an energy-efficient alternative to polyurethane-foam insulation, which also has the disadvantage of containing the gas believed to be responsible for damage to the Earth's ozone layer.

dards will probably require more than the doubling of the thickness of conventional insulation and the reduction or elimination of chlorofluorocarbons (CFCs), thus substantially increasing the cost of insulation. Increased costs for appliances and loss of useful cooled volume will result unless better insulating materials that do not involve the use of CFCs are developed.

Polyurethane foams achieve their performance by the use of CFCs as the gas inside the foam. U.S. refrigerator manufacturing alone uses between 5.4 million and 7.3 million kilograms (12 million and 16 million pounds) of CFCs each year for insulation (two to four times more than is used in the compressors!). A substantial portion of these gases is released during the life cycle of the refrigerator. It is widely believed that CFCs are responsible for damage to the Earth's ozone layer, and there have been many proposals to eliminate their use. Recent measurements suggest that the problem is even more serious than feared earlier. Vacuum-evacuated aerogel represents a leading option for replacing CFCs in high-performance insulating applications.

Although aerogel is a promising substitute insulation, two critical factors continue to hinder its use: cost and performance. Researchers are working to improve the thermal resistance by as much as 100% and to produce less expensive aerogel. To see how this could be done, one should consider how aerogel conducts heat. Heat passes through evacuated aerogel at room temperature in two ways: it is conducted through the solid lattice, and infrared radiation passes through the aerogel. In pure silica aerogel these two are of roughly equal importance. Therefore, reducing the infrared radiant heat transfer could substantially improve the thermal performance. Measurements and calculations have indicated that the largest contribution to the radiant heat transfer at room temperature is radiation in the mid-infrared region. Adding carbon to the aerogel blocks this radiation, resulting in substantially improved performance (a conductivity of 0.0045 watts per meter per degree Kelvin). This and future improvements would reduce aerogel cost and would also allow the use of thinner aerogel panels. Using carbon to block the infrared also blocks the visible radiation; consequently this type of aerogel cannot be used for transparent insulating applications; however, it would be an excellent material for applications in which opaque insulation is accept-

able, such as refrigerators and water heaters.

Additionally, the carbon-doping technique dramatically improves the performance of aerogel at higher temperatures, making its use for applications that require insulation up to 500° C (930° F) appear favorable. Improved aerogel could reduce heat losses (or reduce insulation thickness) by nearly an order of magnitude compared with conventional pipe insulation. For example, this improved aerogel might be used for insulation on steam, heat-recycling, and chemical-process pipes.

Such aerogels could also be used as medium-high temperature insulation in the airplane and aerospace industry. Carbon-doped aerogel may play a role in the development of electric cars equipped with batteries that operate at high temperatures and that need to conserve heat. These high-temperature applications may, however, require additional improvements in aerogel properties and the development of new packaging techniques.

Aerogel insulates a finger from a direct flame. Their remarkable properties cause aerogels to have valuable applications in pipe insulation.

Joel DeGrand

156

ACOUSTICS AND ELECTRICITY

Aerogels may also have acoustic and electrical applications. Because of their unusual structure, aerogels have low sound velocities, as low as 30 meters (98 feet) per second. The sound-dampening properties of aerogel are not well explored, partly because they vary considerably with aerogel preparation methods.

The metallic clang sometimes heard when a piece of aerogel is dropped suggests a lack of sound-dampening properties. However, other aerogels dampen sound when dropped or struck. Establishing production methods that result in aerogels with sound-dampening properties would open up applications in windows and insulations.

Another important acoustic property of aerogel is its mechanical impedance. The impedance of matter is the product of the velocity in, and the density of, the material. Because of aerogel's low density and low sound velocity, the mechanical impedance of aerogel is unusual in that it stands between that of a condensed solid like steel and that of a gas. For that reason aerogel should be an efficient means of coupling sound waves in air to a transducer (a device or element that converts energy from one form to another). This role for aerogel may be useful for either generating or detecting sound.

The pure carbon aerogels described above are quite electrically conductive and may find use as electrodes for batteries, capacitors, or fuel cells. Silica aerogel is an electrical insulator with a low dielectric constant. (The dielectric constant is the measure of the ability of a material to store electrical potential energy under the influence of an electric field, as determined by the ratio of the capacitance of a condenser with the material as a dielectric to its capacitance with a vacuum as a dielectric.) The velocity of signal propagation in a wire or printed circuit board is dependent on the dielectric constant of the surrounding electrical insulation. The lower the dielectric constant, the higher the velocity. Therefore, aerogel dielectrics can substantially speed the operation of microelectronic circuits and computer chips.

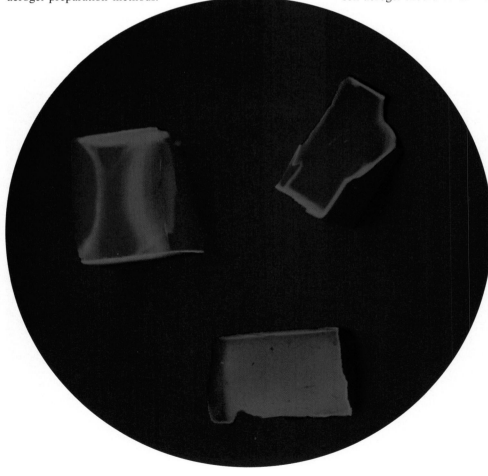

Aerogel composites of silica and silicon exhibit strong photoluminescence—luminescence stimulated by visible or ultraviolet radiation.

Lawrence Berkeley Laboratory

158

Lawrence Berkeley Laboratory

Aerogel composites of silica and iron or iron oxide have strong magnetic properties and may be used to help control cooling cycles in some air conditioners.

COMPOSITE AEROGELS

In developing thermally enhanced aerogel composites, researchers discovered a whole new class of composite aerogel materials. They include composites with nanophase carbon, metallic iron, iron oxides, and elemental silicon incorporated into the aerogel structure. Aerogel composites of silica with iron and iron oxide exhibit magnetic properties and thus may be useful for cooling cycles for automobile or specialty air conditioners. Silica aerogels with silicon exhibit strong photo-luminescence—luminescence stimulated by visible or ultraviolet radiation—and may be used in display devices based on silicon.

The large surface area and high chemical activity of aerogels and aerogel composites make them ideal for use as catalysts in gas-phase chemical reactions. In general, however, aerogels cannot serve as catalysts for reactions involving liquids because the surface tension of the liquid might destroy the structure of the aerogel.

FUTURE PROSPECTS

With so many unusual properties, aerogels will likely find a number of applications in our technological society. In the past, lack of knowledge about aerogel and its limited availability for experimentation have restricted the search for new applications. As aerogel becomes better known and understood, it may indeed find more uses in homes, automobiles, and airplanes.

FOR ADDITIONAL READING

■ *Aerogels: Proceedings of the First International Symposium,* J. Fricke, ed., *Springer Proceedings in Physics,* vol. 6 (Springer, 1986).

■ *Proceedings of the Third International Symposium on Aerogels,* J. Fricke, ed., *Journal of Non-Crystalline Solids,* vol. 145 (1992).

■ *Sol-Gel Science,* C.J. Brinker and G.W. Scherer (Academic Press, 1990).

Indigenous Science: A Star in Africa's Future?

by Thomas A. Bass

Africa possesses a wealth of scientific knowledge developed independently from Western science and its methods. Bringing this knowledge to light and building upon it to benefit the continent are among the concerns of many scientists working in Africa today.

Africa is a natural treasure house. It is endowed with fabulous examples of physical and cultural diversity. These riches hold the keys to answering many questions that can be answered—if they can be answered at all—only in Africa. When did humans first start using tools and fire? How do species evolve? Where do HIV, the virus that causes AIDS, and other new viruses come from? Is the Earth getting hotter and drier, and if so, what can be done about it?

Africa is also a laboratory for studying the clash between modern scientific methods and technologies and traditional practices. As in all traditional societies, African peoples have evolved sophisticated realms of knowledge, derived from experimentation or observation, that explain, predict, or control natural phenomena. This indigenous knowledge often appears to differ from—or even run counter to—the scientific principles brought with the colonial powers. The seeming dichotomy thus raises another important question: Are modern science and its methods alien to traditional African cultures? The answer to this question is crucial to anyone concerned about the less developed world and the future of science in general.

Evidence of Africa's store of indigenous scientific knowledge has emerged recently in a variety of disciplines. Africa's nomadic pastoralists who subsist on the desert's edge are acknowledged to be among the world's experts on famine and range management. The 1,000-year-old cultures living south of Timbuktu along the Niger River in Mali consult written texts that today are appreciated as a model of environmental conservation. The continent's materia medica of more than 1,000 animal, plant, and mineral products for the treatment of illness is a resource that Western-trained scientists are avidly studying. Africa's traditional plant breeders, cultivating tropical gardens that contain as many as 150 species, are now recognized as having developed a remarkably productive agricultural system.

SEEKING A MARRIAGE OF METHODS

The rewards of recognizing and taking seriously Africa's indigenous knowledge are exemplified in the work of Thomas Adeoye Lambo, former deputy director general of the World Health Organization. Born in Abeokuta, Nigeria, in 1923 and one of 30 children fathered by a Yoruba chief with 12 wives, Lambo studied medicine at the University of Birmingham, England, and then earned advanced degrees from the University of London's Institute of Psychiatry. Lambo returned to his own country in 1950 to run the Aro Hospital for Nervous Diseases, Aro, Nigeria, Africa's first mental hospital. While waiting for that facility's buildings to be completed, Lambo decided to billet his patients in neighboring villages. There he discovered that traditional African life, with its close-knit communal structure, had therapeutic value of its own. Even after his hospital was finished, Lambo continued to place patients in the neighboring villages.

Lambo's next experiment—not supported by the British administrators who controlled his government hospital—was even more radical. Using his own money, he hired a dozen traditional healers to practice medicine alongside his regular clinical staff. After studying their techniques and filming them for 12 years, Lambo discovered that the healers, long dismissed by colonial administrators as witch doctors, were employing many of the same psychiatric techniques he had learned at the University

Thomas A. Bass is Scholar-in-Residence at Hamilton College, Clinton, New York. Among his books are Reinventing the Future: Conversations with the World's Leading Scientists *(1994) and* Camping with the Prince and Other Tales of Science in Africa *(1990).*

(Overleaf) A traditional healer from the Qwaqwa region, South Africa.

A child of the Sahelian region of Mali tends a farm during a drought in the late 1980s. Africa's nomadic pastoralists are acknowledged to be among the world's experts on famine and range management.

A Zulu healer is surrounded by items used in his herbal medicines and ointments. Long before the rise of modern psychiatry, Africa's traditional healers were employing psychotherapeutic techniques and dispensing from an extensive collection of herbal remedies and psychotropic drugs.

of London. Independently of Sigmund Freud and his successors—and apparently long before them—Africa's traditional healers had invented the "talking cure," free association, group therapy, and behavioral modification. They also had an extensive pharmacopoeia of herbal remedies and psychotropic (mind-altering) drugs. "We found their techniques to be remarkably effective," Lambo said. "Their psychotherapeutic sessions were vastly superior to ours. They showed us we hadn't got it right."

Lambo's observations included clinical histories such as the following:

A young man was brought to us with his hands and legs tied up after a schizophrenic episode. The healer said, "Take off his ropes, and we'll watch him." They unbound him and the boy didn't do anything violent or aggressive. Then he was given a potion made of ground-up leaves. No Western drugs were used on the patients being treated by traditional healers. They were in charge from beginning to end. The young man slept for two days. Later, when I had these leaves analyzed, I found he had been given a strong dose of tranquilizers and psychotropic chemicals. While the patient slept the healer interviewed his parents. The boy stayed only nine days before he was completely recovered.

To Western psychiatrists, the diagnosis in this case looks simple. "The boy had a spontaneous remission." But I witnessed traditional healers handling hundreds of acute cases the same way. Their management was superb. The patients were usually discharged within a month. If I had admitted that boy into the ward, he wouldn't have been released in nine days. His illness would have been aggravated to such an extent that he would have been there six months.

Lambo devoted the rest of his career to developing a "methodological syncretism," an approach that attempts to fuse Western and traditional medicines. He persuaded African healers to adopt such methods as the use of antibiotics. At the same time, he taught his hos-

162

A variety of traditional medicines are traded in a market in central Johannesburg, South Africa. According to Thomas Adeoye Lambo, former deputy director general of the World Health Organization, "Without a vast herbal pharmacopoeia, most of Africa's tribes would long ago have been wiped out."

pital staff traditional methods, such as the incorporation of the family into psychotherapeutic sessions. Faster, more effective, and one-fifth the price of European-style psychotherapy, Lambo's village-based cure for mental illness already has been adopted in 60 countries around the world.

Lambo explained:

I arranged the marriage of traditional and Western cultures. The Masai were suturing blood vessels, removing appendixes, and practicing other sophisticated surgical techniques long before the British. Without a vast herbal pharmacopoeia, most of Africa's tribes would long ago have been wiped out. Rather than merely imitating the West, Africa should build on its indigenous strengths. Innovate, don't imitate, I tell people, because Westerners themselves are unhappy with what they have.

A WORLDVIEW WITHOUT SCIENCE

Thomas Risley Odhiambo, another leading African scientist, agrees with Lambo that the continent will solve its problems only through the fusion of modern science with Africa's traditional strengths. Born in 1931, the son of a telegraph clerk in the colonial postal service, Odhiambo founded and presently directs the International Centre of Insect Physiology and Ecology, an $8 million-a-year research center in Nairobi, Kenya, staffed by 40 senior scientists. Schooled by missionaries and the *Encyclopædia Britannica*, Odhiambo began his career at the Ugandan Ministry of Agriculture. There he conducted research, on his own time, against the wishes of his British colonial superiors, becoming the first black man in East Africa to publish a scientific paper in an interna-

tional journal. Odhiambo finished college in Uganda and then finished college again at the University of Cambridge, where he also earned a Ph.D.

In the landmark article "East Africa: Science for Development," published in the U.S. journal *Science* in 1967, Odhiambo argued that Africa has to embrace the scientific method—not just its technological results but the worldview inherent in doing science—if it wants to get beyond the "colonial interlude." He called for "centers of excellence" in Africa that would act as "powerhouses for the initiated and for those wishing to be initiated in research."

In his article Odhiambo also examined the philosophical implications of science in Africa. Why, for example, are there so few African scientists? Poor teaching and lack of jobs form part of an answer, "but is it not possible," he speculated, "that there may be

something in the cultural attitude and social philosophy [of Africans] that may discourage a tradition in science?"

Answering his question, Odhiambo wrote, "It is my view that the African's monistic (one world) view of nature has proved an impediment to his becoming a natural scientist." Odhiambo elaborated on that statement by explaining the concept of *jok,* a belief system developed by Africans living at the headwaters of the Nile, the area from which Odhiambo himself came. *Jok* refers to both the body and the spirit that moves it. "The *Jok* concept permeates the Nilotic idea of the universe, of existence, and of destiny" so deeply that nothing distinguishes the living and the dead for these Africans other than the life force, the *jok* that animates them. "Plants, animals, inanimate objects, God, spirits, and men" all share to a lesser or greater extent in this diffusion of energy.

"In this African philosophy there is no sharp distinction between the subjective and objective worlds," wrote Odhiambo—a distinction that in Europe on the eve of the Renaissance was the necessary prerequisite to the development of science. "Science, in the modern sense, has no firm foundations in African

society," he concluded. What Africans have developed instead of science is "a vastly intricate social and communalistic system."

This social system, while opposed to the dualistic worldview of modern science, has benefits of its own. According to Odhiambo:

Africa in the last two centuries has gone through probably the worst period in its history. That we have survived without going mad is due in part to our sense of immortality, the belief that the dead can oversee the affairs of the living. It is a comforting thought to know that the living and the dead are one and the same. The only thing that distinguishes them is what in English is vaguely known as energy. The less you have of it the more you become nonliving. The more you have of it the more you are living, or you may even become a god.

A healer of the Kavango people of Namibia is shown in traditional dress. Rather than see Africa forsake the wealth of indigenous knowledge that is embodied in its healers, Lambo has worked to effect a fusion of traditional and Western medicines.

A Kenyan woman boils herbs for a traditional remedy (left), while nomadic fishermen of the Bozo tribe gather, according to the rhythm of the stars and seasons, for collective fishing on the Niger River (above). Some observers wonder if the differences between Africa's traditional practices and the methods of modern science reflect deeper differences in worldviews. Scientist Thomas Risley Odhiambo has argued that, instead of science, Africans have developed "a vastly intricate social and communalistic system," in which the living, the dead, and the inanimate share in the same *jok,* or life force, and in which "there is no sharp distinction between the subjective and objective worlds."

This African way of thinking is synthetic, rather than analytical. Its truths are arrived at by an additive process that makes them ever more complex and multifaceted. The analytical approach, on the other hand, is reductive. It ends up with a partial truth that is easier to explain for its being an approximation. Unless the African can learn to use analytical tools better, even against his own instincts—indeed, in this case, become schizophrenic about it—then I have a feeling we're not going to get very far. I myself am schizophrenic. I have my cultural life and my scientific life. But I believe that analytical tools are very powerful and that we should use them.

At the end of his *Science* article, Odhiambo called for the creation of a "new" African. He wanted such a person to "reach the basic root of the problem, his monistic world view, and modify it in a manner in which he can begin to regard Nature apart from himself and other beings." Odhiambo then began developing a scientific cadre capable of fusing traditional strengths with Western analytical methods. "My own feeling is that if Africa can rationalize its strengths and incorporate science into its culture, we will have a very powerful instrument."

POTENTIAL VERSUS OUTPUT

One may question Odhiambo's philosophical assumptions, but he is obviously cor-

rect in highlighting the gap between Africa's scientific potential and usable output. A 1992 study of scientific communities in Africa by Jacques Gaillard and Roland Waast of the French Institute of Scientific Research for Development through Cooperation (ORSTOM), Paris, concluded that, because of its scientific underdevelopment, most of Africa's physical and cultural diversity has remained unexplored and underutilized. They estimated that black Africa had 20,000 research engineers and scientists. This was 0.36% of the world's scientists and accounted for 0.4% of the world's expenditure on research and development. Two countries alone monopolized scientific research in Africa, Nigeria and Kenya. They held one-third of the continent's scientists and pro-

duced one-half of its published research. Many African countries that once had viable universities and research stations have descended into political chaos. The one bright spot in African science today is the reintegration of South Africa into the intellectual affairs of the continent.

The gap between Africa's scientific richness and minimal output has been explained by various theories. They range from analyses of external factors (many stemming from the continent's colonial legacy) to discussions of the internal dynamics of African society itself—the difficulty, for example, of transmitting bodies of knowledge in oral cultures that are given to protecting guild secrets. Yet while trying to account for the absence of science in traditional African cultures, many observers over-

African scientists in Kenya carry out tsetse fly research on behalf of the Masai people. According to a recent study of scientific communities in Africa, two countries, Nigeria and Kenya, held one-third of the continent's scientists and produced one-half of its published research. Altogether, black Africa supplied only 0.36% of the world's scientists and accounted for only 0.4% of the world's expenditure on research and development.

look, or fail to recognize, the scientific knowledge indigenous to Africa. If the resources available for scientific research on the continent are scant, the Westerner's familiarity with Africa's traditional knowledge is equally superficial, and much of what is known about science in African cultures was discovered by accident. Foreign experts who had been sent to "fix" the continent's problems suddenly found that the tables were turned. Instead of transferring technology from outside, the experts began adopting methods that Africans long ago had developed on their own.

DEALING WITH DISEASE

Employed by the British colonial medical service, the British entomologist John Ford, beginning in the 1950s, spent a quarter century studying trypanosomiasis, or sleeping sickness, which is caused by a flyborne blood parasite that makes vast tracts of Africa uninhabitable by humans and cattle. Ford, at the end of his career, wrote a classic study on trypanosomiasis, in which he concluded that he and his colleagues "were feebly scratching at the surface of events that we hardly knew existed, and if we achieved anything at all, it was often to exacerbate the ills of the societies we imagined ourselves to be helping." Ford went on:

Unfortunately, with very few exceptions, it was psychologically impossible for men and women concerned in imperial expansion in Africa to believe that their own actions were more often than not responsible for the manifold disasters in which they found themselves caught up. The scientists they called in to help them were as ignorant as they of the problems they had to tackle.

Ford discovered that Africans knew all about the more than 20 species of *Glossina* flies, commonly called tsetse flies, that transmit sleeping sickness. They were also versed in the ecological measures, such as bush clearing and seasonal pasturage, required for controlling the

(Opposite page) Nomadic pastoralists dig trenches that are to carry rainwater into their fields—part of a European strategy to "fix" the drought problems of the Sahel. Due to lack of consistent rainfall in any given locale, however, the concept of encouraging the nomads to work fixed fields has failed. Long ago the farmers already developed their own solution of "chasing" the rain—continually moving to regions where rainfall will be sufficient for the next crop.

British-American explorer and journalist Henry Stanley is pictured on an African expedition in an 1872 engraving. In the late 1870s his steamboats on the Congo River unknowingly spread sleeping sickness in central Africa as they transported the most dangerous species of tsetse fly upriver from its native home in the Congo.

flies. But while Africans long ago had figured out a modus vivendi for living with this and other of the continent's medical challenges, their systems began to break down in the colonial era.

In the European myth of the Dark Continent, Africa was ravaged by disease until the arrival of Western medical science. The truth is actually quite different. In the case of sleeping sickness, it was the British-American explorer Henry Stanley and his steamboats in the late 1870s that unknowingly transported the most dangerous species of tsetse fly upriver from its native home in the Congo and thereby introduced sleeping sickness liberally throughout central Africa. This spread

was further exacerbated by the erroneous colonial policy of evacuating sleeping sickness victims, thereby spreading the disease farther into previously uninfected areas.

Medical historians now agree that the unhealthiest period in Africa's history occurred during the height of colonial contact with Europeans, between 1890 and 1930. Introduced by trade caravans from the eastern coast, cholera reduced the life span of the average Tanzanian male to 25 years. Cholera and smallpox eliminated the nomadic Masai of East Africa as a major tribe. Invading the continent in the 1890s, the rinderpest virus decimated livestock herds from the Nile to South Africa. As a result, East Africa

was largely depopulated during the first three decades of the 20th century.

Precolonial Africa had suffered epidemics during the Bantu migrations from the north, the Zulu expansion from the south, and the days of Arab slaving off the coast, but nothing was equal to the disruption caused by European colonialism. Dispersed populations of hunter-gatherers, pastoralists, and agriculturalists, who had worked out ways to coexist with their pathogens, were suddenly confronted with new diseases and means for spreading them. Viruses and parasites were the advance guard of colonialism, and the continent's present disease environment is one of its legacies.

LIVING ON THE DESERT'S EDGE

Experiences similar to that undergone by Ford have been registered by other researchers sent out to study Africa's problems. One of them is the British economist Jeremy Swift, who has advised many governmental and United Nations agencies on the design of famine early-warning systems in the Sahel, the vast semiarid region of Africa south of the Sahara that stretches from the Atlantic coast to The Sudan. Born in 1939 and currently a professor at the University of Sussex, England, Swift long ago arrived at the conclusion that "the people who really know about famines are the

The Niger's desert wetlands, the source of livelihood for a million people, are also vital to the countless birds that migrate between Europe and Africa. Conservationists seeking to preserve the wetlands ecology with a plan involving multiple-use zones were surprised to find that a traditional system had developed the same concept.

ditional knowledge in African society is attributed by Swift to the inherent limits of modern science. In his view:

People tend to make their reputations in Africa in one narrow area. The model for their research comes from physics and is basically reductionist. But this isolation of elements in the hope of finding one item capable of improvement doesn't work. You have to move forward on all fronts at once. The real challenge is to relate the detail of the mechanism to these larger, more amorphous systems, and to do this, you have to listen very carefully to what farmers and herders say.

Another scientist who was impressed by what he learned from Africa's farmers and herders is British developmental economist Richard Moorehead, former director of a large aid project in the in-

ner delta of the Niger River, south of Timbuktu. In the late 1980s Moorehead was sent by the International Union for Conservation of Nature and Natural Resources (IUCN) to develop an ecological master plan for the area. His project was based on the idea of dividing the delta's resources into multiple-use zones, which would both protect the delta's abundant wildlife and guarantee the livelihood of the million people who live in this desert wetlands. Moorehead was surprised to discover that the concept of multiple-use zones already existed. It was so well developed, in fact, that it had been written down more than a century earlier in Arabic texts called *ta'rikh.*

The traditional system, developed over millennia, arranged these wetlands on the edge of the Sahara into carefully synchronized patterns of land use capable of produc-

ing eight times as much plant matter as the average wheat field. A half-dozen Malian tribes have worked out elaborate protocols for sharing this common ground as it cycles from floodplain to pasture for a million cattle and three million sheep and goats—the highest herd density in Africa.

In the traditional system that existed until the colonial era, the floodplain was divided into 37 *leydi,* or districts, controlled by village elders. They maintained fishing and woodland reserves, organized access to resources, and managed their own highly effective forms of conservation. Cattle crossings, fishing rights, and other rules were codified in a body of law known as the Dina system. "The Dina was a system of multiple land use that imposed a balance on resources and their exploitation," said Moorehead. "These are so-

phisticated, practical people who have known about conservation and multiple use reserves for a long time."

EXPERT FARMERS

Yet another scientist who has come to respect Africa's traditional knowledge is Bede Okigbo, a botanist trained at Cornell University, Ithaca, New York, who served in the 1980s as deputy director general of the International Institute of Tropical Agriculture (IITA), Ibadan, Nigeria. The son of an Ibo farmer in eastern Nigeria and one of Africa's leading scientists, Okigbo is an expert in the area of agriculture known as farming systems.

The development of agriculture traditionally has been credited to the Near East, where the shift from food gathering to food production marked the beginning of

173

the Neolithic revolution. But Okigbo and other botanists now think that agriculture evolved independently in Africa. At the same time that people in southwestern Asia were settling down to village life, Africa was developing its own "Fertile Crescent" along the headwaters of the Niger. Here a Neolithic civilization emerged from the Stone Age and domesticated plants that are now cultivated around the world. These include millet, sorghum, African rice, cowpeas, groundnuts, yams, okra, watermelons, cotton, oil palms, sesame, tamarinds, and kola.

African farmers, to the consternation of colonial administrators, have always preferred to jumble a selection of crops together and grow them all at once. Okigbo and other agronomists have discovered that this system of mixed cropping is actually a prudent

A Malian woman participates in collective fishing on the Niger River. In the traditional system for managing the Niger's wetlands, the floodplain was divided into 37 districts. Fishing rights, land use, and other issues were coordinated through a body of law known as the Dina.

strategy on a continent where crop pests are as numerous as crop varieties. Mixed cropping discourages the insects that attack particular crops from breeding to high levels. The labor of harvesting is staggered, crops are produced over a longer period of time, losses in one crop can be balanced with produce from another, and a wide variety of foods is supplied.

Okigbo has pointed out the tendency of the industrialized world to overspecialize on a handful of crops while ignoring the abundance of varieties often found on indigenous farms. "There are five hundred thousand plant species," he noted. "Ten thousand are utilized by man. Two hundred are grown industrially. But only a few of these are of commercial importance. Fifteen plant species out of the half million that exist in the world give us seventy-five percent of our food."

In recent years Okigbo has devoted himself to studying what are known as compound farms. While cultivating their outlying fields, many African farmers traditionally grow a garden around their family homes, or compounds. Unlike gardens in temperate climates, which are horizontal, these tropical gardens are planted vertically.

Above people's houses rise galleries of palm trees that wave over plantains, which in turn shade the spices and cocoyams planted below. "Tropical rain forests have no fewer than four stories," explained Okigbo, "and the multistoried compound farm is the only agricultural system in the world that tends to mimic nature."

© T.A. Bass

Along the Niger's headwaters Africa may have developed its own "Fertile Crescent" independent of Neolithic agriculture in the Near East.

A recent study of compound farms in eastern Nigeria identified 146 plant species, with as many as 57 grown in a single compound. "At IITA we're working at a much simpler level than the local farmer," said Okigbo. "This means we can only give him information about one or two systems, while he has to deal with something far more complex." It also means that Western

scientists stand to learn many things from African farmers, including the limitations and pitfalls of reductionism.

DEVELOPING AFRICA'S DESTINY

Much bad news has come out of Africa in recent decades—news of civil wars, droughts, famines. Okigbo has cautioned that Africa's food crisis is only one of four crises currently plaguing the continent, the other three being political instability, economic indebtedness, and environmental degradation. In the eyes of many observers, Africa is littered with white elephants—the bleaching bones of animals and aid projects alike. To them the latter are proof that technology transfer, the

dominant model for African development since the end of colonialism, has failed and will continue to fail until policy makers comprehend the real nature of science and development in Africa. In the words of Kenya's Odhiambo:

We don't need any more fire brigades. In an atmosphere of crisis it's natural to want to take shortcuts. Africa has been sold the idea that it can transfer technology from other parts of the world to solve its problems. But it won't work, and we've lost a quarter of a century because of this simplistic view. I believe instead that basic scientific research is what is going to bring Africa to a position where it can control its destiny.

To generalize from the examples cited, if Africa is to overcome the multiple crises it now faces, it must develop the centers of excellence called for by Odhiambo and devote more resources to basic research. It must take advantage of the indigenous knowledge already in place. Finally, it must fuse African wisdom and Western analysis to arrive at a new scientific synthesis, which has the potential to benefit the entire world.

See also Feature Article: THE GODDESS AND THE GREEN REVOLUTION.

A poster (above) teaches the "scientific" way of mixing two crops to African farmers, who long ago learned how to grow dozens of species together on farms resembling natural ecosystems. (Left) A typical Nigerian market is suggestive of the variety of crops grown on indigenous farms.

FOR ADDITIONAL READING

■ *Africa and the Disciplines: The Contributions of Research in Africa to the Social Sciences and Humanities*, Robert H. Bates, V.Y. Mudimbe, and Jean O'Barr, eds. (University of Chicago Press, 1993).

■ *The African Background to Medical Science: Essays on African History, Science, and Civilizations*, Charles S. Finch (Karnak House, 1990).

■ *African Philosophy, Culture, and Traditional Medicine*, M. Akin Makinde (Ohio University, 1988).

■ "African Science Before the Birth of the 'New' World," Ivan Van Sertima, *The Black Collegian* (January–February 1992, pp. 69–71).

■ *Camping with the Prince and Other Tales of Science in Africa*, Thomas A. Bass (Houghton Mifflin, 1990).

■ "East Africa: Science for Development," Thomas R. Odhiambo, *Science* (Nov. 17, 1967, pp. 876–881).

■ *Ngoma: Discourses on Healing in Central and Southern Africa*, John M. Janzen (University of California Press, 1992).

■ *Reinventing the Future: Conversations with the World's Leading Scientists*, Thomas A. Bass (Addison-Wesley, 1994).

■ *The Role of the Trypanosomiases in African Ecology: A Study of the Tsetse Fly Problem*, John Ford (Clarendon Press, 1971).

■ *Science and Technology in Africa*, John W. Forje (Longman, 1989).

■ "The Uphill Emergence of Scientific Communities in Africa," Jacques Gaillard and Roland Waast, *Journal of Asian and African Studies* (January–April 1992, pp. 41–67).

Days of Wine and Science

by Roger Boulton

Since the time of Pasteur, science has worked to put a better bottle of wine on the table. Advances in such fields as analytic chemistry, cellular biology, genetics, and computer science are promising solutions to many of the mysteries and problems that still attend grape growing and wine making.

(Opposite page) "The Last Supper" by Titian (1488/90–1576); (this page) "Les Vendanges" from *Heures ê l'usage de Paris*, attributed to Rohan, early 15th century.

No one is sure if the apostle Paul was downplaying the strict ascetic life or expressing a belief in the benefits of wine when he wrote, "Drink no longer water, but use a little wine for thy stomach's sake and thine often infirmities" (I Timothy 5:23). There is no doubt, however, that wine has been recognized in many cultures and for thousands of years as an important dietary component, even if scientific evidence for its health benefits has been gathered only recently. In Christian celebrations of the Last Supper, wine has played a symbolic role for nearly 2,000 years, and it was known to civilizations for millennia before the birth of Christ. Wine is mentioned by Pliny the Elder, Virgil, and Cato, among other writers in ancient times. It is significant that the Egyptian, Greek, and Roman civilizations each had deities associated with wine—Osiris, Dionysus, and Bacchus, respectively.

Wines and wine making are thought to share a common history with viticulture, the cultivation of grapevines

Roger Boulton is Professor of Enology and Chemical Engineering, University of California, Davis.

Oriental Institute Museum of the University of Chicago

and the production of grapes. Scholars have traced the growing of *Vitis vinifera* (commonly called the European, or vinifera, grape), the species most commonly used in wine making, to the Neolithic Period between 6000 and 5000 BC and to the region between the Black and Caspian seas in Asia Minor.

Egyptian carvings and paintings 4,000–4,500 years old show the cultivation of grapevines and the making and storage of wines. The distribution of grapevines over much of the ancient world is attributed to the Phoenicians and Greeks, although it is perhaps the Roman Empire that contributed most to the introduction and planting of vines throughout Europe between the 1st century BC and the 3rd century AD. *V. vinifera* grapevines were introduced into China from Asia Minor during the Han Dynasty in the 2nd century BC. Other species of *Vitis* are known to have originated in North America and other areas of Asia.

Grape growing and wine making are featured in an ancient Egyptian painting from Thebes (left; tempera facsimile painting). A Roman pavement mosaic (below) depicts a banquet under a grape arbor, while a fanciful Roman ceiling mosaic (bottom) shows cherublike young boys (putti) crushing grapes.

The history of wine during the Dark Ages of Europe is not well documented. Much of the knowledge gained by the Romans appears to have been lost, or at least set aside, during that time. Medieval monasteries became the centers for much of what was known about grape culture, wine making, and the production of distillates because of the importance of wine in Christian liturgy.

The process of wine making begins with the crushing of grapes to release their juice and then separating the juice from the pulp by pressing. Natural sugars in the juice are fermented into ethanol (ethyl alcohol) and carbon dioxide by the action of yeast, traditionally yeast naturally present on the grape. Normally fermentation is completed in about two to four weeks. The new wine commonly is clarified to remove suspended matter and aged—stored for months or years with limited exposure to air—before being bottled. For making red wines the pigmented skins are included in the fermenting juice; for white wines only the juice is used.

(Center and bottom) E.T. Archive

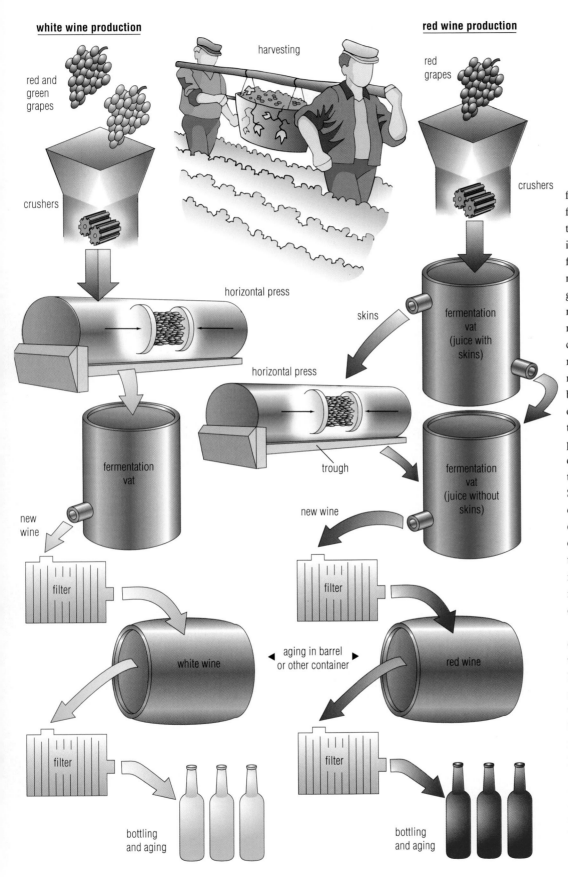

white wine production

red and green grapes

crushers

horizontal press

fermentation vat

new wine

filter

white wine

filter

bottling and aging

red wine production

harvesting

red grapes

crushers

skins

fermentation vat (juice with skins)

horizontal press

trough

fermentation vat (juice without skins)

new wine

filter

◄ aging in barrel or other container ►

red wine

filter

bottling and aging

Although wine makers have followed this simple sequence for centuries, today's practice includes many biochemical and microbiological refinements that allow the wine maker greater retention of grape flavors in the wine, more control of undesirable microbial activity and chemical changes and of the aging reactions, and the means to manufacture bottled products better suited to modern methods of commercial distribution. Historically much of the progress in wine making has come about by empirical, or trial-and-error, developments. Since the 19th century, however, the incorporation of scientific discoveries and methods has helped transform the task of improving wine making from a black art to a modern technology: enology, or scientific wine making.

Today's knowledge of viticulture and enology permits wines of almost any style to be made in temperate climates throughout the world, whereas once they would have been products with only limited distribution or primarily local interest. Three countries,

Basic steps in the production of white and red wines are diagrammed. In wineries around the world many variations exist in the order and number of steps followed and the equipment used.

Vineyards in such diverse places as Tuscany, Italy (left), Napa Valley, California (below left), and the Caucasus of Georgia (below) testify to the broad popularity of wines, although output by country varies widely. Italy, France, and Spain together produce more than half of the world's wines.

(Left) © D. Donadoni—Bruce Coleman Inc.; (below left) © Peter Menzel

Italy, France, and Spain, now account for more than half of the world's production, while seven others, including the U.S., supply another 30%. A wide variation exists in the acceptance of wines in different countries and, thus, in their levels of per capita consumption. Acceptance in a particular country is often strongly influenced by the approval or acceptance of wine by the predominant religions.

FRUIT OF THE VINE

The evolution of wine making has followed the successful establishment of vineyards of vinifera grapes. About 20 cultivars of the species are internationally accepted (*see* Table on pages 184–185), and their widespread cultivation is the basis for the making of most of today's wines. In addition, many traditional cultivars with such names as Peraquita, Furmint, Harslevelu,

Lagrein, Vernaccia, Altesse, Mondeuse, and Mavron are still planted in parts of Europe, where they serve for the making of regional wines with limited distribution.

Several reasons exist for the adoption of particular cultivars in a given region, though the ability to produce acceptably mature grapes would seem to be the main one. Acceptable maturity usually means enough sugar in the grape to provide the wine with a concentration of ethanol (11–13% by volume) that will keep it from spoiling easily. It also means a level of acidity (mainly from tartaric and malic acids in the grape) and an overall flavor that please the taste. For cultivars intended for red wines, color is also an important factor. Secondary considerations include the cultivar's resistance to several vine diseases and its tolerance of frosts or freezing conditions. Vineyards in some regions traditionally grow more than one cultivar in order to reduce seasonal variations in composition and yield and, sometimes, to offset the poor flowering characteristics of certain cultivars.

In some cool areas the overlap of early rains or frost with the final stages of ripening has led to the favoring of cultivars with early-ripening character-istics because they are more likely to reach acceptable maturity in most years. An example is the adoption of early-ripening Pinot Noir and the exclusion of the late-ripening Cabernet Sauvignon in cooler-climate vineyards such as those in the Champagne region of France and in southern Germany. By contrast, in France's Burgundy and Bordeaux regions, the U.S. West Coast, and the coastal regions of Australia, both of these grapes are grown quite successfully.

Grafting has been used to improve a cultivar's ability to grow in a particular region. Cuttings of environmentally more restricted cultivars can be grafted to grapevine rootstocks that, for example, resist plant parasites, grow in poor soil conditions, or tolerate low temperatures. Supported by the hardier rootstocks, the cultivars flourish in conditions under which they would otherwise suffer. In certain regions the number of rootstocks available to support grafts is greatly restricted by the mineral content and acidity of the soil, and the choice of cultivar has been determined primarily by compatibility with those rootstocks. For some of those regions cultivar choice was made even more complicated after a root louse, an aphidlike insect commonly known as phylloxera, destroyed most of the vinifera vineyards of Europe, America, and Australia in the late 1800s. For example, the widespread adoption of the Trebbiano cultivar in the Cognac region of France was based on its compatibility with the few phylloxera-resistant rootstocks that performed satisfactorily in the chalky soils of the region.

Introduction of other *Vitis* species (*e.g.,* the North American species *V. rotundifolia*) into commercial viticulture mostly has been limited to the breeding of hybrid rootstocks that are resistant to attack by phylloxera, nematodes, or other pests. It was the introduction of resistant rootstocks from nonvinifera grape species that subdued the phylloxera epidemic a century ago and allows the successful growing of vinifera cultivars today. Some wine from hybrid cultivars is produced in the colder growing regions of the U.S., parts of Canada and Japan, and regions where fungal growth in humid conditions (*e.g.,* parts of the southern and eastern U.S.) requires the use of native species for successful commercial production. On a world scale, however, hybrid cultivars make only a small contribution to wine production.

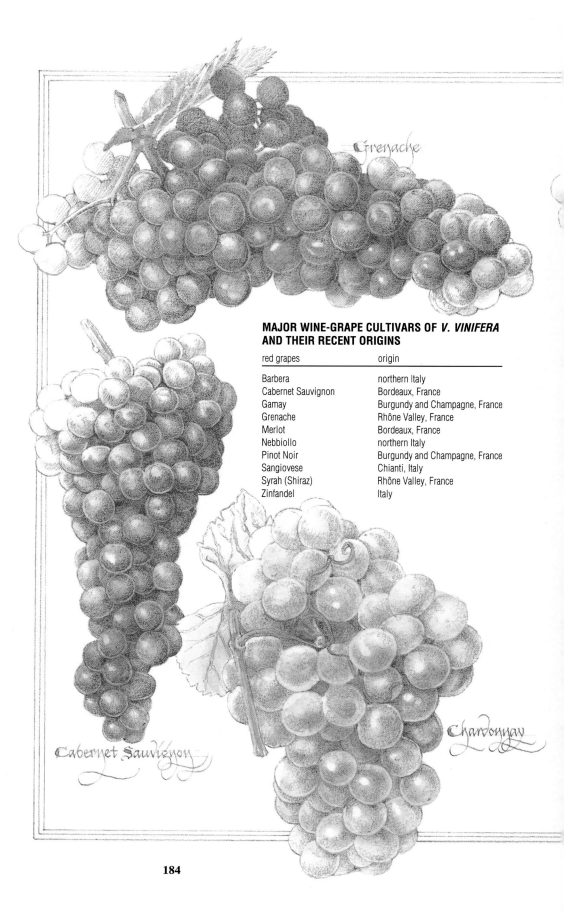

MAJOR WINE-GRAPE CULTIVARS OF *V. VINIFERA* AND THEIR RECENT ORIGINS

red grapes	origin
Barbera	northern Italy
Cabernet Sauvignon	Bordeaux, France
Gamay	Burgundy and Champagne, France
Grenache	Rhône Valley, France
Merlot	Bordeaux, France
Nebbiollo	northern Italy
Pinot Noir	Burgundy and Champagne, France
Sangiovese	Chianti, Italy
Syrah (Shiraz)	Rhône Valley, France
Zinfandel	Italy

184

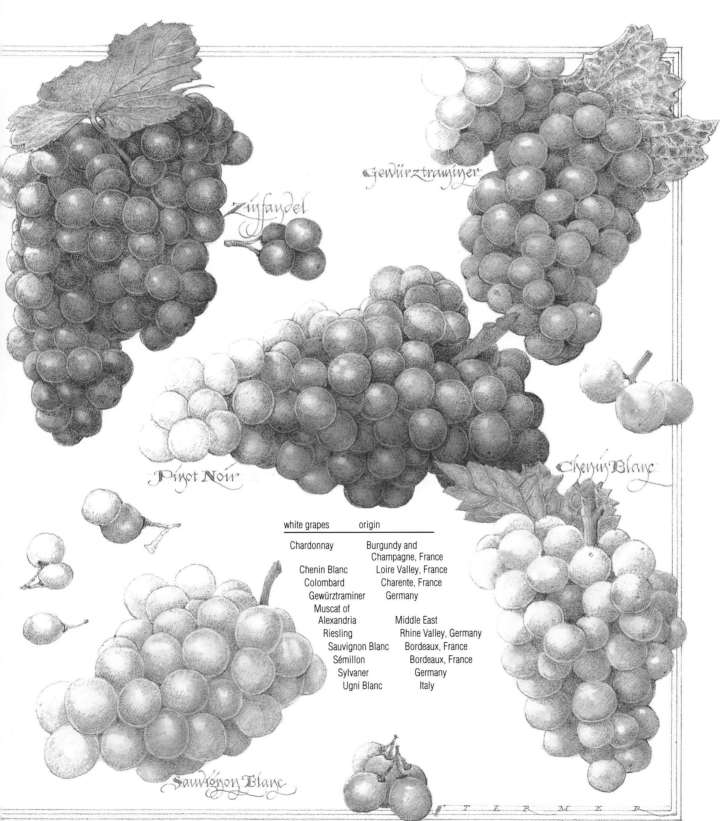

Gewürztraminer

Zinfandel

Pinot Noir

Chenin Blanc

white grapes	origin
Chardonnay	Burgundy and Champagne, France
Chenin Blanc	Loire Valley, France
Colombard	Charente, France
Gewürztraminer	Germany
Muscat of Alexandria	Middle East
Riesling	Rhine Valley, Germany
Sauvignon Blanc	Bordeaux, France
Sémillon	Bordeaux, France
Sylvaner	Germany
Ugni Blanc	Italy

Sauvignon Blanc

Illustration by Dugald Stermer

185

BEGINNINGS OF MODERN WINE MAKING

Significant contributions to modern wine making date to the 17th and 18th centuries, when a number of discoveries, often made by trial and error, brought about important changes in the understanding of wines. Driving the need for those changes were the development of international commerce and the problems encountered with shipping and storing wines. During the period, empirical experiments resulted in bottled wines containing significant dissolved carbon dioxide, which formed long-lasting bubbles when the bottle was opened. These sparkling wines, which later became popular in the royal courts of England, were the earliest form of today's champagne. Although anecdotes of their discovery differ, Dom Pierre Pérignon, wine maker at the Benedictine abbey in Hautvillers, France, is usually—and likely wrongly—credited with encouraging a secondary yeast fermentation within the bottle, wherein carbon dioxide was produced under pressure. The practice of adding sugar to a previously bottled wine to encourage secondary fermentation forms the basis of the *méthode champenoise* for making quality sparkling wines today.

Under quite different circumstances, traders during the period found that wine spirits—that is, distillates of wine—or wines with spirits added could be shipped without the spoilage (which, unbeknownst to them, was due to microbes) exhibited by the traditional wines of the time. According to one story, brandy

originated in the 16th century when Dutch traders distilled light wines from the Cognac region in France so that they would withstand shipment. Although the traders' intention was to reconstitute the wine with water at the port of destination, the wine distillate proved a popular beverage in its own right when softened by aging. It was also found to be an effective preservative, or "fortifying," agent for other wines going to distant places. The addition of brandy to prevent microbial spoilage in wines shipped to England is thought to be the origin of

The *méthode champenoise* for making today's sparkling wines (left) has its roots in empirical experiments in the 17th century. Wooden wine barrels are thought to have been introduced by the Romans; the example above was found at Silchester, England.

the fortified wines known as porto or port, after the principal shipping center Oporto in Portugal. Today this fortification step is added to a partially fermented grape juice rather than to a young wine, and its main purpose is to stop the primary fermentation and so produce a wine that captures some of the sweetness and flavor of the grape juice. Nevertheless, in these fortified wines enhanced microbial stability remains an important feature.

Although the Romans are credited with introducing wooden barrels for storing and shipping wines, it is not known whether they deliberately aged wines in them to extract additional flavor components from the wood, as is the practice today. The availability of suitable timber from surrounding forests, the knowledge related to its harvesting and preparation, and the extent to which the wines from a region were shipped all conceivably contributed to the adoption of the practice of holding wines in small barrels and the acceptance of deliberate aging of wines to modify their flavors. Storing wines in cork-stoppered glass bottles probably came about with the adoption of commercial practices for storing and shipping various commodities

Louis Pasteur (above), often considered the first wine scientist, introduced microbiology and analytic chemistry to wine making. In the same scientific tradition, a researcher at the University of California, Davis (left), listens to ultrasonic emissions from grape plants to assess their water needs.

rather than from the results of deliberate attempts to improve the protection of wine during distribution and sale.

SCIENCE COMES TO THE WINERY

Not until the rise of chemistry, microbiology, biochemistry, and engineering in the 19th century did wine-making practices begin changing significantly. These changes have enabled wine makers to prevent or eliminate most major wine defects and to produce distinctive wines that more faithfully reflect the grape from which they came.

As in other areas of science, the ability to measure a variable of interest usually controls the extent to which useful experiments can be performed. For natural products such as grape juice and wine, it is often the advances in analytic techniques that bring about corresponding advances in knowledge. In wine making it was the technology to analyze acetic acid content that permitted the French scientist Louis Pasteur to accept a challenge from Emperor Napoleon III in 1863 to discover what caused the appearance of acetic acid in wine and its consequent spoilage. His demonstration that oxygen was needed for certain kinds of bacteria present in wine to produce acetic acid was perhaps the first experimental result that changed the way wines were stored. Often considered the first wine scientist, Pasteur also investigated the yield of ethanol and other by-products of wine fermentation, and he made im-

portant chemical discoveries while studying tartaric acid, the major acid in grapes. Pasteur's findings led to some of the most significant innovations in wine making in millennia.

In the decades after Pasteur's pioneering work, microbiology continued to effect changes in wine making, although progress generally was limited by the pace of advances in related fields. Scientists discovered that natural microorganisms were the agents responsible for the production of ethanol in wine fermentation, rather than the spontaneous magical action of an enzyme called zymase. Nevertheless, an understanding of the sequence of chemical reactions underlying the fermentation of sugars such as glucose and fructose into ethanol came only with the evolution of biochemistry and enzymology as sciences in the early 1900s.

Recognition that yeasts on the grapes and in the winery—predominantly strains of *Saccharomyces cerevisiae,* the

same species used in brewing and baking—were conducting the fermentation led to developments in yeast selection, propagation, and inoculation practices by the end of the 19th century. The aim was to make fermentation more consistent from start to finish and reduce the chance of spoilage by undesirable organisms. While reports exist of yeast cultures' being maintained and distributed to farmers in Switzerland and Germany for wine making in the late 1800s, the widespread adoption of selected yeast cultures by the wine-making industry did not occur until the mid-20th century. Advances in yeast identification, the maintenance of cultures, and their propagation on an industrial scale led to the commercial production of yeast in cakes and dried forms that appeared after World War II. Dried yeast pellets that could be rehydrated prior to use were introduced to wine making in California in the 1960s and, after considerable debate in some quarters, have become

A standardized aroma vocabulary for wine assessment is arranged as a wheel. Successive tiers of terms, starting from the center, refine the definition of a particular aroma.

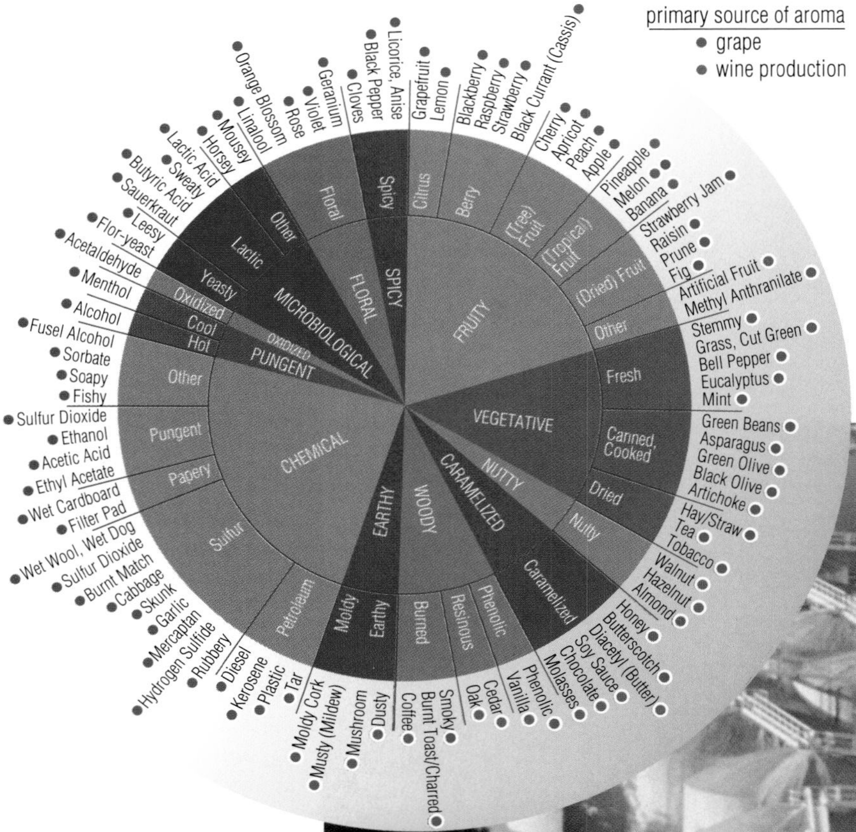

primary source of aroma
● grape
● wine production

accepted throughout the wine regions of the world.

In contrast to the advances in yeast microbiology, scientific understanding of a secondary fermentation process in young wine, called malolactic fermentation, and of the role of lactic acid bacteria in the process lagged until the past few decades. Malolactic fermentation, a bacterial conversion of malic acid in the grape to lactic acid and carbon dioxide, had been recognized for centuries by its effects—some desirable and some not—on the aroma and taste of wines, especially red wines. However, the causal organisms; their sensitivity to acidity level, ethanol, and temperature; their nutritional requirements; and their control by the use of sulfur dioxide have been recent discoveries. The practice of adding selected bacterial cultures to wine to encourage this fermentation began to be investigated only in the late 1950s and was adopted in California in the next decade. Today, despite all the advances, many aspects of lactic acid bacteria and their biochemistry are still mysteries and represent challenges for modern research.

The application of engineering principles to wine making, another relatively recent development, has helped

wineries implement improvements on a commercial scale. Achievements greatly aided by engineering include more efficient grape-pressing systems, improvements in juice preparation, temperature control during fermentation, protection of wines afforded by stainless-steel equipment and efficient refrigeration systems, and control of storage temperature and, thereby, of the rates of certain important chemical reactions in wines as they age. Blanketing wines with inert gases during various stages of transfer and storage to prevent unwanted reactions with oxygen and filtering wine through membranes to remove unwanted microbes, rather than adding chemicals, are examples of how process technologies have contributed to more distinctive wines; they are now used in wineries throughout the world.

The rise of sensory science has had a dramatic effect not only on the commercial assessment of wines but also on the acceptance of certain wine-making practices by the industry and the evaluation of

alternative technologies. Assessment of wines by panels of judges making repeated comparative tastings, introduced during the 1940s, has given way to the use of standardized taste and aroma vocabularies

188

and quantitative descriptive analysis. In descriptive analysis, judges are asked to score single descriptive attributes, such as "bell-pepper" aroma, "buttery" aroma, or "bitterness," on a scale of 0 to 9. The results are usually analyzed by advanced statistical procedures to determine patterns among the wines and their tasting results. Modern sensory evaluation has been very useful in understanding how wines are affected by experimental alterations of procedures in the vineyard or during wine making. Descriptive analysis has passed from the research and teaching arenas into mainstream wine making and is commonly used by wine judges. Its terminology has even invaded the language of wine columnists.

At the end of the 20th century, several fields of science, ranging from biochemistry, cellular biology, and genetics to organic and analytic chemistry and chemical engineering, have the potential to make important contributions to wine making. Some of the more important areas in which science is destined to play a major role are highlighted below.

VINE DISEASES

A number of diseases pose significant threats to the long-term survival of commercial

viticulture as it is known today. In most cases the biological agent has been identified, but the basis of tolerance or resistance in vinifera cultivars—or in *Vitis* species in general—is poorly understood. Examples include (1) Pierce's disease, an infection caused by a widely distributed bacterium, *Xylella fastidiosa,* that leads to block-

age of the fluid channels in the vine and rapid drying out of the vine and leaves, (2) fanleaf degeneration, which results in leaf deformation and severe crop decline and is caused by a virus transmitted by a soilborne nematode, *Xiphema index,* (3) Eutypa dieback, a fungal disease that slowly kills the vascular tissue and leads to withering of the vine wood, caused by *Eutypa armeniacae,* and (4) grape phylloxera (*Daktulosphaira vitifoliae,* formerly *Phylloxera va-*

sitrix), which eats the roots of susceptible vines, causing vine decline and eventual death.

The biological solution developed against phylloxera in the 1880s consisted of grafting European cultivars to phylloxera-resistant rootstocks from North American species of *Vitis.* Over the past 50 years the widespread use

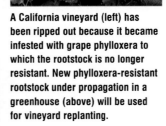

A California vineyard (left) has been ripped out because it became infested with grape phylloxera to which the rootstock is no longer resistant. New phylloxera-resistant rootstock under propagation in a greenhouse (above) will be used for vineyard replanting.

of one rootstock in California has encouraged the emergence of new populations of phylloxera to which that rootstock is no longer resistant. Consequently, a century after the previous disaster, a major costly replanting of vineyards is under way in the coastal regions of the state.

The phylloxera problem is perplexing. Although the insect can reproduce both sexually and asexually, the asexual mode can go on indefinitely and appears to predominate among the phylloxera population in California's vineyards.

Consequently, the insects appear to lack the genetic variation normally introduced by mating, the mechanism that usually accounts for the emergence of subgroups with new traits. Instead, the emergence of variants within the phylloxera population seems to be based on the expression of existing traits under particular environmental pressures. Scientists now regard the use of resistant rootstocks as only a temporary measure in an ongoing battle between vine roots and a complex, versatile organism. Today at least six distinct subgroups of phylloxera are known, and the suitability of the so-called resistant rootstocks, most developed almost 100 years ago, is in question.

Attempts to treat some of these diseases with chemicals has met with little success, and in most cases no preventive measures are known. Prospects for future solutions are seen to rest primarily with rootstock breeding for the root diseases and the use of biotechnology for the other diseases—specifically, the transfer of appropriate genes from naturally resistant plants into existing grape cultivars. While the traditional practice of crossing species to generate new rootstocks has made gains against the fanleaf virus, it offers little hope for solutions to most other vine diseases. Presently the application of biotechnology to viticulture is limited by scientists' poor understanding of grapevine genetics and of the biochemical mechanisms that plants employ to tolerate or resist the diseases in question and by difficulties in introducing functional genes into grape plant cells.

FLAVOR COMPONENTS IN WINES

The wine maker's desire to offer more distinctive and flavorful products has encouraged research into the biochemical origins of the aromas and flavors of grapes and their wines. Study of the factors that influence aroma and flavor was limited for a long time by the inability to measure the chemical components responsible for what is commonly called varietal character. For decades researchers sought in vain to identify the individual compound that they thought to be the essence of a Cabernet Sauvignon, Pinot Noir, or Riesling. Today it is well accepted that varietal character is due to groups of related members of one or more chemical families rather than to single components.

Comstock

Grape phylloxera, an aphidlike insect, kills susceptible vines by eating their roots. Even when it reproduces asexually, phylloxera apparently can produce variant populations able to attack previously resistant rootstock.

In the past 15 years flavor chemists have made major advances in understanding the role of organic compounds known as terpenes. These components, widely distributed in trees and flowers, are primarily responsible for the distinctive, floral aromas of white wine cultivars such as Muscat, Riesling, and Gewürztraminer. The discovery that terpenes exist in the grapes in both a free, volatile form (*i.e.,* present in the vapor above the wine) and a chemically bound, nonvolatile form (typically bound to the sugar glucose) has permitted researchers to study the factors influencing the formation of flavor in these cultivars and occasionally to manipulate them to enhance the corresponding wine aroma.

Similar but more intricate analytic work has uncovered the role of another group of distinctive organic compounds, known as methoxy pyrazines, in Cabernet Sauvignon and Sauvignon Blanc (and perhaps the related cultivars Cabernet Franc, Mer-

lot, and Sémillon). Methoxy pyrazines can be found in these grapes and wines—and, more important, detected by the human senses—at levels of parts per billion. They are often described as giving a bell-pepper aroma; growing the associated cultivars in cool growing regions can accentuate their levels, and certain vineyard practices can alter levels to some degree. On the other hand, the distinguishing components of most other important wine cultivars remain unknown despite the application of very sensitive analytic techniques.

WINE ANALYSIS

Traditional wine analysis has focused on measuring the levels of a number of factors that affect a wine's acceptability to the taste: sugar, acidity, ethanol, and sulfur dioxide, the last of which is both a natural by-product of fermentation and an additive for controlling undesirable microorganisms. Assessing the influence of those trace compounds responsible for varietal character is still, for the most part, the province of sensory descriptive analysis rather than the chemical laboratory.

Wine analysis can be performed at any stage of the wine-making process, from the grape on the vine to the finished wine. The methods used range from older procedures based on titration and on enzyme-based assays for glucose, fructose, and malic acid to chromatographic approaches for ethanol, major organic acids, sugars, and certain phenolic components. Chromatography comprises a collection of techniques for separating mixtures of chemical components; all are based on the strategy of passing the mixture in gaseous or liquid form over a stationary material and exploiting the relative differences in the attraction of the components for the stationary material. The recent introduction of a method called capillary electrophoresis, which makes use of electric fields to separate substances carrying an electric charge, now offers improved methods for analyzing free sulfur dioxide and sugars in wines, as well as alternatives for analyzing organic acids, certain amino acids, and phenolics.

USES FOR ENZYMES

The commercial availability of a number of enzymes, proteins that selectively promote chemical reactions, has led to their use for providing specific chemical effects. The first enzymes employed in wine mak-

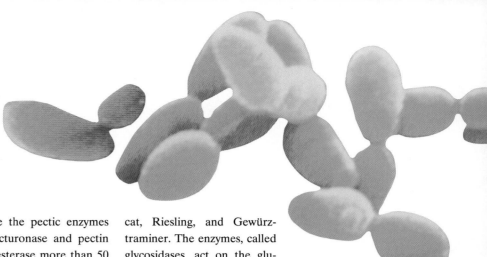

ing were the pectic enzymes polygalacturonase and pectin methyl esterase more than 50 years ago. They were introduced to break down pectin, a polysaccharide (a complex of chemically linked sugar molecules) that serves as a structural material in fruits, and so enhance the release of juice from skins before pressing and the settling of grape pulp in juice afterward. Recent changes in methods of juice draining and clarification and improvements in press design have reduced the need for pectic enzyme treatments.

Another successful enzyme application had its start when researchers identified an unusual polysaccharide of glucose that is produced in grapes infected with the mold *Botrytis cinerea*. Whereas the mold is encouraged in the production of a distinctly flavored type of white wine, the presence of the glucose polysaccharide, called a beta-glucan, leads to rapid plugging of filters prior to bottling. The isolation and use of a glucanase, an enzyme that breaks down glucan into smaller units, has proved to be a very specific and effective solution to the problem.

Specific enzymes have been used with some success to enhance the distinctive varietal aromas arising from terpenes in cultivars such as Mus-

cat, Riesling, and Gewürztraminer. The enzymes, called glycosidases, act on the glucose-bound terpenes, removing the sugar molecules and leaving the terpenes in a volatile form, in which they can contribute to the aroma of the wine.

Wine enthusiasts gather to appreciate a vintner's offerings (left). The wine maker's quest for ever better flavors and aromas has encouraged research into their biochemical origins. (Above) A grape's sugar content is checked in the field with a refractometer.

BIOTECHNOLOGY FOR FERMENTATION PROBLEMS

Strains of *S. cerevisiae* in forms that allow for easy activation are commonly used today in industries that exploit yeast fermentation. Perhaps 10–20 widely distributed

strains are available for wine making. They have been chosen because they can complete fermentation in an acceptable time and provide low levels of undesirable by-products.

Despite the apparent abundance of suitable yeast strains, certain juice conditions can result in fermentations that yield unacceptable levels of certain by-products—for example, hydrogen sulfide, sulfur dioxide, acetic acid, or ethyl acetate at concentrations detectable by the human senses or above legal limits. Studies of juice composition have shown that the problem is due less to deficiencies of certain key nutrients than to unusual proportions of them in the juice. Biologists' incomplete picture of the transport of nutrients into the yeast cell prevents predictions of growth rates and nutrient consumption patterns. Even if such predictions were possible, the way that consumption patterns affect fermentation biochemistry and by-product formation is not yet known.

Recent advances in the understanding of the nature and behavior of sugar trans-

Studies of the way yeast cells (top and previous page, top) transport sugar molecules across their cell membranes has aided fermentation science. Wine is sampled on the production line for microbial testing (left). Filtering through synthetic membranes before bottling is now the preferred method for removing microbes in finished wines.

porters in *Saccharomyces*—proteins in the yeast cell membrane that function to carry sugar molecules into the cell—have provided a basis for predicting how yeast cells utilize sugars from a mixture. Similar advances regarding the transporters of amino acids—the molecular building blocks of proteins—and vitamins in yeast are also needed if juice composition is ever to be related to fermentation behavior. A thorough understanding of fermentation behavior, in turn, must precede any successful application of genetic engineering to yeast or bacteria aimed at reducing unde-sirable fermentation by-products.

The bacteria responsible for malolactic fermentation, mostly strains of *Leuconostoc* or *Lactobacillus,* have slow growth rates and complex nutrient requirements that are poorly understood at present. As a result, they are among the least-favored organisms for microbial research, and it will be many years before they are likely to be improved by means of biotechnology.

MEMBRANES

The use of synthetic membranes to filter particles or even molecules of certain sizes from fluids has many commercial applications. Removing unwanted organisms from wines by means of membranes at the point of bottling has been widely practiced for more than 15 years and is the preferred method for avoiding contamination and unwanted microbial activity in finished wines. The filters are made of inert synthetic polymers with pores of fairly uniform size that are slightly smaller than the diameter of yeast and bacteria. Membrane filtering essentially eliminates the need for additional antimicrobial chemicals. Some wine writers have suggested that such filtration strips flavor components from the wine. It can be shown, however, that even the smallest pore sizes employed (0.45 micrometers, or millionths of a meter) are 100–1,000 times larger than the flavor molecules that interact with taste receptors.

Filters with submicrometer-sized pores pass fluids at a much slower rate than conventional filters. Consequently, they are operated such that the fluid flows parallel to the membrane surface, with only a small fraction actually moving through the membrane. The bulk of the fluid is recirculated across the membrane many times in a process called cross-flow filtration. One advantage is that the particles in suspension are swept across the surface rather than allowed to accumulate and restrict the flow, as occurs in conventional filtration. The wine industry has shown a renewed interest in cross-flow microfilters for the removal of suspended matter in juices and wines as an alternative to filters based on diatomaceous earth. This interest is driven by efforts to reduce industrial solid waste that must be disposed of in landfills, a trend that is likely to continue. The much lower capacities of these filters and the larger capital investment in them have limited their introduction.

The use of semipermeable membranes for making low-alcohol wines by reverse osmosis has been a commercial practice since the early 1980s, although the market for such products has remained small. Wine is placed in contact with the membrane and subjected to high pressure; water and ethanol permeate the membrane and are removed from the wine, while the other wine components are retained. Adding water back to the retained fraction reconstitutes the wine with a lower ethanol content but with its other constituents at their original concentrations. Using two or three such stages allows wines of progressively lower ethanol content to be produced.

One novel separation technique places a strong salt solution and grape juice on opposite sides of a membrane and uses the salt solution to draw water vapor from the juice across the membrane, rather than trying to force it across by pressure. The process, termed osmotic distillation, employs membranes that are more porous and have higher flow rates than those usually associated with reverse osmosis. It has had success in the production of juice concentrates and has the advantages of higher flows and lower pressure requirements than reverse osmosis and of ambient temperature and short contact time compared with traditional evaporative methods. A similar process, in which ethanol vapors from wine permeate this kind of membrane and are captured by a water stream, has been developed for making low-alcohol wines.

COMPUTER APPLICATIONS

How fast and how completely fermentation takes place depends on such factors as fermentation temperature, the amount and condition of the yeast culture added to the grape juice, and the levels of nutrients in the juice. While the first two factors are basically fixed for a given type of wine, nutrient differences in juices will lead to variations in fermentation. The ability to monitor a fermentation directly with instruments and to compare its pattern with that expected, or predicted by computer from a mathematical model of fermentation, would allow the wine maker to identify problem fermentations earlier and to take corrective actions that were more likely to work.

An example of a problem fermentation is one in which yeast growth is less than expected, resulting in a prolonged fermentation and possibly even an incomplete one, in which significant levels of sugar remain in the wine. A lengthy fermentation, in turn, can cause scheduling conflicts, while excess sugar can make the wine too sweet or more vulnerable to microbial spoilage. Mathematical models for wine fermen-

A control panel in a modern winery displays production information. Computers and electronic instrumentation allow wine makers to monitor fermentation and solve a host of logistic and production problems.

tation have been available for several years, and advanced instrumentation coupled with computers now allows measurement of fermentation in progress. Successful pilot-scale and commercial tests have been performed, although the technology has yet to be implemented in a commercial winery.

The most common application of computers at present is in tracking grape and wine movements for government requirements associated with the designations of cultivar, vineyard location, and vintage that appear on wine labels. Commercial database programs exist that make use of data on grape sources and blend histories for grape payments, estimates of blend composition, cost allocation, and wine inventories.

Recent advances in computing power now enable personal computers to perform tasks previously restricted to mainframe machines. Process simulation programs, capable of analyzing and tracking thousands of events and interactions, have been developed to analyze the interaction of

Rinsing and sanitizing of tanks
(below) and other winery
equipment contribute to a water
consumption in wine making that
is normally a multiple of the wine
produced. Ecological concerns are
prompting research into finding
better ways to use and reuse water
and other limited resources.

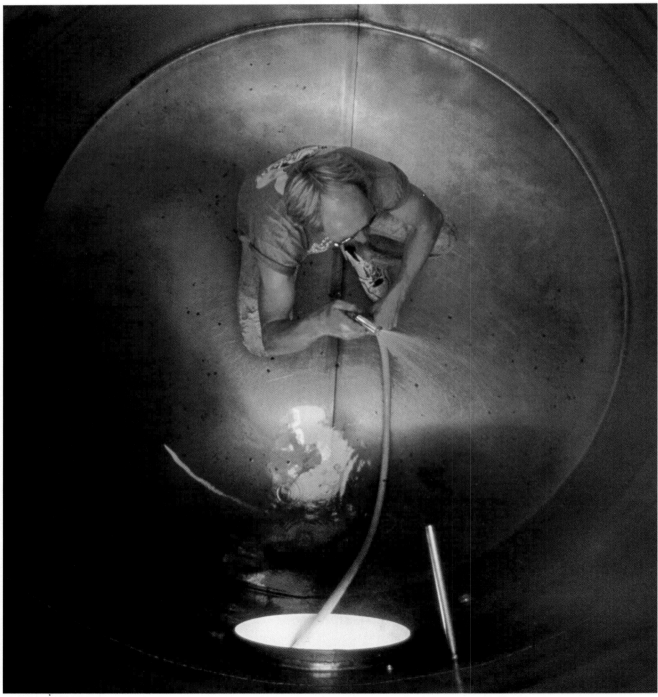

the grape harvesting and delivery patterns with the demands of the winery's receiving system, fermentation equipment, and other resources. Timing of delivery for the grapes, their assignment to various wines, their fermentation time, and the competition for winery equipment can all be analyzed to determine production options and help choose the best strategy ahead of time. The simulations can also evaluate winery designs and modifications and assist in training winery personnel in the logistics of the harvest period.

INDUSTRIAL ECOLOGY

The need is growing for more efficient use and reuse of limited resources such as water in the grape and wine industry, particularly in California. The volume of water consumed in wine making is normally a multiple of the volume of wine produced. Water solutions of chemicals are used to rinse and sanitize all winery equipment and at present are employed only once for that task before being discharged. There are, however, alternative rinsing and recovery systems that would permit reuse of the water solutions and the neutralization of potentially harmful substances in

them before discharge. If introduced, such systems would also benefit the winery by reducing the size of its required wastewater-treatment systems.

For more than 50 years, the practice of adding a clay slurry to white wines to adsorb and remove certain proteins responsible for a cloudy condition called hazing has been a general practice throughout the world. The clay, a type called bentonite, swells in contact with water, thereby enhancing its protein-removing ability. Bentonite use, however, is not without problems, which include difficulty in clarifying the resulting wine, some wine loss due to incomplete recovery from the bentonite, and disposal of the used material. Ceramic-based materials that have been developed for protein recovery in other biotechnology applications compare favorably with bentonite in their ability to remove the unwanted wine proteins. Moreover, the materials can be regenerated and reused many times, reducing the waste-disposal problem.

Present regulations in California require a stepwise reduction in the quantity of industrial solid waste that can be sent to regional landfills. For wineries this has sparked renewed interest in the large-scale composting of grape

skins and the phasing out of such practices as bentonite treatments and diatomaceous earth filtrations in favor of reusable materials. For wine distilleries new approaches exist for the direct recovery of tartaric acid and glycerol, both valuable by-products, from the residues of distillation. In addition to providing salable products, the new techniques promise major reductions in the so-called biochemical oxygen demand (BOD) of the waste stream, the oxygen required for microorganisms to degrade organic materials in the wastewater to safer substances. Reduction in BOD, in turn, means reductions in the extent and cost of wastewater treatment.

It has been said that wine making has progressed more in the last 100 years than it did in the previous 4,000. Science and science-based technology are largely responsible for this progress and in the future will remain crucial to the understanding of many of the still-mysterious aspects of grapevines, wines, and their associated organisms. In addition, their contributions will continue to be sought for better solutions for the wine-making problems that occasionally occur and alternative wine-making practices that are environmentally more benign.

FOR ADDITIONAL READING

■ *Biology of the Grapevine,* M.G. Mullins, A. Bouquet, and L.E. Williams (Cambridge University Press, 1992).

■ "Grape Phylloxera," J. Granett, D. Boubals, M.A. Walker, and J.A. De Benedictis, in *Arthropod and Nematode Management in Vineyards with Emphasis on North America and Western Europe,* L.T. Wilson, T.J. Dennehy, and N.J. Bostanian, eds. (Pergamon Press, 1994).

■ "Red Wines," R. Boulton, in *Fermented Beverage Production,* A. Lea and J.R. Piggott, eds. (Blackie Academic & Professional, 1994).

■ *Wine Microbiology and Biotechnology,* G.H. Fleet (Gordon and Breach Science Publishers, 1993).

■ "Winemaking Yeasts," L.F. Bisson and R.E. Kunkee, in *The Yeasts,* 2nd ed., A.H. Rose and J.S. Harrison, eds. (Academic Press, 1989).

■ "Wines: Wine Tasting," A.C. Noble, in *Encyclopaedia of Food Science, Food Technology and Nutrition,* vol. 7, R. Macrae, R.K. Robinson, and M.J. Sadler, eds. (Academic Press, 1993).

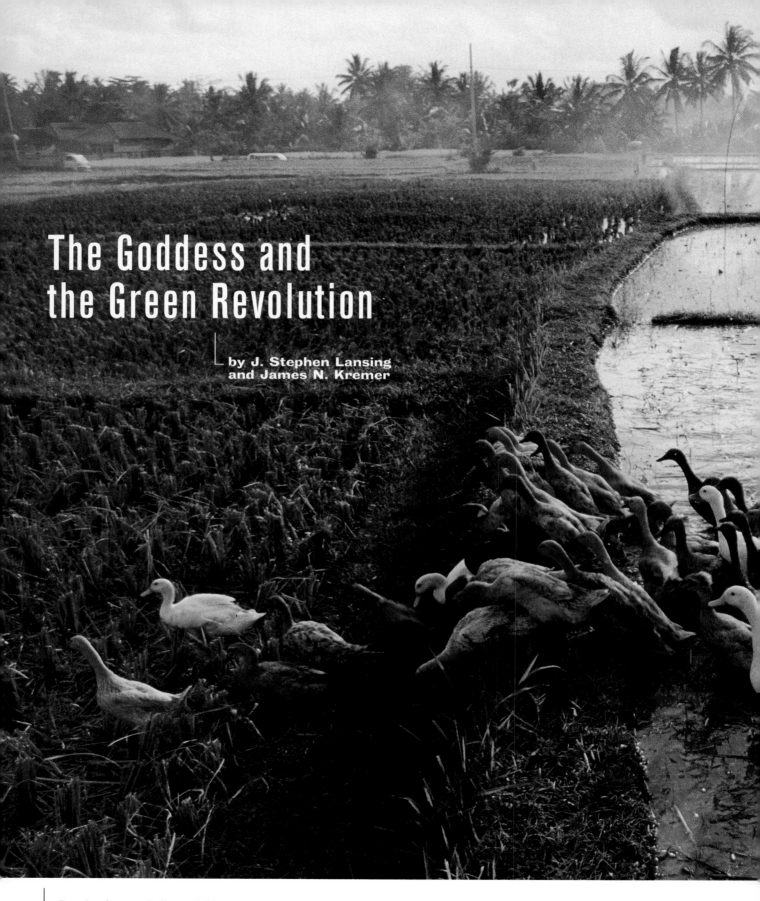

The Goddess and the Green Revolution

by J. Stephen Lansing and James N. Kremer

Drawing from such diverse fields as anthropology, ecology, and complexity theory, scientists have learned what went wrong when the introduction of modern farming practices to Bali nearly destroyed its ancient, highly successful rice-growing system.

A Balinese rice farmer drives a flock of ducks across his fields after the harvest, allowing the animals to glean leftover grain and eat insects that would otherwise damage the next rice crop.

199

For more than 1,000 years, the farmers of Bali, one of about 13,000 islands in the Indonesian archipelago, harvested rice from a complex, engineered system of rice terraces. Their farms formed one of the world's most productive agricultural systems, yielding several tons of rice per hectare every year (a hectare is about 2½ acres). By the 1960s, however, Indonesia found itself hard put to grow enough rice to feed its expanding population, already the fourth largest in the world. Government planners sought an answer in the Green Revolution, a United Nations program to increase food production by encouraging farmers to plant fast-growing hybrid varieties of food crops such as wheat or rice.

The Green Revolution in rice began at the International Rice Research Institute in the Philippines. Institute plant breeders developed rice varieties that could double or triple rice harvests, but the new plants required extensive use of chemical fertilizers and

J. Stephen Lansing is Professor of Anthropology and James N. Kremer is Associate Professor in the Department of Biological Sciences, University of Southern California, Los Angeles.

Om sarwa prani hitangkaram.

("May all that breathes be well.")

–Balinese farmer's prayer

pesticides. Bali was one of the first islands in Indonesia to undergo the Green Revolution; by 1974 nearly 50% of the terraces of south-central Bali had been planted with Green Revolution rice, and three years later the proportion had climbed to 70%.

For the first few years rice harvests increased dramatically. Farmers stopped following their traditional agricultural calendar, which allowed only two crops of rice to be planted each year. Instead, they obeyed the new government directives and planted rice as frequently as possible. Soon, however, district agricultural offices began to report serious problems: population explosions of rice pests and "chaos in the water-scheduling system." A study by World Bank officials concluded that pesticides had "pervasively polluted the island's soil and water resources." Many farmers wanted to return to the traditional system of growing native varieties of rice without chemical fertilizers and pesticides, but officials argued that the old ways could not support

an ever growing population.

Today most farmers in Bali have an answer to the problem of growing high-yielding rice without disrupting the delicate ecological balance in the rice paddies. The answer combines aspects of both systems: the new technology of the Green Revolution and Bali's ancient system of "water temples" that has enabled farmers to manage irrigation and keep pest populations under control. A scientific understanding of the role of the water temples has provided new insights into the ecology of the rice paddies and the adaptive value of an age-old system of cooperation between farmers. The UN Food and Agriculture Organization (FAO) recently launched a new program to apply these lessons in other countries.

One of the key accomplishments that made it possible to integrate the Green Revolution and the traditional system was a shift in perspective—from individual farmers to the ecology of rivers and rice terraces. The Green Revolution approach focused on individuals: how can a farmer grow

as much rice as possible in a year? In Bali, though, groups of farmers who are linked by geographic proximity and a shared water supply traditionally have cooperated in such key tasks as choosing what to plant, setting irrigation schedules, and controlling pests.

Over the course of more than 1,000 years, generations of Balinese farmers have gradually transformed the landscape of their island, clearing forests, digging irrigation canals, and terracing hillsides to enable themselves and their descendants to grow irrigated rice. Paralleling the physical system of dams, terraces, and irrigation works, the Balinese have also constructed intricate networks of shrines and temples dedicated to agricultural deities. These networks of water temples provide a framework for the farmers to coordinate their schedules of irrigation, planting, and harvesting. Computer simulations of the effects of the temple networks on the ecology of the terraces indicate that this cooperative regional planning leads to higher average harvest yields than if each farmer tried to grow as much rice as possible without regard for his neighbors. The reasons for this outcome are rooted in the fundamental ecology of the rice paddies.

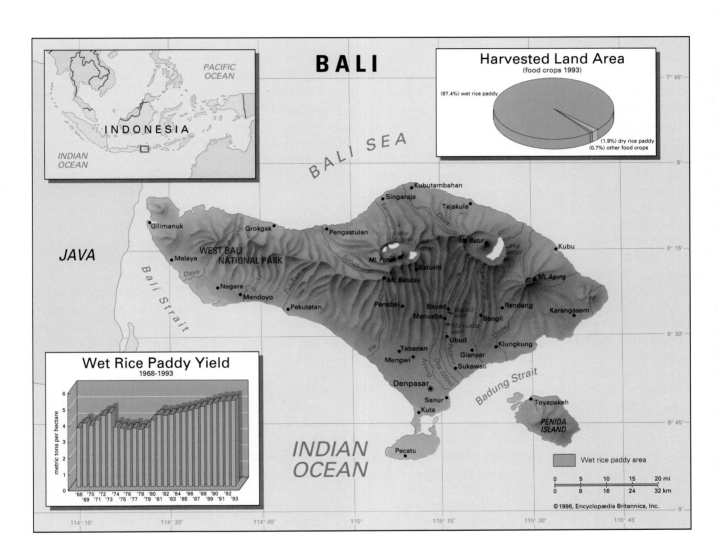

BALI

Harvested Land Area
(food crops 1993)

(97.4%) wet rice paddy
(1.9%) dry rice paddy
(0.7%) other food crops

Wet Rice Paddy Yield
1968-1993

metric tons per hectare

'68 '69 '70 '71 '72 '73 '74 '75 '76 '77 '78 '79 '80 '81 '82 '83 '84 '85 '86 '87 '88 '89 '90 '91 '92 '93

Wet rice paddy area

0   5   10   15   20 mi
0   8   16   24   32 km

©1996, Encyclopædia Britannica, Inc.

BALINESE RICE GROWING

Every year several hundred new articles are added to the scientific literature on rice. The tremendous sustained productivity of wet rice paddies has made rice the single most important food crop for human beings and enabled civilizations like that in Bali to develop. The Balinese are Malayo-Polynesians, whose ancestors colonized the island about 5,000 years ago. Irrigated rice cultivation began in Bali in the 1st millennium AD. One of the earliest known writings in the Balinese language, a royal edict from the 8th century AD, refers to irrigation-tunnel builders as well as taxes on rice harvests. The oldest human settlements in Bali are concentrated in the best rice-growing areas, where some terraces apparently have been under continuous cultivation for a millennium or more. By contrast, all Western systems of irrigated agriculture are subject to a gradual decline in productivity as a consequence of salinization and loss of soil fertility. These processes do not occur in well-managed rice paddies, which resemble self-sustaining artificial ponds.

The vast majority of Balinese live in a south-facing natural amphitheater created by the curving chain of volcanoes that form the geologic backbone of the island. The dimensions are small; from the eastern to the western border of the Balinese rice bowl is about 80 kilometers (a kilometer is about 0.62 mile), and from the uppermost rice terraces to the sea is never more than 40 kilometers. The landscape is constantly being rearranged by volcanic eruptions, which deposit large quantities of ash over whole districts while burying others under lava flows. The land's natural ruggedness is further enhanced by the streams and rivers rushing down the mountainsides. The torrential rains that fall in the rainy season and the steepness of the slopes combine to give the rivers a sharp cutting edge on the soft volcanic rock. About 80 rivers drain the southern rice bowl, and most of them have sliced channels 15–60 meters (50–200 feet) below the surface of the landscape.

Gaining access to such rivers for irrigation poses a difficult engineering challenge. Most Balinese irrigation systems begin at a weir, or diversionary dam, across a river, which sends some of the water into a tunnel. The tunnel may emerge as much as a kilometer or more downstream, at a lower elevation, where the water is routed through a system of canals and aqueducts to the summit of a terraced hillside. In those regions that have been under cultivation the longest, irrigation systems can comprise extraordinarily complex mazes of tunnels and canals for shunting water through blocks of rice terraces. Since the volume of water in the rivers during the wet season can be 10 times greater than the dry-season flow, the irrigation system must cope with conditions ranging from trickles to flash floods. Irrigation systems originating at different weirs are often interconnected, allowing unused water from the tail end of one system to be sent to a different block of terraces or returned to a neighboring stream.

As the rice terraces expanded and the population grew, villages were probably forced to migrate from the valleys to the hillsides and eventually all the way up to the ridge tops, where the irrigation canals could not reach. Today most villages are strung nearly end-to-end along the ridge lines running down the slopes of the volcanoes. The rest of the landscape is almost entirely given over to the rice terraces. Flying over Bali on a sunny day when the terraces are flooded after first harvest, one sees a dazzling shattered mirror of reflections from the paddies, framed by the winding green lines of forested ridges climbing down the mountains.

PADDY ECOLOGY

To appreciate the level of precision required for these irrigation systems to function, it is necessary to understand something about the basic dynamics of the paddy ecosystem. Each paddy has a flat bottom and walls or dikes along the sides, allowing it to hold water. Before planting rice, the farmer floods the paddy and plows it, then smooths and flattens the mud so that the whole field is under a uniform cover of ankle-deep water. Seedlings are grown in a seedbed and transplanted into the paddy in neat rows. The rice remains under water until a few weeks before the harvest, when the paddy is drained and the soil allowed to dry off.

The flow of water—the planned alternation of wet and dry phases—governs the basic biochemical processes of the paddy ecosystem. According to a general theory in ecology, ecosystems characterized by steady, unchanging flows of energy or nutrients tend to be less productive than those in which the flows are supplied in cycles or pulses. Rice paddies are an excellent example of the concept. Controlled changes in water levels create pulses in several important biochemical cycles. The cycle of wet and dry phases in the rice paddies alters the soil's pH (its acidity or alkalinity), induces a cycle of oxygen levels in the top level of the soil that determines the activity of microorganisms, mobilizes mineral nutrients, fosters the growth of algae that extract nitrogen from the air and make it biologically available (nitrogen fixation), excludes some weeds and insect pests, and stabilizes soil temperature. As time passes, paddies actually become more efficient. As the farmer plows his fields, the soil below the disturbed mud is gradually packed into a thick "plow pan" that holds water and prevents nutrients from being leached into the subsoil. Gradually the mineral content of the paddy soil increases.

In addition to the main crop of rice, the paddies produce important sources of animal protein for human consumption such as eels, frogs, and fish. Even the dragonflies that gather over the rice to hunt insects are themselves hunted by children, who roast and eat

A weir, or diversionary dam, across the Petanu River (top left) marks the beginning of a Balinese irrigation system. The weir channels some of the river water into a tunnel and then through a maze of aqueducts and canals, like the canal shown (right), to the summit of a hillside terraced with rice paddies. A tunnel builder (bottom left) sets up a sighting line for checking the alignment of a new irrigation tunnel.

Photos, J. Stephen Lansing

them. Most paddies support a large population of ducks, which must also be carefully managed since they will damage young rice plants if left untended. After each harvest, flocks of ducks are driven from field to field, where they glean leftover grain and eat some of the insects, such as brown plant hoppers, which would otherwise attack the next rice crop. Traditional harvesting techniques remove only the seed-bearing tassels; the rest of the stalks remain in the paddy ecosystem, where their decomposition recycles nutrients and provides an organic energy source that stimulates nitrogen fixation. Depending on the danger from rice pests, the farmer may decide to dry the field after harvest and burn the stalks, thus killing most pests but losing some of the nutrients in the harvested plants. Alternately, the farmer may flood the field and allow the rice stalks to slowly decompose under water.

The effectiveness of drying or flooding the fields as a method of pest control depends on cooperation between all of the farmers in a given block of terraces. For a single farmer to try to reduce the pests in his own field without coordinating with his neighbors is useless, since the pests will simply migrate from field to field. If all of the fields in a large area are either burned or flooded, however, pest populations can be sharply reduced. Both kinds of fallow periods are effective against rice pests by denying them food or habitat, but both depend on synchronization of the harvest and subsequent fallow period over a sufficiently large area. The size of the area and the length of the fallow period depend on the species characteristics of the rice pests. Major pests include rodents, insects, and bacterial and viral diseases.

The role of water in supplying resources in pulses to the individual paddy thus is paralleled on a larger scale by irrigation cycles that control pest populations by flooding or draining large blocks of

Rice plants are started in a seedbed and then are transplanted as seedlings into the flooded paddy (above). The presence in Balinese rice fields of pests such as brown plant hoppers (below) helps explain why farmers who share an irrigation system coordinate their cropping schedules.

paddies. At this level, however, an important trade-off occurs between water sharing and pest control. If all the farmers in a watershed plant the same variety of rice at the same time, they will also harvest at the same time; the consequent widespread fallow period can reduce pests. On the other hand, when all the farmers plant together, the demand for water for irrigation cannot be staggered, and there will be shortages. Striking an optimal balance between the two constraints is not a simple matter, since the choices made by upstream farmers influence conditions for their downstream neighbors, and such constraints as the amount of water available for irrigation vary by location and by season.

Interestingly, the presence of pests in the rice fields may actually help to explain why the farmers cooperate. To understand how this works, consider a simple model consisting of two farmers, one upstream and one downstream. Assume that the water supply is constant but inadequate for meeting the needs of both farmers at once, although it is sufficient if they stagger their planting schedules. Both farmers can suffer losses from the spread of rice pests. Given these assumptions, one can immediately draw several conclusions. The upstream farmer does not care about water scarcity and so is free to choose any irrigation schedule. The downstream farmer faces either water scarcity (under si-

multaneous cropping) or high pest damage (under staggered cropping) and will choose the lesser of two evils. If losses to pests have been running high, both farmers will want to coordinate their planting schedules to create a simultaneous fallow period so that pests will be reduced. If pest losses have been low, the upstream farmer will still want to plant simultaneously to minimize pests, while the downstream farmer will prefer to stagger plantings so that his fields will receive more water.

This simple model yields a basic insight into the reasons why cooperation makes sense for all the farmers in a watershed. If the upstream farmers were to ignore the relationship between fallow periods and pest populations, it would seem that they would lack any incentive to cooperate with their downstream neighbors. By paying attention to the ecology of pests, though, the upstream farmers clearly have much to gain by helping their downstream neighbors satisfy their water needs, since synchronizing irrigation schedules will reduce losses from pests.

Ecological theory shows, then, that a system that enables groups of farmers to find the right balance between water sharing and pest control

Farmers' huts dotting the flooded rice terraces provide places for workers in the paddies to retreat from the midday sun.

J. Stephen Lansing

Bundles of harvested rice dry in front of a traditional rice barn, located on the grounds of the farmer's family residence. In traditional Balinese rice harvesting, only the seed-bearing tassels are gathered; the rest of the stalks remain in the paddy ecosystem.

will be advantageous. But how might such a system come into existence, particularly in a society that until recently lacked telephones or even roads to facilitate communication between villages?

DEITIES AND WATER TEMPLES

From anywhere in central Bali, a farmer need only glance up to the clouds around the central volcano, Mt. Batur, to be reminded of the origin of the water flowing into his fields. In the crater of the volcano, at an elevation well above the height at which rice may be grown, lies a freshwater lake covering more than 1,700 hectares. The farmers

regard the lake as the sacred source of water for the rivers and springs that irrigate the whole of central Bali. Temple priests describe the mountain lake as a sacred mandala, or cosmic map, of waters, fed by springs lying at each of the wind directions, high above the irrigated lands. The steam from the caldera of Mt. Batur represents the zenith of the mandala, while the nadir is found in the depths of the lake. Each of the springs around the lake is regarded as the symbolic origin of waters for a particular hydrologic region of central Bali.

In the Balinese religion, which is a unique blend of Hindu, Buddhist, and Malayo-Polynesian beliefs, the man-

dala of the lake forms the center of a much larger mandala, consisting of the island of Bali and the surrounding seas. Balinese temple priests sometimes speak of the lake as a freshwater ocean, filled with life-giving water, which contrasts with the salt ocean encircling it far below. The lake is the home of one of the two supreme deities of Bali, Dewi Danu, the Goddess of the Lake. Her relationship to the farmers of central Bali is succinctly described in an ancient manuscript kept in her temple: "Because the Goddess makes the waters flow, those who do not follow her laws may not possess her rice terraces."

On the crater rim of Mt. Batur stands a large temple to the Dewi Danu. Hundreds of villages send offerings made of fruits and flowers to the temple once a year to express their thanks for the gift of water. As the water flows down the mountainsides and into irrigation canals, it passes many more water temples and shrines. Symbolically the water temples define connections between groups of farmers and the components of the natural landscape that they seek to control. Each shrine or temple is associated with a particular component of the irrigated landscape. For

example, every irrigation system begins with a spring or, more often, a diversionary weir in a river. Beside each spring or weir stands a shrine. The congregation of the weir-shrine or spring-shrine consists of all the farmers who use the water originating from that source. At the site, delegations of farmers make offerings to both Dewi Danu and the *bhatara empelan,* the Deity of the Weir.

The canal that takes off from the weir eventually reaches a block of terraces. That spot is usually a kilometer or more downstream from the weir and is usually marked by a major water temple, a *pura ulun swi,* or head-of-the-rice-fields temple. The congregation of the temple is the same as that of the weir-shrine: all those farmers who grow rice in the terraces irrigated by that particular canal system. The principal deity of the *pura ulun swi* is a god whose influence extends to all of the terraces watered by the canal. The temple itself is simply a walled courtyard containing a shrine where farmers can make offerings to the temple deity. Additional shrines provide places for offerings to such deities as the Deity of the Weir and Dewi Danu.

Farmers gather in the water temples on a regular calendri-

Balinese women harvest rice in a drained field. Depending on the danger from rice pests, the stalks that remain will either be burned or be covered with water and allowed to decompose.

An entrance gate of the Temple of the Crater Lake leads to another gate to an inner courtyard. Located on the crater rim of Mt. Batur, the temple is dedicated to Dewi Danu, the goddess who is believed by the farmers of Bali to supply the waters that sustain the rice terraces.

© David Sailors

cal schedule, not only to make religious offerings but also to make decisions about the timing of planting and harvesting and other practical questions. The ecological role of the temple networks can be illustrated in the relationship between the irrigation systems of two villages, Bayad and Manuaba, on the upper reaches of the Petanu River. As the map on pages 212–213 shows, the up-

the Manuaba weir diverts water to 350 hectares of rice terraces, controlled by 10 *subaks*. The water temple hierarchy at Bayad consists of a shrine at the weir and a head-of-the-rice-fields temple situated above the terraces. The larger Manuaba system also begins with a shrine beside the weir but includes two head-of-the-rice-fields temples, one for each large block of rice

Farmers' offerings decorate an altar at the Temple of the Crater Lake. The structure, one of 45 altars and shrines at the temple, is believed to serve as a throne for deities who visit their congregation during temple festivals.

© David Sailors

Priests of the Temple of the Crater Lake prepare a blessing of holy water for the rice farmers, whose fields lie on the mountain slopes below.

J. Stephen Lansing

stream Bayad weir diverts water to about 100 hectares of rice terraces. The terraces are managed by a farmers organization, or water-users group, called a *subak,* which comprises about 210 members. A few kilometers downstream,

terraces. The congregations of both of those temples also belong to a larger Masceti temple that is symbolically identified with the entire Manuaba irrigation system. Representatives of all 10 Manuaba *subaks* meet once a year at

the Masceti temple to decide on a cropping pattern—which crops to plant and when to plant them. Thereafter, rituals held at each of the two head-of-the-rice-fields temples help the farmers synchronize their work in the fields. In addition, the Manuaba *subaks* regularly send a delegation to the upstream Bayad weir to request holy water, and the interdependency of the two irrigation systems is given symbolic expression by offerings to the deities of the two weirs.

TURMOIL IN THE TERRACES

Before the Green Revolution the farmers of the two villages followed a traditional two-crop-a-year calendar. Bayad's

farmers planted their first crop of a slow-growing but highly nutritious rice called *padi del* soon after the appearance of the Pleiades star cluster in the night sky. Downstream, Manuaba's farmers followed exactly the same cropping pattern except that they started a month later. In general, irrigation demand is highest at the beginning of a new planting cycle because the dry fields must become saturated. By starting later than their upstream neighbors, the Manuaba *subaks* could avoid water shortages, while a regionwide fallow period helped keep rice pests under control.

The Green Revolution came to Bayad and Manuaba's part of Bali in the mid-1970s. Farmers were instructed to

Lake Batur, covering more than 1,700 hectares, lies in the crater of Mt. Batur. In the cosmology of the Balinese religion, the lake is the sacred source of water for the rivers and springs that irrigate the whole of central Bali.

© David Sailors

stop following the traditional calendar and plant rice as often as possible. Within a few years, losses to pests climbed as high as 100% of each crop. While many farmers urged a return to traditional planting, governmental agricultural policy insisted on continuous cropping. Similar views were expressed by the Asian Development Bank (ADB), which was loaning more than $50 million for *subak* improvement projects in Bali. According to the ADB's head of irrigation at the time, the answer to pests was pesticides, not water temples.

In 1983 one of us, Stephen Lansing, began a year of anthropological research in Bali focusing on the ecology of the rice terraces and the role of water temples in rice production. Earlier, as a graduate student in the mid-1970s, Lansing had spent a year and a half in a Balinese village and had witnessed the confident beginnings of the Green Revolution. By the 1980s, however, farmers and extension workers from all over Bali were reporting unprecedented pest outbreaks and frequent quarrels over water rights. Nyoman Sutawan, a Balinese agricultural expert, wrote a report urging policy makers to take note of "the negative effects experienced as a result

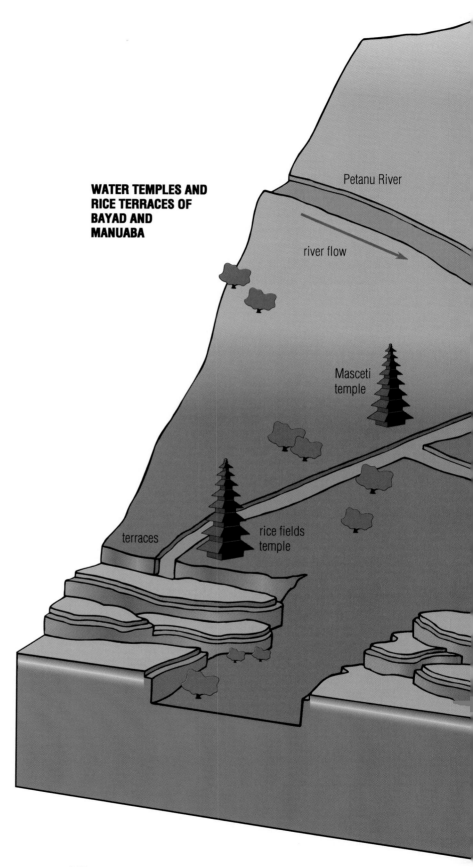

WATER TEMPLES AND RICE TERRACES OF BAYAD AND MANUABA

Petanu River

river flow

Masceti temple

terraces

rice fields temple

212

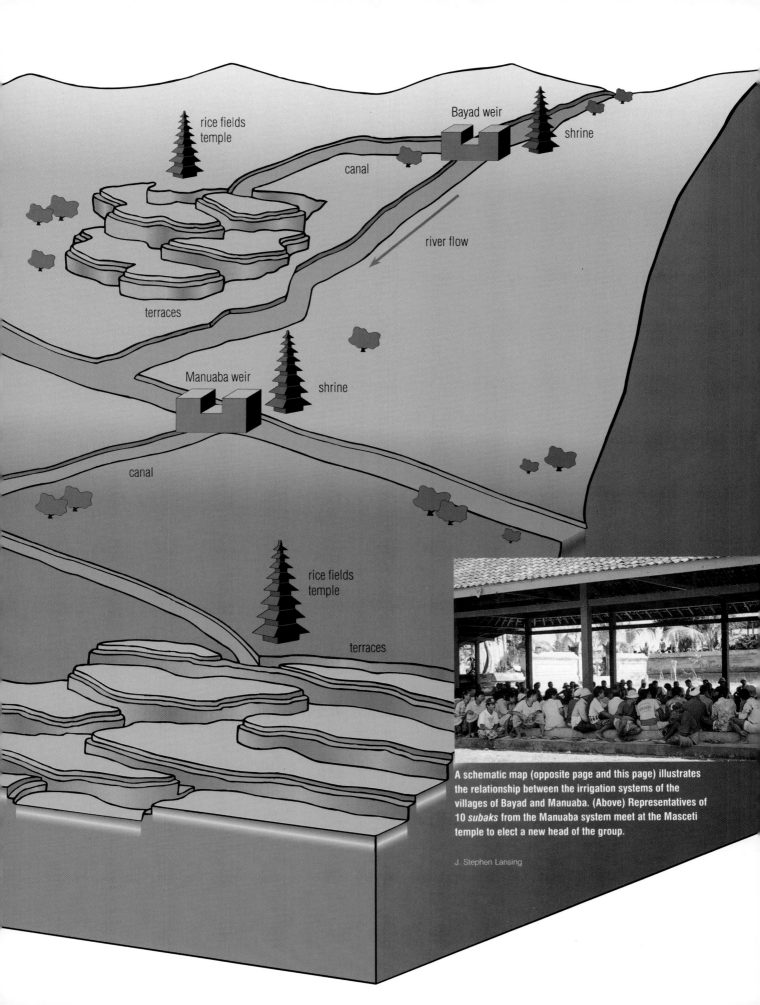

rice fields
temple

Bayad weir

shrine

canal

river flow

terraces

Manuaba weir

shrine

canal

rice fields
temple

terraces

A schematic map (opposite page and this page) illustrates
the relationship between the irrigation systems of the
villages of Bayad and Manuaba. (Above) Representatives of
10 *subaks* from the Manuaba system meet at the Masceti
temple to elect a new head of the group.

J. Stephen Lansing

of the policy of continuous uncoordinated rice planting" and emphasized "the connections between the hierarchy of *subak* temples and cropping patterns." Officials, nevertheless, remained skeptical. As a frustrated civil engineer exclaimed, "They don't need a high priest, they need a hydrologist!"

FARMING RICE BY COMPUTER

In the spring of 1987 the two of us—Lansing, in collaboration with systems ecologist James Kremer—began a computer analysis of the ecological role of the water temples. We were already convinced that the water temples play a key role in allowing the farmers to synchronize cropping schedules. The question that we wished to address was whether they have measurable effects on rice production. While we suspected that the social hierarchy of the water temples could be acting to optimize the conflicting goals of water allocation and pest control, we still needed a way to test the idea quantitatively. Creating a numerical model on a computer to simulate the relevant interactions offered a chance to evaluate them in a rigorous way. Such computer models are widely

used in science, engineering, and economics, yet they seem technical and obscure to many people. In fact, they are fundamentally very logical.

The task of building our

J. Stephen Lansing

A woman makes offerings at a shrine at the upstream edge of her rice fields. Each shrine in the temple system is located at the upstream point of the component of the water system that the farmers seek to control.

computer model began with the identification of features that we thought might be especially important. Because the real rice-growing situation in Bali is vastly complex, we wanted to escape the over-

whelming detail and focus on those aspects that are responsible for determining harvest yields. We considered geography, hydrology, agriculture, and human social behavior,

identifying and clearly stating the essential features in each category. Ultimately we decided on the following set of features for the model:

1. Geographic topography defines the spatial relation-

ship between irrigation systems in different parts of the watershed.

2. River flow results directly from seasonally varying rainfall and water from springs.

3. Farmers, with varying degrees of collaboration, decide what crops to plant.

4. Each crop grows to maturity but may be subject to the stress of inadequate water supply and pest damage.

5. The damage by pests depends on their growth in favorable habitats (*i.e.,* the crops) and their ability to spread to adjacent fields, but their abundance is reduced by fallow periods.

Our goal of evaluating the effects of the coordination among farmers on rice yields dictated the geographic scale of our model. Because downstream farmers are potentially affected by what happens upstream, we decided to model all of the irrigation systems that lie between two rivers in south-central Bali, the Oos (Wos) and the Petanu. The model encompassed all of the canals between the rivers along with some irrigation systems on the other side of each river. The rivers originate high on Mt. Batur and provide irrigation water for about 6,136 hectares of rice terraces, which are managed by 172 *subaks*. From topo-

A statue representing a Balinese water deity, dating from the 11th century, is part of a complex of pools and a cave temple (Elephant Cave) at Goa Gajah near Bedulu in south-central Bali.

J. Stephen Lansing

Offerings are brought to an annual festival at Pura Jati, part of the Temple of the Crater Lake complex. Farmers from more than 200 villages attend and receive a blessing of holy water prepared by the temple priests.

graphic maps we determined the area of the watershed contributing to each tributary of the two rivers. Studies by Balinese hydrologists documented the general relationship between rainfall and river flow via direct runoff. Measurements of the flow volume of major springs were also available for our purposes. Furthermore, long-term weather records allowed us to define a seasonal pattern of average rainfall, which in this case varies with elevation.

We then expressed these features of geography and hydrology in the form of numerical equations for the computer. For example, in January, rainfall at an elevation of 1,000 meters (3,300 feet) is 45 centimeters (18 inches) per month, of which about 5 centimeters (2 inches) are taken up by the forest, with the remainder entering the rivers. Multiplying the unabsorbed rainfall by the effective area of the watershed predicts the river flow leaving the watershed. Such predictions were tested through comparison with measurements at a number of dams and weirs throughout the region. Once the flow of each tributary had been defined, specifying how the streams are connected allowed us to add up the sources to predict the increase in river

flow from the high elevations down to the coastal plains.

We wanted the farmers in our model to be able to grow different varieties of rice. Consequently, we needed to identify the specific features of each rice variety that expressed the important differences between them. We chose five crop options: two traditional Balinese rice varieties, one Green Revolution high-yield variety, a nonrice crop, and a fallow period. We defined the number of months it takes each crop to mature, the yield at harvest, the water demand, the sensitivity to pest damage, and the efficiency with which it uses fertilizer. (*See* Table on opposite page.) In reality the biology of each rice crop is quite complex, and detailed understanding would involve endless research. Yet, for the

purposes of our study, the few attributes that we chose captured the essential differences between traditional rice varieties and modern high-yield strains.

In similar ways we expressed as numbers and equations such features as the growth rates of typical pests and their tendency to migrate from field to field. We then wrote all of the numerical relationships for our model in the form of a computer program, which allowed the computer to simulate the series of real events that determine the growth and harvest yield of crops throughout the landscape. Month by month the computer simulated rainfall and river flow and then updated irrigation demand, rice growth, and pest dynamics for the 172 *subaks* in the region. At the appropriate times the

harvest was adjusted for cumulative water stress and pest damage, yields were tallied, and the next crop cycle was begun.

Once our model was up and running, we used it to evaluate the outcomes of a number of possible management systems for all the *subaks* along the two rivers. The scenarios were as follows:

1. Every *subak* is randomly assigned its own cropping pattern.

2. All the *subaks* follow the same cropping pattern.

3. Half the *subaks* follow one pattern, and half plant a month later.

4. *Subaks* follow one of several other hypothetical patterns of coordination.

5. *Subaks* plant in clusters based on real patterns created by water temples.

The first scenario was designed to resemble the early years of the Green Revolution, when each *subak* set its own independent cropping schedule. After running many simulations we found that when all the *subaks* in a watershed planted in a schedule that was not coordinated by the water temples, crop losses to pests approached 100%, as actually happened in the later 1970s. The computer scenario designed to resemble the actual water temple system produced the highest average yields for all 172 *subaks*—by finding the right balance between water sharing and pest control. It did not matter whether the crops were traditional rice varieties or the faster-growing Green Revolution varieties, since all are affected by water and pests. The results provided objective evidence that the water temples could indeed play a vital role in the ecology of the terraces.

Meanwhile, the farmers of Bali were trying out their own experiments, which in some ways resembled our computer runs. In the 1980s the farmers of Bayad and Manuaba returned to the temple system of crop management but continued to plant high-yielding rice in obedience to government regulations. Just as the computer model predicted, the farmers achieved high yields by balancing the trade-off between water sharing and pest control. To illustrate with a specific case, in September 1988 all 10 *subaks* belonging to the Masceti temple of Manuaba planted IR 64, a high-yielding Green Revolution rice, and harvested an average of 6.5 tons per hectare in December. Subsequently they planted another crop of rice in February and harvested six tons per hectare in May. In June they all

planted vegetables and harvested about two tons per hectare in August. This cropping pattern synchronized harvests for all 10 *subaks*. Pest infestations for the period were reported to be minimal: less than 1% damage to the crops, primarily from brown plant hoppers. Their neighbors upstream at Bayad followed exactly the same cropping pattern as Manuaba except that they started two weeks earlier, which helped their downstream neighbors avoid water shortages.

TEMPLE NETWORKS: A COMPLEX ADAPTIVE SYSTEM?

In the early 1990s a new insight into the workings of the water temple system appeared from an unlikely source: complexity theory. Although complexity theory originated in the late 19th and early 20th centuries in the work of mathematicians Henri Poincaré and John von Neumann, it is a relatively new area of active research. At its core is the concept that surprisingly complex patterns of order can arise from systems made of many individual agents whose interactions are governed by simple rules. One large field of study for complexity research is the dynamics of living systems. Communities of living things—whether they are tissues made of cells, colonies of bacteria, or societies of people—are systems comprising many agents that interact with each other. Importantly, these systems can adapt to change and thus can be regarded as complex adaptive systems. By applying theory, mathematics, and computer simulations, researchers are working to identify complex adaptive systems and understand their essential behavior.

The application of complexity theory to the water temple networks can be illustrated by a second computer model of the farms between the Oos and Petanu rivers. In this model the water temples do not exist, but all the ecological conditions along the two rivers are otherwise the same. As a new year begins, each of the 172 *subaks* plants rice or vegetables in a randomly chosen pattern. At the end of the year, harvest yields are tallied. Next, each *subak* checks to see whether any of its nearest neighbors got a better total yield. If so, it copies the cropping pattern of its most successful neighbor. After all the *subaks* have decided to either copy a neighbor or retain their old cropping schedule, the computer simulates another year of growth. The process continues until each *subak* decides to stick with its current cropping pattern.

ATTRIBUTES FOR FIVE CROP OPTIONS IN THE COMPUTER MODEL

crop	duration (months)	rice yield (tons/hectare)	water demand (depth in meters/day)	maximum yield reduction	
				pests	fertilizer
padi del	6	5	0.015	0.5	0.9
padi chi chi	4	5	0.015	0.75	0.9
high-yield rice	3	10	0.015	1.0	0.5
vegetable	3	0	0.003	na	na
fallow	0	0	0	na	na

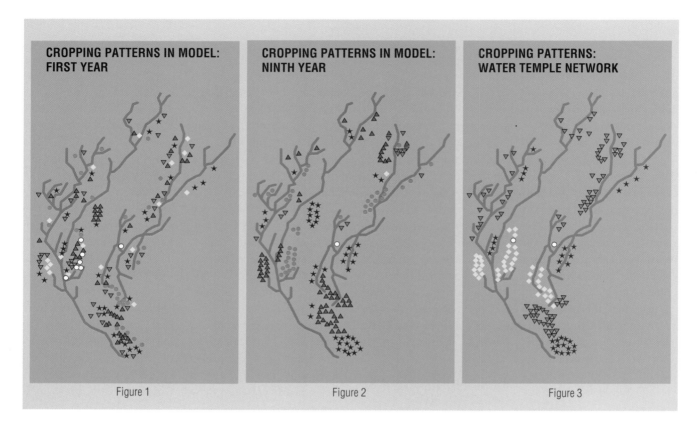

CROPPING PATTERNS IN MODEL: FIRST YEAR

CROPPING PATTERNS IN MODEL: NINTH YEAR

CROPPING PATTERNS: WATER TEMPLE NETWORK

Figure 1

Figure 2

Figure 3

What happens to the overall cropping pattern?

Figure 1 shows the distribution of cropping patterns for the first year of the model. Each kind of symbol indicates a different cropping pattern. No overall pattern exists for the two-river region since the individual cropping patterns were randomly chosen. The average rice harvest for the first-year run was 4.9 tons per hectare. Figure 2 shows the pattern eight years later. By that time the symbols have clustered in groups, representing local groups of *subaks* that are following the same cropping schedule, and the average

harvest has almost doubled to 8.57 tons per hectare. Furthermore, when the spatial pattern of Figure 2 is compared with that of Figure 3, which shows the pattern created by the actual water temple network, the location and size of coordinating *subak* groups are seen to be nearly identical.

The same results occur in computer simulations that incorporate any combination of physical and biological variables—for example, rainfall or pest-dispersal rates—as long as they are within the bounds of biological possibility. In about 10 years the model produces a complex structure of

coordinated cropping patterns that bears a remarkable similarity to the actual pattern of water temple coordination. As these artificial temple networks form inside the computer, harvest yields steadily increase.

Once the artificial water networks appear in the computer, they display another interesting property: the ability to recover quickly from ecological perturbations such as low rainfall or a new kind of pest. Such disturbances trigger a cascade of changes that propagate through one or more clusters of *subaks,* but the temple network quickly

adjusts. Yields remain higher than if the temple system was to stop functioning, as it did during the Green Revolution.

Why should the model *subaks* in the computer organize themselves into networks that look so much like the real water temple networks? A complex adaptive system can be considered to be a network of interacting agents in which each agent is trying to optimize some kind of payoff or reward. The environment of each agent includes other agents as well as the external environment. The water temple networks of Bali fit this definition. Complexity theo-

218

rists such as Murray Gell-Mann, a Nobel laureate in physics, believe that complex adaptive systems are likely to be common because they help their members adapt to changing circumstances. Indeed, the water temple networks of Bali are probably not unique. They may be representative of a class of complex adaptive systems that have evolved among human societies to manage agricultural systems. Nevertheless, as long as researchers focus their attention on the individual agents—the individual farms in the case of Bali—the productive role of systems like the water temples will remain invisible.

APPLYING THE LESSONS LEARNED

Computer-simulation models are always abstractions. They cannot represent reality directly, but they do provide a way to try to capture the underlying dynamics of a system and test possible explanations for its behavior. The concept of Balinese water temple networks as complex adaptive systems has given scientists and planners a new way to think about how human communities relate to the natural environment. As complexity theory would predict, the emergence of temple net-

J. Stephen Lansing

A university student discusses a computer simulation of Balinese rice farming with a high priest of the Temple of the Crater Lake in an effort to help farmers grow high-yield rice without disrupting their traditional system.

works in the computer leads to higher average yields and improvements in sustainability, the ability to cope well with changes in the environment. It appears that the temple networks are intrinsically capable of doing a better job of management than either uncoordinated planting or centralized governmental control.

What we learned about the rice temple system in Bali has begun to influence agricultural policies. In a recent report the ADB, which played a major role in introducing the Green Revolution to Bali, acknowledged the importance of the temple networks:

The substitution of the "high technology and bureaucratic" solution in the event *proved counter-productive, and was the major factor behind the yield and cropped areas declines experienced between 1982 and 1985. . . . The cost of the lack of appreciation of the merits of the traditional regime has been high. Project experience highlights the fact that the irrigated rice terraces of Bali form a complex artificial ecosystem which has been recognized locally over centuries.*

The question of how to apply to other countries the lessons learned from the Balinese example has attracted the attention of the FAO, which in 1993 began sponsorship of a training program for agricultural extension agents

in Bali. Comexap (Computer-Supported Agricultural Extension and Training Program) allows agents to study the patterns of pest outbreaks or water shortages with the help of computers and to use the results to assist the affected farmers in finding optimal cropping patterns. Knowledge of ecological patterns can reduce the need for chemicals such as pesticides and help sensitize planners to the productive role of traditional systems of resource management such as the water temples.

Computer scientist Alan Peterson recently created a new computer application called Watershed for the FAO. Watershed is designed to help first-time computer users in less developed countries carry out the kind of ecological analysis pioneered in Bali. The Indonesian Ministry of Agriculture is planning to introduce Watershed to agricultural extension offices throughout the islands and has requested assistance from the FAO. In the end, what began as an ecological disaster appears on its way toward a happy outcome both for the farmers of Bali and for the scientists who are striving to better understand the complex relationships that exist between humans and their environment.

The Mothers of Aggression

by Laurence G. Frank and Stephen E. Glickman

Steeped in masculinizing hormones in the womb, spotted hyenas are born ready to battle their siblings to the death. As the survivors grow, they learn their place in a complex social structure ruled by females that look and behave much like typical male mammals.

Few animals are as unfairly maligned and as intrinsically fascinating as the spotted hyena. Commonly reviled as a lowly scavenger, it is, in fact, a highly successful predator, the most abundant large carnivore in Africa. It has a complex social system centered on the female of the species, which is more aggressive than the male and is the strongly dominant sex. In fact, the genital organs of the female spotted hyena are highly masculine in form and structure. Her clitoris is penis-sized and fully erectile; through it she urinates, mates, and gives birth. Instead of a vulva she possesses a mock scrotum filled with fatty tissue. This masculinization may be related to another unique aspect of hyena reproduction: spotted hyenas are born with fully erupted teeth and fight violently with each other through the first days of life.

Why should the spotted hyena, among all mammals, develop in such an extraordinary fashion? To biologists the answers can take many forms, but they all fall into

> *The Yena is by its nature at one moment masculine and at another moment feminine, and hence it is a dirty brute.*
>
> –The Bestiary, 13th century

British Library

A hyena pulls a human corpse from its tomb and devours it in an illustration from a mid-13th-century bestiary.

one of two levels of analysis. Ultimate explanations seek to discover the evolutionary origins of a trait—the environmental influences or selective pressures that favored development of the trait, be it a structure, physiological process, or behavior. Proximate explanations deal with the physiological or developmental events that actually produce the trait. For example, an ultimate explanation for the cheetah's remarkable sprinting ability is that it allows the animal to capture fleet prey. The proximate explanation involves anatomic and physiological specialization of the legs, spine, musculature, and cardiovascular system that makes the cheetah a superb running machine. Evolution, then, consists of ultimate causes shaping proximate mechanisms through genetic change and natural selection.

As a result of several long-term field studies of hyena social behavior and a major laboratory study of a hyena colony established at the University of California, Berkeley, scientists are beginning to understand the masculinization of the female spotted hyena at both the proximate and ultimate levels. Moreover, because the phenomenon challenges science's basic understanding of the biology of sex differences, the research is helping to shed light on hormonal processes of sexual differentiation that are common to all mammals, including humans.

Laurence G. Frank, a Zoologist, is a Research Associate in the Psychology Department, and Stephen E. Glickman is Professor of Psychology, University of California, Berkeley.

220

Illustration by Joyce Patti

A SPECIES APART

The spotted hyena (*Crocuta crocuta*) is one of four living species in the family Hyaenidae. Meat-eating mammals, the Carnivora, comprise two large suborders, the Canoidea (dogs, bears, weasels and their allies, and the raccoons and their allies) and the Feloidea (the cats, mongooses and their allies, and the hyenas). Although hyenas resemble dogs in form and hunting behavior, they are evolutionarily closer to cats.

The striped hyena (*Hyaena hyaena*) is found throughout much of Africa and western Asia and is replaced in southern Africa by the brown hyena (*H. brunnea*). Both are true scavengers, living on the carcasses of large mammals supplemented by small vertebrates, insects, and fruits. Because large-mammal carcasses are uncommon, both species are scattered thinly and forage solitarily. Little is known of striped hyena social behavior, but brown hyenas live in small family groups. Neither species shows strong female dominance, and the genital organs of females conform to mammalian standards. Like spotted hyenas, both striped and brown hyenas have specialized, massive, bone-crushing teeth and chewing musculature, allowing them to consume entire carcasses, including the skeletons. The fourth member of the family is the highly specialized aardwolf (*Proteles cristatus*), a fox-sized animal that lives almost exclusively on termites and whose teeth are reduced to small pegs, utterly unlike those of its larger relatives.

The spotted hyena, popularly known as the laughing hyena, is the size of a very

These spotted hyena cubs (left; *Crocuta crocuta*) will grow up to be highly successful predators that cooperate in a group to kill their prey. The spotted hyena's closest relatives, the striped hyena (above; *Hyaena hyaena*) and the brown hyena (right; *H. brunnea*), are both true scavengers and forage alone.

(Left) Nigel Dennis—Photo Researchers, Inc.; (above) Wardene Weisser—Bruce Coleman Inc.; (right) Erwin & Peggy Bauer—Bruce Coleman Inc.

large dog, weighing as much as 85 kilograms (190 pounds); females are about 10% heavier than males. The heavy forequarters contrast with relatively weak hind limbs; the sloping profile may be an adaptation for long-distance movements, allowing hyenas to travel for hours in a seemingly tireless "rocking horse" lope. Some populations of spotted hyenas travel round-trip distances of as much as 160 kilometers (100 miles) between their den and herds of migratory prey. As its name suggests, the animal's coarse coat is covered in dark spots against a background color that ranges from light tan to dark gray. Researchers identify individuals by their unique spot patterns. The black tail is an important display organ, its position communicating its owner's mood to other hyenas. Smell and hearing, as with most mammals, are very acute. In keeping with its nocturnal habits, the hyena sees extremely well at night.

Until recently the spotted hyena was ubiquitous in sub-Saharan Africa except the Congo Basin. Along with most larger mammals, it has been largely extirpated by humans from southern and western Africa. It is, however, still common in wilder parts of eastern Africa. In prehistoric

Hunting at night, spotted hyenas confront a wildebeest (right). A cave drawing (above), discovered in 1994 in southern France as part of a large and unique cache of Paleolithic art, appears to depict a spotted hyena. In prehistoric times the animal ranged throughout Europe, Asia, and Africa and must have posed a considerable threat to early humans.

times it ranged throughout Europe and Asia, disappearing only recently with many other large mammals after the last ice age. For millions of years it must have been a major predator on the ancestors of humans and a competitor for kills.

The long-distance call, the whoop, of the spotted hyena is one of the most characteristic sounds of the African night, but its vocal repertoire is varied. Its giggle, from which it gets the name laughing hyena, signifies fear rather than frivolity and is most often given by an individual being chased or bitten by another. A variety of groans and moans are used by mothers to call their cubs or among close relatives to greet each other. A similar sound may be used during aggression, giving way to a deep rumbling growl when the hyena is simultaneously frightened and threatening.

Spotted hyenas feed exclusively on large mammals, typically wildebeests, zebras, and gazelles. Like most carnivores they will readily scavenge from a carcass, but typically they kill the vast majority of their food. A single hyena is quite capable of bringing down a 250-kilogram (550-pound) bull wildebeest, but by hunting in groups they are able to kill animals as large as zebras and even the awesome Cape buffalo, weighing as much as 750 kilograms (1,650 pounds). Hyenas do not hunt by stealth or guile, like the cats. Rather, they hunt like wolves, "testing" herds of prey by chasing them to identify the individuals that, because of age or infirmity, cannot keep up with the rest. In the high-density hyena populations of East Africa, the sounds of the kill attract many more hungry mouths, and soon the kill site is a noisy, quarreling mass of hyenas, each eating as fast as it can. Under the ravenous attentions of 20 hyenas, a wildebeest may disappear completely within 20 minutes.

Female hyenas nearly always give birth to twins. They bear their young at the mouths of abandoned aardvark burrows, which are too narrow to admit potential predators such as lions or other hyenas. The cubs live in the depth of the burrow, going to the entrance to nurse. When they are two to six weeks of age, the mother takes them to join the rest of the clan's youngsters in the communal den, another burrow system, which is the clan's social cen-

Robert Caputo—AURORA

Spotted hyenas feed exclusively on large mammals, which may include giraffes, zebras, and even Cape buffalo. They hunt like wolves, "testing" herds of prey to identify the weaker individuals. A single hyena is capable of downing a full-grown bull wildebeest.

ter. Females go to the communal den to nurse their cubs in the evening; older juveniles go to socialize with their mothers and younger siblings; and males wander through to check on the reproductive status of the adult females.

BENDING THE GENDER

Since ancient times the spotted hyena had been thought to be a hermaphrodite, either possessing the organs of both sexes or able to change from male to female and back. The animal was first studied scientifically in 1939, when British zoologist Leonard Harrison Matthews collected more than 100 hyenas in Tanganyika Territory (present-day Tanzania) for anatomic studies of the reproductive tract. He found that all individuals are either male or female and that, internally, the reproductive organs of the female hyena conform to standard carnivore anatomy. Externally, however, Matthews observed, the female's clitoris is greatly enlarged and very similar to the male's penis in anatomy, size, and function. The labia of the vulva are fused to form a pseudoscrotum that contains fat and connective tissue, giving the appearance of testicles.

The reproductive and urinary tracts join within the abdomen and form the urogenital canal, which runs the length of the clitoris. The female urinates, copulates, and gives birth through the penile clitoris. Mating is aided by a pair of robust retractor muscles that run the length of the organ, allowing the female to retract the clitoris, much like pushing up a sleeve, to form a functional vagina into which the male inserts his penis when mating. At puberty the female urogenital canal enlarges under the influence of estrogens (female sex hormones), but a female's first birth is protracted and difficult, causing high rates of stillbirths and maternal deaths. The opening in the end of the urogenital canal tears during the first delivery such that subsequent births tend to be easy.

When two animals meet after a period of separation, they perform a "greeting ceremony"; standing head to tail, each raises the inner hind leg and offers its penis or clitoris, which may or may not be erect, for inspection by the other. An erection also serves both genders in many other social displays, usually having

Like its striped- and brown-hyena relatives, the spotted hyena has specialized, massive teeth and chewing musculature that allow it to devour entire carcasses, including the bones. Its vocal repertoire ranges from a characteristic long-distance call and its famous giggle to a variety of moans, groans, and growls.

nothing to do with sex, and always signifies subordinate status.

How can females develop such profoundly masculine features? To answer this question it is necessary to consider the process of sexual differentiation in humans and other typical mammals. Sex is determined at the time of conception by the sex chromosome contributed by the fertilizing sperm. All eggs contain a single X chromosome; a sperm contains either an X chromosome or a Y chromosome. If the resulting fertilized egg contains two X's, the embryo develops as a female; if it contains an X and a Y, it develops as a male.

A major product of the Y chromosome is H-Y antigen. This protein causes the embryonic gonad to develop as a testis and start producing testosterone, the primary androgen (male sex hormone). In the absence of a Y chromosome, the gonad develops as an ovary and produces little testosterone during development. Testosterone from the fetal testis is converted by means of an enzyme to dihydrotestosterone (DHT), which induces certain tissues in the embryo to develop into the penis and the scrotum. In the absence of testosterone and DHT, those tissues develop

into the clitoris and the labia of the vulva.

A number of developmental anomalies exist that can cause human babies to be born with the "wrong" genitals for their chromosomal sex. For example, a defect in the enzyme that converts testosterone to DHT causes the genitals of a

Two adult spotted hyenas engage in the "greeting ceremony," while two cubs join in. Standing head to tail, each animal offers its penis or clitoris to the other for inspection.

male fetus to remain in the female state, even though he has internal testes and produces testosterone. Conversely, a metabolic error may result in the production of large amounts of testosterone by the adrenal gland. If the affected fetus is a female, she may be born with strongly masculinized genitals—an enlarged clitoris and fused labia—even though she has the internal reproductive tract of a female.

In addition to its effects on genital development, testosterone causes sexual differentiation of the fetal brain and is probably responsible for many of the behavioral differences between females and males. Similar to genital differentiation, in the absence of testosterone the brain develops in a female condition. Exposure to testosterone during fetal development produces male sexual behavior and in many species is probably at least partially responsible for the higher levels of aggression seen in adult males than in adult females.

Clearly, the female spotted hyena presents a challenge to this basic understanding of sexual differentiation. It is, in effect, a powerful natural experiment with which to test what scientists think they know about male-female differences. If testosterone is required for producing a penis and scrotum and is implicated in the development of aggressive behavior, one would expect to find a potent source of testosterone in female hyena fetuses. The primary questions, therefore, are twofold. Does female masculinization require testosterone, as in development of normal male genital organs? And if so, what is the source of the testosterone?

LABORATORY STUDIES

In 1984 we started a laboratory colony of spotted hyenas at the University of California, Berkeley. Since that time collaborative research with endocrinologists Julian Davidson of Stanford University, Paul Licht of Berkeley, and Pentti Siiteri and his colleagues at the University of California, San Francisco, has produced a detailed picture of the endocrine mechanisms that seem to underlie female masculinization.

We started the colony with 20 infants captured in the wild and hand reared. It soon became apparent that in juveniles as well as adults, females had unusually high levels of the hormone androstenedione in their blood. Androstenedione is formed in all mammalian ovaries, where it is converted to an estrogen by the enzyme aromatase, but it normally occurs only in low levels in the female blood circulation. It can also be converted to testosterone and is produced at low levels by the male testis and the adrenal gland. It has the effects of a weak androgen, and the finding that it was consistently elevated in females suggested that it may be responsible for at least some of the characteristics of female hyenas.

After three years the Berkeley hyenas were old enough to breed, and blood samples showed that pregnant females do indeed possess high levels of circulating testosterone. By sampling blood from mothers and fetuses and by tracing the fate of radioactively labeled androstenedione administered to pregnant females, we discovered some of the secrets taking place in the hyena's body.

In pregnancy the hyena ovary produces high levels of androstenedione, which the blood carries to the placenta. Normally the mammalian placenta protects the female fetus from "stray" androgens from the mother by convert-

ing them to estrogens with the enzyme aromatase. The hyena placenta, however, is deficient in aromatase. Moreover, it contains another enzyme, 17β-hydroxysteroid dehydrogenase, which converts androstenedione to testosterone. The placental circulation thus carries high levels of testosterone to fetuses of both sexes, where it presumably masculinizes the female genital organs and brain. Through the latter half of gestation, the fetuses are exposed to levels of testosterone at least as high as those found in adult males. Further, the hyena fetus is deficient in a protein that normally binds and inactivates a significant portion of circulating androgens. Thus, all the testosterone in the fetus is physiologically available. At birth, when the fetus separates from the placenta, testosterone levels fall abruptly.

From experiments with laboratory rodents it is known that a fetal ovary exposed to testosterone develops in a way remarkably similar to the hyena ovary; egg-producing tissue decreases, while hormone-producing tissue increases. Thus, it may be that a female fetus exposed to androgens during development will grow up to produce excess androgens as an adult, and in turn she will carry a fetus

that is also exposed to androgens. By this scenario the primary mutation—the genetic change in the spotted hyena's ancestors that led to the masculinization of females—may have been a simple regulatory change in production of aromatase by the placenta. The rest of the process would have been self-perpetuating. In women this condition is found in the common syndrome of polycystic ovaries, associated with both infertility and changes due to excess androgens, such as unwanted hair growth and deepening of the voice.

This mechanism for producing potentially masculinizing hormones in pregnant females certainly suggests that biologists' standard ideas of sexual differentiation are sufficient to explain male genital development in female hyenas and possibly their aggressive nature. However, in order to prove that exposure to testosterone is responsible for masculinized females, it is necessary to examine infant hyenas that have developed in the absence of the hormone. We would predict that under such conditions all infants, genetic males as well as females, would be born with normal mammalian female genital organs. We are currently testing this prediction in a series

of experiments that involve administering antiandrogens, drugs that block the action of testosterone, to pregnant females. Very early results suggest that the process of female masculinization may be more complex than we yet realize.

By means of such laboratory studies, we are beginning to understand the proximate mechanisms—the endocrinology—of hyena masculinization. To understand its ultimate evolutionary basis, however, it is necessary to study the social animal in the wild.

IMPORTANCE OF SOCIAL FORCES

Some of the most powerful evolutionary forces acting on animals are those imposed by group living, the interactions between and competition among members of the same species. The study of social behavior, called behavioral ecology or sociobiology, seeks to understand how relationships between individuals shape the social system and mold the evolution of individual form and behavior.

Most anatomy, physiology, and behavior are to a large degree determined by genes and thus are passed from parent to offspring. The key to evolutionary success is very simple: leave more offspring than other members of your species. Genetic changes that increase the number of one's descendants (or the descendants of one's close relatives) will spread through the species. Since a great many aspects of a species' social behavior ultimately affect individual survival and reproductive success, social forces have profound implications for the evolution of most animals, including humans.

Biologists measure an organism's relative genetic potential with a theoretical construct termed fitness. An individual with greater fitness is more likely to leave descendants than one with less. All aspects of an organism's biology—for instance, longevity, tolerance of environmental extremes, and the abilities to feed itself, escape predators, find mates, and raise offspring—contribute to its fitness. One of the most important components of fitness is reproductive success, which can also be measured in various ways: number of mates, number of offspring born, number of offspring that survive infancy, or number of offspring that survive to reproduce. Each of the four aforementioned measurements gives a better tally of descendants than the pre-

ceding one, but each is successively more difficult to measure in practical terms. Only through long-term studies of known individuals can one gain good measures of reproductive success and understand the behavioral characteristics that contribute to it and, hence, to fitness.

The first ecological research on the spotted hyena was carried out by Dutch zoologist Hans Kruuk, working in Tanzania's Ngorongoro Crater and Serengeti National Park. By following them at night, he established that hyenas are primarily hunters rather than scavengers and that they have elaborate and complex social behaviors. He

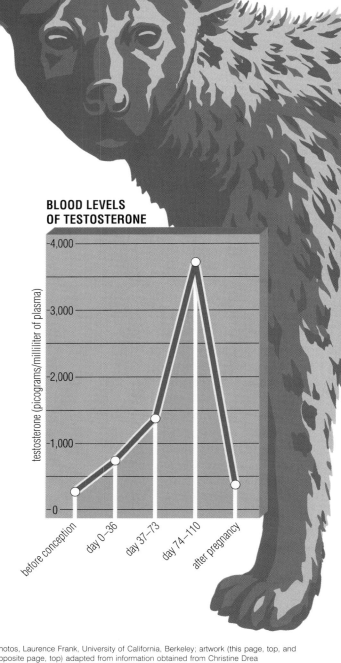

BLOOD LEVELS OF TESTOSTERONE

Photos, Laurence Frank, University of California, Berkeley; artwork (this page, top, and opposite page, top) adapted from information obtained from Christine Drea

The clitoris of the female spotted hyena (left, top) closely resembles the penis of the male (left, bottom) in form and size and is fully erectile. At birth the hyena fetus follows a circuitous route (opposite page, top), passing through the urogenital canal in the clitoris. In the womb (opposite page, bottom) fetuses of both sexes are exposed to high levels of testosterone, which is made in the placenta by conversion of maternal androstenedione (see text pages 228–229). As the graph shows, testosterone levels in the blood of the adult female hyena rise dramatically during pregnancy and then fall after the cubs are born.

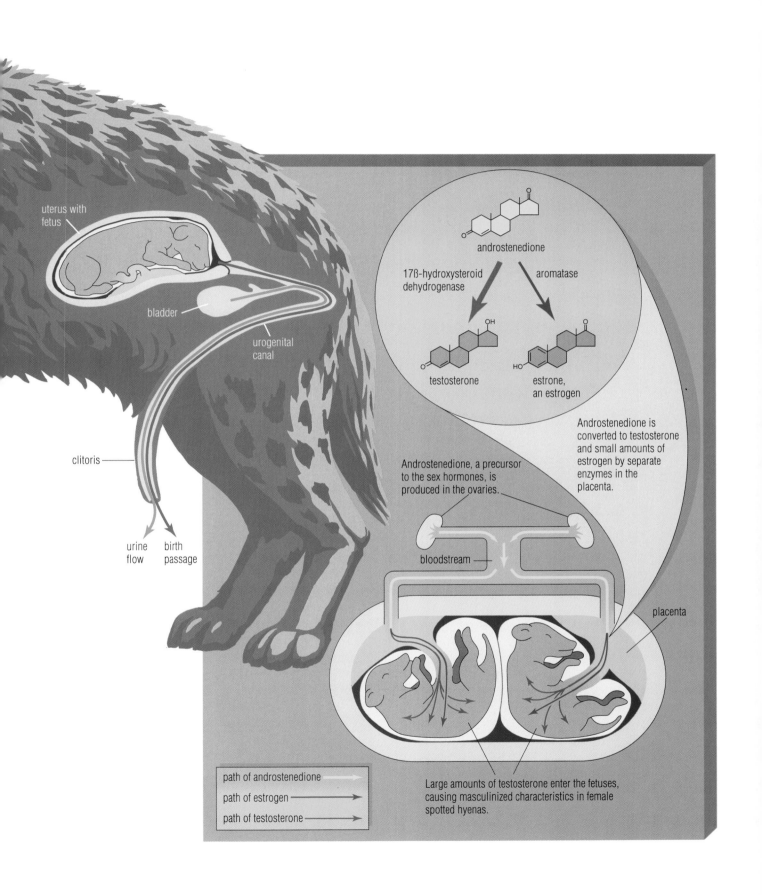

uterus with fetus

bladder

urogenital canal

clitoris

urine flow

birth passage

androstenedione

17ß-hydroxysteroid dehydrogenase

aromatase

testosterone

estrone, an estrogen

Androstenedione is converted to testosterone and small amounts of estrogen by separate enzymes in the placenta.

Androstenedione, a precursor to the sex hormones, is produced in the ovaries.

bloodstream

placenta

path of androstenedione

path of estrogen

path of testosterone

Large amounts of testosterone enter the fetuses, causing masculinized characteristics in female spotted hyenas.

found that they live in social groups that he termed clans, animals that all inhabit the same area and defend it against neighboring clans at well-defined territorial boundaries. Border clashes between clans are dramatic events, with as many as 30 animals on a side chasing each other in the moonlight back and forth across the boundary amid an ear-splitting din of whoops, roars, screams, and giggles. Only at a large kill will most clan members congregate; typically, they forage alone or in small groups.

Kruuk also discovered that female spotted hyenas are always dominant over males. The highest-ranking adult male gives way to the lowest-ranking adult female and even to her cubs. Such extreme female dominance is rare among mammals, and it was inevitable that it would be studied for its possible relationship to the hyena's female mas-

(Opposite page) A spotted hyena (on left) appeases another at a kill site. Among spotted hyenas a separate dominance hierarchy exists for each sex, with all adult females ranking above all adult males. Young cubs of both sexes possess the social position of their mothers in the female hierarchy. Thus, the offspring of high-ranking females are able to feed without interference by other hyenas.

culinization. Whereas Kruuk's work made it clear that hyenas are highly social, he did not delve into the patterns of associations and interactions among individuals that comprise a species' social organization.

AFRICAN FIELD STUDIES

In the late 1970s, one of us, Laurence G. Frank, started to study the social organization of a single large group, the Talek Clan, in Kenya's Masai Mara National Reserve, a project that by 1995 was in its 17th year. At the same time, M.G.L. ("Gus") Mills of South Africa's National Parks Board of the University of Pretoria was observing the much smaller clans in South Africa's Kalahari Desert. In the 1980s Johannes S. Henschel, another National Parks Board scientist, studied spotted hyenas in the bush country of Kruger National Park, also in South Africa, while Heribert Hofer and Marion L. East of the Max Planck Institute for Behavioral Physiology in Germany initiated a very productive ongoing study of the "commuting" hyena clans of the Serengeti. The following description is taken largely from the study of the Talek Clan, which numbers about

70 individuals and inhabits a home range of about 70 square kilometers (27 square miles).

In many respects social organization of the spotted hyena is remarkably similar to that of baboons and other terrestrial monkeys that have long served as models for understanding human social behavior. The stable core of the clan is a series of female families; maturing females stay in the clan of their birth, while males leave around puberty, eventually joining other clans. Spotted hyena social organization is also far more complex than that of any other carnivore. For example, packs of wolves, coyotes, or African wild dogs are simple nuclear families, comprising the dominant pair and their grown offspring. A lion pride is a group of closely related females that are joined by a succession of small groups of males.

Among social animals, stable groups are almost always characterized by dominance hierarchies such that certain individuals have priority of access to food, mates, sleeping sites, or other limited resources. In the absence of stable relations among individuals, life would be an endless squabble over resources. Dominance relations impose order and reliability, albeit of-

ten to the detriment of low-ranking individuals.

Among spotted hyenas there is a separate hierarchy in each sex, with all adult females ranking above all adult males. An individual's dominance rank profoundly affects most aspects of its life. An early finding was that young cubs of both sexes acquire the social position of their mother in the female dominance hierarchy; a male loses his rank when he leaves his natal clan, but a female retains her mother's rank for life. As a result, the female lineages, or matrilines, comprising the clan maintain their relative ranks for generations. The alpha, or top-ranked, female in the Talek Clan in 1995 was the great-granddaughter of the alpha female in the early 1980s. Studying the process of rank acquisition in the Talek Clan, Kay E. Holekamp and Laura Smale of Michigan State University found that females teach their cubs their social rank by intervening in squabbles with cubs of lower-ranking females and attacking lower-ranking females in the presence of their own cubs.

High-ranking females and their cubs take priority in the quarrelsome feeding melee of a hyena kill. Probably owing to their improved access to food, high-ranking females

leave more surviving offspring than low-ranking ones. Many low-ranking female juveniles do not survive to breed, whereas survival of high-ranking ones is much more likely. In the Talek Clan the highest-ranking matriline has been 2.5 times more successful in raising both males and females to the age of reproductive maturity (three years for females, two years for males) and has increased in size, while all other matrilines have decreased. The greater reproductive success of the most dominant family in a clan means that within 15 generations, or 45 years, all clan females will be descended from one individual. Thus, all clan females are closely related through their mothers.

When a male leaves his natal clan and attempts to join a new one, he must deal with an established male hierarchy that does not welcome newcomers. He is eventually assimilated as the lowest-ranking male, rising gradually in rank with the length of time spent in the clan. The mating system is polygynous; that is, most mating is accomplished by the highest-ranking males, who thus leave a disproportionate number of offspring. To achieve mating success then, a male must outlive his competitors. This situation is quite unlike that found typically in mammals with polygynous mating systems, where outright aggression among competing males determines male rank.

CAIN AND ABEL IN THE BURROW

When the hyenas in the Berkeley colony started to breed, we were astonished to discover that newborn twins fought violently and that they were highly specialized for winning the fight. While most mammals develop teeth only at a few weeks of age, spotted hyenas are born with their canines and incisors fully erupted. Unlike other carnivores (including the other species of hyenas), which start life as helpless little bundles of fur, spotted hyena neonates are capable of strong, directed behavior. They are also larger than other hyena infants. Their size, precocial behavior, and erupted teeth are the result of an extended gestation period, which at 110 days is 20 days longer than that of other hyenas.

Within minutes of birth, a newborn attempts to fasten its teeth into the neck and shoulders of its sibling and shake it violently. Fighting is most intense and prolonged on the day of birth and soon produces a dominant twin. The hierarchy lasts as long as the twins stay together. The dominant cub continues to punish the subordinate, inflicting wounds over the entire neck and shoulders. In the wild we have found emaciated, dying cubs with most of the shoulder skin gone and deep infected wounds in the muscles. We believe that in the confines of the natal burrow, the dominant cub continues to attack the subordinate and in many cases prevents it from moving to the mouth of the burrow to nurse. When death occurs, it is probably a result of malnutrition and infection.

The discovery of neonatal fighting in the captive hyenas solved a major puzzle that had emerged from field research. Although we knew from captive mothers that litters are normally born as twins, nearly half of all litters that wild females take from the natal burrow to the communal den are singletons. The ferocious fighting that we observed in the Berkeley colony appears to explain the difference.

In most animals males and females are born in roughly equal numbers. Simple mathematics shows that if twins are the norm, the composition of twin litters should be on average one-fourth male-male pairs, one-fourth female-

female pairs, and one-half male-female pairs. Given the similarity between the sexes, initially it was difficult to determine the sex of wild juveniles under one year of age, but as our ability to sex them improved, an unexpected pattern emerged. Nearly all wild litters that survived as twins were male-female pairs. Only a few male-male pairs were taken to the communal den, and until the past few years no female-female pairs were known, either in the Talek Clan or in any of the other hyena field studies. Since we knew that most litters started as twins, it seemed inescapable that most singletons originally had had siblings and that when both cubs were of the same sex, one of them had died in the natal burrow.

Siblicide, the killing of one sib by another, is well known among eagles, herons, pelicans, and other predatory birds but had not been previously described in mammals. In birds it is called siblicidal brood reduction and seems to serve the purpose of tailoring brood size to available food resources. Fighting among the newborn chicks establishes dominance. In years in which food is in short supply, the more dominant chicks eat well at the expense of the more subordinate, which

die of starvation. In plentiful years enough food is available for even the most subordinate chicks to survive.

Siblicide has a genetic cost, however. An animal's inclusive fitness is the sum of its direct fitness, derived from its own offspring, and indirect fitness, derived from the offspring of its relatives, with

which it shares genes. Full siblings hold about half their genes in common. Killing a sibling reduces one's indirect fitness and can evolve in a species only if there is a compensatory increase in direct fitness; that is, if one gains more from killing a sib than one loses through the loss of shared genes in that sib.

A tranquilized hyena yields a blood sample for use in hormone assays, paternity determination, or disease studies. When animals are captured, they are also measured and weighed and their physical condition assessed.

Laurence Frank, University of California, Berkeley

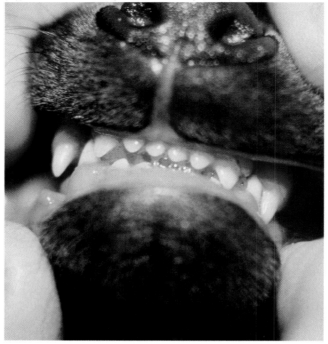

A spotted hyena cub on the day of birth possesses fully erupted canines and incisors (top). During the first few days of life, newborn cubs fight violently, each attempting to sink its teeth into the neck and shoulders of its twin (above). The fighting soon produces a dominant twin, which continues to subjugate its littermate as long as the two remain together.

In hyenas the function of siblicide remains to be explained. If females were able to raise two young only in years of high food supply, its use would appear similar to that in birds. However, we know that hyenas usually raise mixed-sex litters successfully. In some ecosystems in which the hyenas' prey is fairly scarce, siblicide may well serve an occasional brood-reduction function. Nonetheless, it does not explain why the fighting should proceed to death most often in same-sex litters and why it occurs at such an early age, well before food shortage is likely to be an issue.

There are intriguing hints in our studies that female hyenas use siblicidal fighting to their own genetic advantage. For example, when in 1990 the departure of several mid-ranking Talek females caused the population of the clan to drop suddenly below its long-term stable level, we began to see twin female cubs surviving. Thus, it may be that when ecological conditions favor producing either more sons or more daughters, a mother is able to influence the outcome of the fighting by various means such that more of the preferred sex survive. Influencing siblicide to maximize her reproductive success may be one way she minimizes the genetic cost of the infants that die in the process.

Neonatal fighting in spotted hyenas is an exceptionally "pure" form of aggression and, as such, appears to offer a superb opportunity to examine the biological roots of aggression. Studies, for example, on hormonal influences on fighting in males are often difficult to interpret because there is always a social context and because the combatants have a social history (even those that have been experimentally deprived of previous social contact). It is certain that testosterone has subtle and complex effects on aggression in many species, but the results may not be readily predictable. For instance, administering excess testosterone to a male monkey may not improve his social status. He may indeed become more aggressive, but by picking fights he cannot win, he may actually lose social status. Hyenas' neonatal fighting may prove to be an excellent model for studies of hormones and aggression simply because they have no previous social experience; there is no evidence that they fight in the womb.

That hyenas in the womb are exposed to very high levels of testosterone suggests that hormonal effects may underlie their neonatal fighting. However, even though newborns are highly adapted for winning the fight, their tendency to fight so early in life may be a secondary effect of prenatal hormone exposure that originally evolved for other reasons. We await the outcome of experiments with antiandrogens to see if they decrease fighting in neonates.

WHY DID FEMALE MASCULINIZATION EVOLVE?

Because neither behaviors nor soft parts like genitals

leave fossils, any understanding of the evolution of female masculinization in the spotted hyena must be conjectural. However, we understand enough about the ecology and social system of the species to offer a reasonable conjecture. The keys to the hypothetical scenario are the hyena's uniquely competitive feeding melee and the reproductive advantages gained by high-ranking females. Long-term data from the Talek Clan clearly demonstrate that the highest-ranking females are much more successful in raising their cubs, probably because they are the only animals that have essentially unlimited access to food. The ability to dominate other hyenas at a kill is an enormous reproductive advantage; because females "inherit" their mother's rank, the effect snowballs over generations.

We speculate that the ancestor of the spotted hyena closely resembled the other species of living hyenas. It was primarily a scavenger, with normal male dominance and female anatomy. Because carcasses are a rare commodity, it lived at low density and fed in relative solitude. With the development of cooperative predation on living prey, a vast

Postulated major events in the evolution of female masculinization in the spotted hyena are summarized. (*See* text beginning on page 236.)

Nearly half of the litters that wild hyena females bring to the communal den from the natal burrow are singletons, although litters are normally born as twins. The discovery of neonatal fighting—which often ends in the death of one of the cubs—has explained why.

237

new food resource opened up. Many hyenas now gathered at each carcass, and the hyena population increased. Those two developments led to the present situation, in which feeding is a mad scramble for a rapidly disappearing meal. In another social carnivore, the African lion, similar pres-sures result in severe cub mor-tality because youngsters feed only after the adults; only in times of plenty do many cubs survive. In wolves and African wild dogs (but not in lions or spotted hyenas), adults pro-vision the young, partly pro-tecting them in times of food shortage.

Under such ecological pres-sure any evolutionary develop-ment, such as increased female aggressiveness, that allowed more cubs to survive would have been strongly favored by natural selection and would have spread rapidly through the population. We know from experiments on laboratory an-imals that prenatal androgen exposure can increase aggres-siveness in the adult, especially in the presence of circulating androgens. If our current view of endocrinology in the spot-ted hyena is correct, a fairly modest change in a gene that regulates aromatase produc-tion in the placenta may have

initiated a series of events culminating in more aggressive females, able to ensure adequate nutrition for themselves and their cubs.

An inevitable result of prenatal androgen exposure, however, is masculinization of the female genitals and the consequent problems in mating and giving birth. The evolutionary pressure on the hyena to undergo changes that would deal with these problems must have been strong, or the new mutation would have rapidly disappeared. The fact that birth difficulties still exist suggests that the process is not yet complete.

The dominance of females over males may not necessarily have evolved for that purpose. The great reproductive advantages of high female rank suggest that dominance over other females is a strong reason for evolution to select for females with high levels of aggressiveness. If lower levels of aggressiveness serve males better (and there is no doubt that humans and other animals can be too aggressive for their own good), they would end up being less aggressive than females. Thus, female dominance over males may be a side effect of selection for aggressive females.

Obviously, many questions remain. For instance, given apparently identical hormonal exposure in the womb, why are males less aggressive than females? If there is a survival benefit for cubs, why has a similar system not arisen in the lion or other carnivores that face similar ecological pressures? Was there something special about ancestral hyena endocrinology that permitted this evolution, or was it a one-time mutation that, against all odds, happened to work? Were the initial development and subsequent evolution of siblicidal fighting a side effect of prenatal androgens that evolved to make aggressive adults and unavoidably created aggressive infants as well? Clearly, spotted hyenas will provide rich grounds for physiological and behavioral research for years to come. The results eventually may offer valuable insights into the characteristics of aggression and sexual development in mammals in general and humans in particular.

What does the spotted hyena gain from neonatal fighting and the frequent survival of only one twin? One theory is that a mother may be able to influence the outcome of the fighting to maximize her own reproductive success.

Nigel Dennis—NHPA

FOR ADDITIONAL READING

■ "Costs and Benefits of 'Androgenization' in the Female Spotted Hyena: The Natural Selection of Physiological Mechanisms," S.E. Glickman *et al.*, in *Perspectives in Ethology*, P.P.G. Bateson, N. Thompson, and P. Klopfer, eds. (Plenum Press, 1993).

■ "Dominance, Demographics and Reproductive Success in Female Spotted Hyenas: A Long Term Study," L.G. Frank, H.E. Holekamp, and L. Smale, in *Serengeti II: Dynamics, Management, and Conservation of an Ecosystem*, A.R.E. Sinclair and P. Arcese, eds. (University of Chicago Press, 1995).

■ "Fatal Sibling Aggression, Precocial Development, and Androgens in Neonatal Spotted Hyenas," L.G. Frank, S.E. Glickman, and P. Licht, *Science* (May 3, 1991, pp. 702–704).

■ "Female Masculinization in the Spotted Hyena: Endocrinology, Behavioral Ecology, and Evolution," L.G. Frank, in *Carnivore Behavior, Ecology, and Evolution*, vol. 2, J.L. Gittleman, ed. (Cornell University Press, 1995).

■ "The Hormonal Control of Sexual Development," J.D. Wilson, F.W. George, and J.E. Griffin, *Science* (March 20, 1981, pp. 1278–84).

■ "A Mechanism for Virilization of Female Spotted Hyenas in Utero," T.M. Yalcinkaya *et al.*, *Science* (June 25, 1993, pp. 1929–31).

■ *Reproduction in Mammals*, book 2: *Embryonic and Fetal Development*, C.R. Austin and R.V. Short (Cambridge University Press, 1982).

■ *Sexual Differentiation of the Brain*, R.W. Goy and B.S. McEwen (MIT Press, 1980).

■ *The Spotted Hyena: A Study of Predation and Social Behavior*, H. Kruuk (University of Chicago Press, 1972).

Thomas Eisner:

Nature plays out boundless numbers of scenes that await our appreciation. Entomologist Thomas Eisner has spent his career seeking out the beauty and enigma of an enthralling world that most of us take for granted. This photo essay features the work of a scientist whose love of nature is complemented by his devotion to photography, which began in his teens. With his cameras and scientific tools and with an intense curiosity and respect for all living things, he ex-

Capturing Nature's Theater

plores the hidden drama that unfolds in the world beyond our sight.

The Jacob Gould Schurman professor of chemical ecology at Cornell University, Ithaca, N.Y., Eisner lists chemical ecology, evolution, behavior, and conservation among his research interests. He has written five books and more than 300 technical articles, and his photographs have appeared in many magazines and newspapers, including *Science*, *Scientific American*, *National Geographic*, *Time*, and the *New York Times*.

Head of a praying mantid.

Demonstrating protective camouflage, a caterpillar is concealed on a flower.

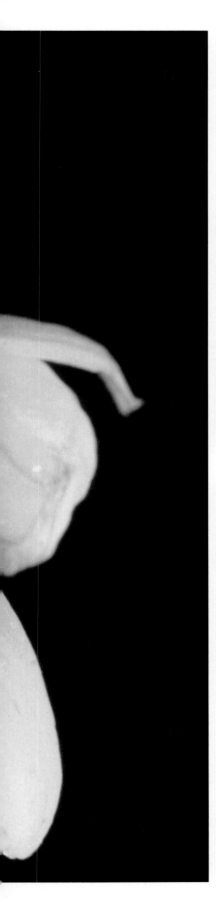

Noctuid moth rests on flower that it imitates.

Desert weevil feeds on plants.

Praying mantid is camouflaged by lichens.

Pentatomid bug is camouflaged against pine tree bark.

Below, defensive secretion oozes from the flank of a millipede. Opposite page top left to bottom right, a spittle bug surrounds itself with defensive froth; a lubber grasshopper regurgitates defensive gut fluid; poisonous spines line the back of an io moth caterpillar; and defensive droplets are emitted from the neck of a ctenuchid moth.

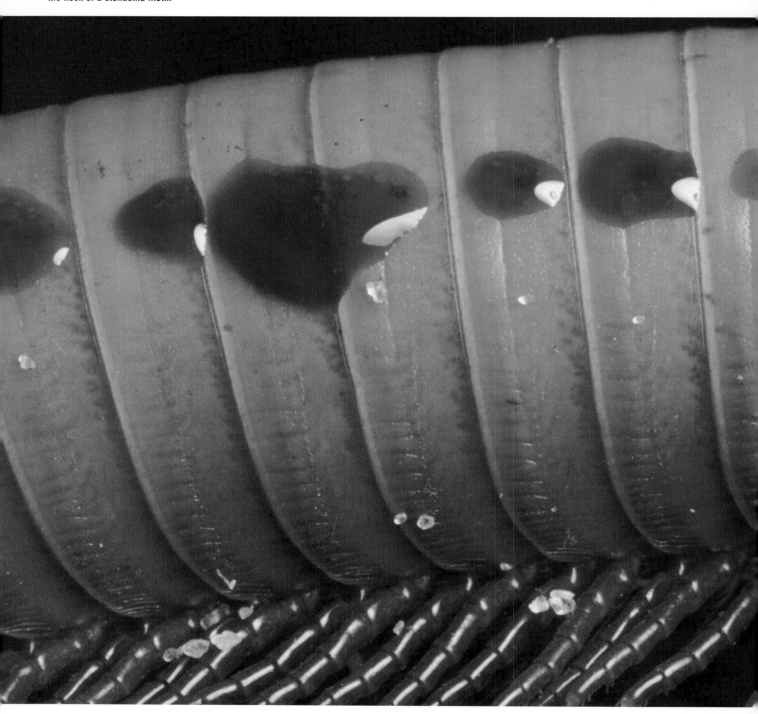

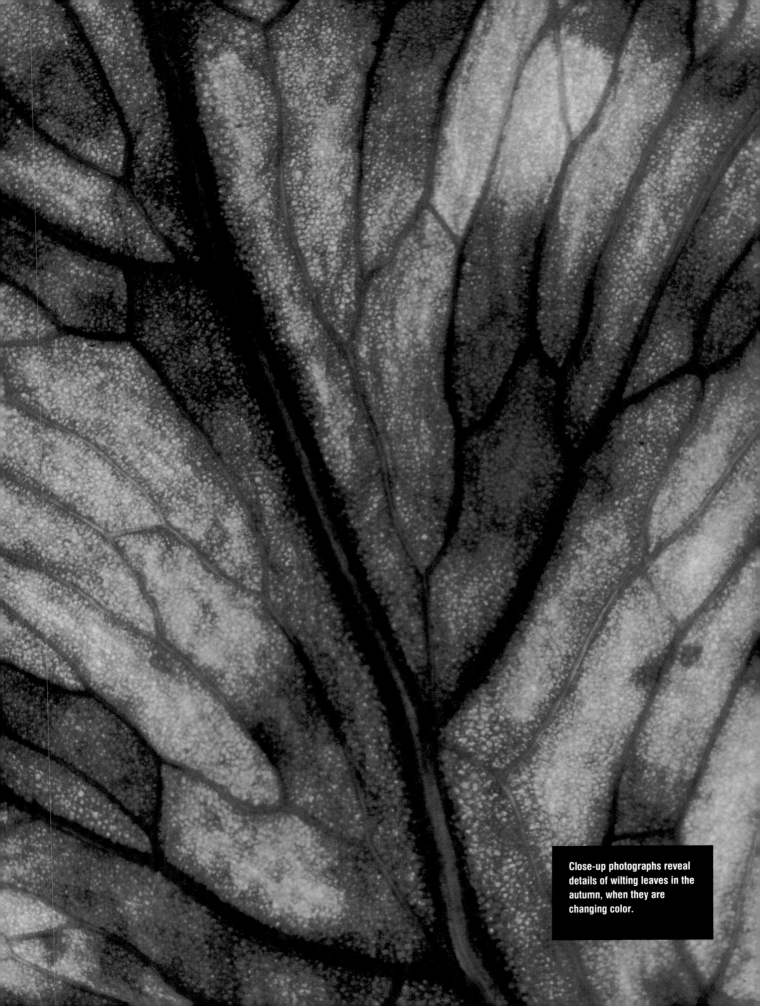

Close-up photographs reveal details of wilting leaves in the autumn, when they are changing color.

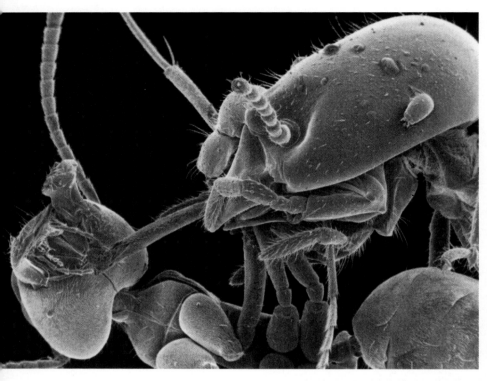

Left, a termite (right) bites an attacking ant. The tiny drop-shaped structure on the termite's head is a parasitic mite. Below, newly emerged larvae of Mexican bean beetles munch on leaves. Opposite page, an ant of the genus *Formica* attacks a tortoise-shell beetle.

Opposite page, pupa of a moth
is protected by a silken web.

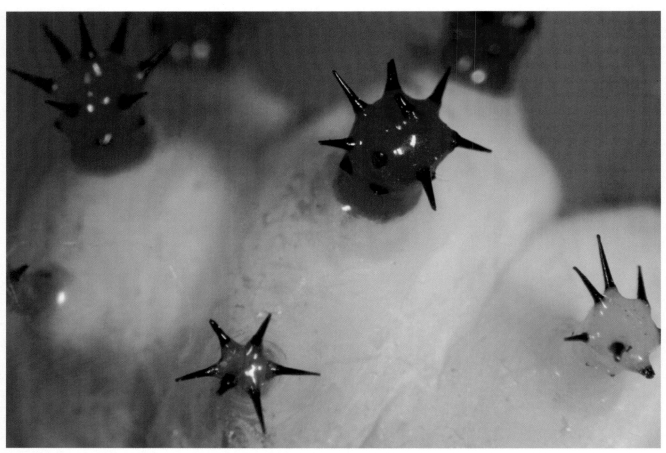

Spiny knobs provide a defense for the caterpillar of the giant silkworm moth.

Shield (top) protects the larva of a tortoise-shell beetle.

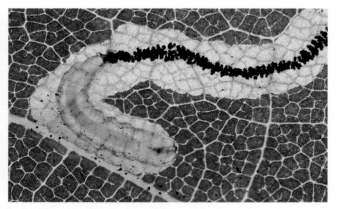

Leaf-mining caterpillar burrows within an oak leaf.

The Max Planck Society: A Stronghold of German Science

by Bernd Ebersold

The eye movements of a goldfish held motionless in a tank of water (above) are studied in perception experiments at the Max Planck Institute for Biological Cybernetics, Tübingen, Germany. (Opposite page) At the same institute, a human head is scanned by laser to create a three-dimensional computer model for research into artificial recognition systems.

Photographs by Wolfgang Filser

Although its 80th birthday is securely behind it, the venerable Max Planck Society for the Advancement of Science (in German, Max-Planck-Gesellschaft zur Förderung der Wissenschaften, or MPG) maintains a flexibility in its structure and a quickness to embrace new fields of research that many younger institutions might envy. Established in 1911 as the Kaiser Wilhelm Society (KWG), the MPG, together with its sprawling collection of research institutes, is now Germany's premier nonprofit organization for the support of basic scientific research. Today the concept on which its predecessor was founded remains the MPG's overarching principle—that of putting the responsibility for running well-equipped institutes devoted to basic research into the hands of the best researchers and granting them almost complete autonomy. Consequently, the MPG possesses a degree of freedom to pursue science that few research organizations in other countries can match.

Bernd Ebersold is Personal Assistant to the President of the Max Planck Society, Munich, Germany.

For more than eight decades, Germany's Max Planck Society has been living proof that an organization committed to "pure" research carried out with scientific and administrative autonomy can reap valuable rewards for a nation's industry and society.

Two KWG scientific members, Fritz Haber (left) and Albert Einstein, pose in 1914 at Haber's Institute for Physical Chemistry and Electrochemistry. Haber won a Nobel Prize in 1918 for developing a method for synthesizing ammonia. Einstein won one in 1921 for contributions to theoretical physics.

FOUNDING YEARS

Nearly a century ago a group of farsighted German scholars, policy makers, and industrialists recognized the need to complement their nation's scientific research system, which since the time of the early 19th-century educational reformer Wilhelm von Humboldt had been based primarily on universities, with their twofold commitment to education and research. They believed that Germany needed "pure" research institutes, unencumbered with the burdens of educational necessities. Rapid growth in the sciences and increasing numbers of students in the first decade of the 20th century had made the shortcomings of the universities quite apparent. Rigid adherence to

the traditional disciplines was impeding the pursuit of innovative, interdisciplinary subjects in chemistry and physics. Furthermore, the universities seemed unable to bear the growing costs of modern research equipment and other investments.

In 1909 in a memorandum addressed to Kaiser Wilhelm II, Adolf von Harnack, a professor of theology at the University of Berlin, combined all of these arguments with the admonition that a high standard of technology could not be achieved without a high standard of scientific research and that both were "communicating tubes" of the utmost importance to a nation's wealth and economic status in the world. In Harnack's view, given the aggressive worldwide competition for markets and

products and the astonishing energy of the U.S. research and development (R&D) effort at the time, it was imperative for Germany not to lose ground. He pointed out that newly established foundations such as Sweden's Nobel Foundation (established in 1900) and the U.S.'s Rockefeller Institute for Medical Research (1901) and Carnegie Institution of Washington (1902) had successfully broadened the research systems in those countries.

In addition, the memorandum contained two points that had a great influence on the way the KWG and its successor would see themselves. First, the institutes that Harnack proposed to be established should only complement the universities and not diminish their basic commitment to research. In this respect, the new institutes necessarily would play a subsidiary role. Second, whereas the institutes would be devoted primarily to basic research in the sciences as well as the humanities and financed by both private and public sources, the responsibility for running them and for defining their fields of inquiry should lie with outstanding researchers alone. In other words, industry, governments, and society would have to set aside their

own particular interests in realizing short-term gains and trust that independent, nonindustrial research would be economically more fruitful in the long run.

At the time, Harnack's arguments were shared by many influential people in science, industry, and government in Germany. The tremendous success of a fund-raising campaign among industrialists and bankers and the support of Wilhelm II and the Prussian government paved the way for the founding of the KWG in 1911 and led to the opening of the first two Kaiser Wilhelm institutes in Berlin in the same year: the Institute for Physical Chemistry and Electrochemistry, headed by Fritz Haber, and the Institute for Chemistry, with Ernst Beckmann, Richard Willstätter, and Otto Hahn as its leading scientists. Harnack was elected first president of the KWG, to which belonged all "scientific members" appointed by the society to its institutes as well as all "supporting members" (private persons, industrial enterprises, and municipal organizations).

The history of the KWG proved the wisdom of the idea to build each research institute around an excellent scientist, the so-called Harnack principle. In fact, three of its first scientific members mentioned above—Haber, Willstätter, and Hahn—later received Nobel Prizes. Hahn, for instance, working with Lise Meitner and Fritz Strassmann at the Institute for Chemistry in 1938, unexpectedly discovered nuclear fission while attempting to create elements heavier than uranium. Six years later Hahn received the Nobel Prize for Chemistry for this discovery. By 1944 the KWG could boast of having 15 Nobel Prize-winning scientists. Its scientific achievements helped it to survive under quite unfavorable circumstances—World War I, the monetary inflation and socioeconomic turmoil of the 1920s and '30s, Hitler's dictatorship, and then World War II.

Other examples of the high quality of science in the KWG's history are connected with the Institute for Coal Research, which was founded in 1914 in Mülheim. In the 1920s its laboratories yielded the famous Fischer-Tropsch reaction for the production of gasoline by coal liquefaction. In 1943 organic chemist Karl Ziegler was appointed director of the institute. In the 1950s, taking advantage of a lucky accident, Ziegler developed a fast, low-pressure process for catalytically converting the gaseous hydrocarbon ethylene into a polymer with valuable plastic properties. The approach, which could also be used to make other polymers, became the basis for the worldwide production of numerous synthetic plastics, fibers, rubbers, and films, and it earned for Ziegler a Nobel Prize in 1963.

THE MODERN SOCIETY

Three years after the end of World War II, the KWG was reestablished as the Max Planck Society within what was soon to become West Germany. Its new name honored the great theoretical physicist Max Planck, then recently deceased, who had originated quantum theory in the early 1900s and had served as president of the KWG in the 1930s and as acting president in the transition period after the war.

Today, as then, the society's explicit aim is to continue supporting research in the spirit of its predecessor. In the context of the highly differentiated German R&D system, its primary task can be summarized in three imperatives: (1) to work in particularly important or promising research fields with sufficient personnel and funds; (2) to quickly embrace newly developing fields outside established disciplines, particularly those not yet, or only slowly, being introduced in universities; (3) to carry out research that because of facilities requirements or high cost is either impossible or impractical for universities.

Operating within these guidelines, the MPG forms an integral part of the well-orchestrated concert of public, nonindustrial research activities in Germany. By tradition as well as by sheer number, the universities remain the foundation of the publicly funded research system. Being committed as much to research as to teaching, they are essential for recruiting future scientists. In general, university research is aimed at raising the level of knowledge in all scientific disciplines and at introducing young scientists to research. Apart from a few private ones, all German universities are the responsibility of the constituent German states (*Länder*); they are not federal institutions. The German government supports them only by providing half the cost of institutional support—investments in buildings and large-scale facilities—or by funding research projects directly. Furthermore, in conjunction with the states, the federal government backs research work at universities through shared sponsorship of the German Research Association (Deutsche Forschungsgemeinschaft, or DFG). Like the Max Planck Society, the DFG is a self-administered organization, but it does not operate research institutes. The major part of its budget is devoted to grants awarded on the basis of an efficient peer-review system. The DFG's budget, DM 1.6 billion (about $1 billion) in 1993, is roughly that of the MPG.

The universities, the MPG, and the DFG form the three

UPI/Bettmann

Max Planck, who received a Nobel Prize in 1918—the same year that Haber won the award—for laying the foundations of quantum theory, served as KWG president from 1930 to 1937 and for a short time after World War II. In 1948, a year after his death, the KWG was reestablished and, in Planck's honor, given its present name.

255   The Institute for Chemistry, Berlin, one of the first two Kaiser Wilhelm institutes, is pictured in 1912.

Archive on the History of the Max Planck Society, Berlin

pillars of German basic research. They are also highly interconnected. In general, MPG scientists may apply for DFG grants on the same basis as their university colleagues. Representatives of the MPG and the DFG are each included in the organizational framework of the other body. Cooperation with the universities gives scientific members of the MPG the freedom to work with their academic counterparts on common projects. Although there is no commitment for MPG researchers to teach at the universities, more than 80% of its institute directors are so associated, mostly as honorary professors. By the same token, university professors are members of the MPG's central organizational body, the Senate, and of MPG committees convened to consider future appointments. Finally, although the MPG has no graduate program of its own, its research institutes offer many young scientists preparing for their diplomas or doctoral degrees opportunities to take part in research. In 1993, for example, 1,596 students supported by the MPG prepared Ph.D. theses for submission to universities.

As an independent, autonomous institution, the MPG differs from other German nonuniversity research organizations and is arguably unique in the industrialized world. It will take up promising fields in basic research, but only if there is a possibility of exploring them in an institute of manageable size and only if an outstanding researcher is available whose past achievements suggest that the freedom and research opportunities offered by the MPG will result in further exceptional progress. It rarely performs research on request from industry, government ministries, or other outside agencies and then only on the condition that the projects fit into the institutes' research agenda. In this respect the MPG differs fundamentally from Germany's Fraunhofer Society for Applied Research (Fraunhofer-Gesellschaft zur Förderung der angewandten Forschung, or FhG), whose 47 institutes work mainly on applied research problems at the request of its public and private financiers. Consequently, Fraunhofer institutes must attract research contracts from

Ernst Beckmann (right), first director of the Institute for Chemistry, works with a staff member in a laboratory of the institute about 1913. Beckmann's research added to an understanding of organic chemical reactions.

Scientists who contributed to the distinguished history of the KWG and MPG include biologist Hans Spemann, a 1935 Nobel laureate honored for discoveries in embryonic development. During World War I Spemann directed the Institute for Biology.

industry or government organizations, although they do receive some basic federal support.

In addition to the FhG, Germany has 16 national research centers that help to bridge the gap between fundamental science and technological development. They pursue specific research topics that either are in the public interest (*e.g.,* cancer or ecology) or need facilities so expansive that they cannot be provided by a single university or Max Planck institute (*e.g.,* for atomic-energy or particle-accelerator research). Only one national research center, the Institute for Plasma Physics, Garching, is run by the MPG. It carries out studies on nuclear

fusion and is well integrated into the national and international fusion-power program. The nonindustrial German research system is completed by research institutions run directly by federal or state ministries and by various types of other individual research facilities, the so-called Blue List Institutes, which, apart from a common method of financing, have no common rationale.

SCIENTIFIC SPECTRUM

Although the MPG must be selective in the research activities that it undertakes, the sum of its endeavors covers a broad scientific spectrum. Max Planck institutes are grouped into three sections: chemistry,

Werner Heisenberg, a 1932 Nobel laureate and another pioneer of quantum theory, directed the Institute for Physics during much of World War II. After the war he organized and directed the Institute for Physics and Astrophysics.

Lise Meitner (left) and Otto Hahn are pictured in their laboratory at the Institute for Chemistry in 1928. A decade later at the institute, while trying to create elements heavier than uranium, they and Fritz Strassmann discovered nuclear fission.

Adolf Butenandt became director of the Institute for Biochemistry in 1936, and from 1960 to 1972 he served as president of the MPG. In 1939 he was co-winner of a Nobel Prize for his work on sex hormones.

The flame of an oil-burning furnace is probed with ultraviolet laser light in ongoing studies at the Institute for Flow Research, Göttingen. At some MPG institutes basic research is often guided by problems of practical significance or in areas with high applications potential.

Wolfgang Filser

physics, and technology; biology and medicine; and the humanities.

Basic research in the chemistry, physics, technology section, which includes astronomy and mathematics, is the classical basis for technological progress; at the same time, it fulfills our desire to understand more about the structure of matter and the history of the universe. Two great themes permeate basic chemical and physical research: the search for a standard, all-encompassing explanation of nature's processes and the search to understand our own place in the world around us. In addressing those themes, research at Max Planck institutes explores phenomena that range in size from the dimensions of elementary particles to the breadth of the cosmos and in time from a thousandth of a trillionth of a second to billions of years.

MPG chemists observe the dynamics and the atomic de-

tails of important chemical reactions such as photosynthesis and catalysis, examine processes taking place in the Earth's upper atmosphere, and study the history of the solar system. Research topics in physics range from the fundamental building blocks of matter and atomic-scale surface processes to questions concerning the origins and evolution of stars, galaxies, and the universe itself. Basic research in chemistry, physics, and technology is also guided by problems that are either of considerable practical significance—for example, fusion power or human-caused climate change—or in areas that have high applications potential—for example, solid-state physics (semiconductor or metals research) or polymer chemistry (synthetic materials, coatings, or adhesives).

Max Planck institutes in the biology and medicine section study the basic life sciences,

which subsume such areas as evolution, genetics, biochemistry, processes of adaptation to altered living conditions, and mechanisms of neuronal activity. The different institutes' activities cover structural and functional investigations of biologically important molecules and cell components, research on single-celled and multicellular organisms, and studies of interactions between individual organisms and between organisms and their environment. Since biological processes are universal, a great deal of general research is relevant for human beings. Nevertheless, some MPG institutes and research groups focus specifically on questions of human biology and on fields of science pertaining to human physiological, mental, and intellectual performance.

The MPG sees inquiry into human culture and values and the ability of the human spirit for self-expression as an essential counterpart to science. Therefore, the society's approach to research in its entirety involves a section for the humanities. This section comprises institutes that deal with the mental and intellectual aspects of our existence and development (psychological and educational research), social coexistence (social re-

search), legal systems (jurisprudence) the story of civilization (research in history), and art (history of art).

RESPONSIVENESS THROUGH RESTRUCTURING

The dynamic nature of basic research and the restraints of an inflexible civil-service system in Germany have required special organizational efforts for the Max Planck Society to remain responsive to new developments. Recognizing that any institute tends toward its own perpetuation, sometimes at the expense of progress, the MPG continually questions the feasibility of its research programs and institutes. This process is particularly active when a scientific member, who normally holds lifelong tenure with the MPG as an institute director, retires.

If it is apparent that a special interest no longer exists in the research work done at an institute or in one of its departments, the MPG moves either to redirect the facility thematically through the appointment of a new institute director or, as a last resort, to close it. Concurrently, by establishing new institutes, the MPG takes up innovative topics not yet being pursued. In the 1980s the society closed two institutes, four research units, two subinstitutes, and 19 departments. In the same period, 8 new institutes were founded, 2 subinstitutes were reorganized as independent institutes, and 10 new project groups, research units, or working groups were established. As a result of the restructuring, it was possible to transfer almost 700 permanent posts within MPG research facilities.

With the reunification of East Germany and West Germany in 1990, the need to establish a balanced scientific landscape offered opportunities for further innovation through the founding of new facilities and programs. Between 1990 and 1994, budget increases allowed the MPG to create 10 new institutes. During the same period, it also established 27 working groups in order to revitalize research in former East German universities. The MPG's long-range plan is to set up 15–20 institutes in eastern Germany.

As of 1994 the Max Planck Society operated more than 70 institutes and other re-

A scientist at the Institute for Nuclear Physics, Heidelberg, collects radioactive germanium atoms as part of the GALLEX solar-neutrino experiment.

Wolfgang Filser

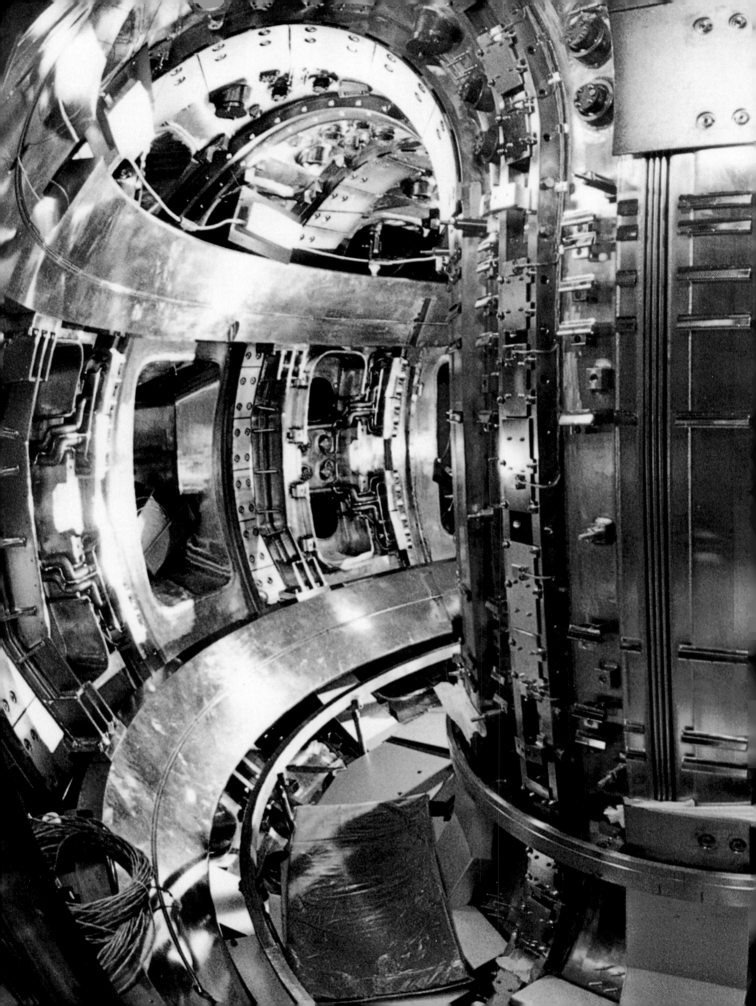

A hollow toroidal (doughnut-shaped) vessel forms the core of the ASDEX (Axially Symmetric Divertor Experiment) Upgrade tokamak at Garching. Developed by researchers of the Institute for Plasma Physics, ASDEX is an experimental fusion-power device of tokamak design that uses a powerful, complex magnetic field to confine a hot ionized gas, or plasma, wherein atomic nuclei can collide, fuse, and produce energy. A major problem with the tokamak design is damage to the vessel wall caused by contact with the hot plasma. The ASDEX Upgrade is being used to investigate a special magnetic field configuration that removes the outer boundary layer of the plasma before it can interact with the wall.

Institute for Plasma Physics

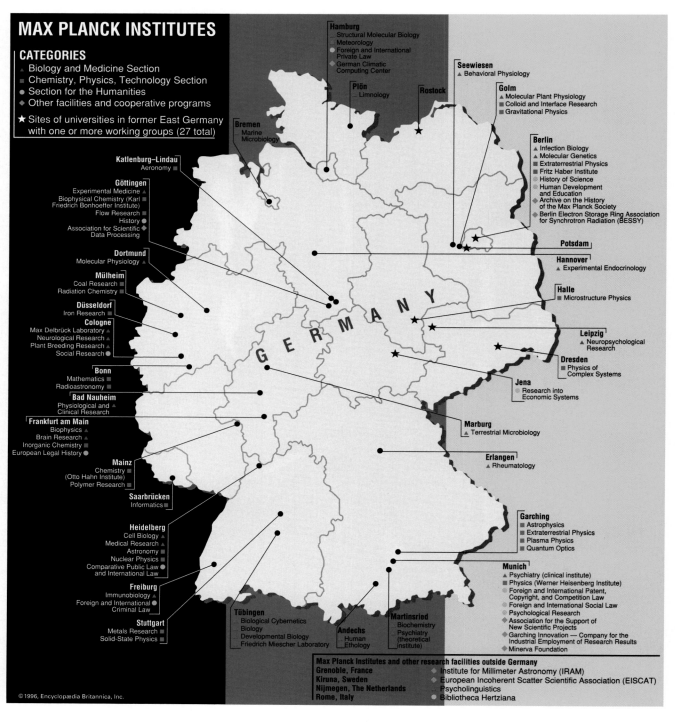

MAX PLANCK INSTITUTES

CATEGORIES

▲ Biology and Medicine Section
■ Chemistry, Physics, Technology Section
● Section for the Humanities
◆ Other facilities and cooperative programs

★ Sites of universities in former East Germany
with one or more working groups (27 total)

Hamburg
Structural Molecular Biology
Meteorology
● Foreign and International
Private Law
◆ German Climatic
Computing Center

Plön
Limnology

Rostock

Seewiesen
▲ Behavioral Physiology

Golm
▲ Molecular Plant Physiology
■ Colloid and Interface Research
■ Gravitational Physics

Bremen
Marine
Microbiology

Katlenburg–Lindau
Aeronomy ■

Göttingen
Experimental Medicine ▲
Biophysical Chemistry (Karl ■
Friedrich Bonhoeffer Institute)
Flow Research ■
History ●
Association for Scientific ◆
Data Processing

Dortmund
Molecular Physiology ▲

Mülheim
Coal Research ■
Radiation Chemistry ■

Düsseldorf
Iron Research ■

Cologne
Max Delbrück Laboratory ▲
Neurological Research ▲
Plant Breeding Research ▲
Social Research ●

Bonn
Mathematics ■
Radioastronomy ■

Bad Nauheim
Physiological and ▲
Clinical Research

Frankfurt am Main
Biophysics ▲
Brain Research ▲
Inorganic Chemistry ■
European Legal History ●

Mainz
Chemistry ■
(Otto Hahn Institute)
Polymer Research ■

Saarbrücken
Informatics ■

Heidelberg
Cell Biology ▲
Medical Research ▲
Astronomy ■
Nuclear Physics ■
Comparative Public Law ●
and International Law

Freiburg
Immunobiology ▲
Foreign and International ●
Criminal Law

Stuttgart
Metals Research ■
Solid-State Physics ■

Tübingen
Biological Cybernetics
Biology
Developmental Biology
Friedrich Miescher Laboratory

Andechs
Human
Ethology

Martinsried
Biochemistry
Psychiatry
(theoretical
institute)

Berlin
▲ Infection Biology
▲ Molecular Genetics
■ Extraterrestrial Physics
■ Fritz Haber Institute
● History of Science
● Human Development
and Education
◆ Archive on the History
of the Max Planck Society
◆ Berlin Electron Storage Ring Association
for Synchrotron Radiation (BESSY)

Potsdam

Hannover
▲ Experimental Endocrinology

Halle
■ Microstructure Physics

Leipzig
▲ Neuropsychological
Research

Dresden
■ Physics of
Complex Systems

Jena
● Research into
Economic Systems

Marburg
▲ Terrestrial Microbiology

Erlangen
▲ Rheumatology

Garching
■ Astrophysics
■ Extraterrestrial Physics
■ Plasma Physics
■ Quantum Optics

Munich
▲ Psychiatry (clinical institute)
■ Physics (Werner Heisenberg Institute)
● Foreign and International Patent,
Copyright, and Competition Law
● Foreign and International Social Law
● Psychological Research
◆ Association for the Support of
New Scientific Projects
◆ Garching Innovation — Company for the
Industrial Employment of Research Results
◆ Minerva Foundation

Max Planck Institutes and other research facilities outside Germany
Grenoble, France — ◆ Institute for Millimeter Astronomy (IRAM)
Kiruna, Sweden — ◆ European Incoherent Scatter Scientific Association (EISCAT)
Nijmegen, The Netherlands — ● Psycholinguistics
Rome, Italy — ● Bibliotheca Hertziana

search units. Two institutes, the Bibliotheca Herztiana, Rome, which is devoted to research on the history of art, and the Max Planck Institute for Psycholinguistics, Nijmegen, The Netherlands, are located abroad. At the start of 1994, 11,074 employees held a contract with the MPG. Scientific members numbered 218, and they were assisted by a scientific staff of 2,832. In addition, 5,728 scholarship holders and guest scientists worked in MPG facilities during 1993.

ORGANIZATION FOR AUTONOMY

Although the MPG is financed almost entirely through public funds, it is not a governmental organization but a registered society organized under private law. In addition to the scientific members appointed to it, any private person, company, township, or public corporation in Germany or abroad with an interest in the advancement of science can obtain membership. The MPG's sponsorship of these supporting members is an essential guarantee of its independence from undue governmental influence and a demonstration of its societal basis. At the start of 1994, 515 private and 485 corporate members belonged to it.

The societal basis of the MPG is further underscored by its self-administration and scientific autonomy. The society's organizational framework reflects a highly differentiated decision-making process with checks and balances. Its main body, the General Assembly of its members,

(Top) Karl-Hermann Tacke, Institute for Iron Research; (bottom) Wolfgang Filser

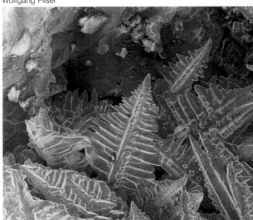

Dendrites (right), microscopic structures that form as steel solidifies, are studied at the Institute for Iron Research, Düsseldorf. (Below) A dye laser developed at the Institute for Biophysical Chemistry, Göttingen, has uses in pollution analysis and stratospheric ozone research.

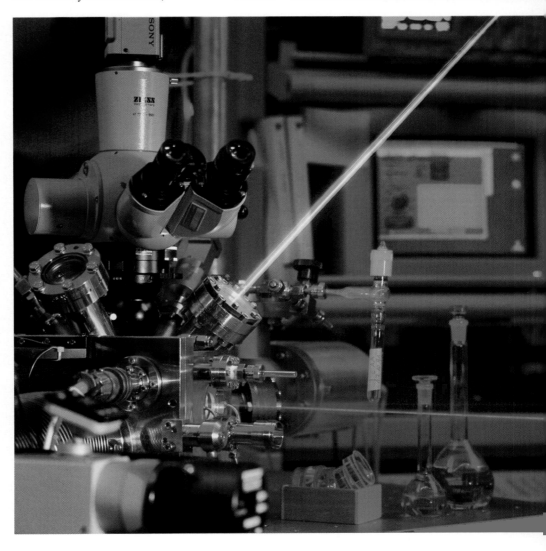

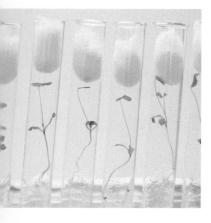

Wolfgang Filser

is responsible for the entire structure of the organization, especially for the resolution of amendments to the society's statutes and the election of its senators. The Senate, the society's central policy-making body, elects the president and the members of the Executive Committee. It also appoints the MPG's scientific members; deals with budgetary matters; makes decisions regarding the foundation, closure, and reorganization of Max Planck institutes (or parts of them); and has the responsibility for approving or amending the institutes' statutes. In order to represent the public and to broaden the basis of its decisions, the Senate includes elected members in addition to official representatives of the MPG: scientists from within and outside the society, representatives of the German states and the federal government, and outstanding individuals from in-

dustry or other spheres of society.

The MPG is headed by its president, who during a six-year term represents the society, drafts the fundamental aspects of its policy, and ensures the smooth running of its internal decision-making process. The names of the MPG's presidents testify to this demanding commitment as well as to the successful history of German science: Adolf von Harnack, Max Planck, Carl Bosch, Albert Vögler, Otto Hahn, Adolf Butenandt, Reimar Lüst, Heinz A. Staab, and, presently, Hans F. Zacher. As chairman of the General Assembly and the Senate, the president has full executive responsibility. He also chairs the Executive Committee, which, as prescribed by German law for this kind of association, acts together with the secretary-general as a board of trustees. A head office, located in Munich, attends to the society's day-to-day work and helps the various bodies fulfill their duties.

The heart of the MPG is the scientific life in its institutions. Scientists who are appointed by the Senate to lead Max Planck institutes, either solely or with colleagues, are

264

Studies of leguminous crops grown in vitro (opposite page, far left), Mendelian inheritance in maize, or corn (opposite page, bottom), and cross breeding of barley in the field (right) are representative of activities carried out at the Institute for Plant Breeding Research, Cologne. (This page) An institute scientist in a wheat field planted with hybrids checks plants for desired characteristics. The search for new combinations of genes that will improve cereal crops is still largely conducted by means of conventional crossbreeding studies. When interesting gene combinations appear in the offspring of selected parental pairs, thousands of third-, fourth-, and fifth-generation plants must be cultivated in the field and evaluated.

autonomous in their research endeavors. An institute director works free of preconditions regarding the research program, choice of staff, or limitations on time. Every institute is supported by an internationally composed advisory board, which assists the institute in defining its research objectives and carrying out its work. The board also assesses the relevance and the success of the research activities of an institute in regular reports to the president.

All scientific members are related to one of the three sections described above. For MPG decisions that require scientific competence, especially the appointment of future scientific members, recommendations are prepared by the sections, which together form the MPG's Scientific Council. Owing to the

(Above, inset, and left) photos, Wolfgang Filser

265

Daphnia, tiny algae-eating crustaceans, are sampled at different depths from a German lake in research at the Institute for Limnology, Plön. Studies show that lake fish indirectly affect the amount of algae in the lake's upper layers and hence the water clarity. Daytime feeding by the fish on *Daphnia* forces the crustaceans to retreat to the lake's bottom waters during the day and limit their own feeding to nighttime hours.

Wolfgang Filser

high standards required of the society's personnel, future scientific members are appointed only after passing a rigorous peer review.

AN INTERNATIONAL REACH

Reflecting the idea that the human endeavor to know more and more transcends national boundaries, the activities of the MPG are internationally oriented. Of 218 directors of institutes or departments in 1994, 33 (about one in seven) were from abroad, representing 16 different countries. Ninety-three Americans and 169 Europeans from outside Germany numbered among the 453 members of the advisory boards. Nearly half of the so-called external scientific members, which are loosely bound to the institutes, were foreign scientists. Financed by the MPG to a total figure of DM 25 million ($16 million), more than 2,100 foreign guest scientists, scholarship holders, and doctoral students from more than 60 countries stayed at Max Planck institutes in 1993. Moreover, nearly 3,000 Max Planck researchers annually take the opportunity to conduct science outside Germany with the help of funds from the society or other sources.

Photos, Wolfgang Filser

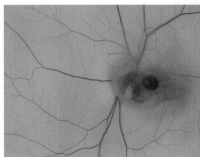

The list of frontier-crossing cooperative science is long. Researchers in some 50 countries work with Max Planck colleagues on a fairly informal basis. There also exist long-term cooperative programs based on written agreements, such as the Institute for Millimeter Astronomy, Grenoble, France, which is jointly financed and managed by the MPG and research organizations in France and Spain; the Calar Alto Observatory jointly operated with Spain; and the cooperative venture with British, French, and Scandinavian research organizations on the investigation of the Earth's ionosphere within the framework of the European Incoherent Scatter Scientific Association (EISCAT), Kiruna, Sweden. Outside Europe the society maintains close scientific relations with the U.S., China, and Israel.

FUNDING

Over the past 80 years, the ways of financing the Max Planck Society and its predecessor have changed radically. When the Kaiser Wilhelm Society was founded in 1911, it existed on private donations supplemented to a limited extent by governmental support. During the economic crisis of the Weimar Republic, as the German government was called between 1919 and 1933, public sources of funding became increasingly more important. In 1949 the new MPG received a solid financial basis through the support of the state governments, which at the time were regarded as the main sponsors of science. Later, owing to the growing

At the Institute for Biochemistry, Martinsried, a bloodsucking insect that carries Chagas' disease (top) is studied for its response to natural insecticides. Observations of blood-vessel formation in bird embryos (above) at the Institute for Physiological and Clinical Research, Bad Nauheim, offer insight into early development.

DNA fragments that have been separated according to size and labeled with fluorescent dyes stand out under ultraviolet (UV) light as glowing bands in a sheet of gel. A face mask shields the researcher, a scientist of the Institute for Biochemistry, from harmful UV exposure.

Wolfgang Filser

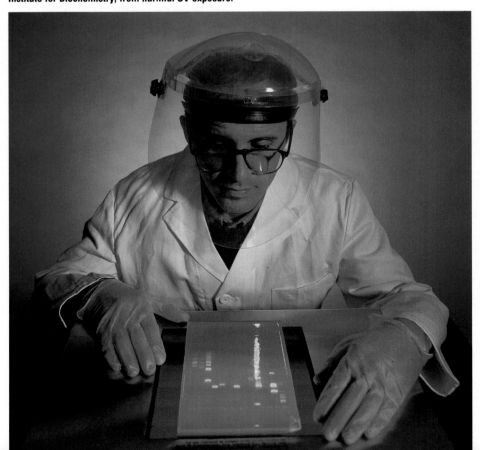

Retinal cells are observed under a microscope in a patch-clamp measuring station at the Institute for Biophysical Chemistry. The patch-clamp technique, which allows scientists to measure tiny electrical currents associated with individual ion channels in cell membranes, earned MPG researchers Erwin Neher and Bert Sakmann a Nobel Prize in 1991.

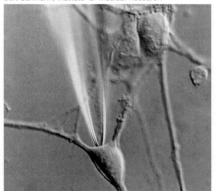

A hollow glass pipette with a microscopically small tip is the key to the patch-clamp technique. When the tip is sealed against the surface of a single cell (left), it electrically isolates a portion of the cell membrane and the ion channels within it for study.

influence of the federal government in R&D, institutional support for the MPG came to be split equally between the states and the federal government, an arrangement that became fixed by agreement in 1975. In 1993 the society's institutional support accounted for 88% of the MPG's total budget of DM 1.6 billion, 6.3% of the budget was financed through funds earmarked for scientific projects, and another 5.7% came from other income.

The MPG receives only a marginal part of the whole financial support for R&D in Germany. In fact, its annual budget is comparable to that of two or three large German universities. In 1992, for example, total R&D expenditures in Germany amounted to DM 80.6 billion ($50 million), of which industry provided about 60%. The MPG's share of that total was 1.8%.

RECENT SCIENTIFIC HIGHLIGHTS

As of 1994, Nobel Prizes had been bestowed on 28 scientists of the KWG and MPG. The most recent winners, Erwin Neher and Bert Sakmann, received the 1991 Nobel Prize for Physiology or Medicine for the patch-clamp technique, whose development and use they pioneered in the 1970s at the Max Planck Institute for Biophysical Chemistry, Göttingen. The patch-clamp technique marked the beginning of a new era in cell biology, making it possible for the first time to take individual, detailed measurements of tiny electrical currents in the form of streams of ions (electrically charged atoms) as they pass through the cell membrane. These streams, only billionths of an ampere in magnitude and lasting only thousandths of a second, flow into or out

of cells through minute pores, or channels, that are controlled by special proteins in the membrane. The streams transfer signals between cells and help govern their physiological functions; *e.g.,* the conduction of nerve impulses or the release of hormones.

In order to monitor this electrical flow, Neher and Sakmann developed glass pipettes with fine tips a thousandth of a millimeter in diameter. When a pipette tip is pressed against the cell membrane, it forms a tight seal and isolates the ion channels in that portion of the membrane for study. With the aid of the patch-clamp technique, researchers have discovered the roles that ion channels play in such diseases as cystic fibrosis, diabetes, epilepsy, and certain neuromuscular disorders.

Remarkable scientific progress took place at the Max Planck Institute for Biochemistry, Martinsried, in the 1980s, when a group of young researchers succeeded in revealing the exact molecular structure of the photosynthetic reaction center in purple bacteria. The reaction center is a membrane-embedded protein complex with which the bacteria, in a way similar to photosynthesis in plants, convert sunlight into chemical energy, which then is used to

power vital cellular processes such as growth, repair, and reproduction. Since knowledge of a protein's structure reveals much about its function, it became possible to understand key processes in photosynthesis step-by-step—processes that had been known only indirectly or partially. The reaction center was the first membrane-bound protein to be isolated and crystallized; at that time it was also the most complex molecule whose structure was determined with the help of X-ray diffraction, a technique for deducing the positions of individual atoms in a crystallized substance from the way that the atoms scatter a beam of X-rays. Johann Deisenhofer, Robert Huber, and Hartmut Michel received the 1988 Nobel Prize for Chemistry in recognition of their achievement.

The program at the Max Planck Institute for Quantum Optics, Garching, covers a broad spectrum of research in which lasers serve as both subjects of study and the main tools of experiments. Laser-based research recently achieved an extremely precise determination of the Lamb shift in the energy levels of the ground, or unexcited, states of the hydrogen and deuterium atoms—a key measurement for quantum electrodynamics,

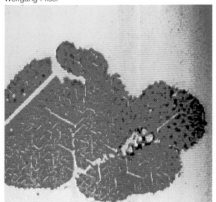

Wolfgang Filser

Cell-wall details of the purple bacterium are revealed in false color by scanning tunneling microscopy. Studies of the bacterium's photosynthetic reaction center brought a Nobel Prize to three MPG researchers in 1988.

the modern theory that describes all the interactions of electromagnetic radiation with matter and of charged particles with each other. Another important numerical value associated with the interactions of radiation and atoms, the Rydberg constant, was determined with an accuracy better than that of any other fundamental constant in physics. Yet another recent achievement in investigations of radiation-atom interactions is the one-atom maser, or micromaser, with which scientists can study the ideal case of the interaction of a single atom with a single quantized packet of electromagnetic energy—a single photon—in a confining cavity. A final example of the institute's research activities is the investigation of small numbers of atoms and ions held in special electromagnetic traps. In those experiments laser radiation is used to slow the particles down, cooling them to temperatures only a mil-

lionth of a degree above absolute zero. In experiments involving ions, researchers have observed the trapped particles undergoing transitions between a disordered cloud and an ordered array resembling the atoms in a solid crystal.

The program at the Max Planck Institute for Meteorology, Hamburg, stands as an example of research focused on environmental problems. Scientists are concerned that during the coming decades the world's climate will change as a result of an additional greenhouse effect caused by rising levels of carbon dioxide and other trace gases in the atmosphere. One of the most urgent tasks confronting current climate research is to predict correctly the extent of such changes in climate. For this purpose, climate models must be developed that make it possible to simulate on computers the complex interplay of atmosphere, ocean, land and ice masses, and the bio-

sphere. On an international level the Institute for Meteorology holds a leading position in this field. After having developed "coupled" models, which for the first time reproduce the interplay between ocean and atmosphere quite realistically, scientists at the institute have been working to add the global circulation of carbon dioxide to the mix. Institute work also has focused on improved understanding of cloud formation and the role that clouds play in climate and on including those aspects in the models.

Understanding the nature and activity of the Sun, a question that has intrigued human beings since the earliest times, is the special concern of the international GALLEX collaboration led by the Max Planck Institute for Nuclear Physics, Heidelberg. The Sun is central to us as the primary source of energy for life on Earth and for the environment that makes Earth hospitable to life, yet it is also a prototype for most stars in the universe. Well-founded theoretical models describe the Sun as a massive ball of gas that is ionized in its dense core and produces energy by means of the nuclear fusion of hydrogen into helium. As plausible as the models may be, they have never been checked by

direct observation since the solar core is totally inaccessible. Only one type of particle produced in the Sun's fusion reactions, the neutrino, leaves the Sun freely. By monitoring the rate at which neutrinos arrive at the Earth and comparing it with predictions from the models, scientists can gain some idea about whether their picture of the solar interior is correct.

The GALLEX detector, operated by an international collaboration working at an underground laboratory in the Gran Sasso Tunnel in Italy, aims to verify the theory of solar energy production and to explore fundamental properties of neutrinos. In a reaction vessel containing 30 tons of the rare metal gallium, solar neutrinos convert gallium atoms into radioactive germanium atoms at a rate of only a few per month. The germanium atoms are then chemically separated from the gallium and analyzed by means of extremely sensitive radiation detectors. The experiment is protected from the interfering cosmic rays by 1,200 meters (3,900 feet) of overlying rocks. Since 1991 the experiment has succeeded in general in finding the neutrinos expected from the Sun's nuclear processes and thus has helped to confirm theoretical ideas with experimental facts. Nevertheless, the rate of neutrino detection is smaller than expected. Some theorists interpret this shortfall as evidence that neutrinos, which come in three types, may be able to change from one type to another while traveling from the Sun to Earth and so possibly escape detection. The ability to change between types, however, requires that neutrinos have a small rest mass (rather than the zero rest mass heretofore accepted)—an implication of major importance for particle physics.

Investigation beyond the Earth is another pursuit of the MPG, which has the primary responsibility for the astronomical and astrophysical research conducted in Germany. For instance, work at the Max Planck Institute for Extraterrestrial Physics, with locations in Garching and Adlershof, encompasses studies of the Earth's nearer environments—its ionosphere and magnetosphere and the realm of interplanetary space—and more distant astronomical observations in those regions of the electromagnetic spectrum

that, because of the absorbing effect of the Earth's atmosphere, are accessible only from outer space: infrared, X-ray, and gamma radiation. A special project of recent years was the development of a large imaging X-ray telescope for the Earth-orbiting astronomical satellite ROSAT. A German-U.K.-U.S. collaboration, ROSAT was launched into space in June 1990 in order to measure X-ray emission and the temperature distribution in the Milky Way Galaxy and beyond. The 60,000 X-ray

sources surveyed by ROSAT will form the pillar of X-ray astronomy for the coming decades. X-ray data from ROSAT, for example, will add to knowledge of the nature of young stars, particularly the activity at the star's surface and in its atmosphere, and of the structure of the cold, dense gas that lies between the stars of the Milky Way.

POURING OUT ITS BLESSING

Over the course of the 20th century, the world's perceptions of the value and functions of science have changed greatly. The Max Planck Society has also changed to meet new demands and to pursue new directions of inquiry, but its founding philosophy has remained largely the same. It is this philosophy—that society and industry can prosper from an efficient, disciplined nurturing of basic science—to which the MPG confidently

A dye laser at the Institute for Quantum Optics, Garching, is used in experiments in which magnesium ions are confined in a special electromagnetic trap and cooled to temperatures a tiny fraction of a degree above absolute zero.

Wolfgang Filser

(Top) Deutsche Aerospace; (bottom) Institute for Extraterrestrial Physics

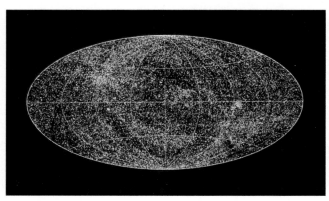

The ROSAT observatory (above), launched in June 1990, included a large imaging X-ray telescope developed at the Institute for Extraterrestrial Physics, Garching. ROSAT's all-sky survey yielded a map of some 60,000 X-ray sources (left). Colors represent the comparative "hardness" of the radiation from a given source, red being less energetic (softer) X-rays and blue being more energetic (harder) X-rays.

looks for its continued success. In view of today's debate over the societal and economic relevance of curiosity-driven basic research, it is enlightening to cite a central passage of Harnack's 1909 memorandum:

> Organic chemistry, which was without doubt the domain of chemistry laboratories at German universities until a short time ago, has now moved from there to large factory laboratories almost completely. This entire line of research to a large extent is thus lost for pure science, for factories always continue this research only as long as it promises practical results, and they guard these results as a secret or patent them. Support of science by laboratories at individual factories operating with very ample funds can, therefore, seldom be expected. The contrary, however, has always been apparent, and industry itself is aware of this fact: pure science has given the greatest support to industry by exploring really advanced fields of research. . . . Humboldt's words continue to be accurate: "Science often pours out its richest blessing on life when it would seem to be removed from life."

update

ENCYCLOPÆDIA BRITANNICA SCIENCE

Major Revisions from the 1995 *Macropædia*

The purpose of this section is to introduce to continuing *Yearbook of Science and the Future* subscribers selected *Macropædia* articles or portions of them that have been revised or written anew. It is intended to update the *Macropædia* in ways that cannot be accomplished fully by reviewing the year's events or by revising statistics annually, because the *Macropædia* texts themselves—written from a longer perspective than any yearly revision—supply authoritative interpretation and analysis as well as narrative and description.

Sections from two articles have been chosen from the 1995 printing: CHEMICAL BONDING and ELECTRONICS. Each is the work of distinguished scholars, and each represents the continuing dedication of the *Encyclopædia Britannica* to bringing such works to the general reader.

Chemical Bonding

Bonds between atoms

It has been shown that, for reasons related to the energy requirements for electron removal or addition, only the electrons in valence shells play a significant role in the formation of bonds between atoms. Henceforth this article will concentrate on these electrons alone. Lewis introduced the conventions of representing valence electrons by dots arranged around the chemical symbol of the element, as in H·, Na·, and ·Cl:, and of discussing bond formation as the transfer of dots from one symbol to another. This seemingly simplistic device turns out to be very useful for establishing the characteristics of chemical bonds and will be examined in this section.

THE FORMATION OF IONIC BONDS

Electron transfer

Lewis formulation of an ionic bond. In Lewis terms, the formation of an ionic bond stems from the transfer of electrons from one atom to another. When such a transfer occurs, all the valence electrons on the more electropositive element (from one of the first three groups on the left in the periodic table) are removed to expose the core of the atom. The electrons so released are accepted into the empty orbitals of the valence shell of the more electronegative atom (typically from the groups immediately to the left of the noble gases); the valence shell is thereby filled. Thus, the formation of the ionic compound sodium chloride can be represented by the following process:
The formation of aluminum oxide (alumina) involves

$$Na\cdot\ \cdot\ddot{C}l: \longrightarrow Na^+ :\ddot{C}l:^-$$

selecting enough aluminum and oxygen atoms to ensure that all the electrons released by the aluminum atoms (three from each one) are accommodated by oxygen atoms (each of which can accept two electrons):
(The numbers of atoms required to balance the electrons

$$2\dot{A}l\cdot\ \ 3:\ddot{O}\cdot \longrightarrow 2Al^{3+}\ \ 3:\ddot{O}:^{2-}$$

donated and accepted is indicated by the chemical formula Al_2O_3 for aluminum oxide.)

That the transfer of electrons represented by these diagrams leads to a lowering of energy can be checked by assessing the energies associated with them. There is more to the process than a straightforward consideration of ionization energy and electron affinity. The ionization energy of sodium is larger than the electron affinity of chlorine, so energy is required to remove an electron from a sodium atom and attach it to a chlorine atom. That is, at first sight it appears that the total energy of a Na^+ ion and a Cl^- ion is greater than that of a sodium atom and a chlorine atom. If that were the case, then it would be hard to understand how sodium chloride could be a stable species relative to a gas of sodium and chlorine atoms.

There are in fact two errors in such a simple approach. First, the argument has ignored the favourable energy of interaction between the cation and the anion. The net energy of formation of a Na^+ ion and a Cl^- ion is the sum of three terms. The first is the energy investment needed to ionize a sodium atom. The second is a somewhat smaller energy that is released when the electron from the sodium atom attaches to a chlorine atom. At this stage, the net energy change is positive, indicating a higher energy than for the two atoms. However, because there is an attraction between opposite charges, there is a further release of energy as a result of the interaction of the two ions. This additional favourable contribution to the energy varies with the separation of the ions and strengthens as the two ions approach one another. Thus, at large separations the neutral atoms have the lowest energy, but as the two atoms are brought together a point is reached at which the lowest total energy is obtained if an electron transfers from the sodium atom to the chlorine atom. At this distance, and

Energy of ion-ion interaction

at shorter distances, Na^+Cl^- is the lower-energy species.

The second feature omitted from the argument is that an ionic compound does not consist of an isolated cation and anion. An ionic compound is typically a solid formed from an array of alternating cations and anions (Figure 7). The packing of ions together and their electrostatic interactions with one another account for the typical features of ionic compounds—namely, their brittleness and high melting points. Moreover, when studying the stability of such compounds, one should more appropriately consider the energy changes associated with their formation from the elements in their standard state (such as solid metallic sodium and gaseous chlorine molecules) than from a gas of atoms of the elements.

The Born-Haber cycle. The analysis of the formation of an ionic compound from its elements is commonly discussed in terms of a Born-Haber cycle, which breaks the overall process into a series of steps of known energy. The Born-Haber cycle for the formation of sodium chloride is shown in Figure 8. At the start of the cycle, the elements are considered to be in the form in which they exist at normal pressure and temperature. First, sodium metal is vaporized to a gas of sodium atoms. This step requires an input of energy known as the atomization energy of sodium metal. Next, the appropriate number of chlorine molecules (Cl_2) are broken apart to provide a gas of chlorine atoms. This step also requires a considerable input of energy that is called the dissociation energy of chlorine. The origin of these two contributions to the energy can be clarified by considering metallic and covalent bonding in more detail (specifically, the lowering of energy that occurs when metallic or covalent bonds form); here they can be treated as empirical quantities. At this stage, an electron is removed from each sodium atom and attached to each chlorine atom. The ionization requires a considerable input of energy, and a fraction of that investment is recovered from the electron affinity of the chlorine atoms. Overall, however, there is a considerable increase in energy as compared to the two starting materials.

At this stage, the ions are allowed to come together to form a crystalline array. This step releases a large quantity of energy called the lattice energy of the compound. Energy is released in the process of crystal formation because first a cation becomes surrounded by anions, then that cluster of anions becomes surrounded by cations, and so on. As a result of this packing, every cation has anions as neighbours, and every anion has cations around it (as depicted in Figure 7), and there is a strong overall attractive

Lattice energy

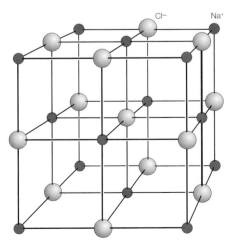

Figure 7: *The crystal structure of sodium chloride in the common mineral form known as rock salt.* Each sodium cation (Na^+) is surrounded by six chloride anions (Cl^-) and vice versa. The small spheres mark the centres of the ions; the ions virtually fill the available volume.

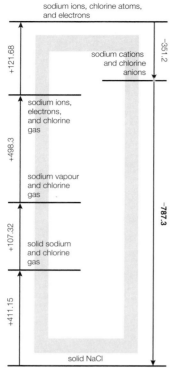

sodium ions, chlorine atoms, and electrons

+121.68

-351.2

sodium cations and chlorine anions

sodium ions, electrons, and chlorine gas

+498.3

sodium vapour and chlorine gas

-787.3

+107.32

solid sodium and chlorine gas

+411.15

solid NaCl

Figure 8: *The Born-Haber cycle for the formation of solid sodium chloride from solid sodium and chlorine gas.* The energies involved (strictly, the enthalpies) are expressed in kilojoules per mole.

interaction among the many ions of opposite charge in the crystal. For sodium chloride, the lattice energy is so great that more energy is released in this step than is required for all the preceding steps combined, and solid sodium chloride therefore has a lower energy than sodium metal and chlorine gas. It is for this reason that, when sodium reacts with chlorine, a large quantity of heat is released.

Factors favouring ionic bonding. A Born-Haber cycle gives an indication of the factors that favour ionic bonding. Overall, the lattice energy must be great enough to overcome the energy required for ion formation. It follows that only elements with reasonably low ionization energies can contribute, as cations, to ionic materials, for too large an ionization energy could not be recovered from the resulting lattice energy. In practice, this criterion means that only metallic elements are likely to form cations, and two elements are unlikely to form an ionic compound unless one of them is a metal. Moreover, the steep increase in ionization energy required to break into a closed shell precludes the loss of all but the valence electrons. Furthermore, no more than about three electrons per atom can be lost before the increase in ionization energy becomes prohibitive.

It can also be seen from the Born-Haber cycle that elements will contribute anions to an ionic compound only if their electron affinity is positive or, at least, not too strongly negative. Elements with positive electron affinities are likely to form anions (as long as a metal is present). A negative electron affinity can be tolerated provided it is not too great and the additional energy investment can be recovered from a greater lattice energy. That is the reason why ionic oxides are so common: although energy is required to push the second electron on an oxygen atom to make an O^{2-} ion, the resulting ion produces such a high lattice energy that the energy investment is overcome.

Ionic bonding is likely to occur if the lattice energy of the compound is large, for a large lattice energy can compensate for some strongly demanding energy requirements, most notably for cation formation, earlier in the cycle. High lattice energies are achieved if the ions that form the lattice are small and highly charged, for small ions can pack together closely and interact strongly with one another. The O^{2-} ion of oxides is small (oxygen lies well to the right in the periodic table) and is reasonably highly charged (it has two negative charges; three negative charges is about the limit for monatomic anions). As a result, ionic oxides are widely formed by metallic elements. Although it is conceivable that O^{3-} ions could be formed if enough energy were provided to overcome the repulsion from the many electrons present in O^{2-}, the necessary energy would not be recovered from the lattice energy, for O^{3-} anions are so large that the lattice energy of any compound they would form would be small. Once again, the termination of electron gain at a noble gas configuration is not so much a sign of some magic stability of such a species but rather a consequence of the fact that after such a configuration has been attained there is insufficient opportunity for achieving a lower energy.

The actual pattern in which cations and anions pack together is the one that results in the greatest lattice energy (that is, the greatest lowering of energy of the ions relative to the gas of ions). The arrangement shown in Figure 7 is adopted by sodium chloride and a number of other compounds. More complex arrangements are adopted by species such as aluminum oxide. For further details on crystal arrangements, see MATTER: *Solid state: Crystalline solids.*

Crystal arrangements

COVALENT BONDS

When none of the elements in a compound is a metal, no atoms in the compound have an ionization energy low enough for electron loss to be likely. In such a case, covalence prevails. As a general rule, covalent bonds are formed between elements lying toward the right in the periodic table (*i.e.*, the nonmetals). Molecules of identical atoms, such as H_2 and buckminsterfullerene (C_{60}), are also held together by covalent bonds.

Lewis formulation of a covalent bond. In Lewis terms a covalent bond is a shared electron pair. The bond between a hydrogen atom and a chlorine atom in hydrogen chloride is formulated as follows:

$$H\cdot \ \cdot\ddot{\underset{\cdot\cdot}{Cl}}: \longrightarrow H:\ddot{\underset{\cdot\cdot}{Cl}}:$$

In a Lewis structure of a covalent compound, the shared electron pair is represented by a line, so the Lewis structure of hydrogen chloride is denoted $H-\ddot{\underset{\cdot\cdot}{Cl}}:$. The electron pair represented by the line is called a bonding pair; the three other pairs of electrons on the chlorine atom are called lone pairs and play no direct role in holding the two atoms together.

Each atom in the hydrogen chloride molecule attains a closed-shell octet of electrons by sharing and hence achieves a maximum lowering of energy. In general, an incomplete shell means that some attracting power of a nucleus may be wasted, and adding electrons beyond a closed shell would entail the energetic disadvantage of beginning the next shell of the atom concerned. Lewis' octet rule is again applicable and is seen to represent the extreme means of achieving lower energy rather than being a goal in itself.

A covalent bond forms if the bonded atoms have a lower total energy than the widely separated atoms. The simplest interpretation of the decrease in energy that occurs when electrons are shared is that both electrons lie between two attracting centres (the nuclei of the two atoms linked by the bond) and hence lie lower in energy than when they experience the attraction of a single centre. This explanation, however, requires considerable modification to capture the full truth about bonding, and it will be discussed further below when bonding is considered in terms of quantum mechanics.

Lewis structures of more complex molecules can be constructed quite simply by extending the process that has been described for hydrogen chloride. First, the valence electrons that are available for bonding are counted ($2 \times 1 + 6 = 8$ in H_2O, for example, and $4 + 4 \times 7 = 32$ in carbon tetrachloride, CCl_4), and the chemical symbols for the elements are placed in the arrangement that reflects which are neighbours:

Construct- ing Lewis structures

$$H \quad O \quad H \qquad\qquad Cl \quad C \quad Cl$$

with Cl above and below the C.

Next, one bonding pair is added between each linked pair of atoms:

$$H:O:H \qquad\qquad Cl:C:Cl$$

The remaining electrons are then added to the atoms in such a way that each atom has a share in an octet of electrons (this is the octet-rule part of the procedure):

$$H:\ddot{O}:H \qquad\qquad :\ddot{Cl}:\ddot{C}:\ddot{Cl}:$$

Finally, each bonding pair is represented by a dash:

$$H-\ddot{O}-H \qquad\qquad :\ddot{Cl}-C-\ddot{Cl}:$$

(Note that Lewis structures do not necessarily show the actual shape of the molecule, only the topological pattern of their bonds.)

In some older formulations of Lewis structures, a distinction was made between bonds formed by electrons that have been supplied by both atoms (as in H—Cl, where one shared electron can be regarded as supplied by the hydrogen atom and the other by the chlorine atom) and covalent bonds formed when both electrons can be regarded as supplied by one atom, as in the formation of OH⁻ from O²⁻ and H⁺. Such a bond was called a coordinate covalent bond or a dative bond and symbolized O → H⁻. However, the difficulties encountered in the attempt to keep track of the origin of bonding electrons and the suggestion that a coordinate covalent bond differs somehow from a covalent bond (it does not) have led to this usage falling into disfavour.

Coordinate covalent bond

Advanced aspects of Lewis structures. The Lewis structures illustrated so far have been selected for their simplicity. A number of elaborations are given below.

Multiple bonds. First, an atom may complete its octet by sharing more than one pair of electrons with a bonded neighbour. Two shared pairs of electrons, represented by a double dash (=), form a double bond. Double bonds are found in numerous compounds, including carbon dioxide:

$$\ddot{O}=C=\ddot{O}$$

Three shared pairs of electrons are represented by a triple dash (≡) and form a triple bond. Triple bonds are found in, for example, carbon monoxide, nitrogen molecules, and acetylene, shown, respectively, as:

$$:C≡O: \qquad :N≡N: \qquad H-C≡C-H$$

A double bond is stronger than a single bond, and a triple bond is stronger than a double bond. However, a double bond is not necessarily twice as strong as a single bond, nor is a triple bond necessarily three times as strong. Quadruple bonds, which contain four shared pairs of electrons, are rare but have been identified in some compounds in which two metal atoms are bonded directly together.

Resonance. There is sometimes an ambiguity in the location of double bonds. This ambiguity is illustrated by the Lewis structure for ozone (O₃). The following are two possible structures:

$$:\ddot{O}-\ddot{O}=\ddot{O} \qquad\qquad \ddot{O}=\ddot{O}-\ddot{O}:$$

In such cases, the actual Lewis structure is regarded as a blend of these contributions and is written:

$$:\ddot{O}-\ddot{O}=\ddot{O} \longleftrightarrow \ddot{O}=\ddot{O}-\ddot{O}:$$

The blending together of these structures is actually a quantum mechanical phenomenon called resonance, which will be considered in more detail below. At this stage, resonance can be regarded as a blending process

that spreads double-bond character evenly over the atoms that participate in it. In ozone, for instance, each oxygen-oxygen bond is rendered equivalent by resonance, and each one has a mixture of single-bond and double-bond character (as indicated by its length and strength).

Hypervalence. Lewis structures and the octet rule jointly offer a succinct indication of the type of bonding that occurs in molecules and show the pattern of single and multiple bonds between the atoms. There are many compounds, however, that do not conform to the octet rule. The most common exceptions to the octet rule are the so-called hypervalent compounds. These are species in which there are more atoms attached to a central atom than can be accommodated by an octet of electrons. An example is sulfur hexafluoride, SF₆, for which writing a Lewis structure with six S—F bonds requires that at least 12 electrons be present around the sulfur atom:

$$F \cdots S \cdots F$$

(Only the bonding electrons are shown here.) In Lewis terms, hypervalence requires the expansion of the octet to 10, 12, and even in some cases 16 electrons. Hypervalent compounds are very common and in general are no less stable than compounds that conform to the octet rule.

The existence of hypervalent compounds would appear to deal a severe blow to the validity of the octet rule and Lewis' approach to covalent bonding if the expansion of the octet could not be rationalized or its occurrence predicted. Fortunately, it can be rationalized, and the occurrence of hypervalence can be anticipated. In simple terms, experience has shown that hypervalence is rare in periods 1 and 2 of the periodic table (through neon) but is common in and after period 3. Thus, the octet rule can be used with confidence for carbon, nitrogen, oxygen, and fluorine, but hypervalence must be anticipated thereafter. The conventional explanation of this distinction takes note of the fact that, in period-3 elements, the valence shell has $n = 3$, and this is the first shell in which d orbitals are available. (As noted above, these orbitals are occupied after the $4s$ orbitals have been filled and account for the occurrence of the transition metals in period 4.) It is therefore argued that atoms of this and subsequent periods can utilize the empty d orbitals to accommodate electrons beyond an octet and hence permit the formation of hypervalent species.

In chemistry, however, it is important not to allow mere correlations to masquerade as explanations. Although it is true that d orbitals are energetically accessible in elements that display hypervalence, it does not follow that they are responsible for it. Indeed, quantum mechanical theories of the chemical bond do not need to invoke d-orbital involvement. These theories suggest that hypervalence is probably no more than a consequence of the greater radii of the atoms of period-3 elements compared with those of period 2, with the result that a central atom can pack more atoms around itself. Thus, hypervalence is more a steric (geometric) problem than an outcome of d-orbital availability. How six atoms can be bonded to a central atom by fewer than six pairs of electrons is discussed below.

Incomplete-octet compounds. Less common than hypervalent compounds, but by no means rare, are species in which an atom does not achieve an octet of electrons. Such compounds are called incomplete-octet compounds. An example is the compound boron trifluoride, BF₃, which is used as an industrial catalyst. The boron (B) atom supplies three valence electrons, and a representation of the compound's structure is:

Boron trifluoride

$$:\ddot{F}-B-\ddot{F}: \quad (\ddot{F} \text{ above})$$

The boron atom has a share in only six valence electrons. It is possible to write Lewis structures that do satisfy the octet rule.

$$:\ddot{F}=B-\ddot{F}: \qquad :\ddot{F}-B-\ddot{F}: \qquad :\ddot{F}-B=\ddot{F}:$$

However, whereas in the incomplete octet structure the fluorine atoms have three lone pairs, in these resonance structures one fluorine atom has only two lone pairs, so it has partly surrendered an electron to the boron atom. This is energetically disadvantageous for such an electronegative element as fluorine (which is in fact the most electronegative element), and the three octet structures turn out to have a higher energy than the incomplete-octet structure. The latter is therefore a better representation of the actual structure of the molecule. Indeed, it is exactly because the BF₃ molecule has an incomplete-octet structure that it is so widely employed as a catalyst, for it can use the vacancies in the valence shell of the boron atom to form bonds to other atoms and thereby facilitate certain chemical reactions.

Electron-deficient compounds. Another type of exception to the Lewis approach to bonding is the existence of compounds that possess too few electrons for a Lewis structure to be written. Such compounds are called electron-deficient compounds. A prime example of an electron-deficient compound is diborane, B₂H₆. This compound requires at least seven bonds to link its eight atoms together, but it has only $2 \times 3 + 6 \times 1 = 12$ valence electrons, which is enough to form only six covalent bonds. Once again, it appears that, as in hypervalent compounds, the existence of electron-deficient compounds signifies that a pair of electrons can bond together more than two atoms. The discussion of the quantum mechanical theory of bonding below shows that this is indeed the case.

A number of exceptions to Lewis' theory of bonding have been catalogued here. It has further deficiencies. For example, the theory is not quantitative and gives no clue to how the strengths of bonds or their lengths can be assessed. In the form in which it has been presented, it also fails to suggest the shapes of molecules. Furthermore, the theory offers no justification for regarding an electron pair as the central feature of a covalent bond. Indeed, there are species that possess bonds that rely on the presence of a single electron. (The one-electron transient species H₂⁺ is an example.) Nevertheless, in spite of these difficulties, Lewis' approach to bonding has proved exceptionally useful. It predicts when the octet rule is likely to be valid and when hypervalence can be anticipated, and the occurrence of multiple bonds and the presence of lone pairs of electrons correlate with the chemical properties of a wide variety of species. Lewis' approach is still widely used as a rule of thumb for assessing the structures and properties of covalent species, and modern quantum mechanical theories echo its general content.

The following sections discuss how the limitations of Lewis' approach can be overcome, first by extending the theory to account for molecular shapes and then by developing more thorough quantum mechanical theories of the chemical bond.

MOLECULAR SHAPES AND VSEPR THEORY

There is a sharp distinction between ionic and covalent bonds when the geometric arrangements of atoms in compounds are considered. In essence, ionic bonding is nondirectional, whereas covalent bonding is directional. That is, in ionic compounds there is no intrinsically preferred direction in which a neighbour should lie for the strength of bonding to be maximized. In contrast, in a covalently bonded compound, the atoms adopt specific locations relative to one another, as in the tetrahedral arrangement of hydrogen atoms around the central carbon atom in methane, CH₄, or the angular arrangement of atoms in H₂O.

The lack of directionality of ionic bonds stems from the isotropy (spherical symmetry) of the electrostatic forces between ions. As has already been pointed out, the result of this isotropy is that ions stack together in the locations necessary to achieve the lowest energy and in this way give rise to the common packing patterns characteristic of many ionic solids. When deviations from stacking schemes are observed that seem to indicate that the ions are being held in certain orientations relative to their neighbours, it is a sign that covalent bonding is beginning to influence the structure of the solid and that the bonding

Direction-ality of bonds *(margin note)*

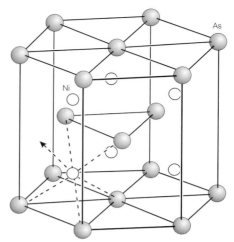

Figure 9: *The crystal structure of nickel arsenide.* This type of structure departs strongly from that expected for ionic bonding and shows the importance of covalence. There is also some direct nickel-nickel bonding that tends to draw the nickel atoms together.

is not purely ionic. This is the case, for example, in the compound nickel arsenide (NiAs), which has a structure that suggests that a degree of covalent bonding is present (Figure 9). It is fully apparent in the structure of diamond (Figure 10), in which each carbon atom is in a tetrahedral position relative to its neighbour and in which the bonding is essentially purely covalent.

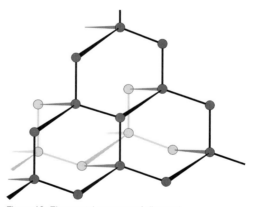

Figure 10: *The crystal structure of diamond.* Each carbon atom is bonded covalently to four neighbours arranged tetrahedrally around the central atom. The structure is highly rigid.

The rationalization of the structures adopted by purely ionic solids is essentially a straightforward exercise in the analysis of electrostatic interactions between ions. The problem of the structures of covalent compounds, both individual molecules, such as methane, and covalently bonded solids, such as diamond, is much more subtle, for it involves delving into the characteristics of the electron arrangements in individual atoms. Thus, if the formation of a covalent bond is regarded as corresponding to the accumulation of electrons in a particular region of an atom, then, to form a second bond, electrons can be accumulated into only certain parts of the atom relative to that first region of enhanced electron density. As a result, the bonds will lie in a geometric array that is characteristic of the atom. The remainder of this section focuses on this problem, but a detailed quantum mechanical analysis is required for a full understanding of the matter.

The theory of molecular shape known as valence-shell electron-pair repulsion (VSEPR) theory grew out of Lewis' theory, and, like that approach to bonding, VSEPR focuses on the role of electron pairs. It stems from the

Development of VSEPR theory *(margin note)*

work of the British chemists H.M. Powell and Nevil V. Sidgwick in the 1940s and was extensively developed by R.J. Gillespie in Canada and Ronald S. Nyholm in London during the 1960s. As such, it postdates quantum mechanical theories of bonding and shape but should be seen (as is so common a motivation in chemistry) as an attempt to identify the essential features of a problem and to formulate them into a simple qualitative procedure for rationalization and prediction.

A Lewis structure, as shown above, is a topological portrayal of bonding in a molecule. It ascribes bonding influences to electron pairs that lie between atoms and acknowledges the existence of lone pairs of electrons that do not participate directly in the bonding. The VSEPR theory supposes that all electron pairs, both bonding pairs and lone pairs, repel each other—particularly if they are close—and that the molecular shape is such as to minimize these repulsions. The approach is commonly applied to species in which there is an identifiable central atom (the oxygen atom in H_2O, for instance), but it is straightforward to extend it to discussions of the local shape at any given atom in a polyatomic species.

Applying VSEPR theory to simple molecules. The methane molecule, CH_4, can be used to illustrate the procedure for predicting molecular shape. The Lewis structure of this molecule ascribes four bonding electron pairs to the carbon atom (Figure 11). These pairs repel one another, and their separation is maximized if they adopt a tetrahedral disposition around the central carbon atom. A hydrogen atom is attached by each bonding pair, so it can be predicted that CH_4 is likely to be a tetrahedral species, which is in fact the case.

When applying VSEPR theory, attention is first focused on the electron pairs of the central atom, disregarding the distinction between bonding pairs and lone pairs. These pairs are then allowed to move around the central atom (at a constant distance) and to take up positions that maximize their mutual separations. As in the methane molecule, four pairs adopt a tetrahedral disposition. The arrangements adopted by two through six pairs are summarized in the table. At this stage, the atoms that are attached by the bonding pairs are introduced, and the shape of the molecule is reported on the basis of the arrangement of these atoms.

The water molecule, H_2O, provides a simple example. The oxygen atom has four electron pairs, so these pairs adopt a tetrahedral arrangement. Two of the pairs are bonding, and hydrogen atoms are attached to them. Hence, the molecule is angular. (Note that the shape of the molecule is determined by the disposition of the atoms, not the disposition of the electron pairs.) The ammonia molecule, NH_3, has four electron pairs in a tetrahedral arrangement around the nitrogen atom; three of these pairs are used to bond hydrogen atoms, so the molecule is predicted to be

VSEPR Electron-Pair Arrangements and Associated Molecular Shapes	
number and arrangement of electron pairs	molecular shapes
2 linear	linear
3 trigonal planar	trigonal planar angular
4 tetrahedral	tetrahedral trigonal pyramidal angular
5 trigonal bipyramidal	trigonal bipyramidal seesaw T-shaped
6 octahedral	octahedral square pyramidal square planar

trigonal pyramidal, with a lone pair in the apical position. Some of the names of the shapes of simple molecules are summarized in the table.

The angle between electron pairs in a tetrahedral arrangement is 109.5°. However, although H_2O is indeed angular and NH_3 is trigonal pyramidal, the angles between the bonds are 104° and 107°, respectively. In a sense, such close agreement is quite satisfactory for so simple an approach, but clearly there is more to explain. To account for variations in bond angle, it is supposed that electron pair repulsions are greatest between lone pairs, less between lone pairs and bonding pairs, and least between bonding pairs. The justification of this ordering has proved somewhat elusive; qualitatively it is presumed that lone pairs, being attached only to a single centre, spread over a greater volume than bonding pairs, which are pinned between two attracting centres. Whatever the reason may be, the order correlates quite well with observation. Thus, in H_2O, the two lone pairs move apart a little, and the two bonding pairs move away from them by closing the angle between one another. Likewise, in NH_3 the three bonding pairs move back from the single lone pair to minimize their interaction with it. As a result, the H—N—H bond angle decreases slightly. In each case, the predicted angle is less than the tetrahedral angle, as is observed experimentally.

VSEPR theory is quite successful at predicting (or, at least, rationalizing) the overall shapes of molecules. Thus, the hypervalent species SF_6 (sulfur hexafluoride), with six bonding pairs, is predicted and found to be a regular octahedron, and PCl_5 (phosphorus pentachloride), with five bonding pairs, is predicted and found to be a trigonal bipyramid. The XeF_4 (xenon tetrafluoride) molecule is hypervalent with six electron pairs around the central xenon (Xe) atom. These pairs adopt an octahedral arrangement. Four of the pairs are bonding pairs, and two are lone pairs. According to VSEPR theory, the repulsion between

Variations in bond angle

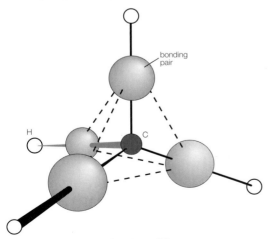

Figure 11: *The structure of methane, CH_4.*
This regular tetrahedral structure is explained in the VSEPR theory of molecular shape by supposing that the four pairs of bonding electrons (represented by the gray clouds) adopt positions that minimize their mutual repulsion.

the lone pairs is minimized if they lie on opposite sides of the xenon atom, leaving the four equatorial pairs as bonding pairs.

F⋮Xe⋮F / F⋮⋮F

This analysis suggests that XeF_4 should be a planar species, which is found to be the case.

Molecules with multiple bonds. There are further rules in VSEPR theory that simplify the discussion of species with multiple bonds and of species in which resonance must be considered. An analysis of the shapes adopted by species with multiple bonds suggests that each multiple bond can be treated as a single "superpair" of electrons. This rule can be justified by considering the geometric shapes that stem from two atoms sharing two or more pairs of electrons (Figure 12). Thus, the sulfate ion, SO_4^{2-}, for which a Lewis structure is

:Ö: ⎤²⁻ / :Ö—S—Ö: , / .Ö.

can be treated as having the equivalent of four pairs (two ordinary pairs and two superpairs) around the sulfur atom in a tetrahedral arrangement. All four pairs are bonding, so the ion is predicted to be a regular tetrahedron, which it indeed is. The same conclusion about the shape of the molecule would be drawn from another possible Lewis structure, in which each bond is single:

:Ö: ⎤²⁻ / :Ö—S—Ö: / :Ö:

The actual molecule is a resonance hybrid of these and related structures; but, as each one corresponds to the same geometry, no particular Lewis structure need be selected before one can make a prediction based on VSEPR theory. In other words, resonance does not affect the shapes of molecules.

Molecules with no central atom. Examples of the manner in which VSEPR theory is applied to species in which there is no central atom are provided by ethane (C_2H_6), ethylene (C_2H_4), and acetylene (C_2H_2), the Lewis structures for which are, respectively, the following:

H H / | | / H—C—C—H   C=C   H—C≡C—H / | | / H H

Local environment of atoms

In each case, consider the local environment of each carbon atom. In ethane there are four bonding pairs around each carbon atom, so every carbon atom is linked to its four neighbours (one carbon atom and three hydrogen atoms) by a tetrahedral array of bonds (Figure 13). The bond angles in ethane are indeed all close to 109°. In ethylene each carbon atom possesses two ordinary bonding pairs (linking it to hydrogen atoms) and one superpair (linking it to the other carbon atom). These three pairs, and the corresponding bonds, adopt a planar triangular arrangement, and the H—C—H and H—C=C angles are predicted to be close to 120°, as is found experimentally. It is less apparent from this analysis, but understandable once it is realized that the superpair is actually two shared pairs (Figure 12), that the ethylene molecule is predicted to be planar. Each carbon atom in an acetylene molecule has one bonding pair (to hydrogen) and one superpair (to the other carbon atom). The molecule is therefore expected to be linear, as is found in practice. The linearity of the molecule can be appreciated by referring to Figure 12.

Limitations of the VSEPR model. The VSEPR theory is simple yet powerful. Nevertheless, like any simplified model, it has its limitations. First, although it predicts that the bond angle in H_2O is less than the tetrahedral angle, it does not make any attempt to predict the magnitude of the

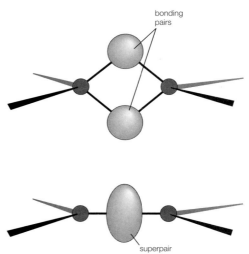

Figure 12: *Double bonds.*
The geometric arrangement of atoms linked by two shared pairs of electrons in a double bond (top) can be simulated by treating the double bond as the result of the sharing of a single superpair of electrons (bottom).

decrease. Second, the theory makes no predictions about the lengths of the bonds, which is another aspect of the shape of a molecule. Third, it ascribes the entire criterion of shape to electrostatic repulsions between bonding pairs, when in fact there are numerous contributions to the total energy of a molecule, and electrostatic effects are not necessarily the dominant ones. Fourth, the theory relies on some vague concepts, such as the difference in repelling effects of lone pairs and bonding pairs. There also are some species for which VSEPR theory fails. Nevertheless, despite these limitations and uncertainties, VSEPR theory is a useful rule of thumb and can be used with reasonable confidence for numerous species.

THE POLARITY OF MOLECULES

There are three main properties of chemical bonds that must be considered—namely, their strength, length, and

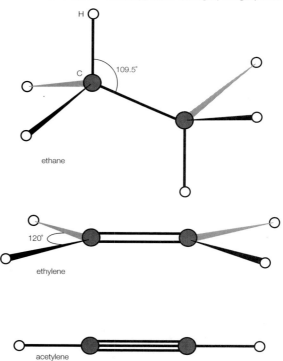

Figure 13: The shapes of molecules of ethane, C_2H_6; ethylene, C_2H_4; and acetylene, C_2H_2, according to VSEPR theory. These shapes correspond closely to the observed shapes of the molecules.

polarity. The polarity of a bond is the distribution of electrical charge over the atoms joined by the bond. Specifically, it is found that, while bonds between identical atoms (as in H_2) are electrically uniform in the sense that both hydrogen atoms are electrically neutral, bonds between atoms of different elements are electrically inequivalent. In hydrogen chloride, for example, the hydrogen atom is slightly positively charged whereas the chlorine atom is slightly negatively charged. The slight electrical charges on dissimilar atoms are called partial charges, and the presence of partial charges signifies the occurrence of a polar bond.

The polarity of a bond arises from the relative electronegativities of the elements. Electronegativity, it will be recalled, is the power of an atom of an element to attract electrons toward itself when it is part of a compound. Thus, although a bond in a compound may consist of a shared pair of electrons, the atom of the more electronegative element will draw the shared pair toward itself and thereby acquire a partial negative charge. The atom that has lost its equal share in the bonding electron pair acquires a partial positive charge because its nuclear charge is no longer fully canceled by its electrons.

The existence of equal but opposite partial charges on the atoms at each end of a heteronuclear bond (*i.e.,* a bond between atoms of different elements) gives rise to an *Dipole* electric dipole. The magnitude of this dipole is expressed *moment* by the value of its dipole moment, μ, which is defined as the product of the magnitude of the partial charges times their separation (essentially, the length of the bond). The dipole moment of a heteronuclear bond can be estimated from the electronegativities of the atoms A and B, χ_A and χ_B, respectively, by using the simple relation

$$\frac{\mu}{D} = \sqrt{(\chi_A - \chi_B)},$$

where D denotes the unit debye, which is used for reporting molecular dipole moments (1 $D = 3.34 \times 10^{-30}$ coulomb · metre). Moreover, the negative end of the dipole lies on the more electronegative atom. If the two bonded atoms are identical, it follows that the dipole moment is zero and the bond is nonpolar.

As the difference in electronegativity between two covalently bonded atoms increases, the dipolar character of the bond increases as the partial charges increase. When the electronegativities of the atoms are very different, the attraction of the more electronegative atom for the shared electron pair is so great that it effectively exercises complete control over them. That is, it has gained possession of the pair, and the bond is best regarded as ionic. Ionic and covalent bonding therefore can be regarded as constituting a continuum rather than as alternatives. This continuum can be expressed in terms of resonance by regarding a bond between atoms A and B as a resonance between a purely covalent form, in which the electrons are shared equally, and a purely ionic form, in which the more electronegative atom (B) has total control over the electrons:

$$:\ddot{A}:\ddot{B}: \longleftrightarrow \quad :\ddot{A}:\ddot{B}:^-$$

As the electronegativity difference increases, the resonance lies increasingly in favour of the ionic contribution. When the electronegativity difference is very large, as between an electropositive atom like sodium and an electronegative atom like fluorine, the ionic structure dominates the resonance, and the bonding can be regarded as ionic. Thus, as the electronegativity difference of the two bonded elements increases, a nonpolar bond gives way to a polar bond, which in turn becomes an ionic bond. There are, in fact, no purely ionic bonds, just as there are no purely covalent bonds; bonding is a continuum of types.

Ionic- Even a homonuclear bond, which is a bond between *covalent* atoms of the same element (as in Cl_2), is not purely co- *resonance* valent, because a more accurate description would be in terms of ionic-covalent resonance:

$$Cl^-Cl^+ \leftrightarrow Cl-Cl \leftrightarrow Cl^+Cl^-$$

That the species is nonpolar despite the occurrence of ionic contributions stems from the equal contributions of the ionic structures Cl^-Cl^+ and Cl^+Cl^- and their canceling dipoles. That Cl_2 is commonly regarded as a covalently bonded species stems from the dominant contribution of the structure $Cl-Cl$ to this resonance mixture. In contrast, the valence bond theory wavefunction (see below *The quantum mechanics of bonding: Valence bond theory*) of hydrogen chloride would be expressed as the resonance hybrid

$$H^-Cl^+ \leftrightarrow H-Cl \leftrightarrow H^+Cl^-$$

In this case, the two ionic structures would contribute different amounts (because the elements have different electronegativities), and the larger contribution of H^+Cl^- is responsible for the presence of partial charges on the atoms and the polarity of the molecule.

A polyatomic molecule will have polar bonds if its atoms are not identical. However, whether or not the molecule as a whole is polar (*i.e.,* has a nonzero electric dipole moment) depends on the shape of the molecule. For example, the carbon-oxygen bonds in carbon dioxide are both polar, with the partial positive charge on the carbon atom and the partial negative charge on the more electronegative oxygen atom. The molecule as a whole is nonpolar, however, because the dipole moment of one carbon-oxygen bond cancels the dipole moment of the other, for the two bond dipole moments point in opposite directions in this linear molecule. In contrast, the water molecule is polar. Each oxygen-hydrogen bond is polar, with the oxygen atom bearing the partial negative charge and the hydrogen atom the partial positive charge. Because the molecule is angular rather than linear, the bond dipole moments do not cancel, and the molecule has a nonzero dipole moment.

The polarity of H_2O is of profound importance for the properties of water. It is partly responsible for the exis- *Signifi-* tence of water as a liquid at room temperature and for *cance of* the ability of water to act as a solvent for many ionic *the polarity* compounds. The latter ability stems from the fact that the *of water* partial negative charge on the oxygen atom can emulate the negative charge of anions that surround each cation in the solid and thus help minimize the energy difference when the crystal dissolves. The partial positive charge on the hydrogen atoms can likewise emulate that of the cations surrounding the anions in the solid.

The quantum mechanics of bonding

The preceding discussion has outlined the general approach to covalent bonding and has shown how it is still widely employed for a qualitative understanding of molecules. It is incomplete in many respects, however. First, the role of the electron pair remains unexplained but appears to be the hinge of both Lewis' theory and the VSEPR theory. Second, there is evidence that suggests that Lewis' theory overemphasizes the role of electron pairs. More fundamentally, little has been said about the distribution of bonding electrons in terms of orbitals, although it has been shown that in atoms the distributions of electrons are described by wavefunctions. Finally, the models that have been described have little quantitative content: they do not lead to bond lengths or precise bond angles, nor do they give much information about the strengths of bonds.

A full theory of the chemical bond needs to return to the roots of the behaviour of electrons in molecules. That is, the role of the electron pair and the quantitative description of bonding must be based on the Schrödinger equation and the Pauli exclusion principle. This section describes the general features of such an approach. Once again, the discussion will be largely qualitative and conceptual rather than mathematical and numerical. However, the character of the presentation here should not be taken to imply that the current understanding of molecules is not rigorous, quantitative, and precise.

Several difficulties are encountered at the outset of the application of the Schrödinger equation to molecules. Even the simplest molecules consist of two nuclei and several electrons, and interesting molecules may contain a thousand atoms and tens of thousands of electrons. So that any progress of a generally applicable kind can be made, approximations are necessary.

One approximation is common to all discussions of molecules. The Born-Oppenheimer approximation, which was introduced by Max Born and J. Robert Oppenheimer in 1927, separates the motion of the electrons in a molecule from the motion of the nuclei. The separation is based on the fact that the nuclei are much heavier than the electrons and move more slowly. Hence, even though nuclei do move, the electrons can respond to their new positions almost instantaneously. That being the case, it is permissible to consider the nuclei as stationary in a given arrangement and then to solve the Schrödinger equation for the electrons in that stationary framework of nuclei. In order to explore how the energy of the molecule changes as the nuclei change their positions, a series of static nuclear arrangements can be selected, and the Schrödinger equation solved for the electrons in each stationary arrangement.

The data obtained from such a procedure can be used to construct a molecular potential energy curve, a graph that shows how the energy of the molecule varies as bond lengths and bond angles are changed. A typical curve for a diatomic molecule, in which only the internuclear distance is variable, is shown in Figure 14. The energy minimum of this curve corresponds to the observed bond length of the molecule. The depth of the minimum is (apart from a small correction for the vibrational properties of the bond) equal to the bond dissociation energy and hence indicates the tightness with which the two atoms are held together. The steepness of the walls of the curve, which shows how rapidly the energy changes as the nuclear separation changes, indicates the rigidity of the bond. Thus, quantitative information can be obtained from such an approach.

Even the Born-Oppenheimer approximation is only one of the approximations needed for the study of the molecule. It separates out the nuclear motion and leaves untouched the need to solve the Schrödinger equation for several (and perhaps tens of thousands) of electrons. Two major alternative approximations beyond the Born-Oppenheimer approach have been devised to tackle this aspect of the problem. The first to be proposed (by Walter Heitler and Fritz London in 1927 and substantially developed by John Slater and Linus Pauling in the 1930s) is valence bond (VB) theory. This theory introduced language into chemistry that is still widely used, particularly in the discussion of organic compounds, but it has been somewhat overshadowed in quantitative investigations by its rival. The latter, molecular orbital (MO) theory, was introduced in 1927 by Robert S. Mulliken and Friedrich Hund. It has undergone considerable development and is the principal model for the calculation of molecular properties and for general discussions of compounds.

VALENCE BOND THEORY

The basis of VB theory is the Lewis concept of the electron-pair bond. Broadly speaking, in VB theory a bond between atoms A and B is formed when two atomic orbitals, one from each atom, merge with one another (the technical term is overlap), and the electrons they contain pair up (so that their spins are ⇅). The merging of orbitals gives rise to constructive interference—*i.e.,* an enhancement of amplitude—between the wavefunctions in the areas where they overlap, and hence an enhanced amplitude results in the internuclear region. As a consequence of the formation of this region of heightened amplitude, there is an increased probability of finding the electrons in the internuclear region (so echoing Lewis' conception of the bond) and, by implication, a lowering of the energy of the molecule.

The VB theory can be put in the broader context of quantum mechanics by drawing on the superposition principle and the Pauli exclusion principle (see MECHANICS: *Quantum mechanics*). The two principles establish more precisely the type of orbital merging that is required and also show that, to achieve that merging, the two electrons must pair their spins. The technical justification will not be presented here.

Formation of σ and π bonds. As an illustration of the VB procedure, consider the structure of H_2O. First, note that the valence-shell electron configuration of an oxygen

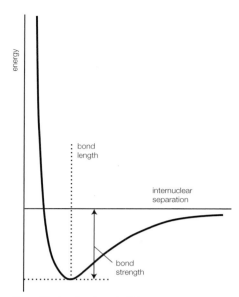

Figure 14: *A molecular potential energy curve.*
The strength of the bond is indicated by the depth of the well below the energy of the separated atoms (to the right), and the bond length is the corresponding internuclear separation.

atom is $2s^2 2p_x^2 2p_y^1 2p_z^1$, with an unpaired electron in each of two $2p$ orbitals, and :Ö· is the Lewis diagram for the atom. Each hydrogen atom has an unpaired $1s$ electron (H·) that can pair with one of the unpaired oxygen $2p$ electrons. Hence, a bond can form by the pairing of each hydrogen electron with an oxygen electron and the overlap of the orbitals they occupy (Figure 15). The electron distribution arising from each overlap is cylindrically symmetrical around the respective O—H axis and is called a σ bond. The VB description of H_2O is therefore that each hydrogen atom is linked to the oxygen atom by a σ bond formed by pairing of a hydrogen $1s$ electron and an oxygen $2p$ electron. Because a wavefunction can be written for this structure, an energy can be calculated by solving the Schrödinger equation, and a bond length can be determined by varying the nuclear separation and identifying the separation that results in the minimum energy.

The term σ bond is widely used in chemistry to denote an electron distribution like that in an oxygen-hydrogen bond, specifically one that has cylindrical symmetry about the line between the two bonded atoms. It is not the only type of bond, however, as can be appreciated by considering the structure of a nitrogen molecule, N_2. Each

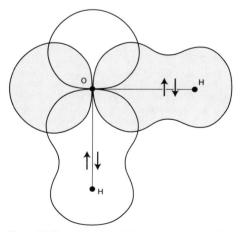

Figure 15: *The valence-bond description of the bonding in a water molecule in the simplest approximation.*
Each bond is formed when an electron in a hydrogen $1s$ orbital pairs with an electron in a $2p$ orbital of oxygen. The resulting electron distributions are called σ bonds owing to their cylindrical symmetry around the bond axis.

nitrogen atom has the valence-shell electron configuration $2s^2 2p_x{}^1 2p_y{}^1 2p_z{}^1$. If the z direction is taken to lie along the internuclear axis of the molecule, then the electrons in the two $2p_z$ orbitals can pair and overlap to form a σ bond. However, the $2p_x$ orbitals now lie in the wrong orientation for head-to-head overlap, and they overlap side-to-side instead. The resulting electron distribution is called a

π bond (Figure 16). A π bond also helps to hold the two atoms together, but, because the region of maximum electron density produced by the overlap is off the line of the internuclear axis, it does not do so with the same strength as a σ bond. The $2p_y$ electrons can pair and overlap in the same way and give rise to a second π bond. Therefore, the structure of an N_2 molecule consists of one σ bond and two π bonds. Note how this corresponds to and refines the Lewis description of the :N≡N: molecule.

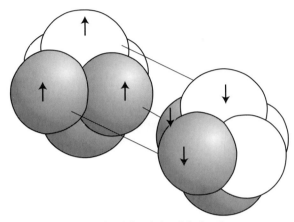

Figure 16: *The valence-bond description of the bonding in a nitrogen molecule, N_2.*
In addition to a σ bond, there are two π bonds formed by the broadside overlap of p orbitals on each atom.

In summary, a single bond in a Lewis structure corresponds to a σ bond of VB theory. A double bond corresponds to a σ bond plus a π bond, and a triple bond corresponds to a σ bond plus two π bonds.

Promotion of electrons. Valence bond theory runs into an apparent difficulty with CH_4. The valence-shell electron configuration of carbon is $2s^2 2p_x{}^1 2p_y{}^1$, which suggests that it can form only two bonds to hydrogen atoms, in which case carbon would have a valence of 2. The normal valence of carbon is 4, however. This difficulty is resolved by noting that only the overall energy of a molecule is important, and, as long as a process leads to a lowering of energy, it can contribute even if an initial investment of energy is required. In this case, VB theory allows promotion to occur, in which an electron is elevated to a higher orbital. Thus, a carbon atom is envisaged as undergoing promotion to the valence configuration $2s^1 2p_x{}^1 2p_y{}^1 2p_z{}^1$ as a CH_4 molecule is formed. Although promotion requires energy, it enables the formation of four bonds, and overall there is a lowering of energy. Carbon is particularly suited to this promotion because the energy involved is not very great; hence the formation of tetravalent carbon compounds is the rule rather than the exception.

Hybridization. The discussion is not yet complete, however. If this description of carbon were taken at face value, it would appear that, whereas three of the CH bonds in methane are formed from carbon $2p$ orbitals, one is formed from a carbon $2s$ orbital. It is well established experimentally, however, that all four bonds in methane are identical.

Quantum mechanical considerations resolve this dilemma by invoking hybridization. Hybridization is the mixing of atomic orbitals on the same atom. When the $2s$ and three $2p$ orbitals of a carbon atom are hybridized, they give rise to four lobelike sp^3 hybrid orbitals that are equivalent to one another apart from their orientations, which are toward the four corners of a regular tetrahedron (Figure 17). Each hybrid orbital contains an unpaired electron and can form a σ bond by pairing with a $1s$ electron of a hydrogen

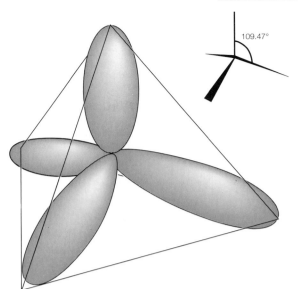

Figure 17: The tetrahedral disposition of the four sp^3 hybrid orbitals of a carbon atom.

atom. Hence, the VB structure of methane is described as consisting of four equivalent σ bonds formed by overlap of the s orbitals of the hydrogen atoms with sp^3 hybrid orbitals of the carbon atom.

Hybridization is a major contribution of VB theory to the language of chemistry. The structure of ethylene can be examined in VB terms to illustrate the use of hybridization. To reproduce the Lewis structure given earlier, it is necessary to contrive a double bond (*i.e.,* a σ bond plus a π bond) between the two carbon atoms. Such a bonding pattern can be achieved by selecting the carbon $2s$ orbital, from which an electron has been promoted, and two of its $2p$ orbitals for hybridization, leaving one $2p$ orbital unhybridized and ready for forming a π bond. When one $2s$ and two $2p$ orbitals are hybridized, they form sp^2 hybrid orbitals, which have lobelike boundary surfaces that point to the corners of an equilateral triangle; the unhybridized $2p$ orbital lies perpendicular to the plane of the triangle (Figure 18). Each of the orbitals contains a single electron. Two of the hybrids can form σ bonds to two hydrogen atoms, and one of the hybrids can form a σ bond to the other carbon atom (which has undergone similar hybridization). The unhybridized $2p$ orbitals are now side-by-side and can overlap to form a π bond.

This description conforms to the Lewis description. It also explains naturally why ethylene is a planar molecule, because twisting one end of the molecule relative to the

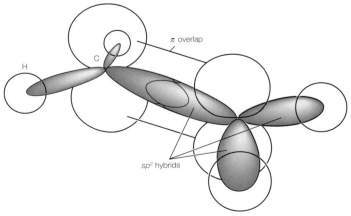

Figure 18: *The shape of sp^2 hybrid orbitals and the structure of an ethylene molecule.*
The σ bond is formed by the overlap of hybrid atomic orbitals, and the π bond is formed by the overlap of unhybridized p orbitals. The entire structure is resistant to twisting around the carbon-carbon bond.

other reduces the overlap between the $2p$ orbitals and hence weakens the π bond. All double bonds confer a torsional rigidity (a resistance to twisting) to the parts of molecules where they lie.

Resonant structures. The description of the planar hexagonal benzene molecule, C_6H_6, illustrates another aspect of VB theory. Each of the six carbon atoms is taken to be sp^2 hybridized. Two of the hybrid orbitals are used to form σ bonds with the carbon atom neighbours, and one is used to form a σ bond with a hydrogen atom. The unhybridized carbon $2p$ orbitals are in a position to overlap and form π bonds with their neighbours (Figure 19). However, there are several possibilities for pairing; two are as follows:

Kekulé structures

There is a VB wavefunction for each of these so-called Kekulé structures. (They are so called after Friedrich August Kekulé, who is commonly credited with having first proposed the hexagonal structure for benzene in 1865; however, a cyclic structure had already been proposed by Joseph Loschmidt four years earlier.) The actual structure is a superposition (sum) of the two wavefunctions: in VB terms, the structure of benzene is a resonance hybrid of the two canonical structures. In quantum mechanical terms, the blending effect of resonance in the Lewis approach to bonding is the superposition of wavefunctions for each contributing canonical structure. The effect of resonance is the sharing of the double-bond character around the ring, so that each carbon-carbon bond has a mixed single- and double-bond character. Resonance also (for quantum mechanical reasons) lowers the energy of the molecule relative to either contributing canonical structure. Indeed, benzene is a molecule that is surprisingly resistant to chemical attack (double bonds, rather than being a source of molecular strength and stability, are usually the targets of chemical attack) and is more stable than its structure suggests.

One of the difficulties that has rendered VB computationally unattractive is the large number of canonical structures, both covalent and ionic, that must be used in order to achieve quantitatively reliable results; in some cases tens of thousands of structures must be employed. Nevertheless, VB theory has influenced the language of chemistry profoundly, and the concepts of σ and π bonds, hybridization, and resonance are a part of the everyday vocabulary of the subject.

MOLECULAR ORBITAL THEORY

The alternative quantum mechanical theory of the electronic structures of molecules is MO theory. This approach was introduced about the same time as VB theory but has proved more amenable to quantitative implementation on computers. It is now virtually the only technique employed in the computational investigation of molecules. Like VB theory, it has introduced a language that is widely used in chemistry, and many chemists discuss chemical bonds in terms that combine both theories.

Just as an atomic orbital is a wavefunction that describes the distribution of an electron around the nucleus of an atom, so a molecular orbital (an MO) is a wavefunction that describes the distribution of an electron over all the nuclei of a molecule. If the amplitude of the MO wavefunction is large in the vicinity of a particular atom, then the electron has a high probability of being found there. If the MO wavefunction is zero in a particular region, then the electron will not be found there.

Although an MO can in principle be determined by solving the Schrödinger equation for an electron in the electrostatic field of an array of nuclei, in practice an approximation is always adopted. In this approximation, which is known as the linear combination of atomic orbitals (LCAO) approximation, each MO is constructed from a superposition of atomic orbitals belonging to the atoms in the molecule. The size of the contribution of an orbital from a particular atom indicates the probability

Molecular orbitals

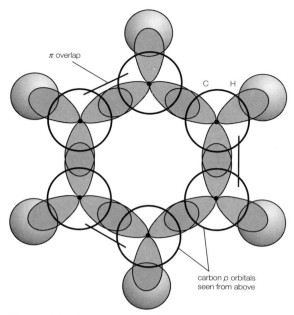

Figure 19: *The valence-bond description of a benzene molecule.*
The sp^2 hybridized carbon atoms form σ bonds with their neighbours, and the unhybridized p orbitals overlap to form π bonds. This bonding pattern corresponds to one of the Kekulé structures (see text).

that the electron will be found on that atom. The actual shape of the molecular orbital (and indirectly its energy) is a reflection of the extent to which the individual atomic orbitals interfere with one another either constructively or destructively.

Molecular orbitals of H_2 and He_2. The procedure can be introduced by considering the H_2 molecule. Its molecular orbitals are constructed from the valence-shell orbitals of each hydrogen atom, which are the $1s$ orbitals of the atoms. Two superpositions of these two orbitals can be formed, one by summing the orbitals and the other by taking their difference (Figure 20). In the former, the amplitudes of the two atomic orbitals interfere constructively with one another, and there is consequently an enhanced amplitude between the two nuclei. As a result, any electron that occupies this molecular orbital has a high probability of being found between the two nuclei, and its energy is lower than when it is confined to either atomic orbital alone. This combination of atomic orbitals is therefore called a bonding orbital. Moreover, because it has cylindrical symmetry about the internuclear axis, it is designated a σ orbital and labeled 1σ.

The MO formed by taking the difference of the two $1s$ orbitals also has cylindrical symmetry and hence is also a σ orbital. Taking the difference of the two atomic orbitals, however, results in destructive interference in the internuclear region where the amplitude of one orbital is subtracted from the other. This destructive interference is complete on a plane midway between the nuclei, and hence there is a nodal plane—*i.e.,* a plane of zero amplitude—between the nuclei. Any electron that occupies

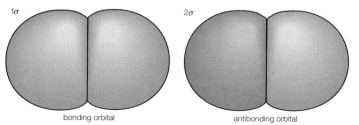

Figure 20: The formation of bonding and antibonding molecular orbitals by constructive and destructive interference, respectively, of neighbouring atomic orbitals. Both molecular orbitals are σ orbitals.

this orbital is excluded from the internuclear region, and its energy is higher than it would be if it occupied either atomic orbital. The orbital arising in this way is therefore called an antibonding orbital; it is often denoted σ^* (and referred to as "sigma star") or, because it is the second of the two σ orbitals, 2σ.

MO energy-level diagrams

The molecular orbital energy-level diagram, which is a diagram that shows the relative energies of molecular orbitals, for the H_2 molecule is shown in Figure 21. On either side of the central ladder are shown the energies of the $1s$ orbitals of atoms A and B, and the central two-rung ladder shows the energies of the bonding and antibonding combinations. Only at this stage, after setting up the energy-level diagram, are the electrons introduced. In accord with the Pauli exclusion principle, at most two electrons can occupy any one orbital. In H_2 there are two electrons, and, following the building-up principle, they enter and fill the lower-energy bonding combination. Hence the electron configuration of the molecule is denoted $1\sigma^2$, and the stability of the molecule stems from the occupation of the bonding combination. Its low energy results in turn (in the conventional interpretation, at least) from the accumulation of electron density in the internuclear region because of constructive interference between the contributing atomic orbitals.

The central importance of the electron pair for bonding arises naturally in MO theory via the Pauli exclusion principle. A single electron pair is the maximum number that can occupy a bonding orbital and hence give the greatest lowering of energy. However, MO theory goes beyond Lewis' approach by not ascribing bonding to electron pairing; some lowering of energy is also achieved if only one electron occupies a bonding orbital, and so the fact that H_2^+ exists (with the electron configuration $1\sigma^1$) is no longer puzzling.

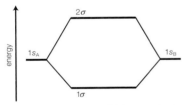

Figure 21: A molecular orbital energy-level diagram showing the relative energies of the atomic orbitals of atoms A and B ($1s_A$ and $1s_B$) and the bonding (1σ) and antibonding (2σ) molecular orbitals they form.

Instability of He₂

The molecular orbital energy-level diagram shown in Figure 21 also applies (with changes of detail in the energies of the molecular orbitals) to the hypothetical species He_2. However, this species has four valence electrons, and its configuration would be $1\sigma^2 2\sigma^2$. Although there is a bonding influence from the two bonding electrons, there is an antibonding influence from two antibonding electrons. As a result, the He_2 molecule does not have a lower energy than two widely separated helium atoms and hence has no tendency to form. (The overall effect is in fact slightly antibonding.) The role of the noble gas configuration now can be seen from a different perspective: the electrons that are provided by each closed-shell atom fill both the bonding and antibonding orbitals, and they result in no net lowering of energy; in fact, they give rise to an increase in energy relative to the separated atoms.

The molecular orbitals of other species are constructed in an analogous way. In general, the orbitals in the valence shells of each atom are considered first (not, initially, the electrons those orbitals contain). Then the sets of these orbitals that have the same symmetry with respect to the internuclear axis are selected. (This point is illustrated below.) Bonding and antibonding combinations of each set are then formed, and from n atomic orbitals n such molecular orbitals are formed. The molecular orbital energy-level diagram that results is constructed by putting the molecular orbitals in order of increasing number of internuclear nodal planes, the orbital with no such nodal plane

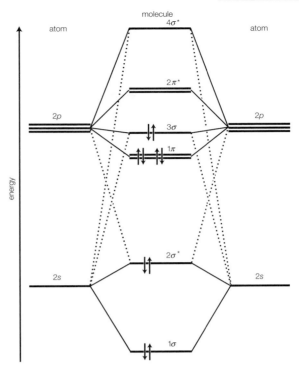

Figure 22: The molecular orbital energy-level diagram for diatomic molecules of period-2 elements. The occupation of the orbitals is characteristic of N_2.

lying at lowest energy and the orbital with nodal planes between all the atoms lying at highest energy. At this stage, the valence electrons provided by the atoms are allowed to occupy the available orbitals in accord with the general rules of the building-up principle, with no more than two electrons in each orbital and in accord with Hund's rule if more than one orbital is available for occupation.

Molecular orbitals of period-2 diatomic molecules. As a first illustration of this procedure, consider the structures of the diatomic molecules formed by the period-2 elements (such as N_2 and O_2). Each valence shell has one $2s$ and three $2p$ orbitals, and so there are eight atomic orbitals in all and hence eight molecular orbitals that can be formed. The energies of these atomic orbitals are shown on either side of the molecular orbital energy-level diagram in Figure 22. (It may be recalled from the discussion of atoms that the $2p$ orbitals have higher energy than the $2s$ orbitals.) If the z axis is identified with the internuclear axis, the $2s$ and $2p_z$ orbitals on each atom all have cylindrical symmetry around the axis and hence may be combined to give σ orbitals. There are four such atomic orbitals, so four σ orbitals can be formed (Figure 23). These four molecular orbitals lie typically at the energies shown in the middle of Figure 22. The $2p_x$ orbitals on each atom do not have cylindrical symmetry around the internuclear axis. They overlap to form bonding and antibonding π orbitals (Figure 24). (The name and shape reflects the π bonds of VB theory.) The same is true of the $2p_y$ orbitals on each atom, which form a similar pair of bonding and antibonding π orbitals whose energies are identical to those of bonding and antibonding π orbitals, respectively, formed from the $2p_x$ orbitals. The precise locations of the

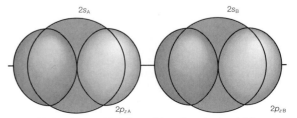

Figure 23: The four σ orbitals formed from four atomic orbitals ($2s$ and $2p_z$ on each atom).

The
structure
of N₂

π orbitals relative to those of the σ orbitals depend on the species: for simplicity here they will be taken to be as shown in Figure 22.

Now consider the structure of N_2. There are $2 \times 5 = 10$ valence electrons to accommodate. These electrons occupy the five lowest-energy MOs and hence result in the configuration $1\sigma^2 2\sigma^2 1\pi^4 3\sigma^2$. Note that only the orbitals in the lower portion of the diagram of Figure 22 are occupied. This configuration accounts for the considerable strength of the bonding in N_2 and consequently its ability to act as a diluent for the oxygen in the atmosphere, because the O_2 molecules are much more likely to react than the N_2 molecules upon collision with other molecules. An analysis of the identities of the orbitals shows, after allowing for the cancellation of bonding effects by antibonding effects, that the form of the electron configuration is (σ bonding orbital)^2(π bonding orbitals)^4. If each doubly occupied σ orbital is identified with a σ bond and each doubly occupied π orbital with a π bond, then the structure obtained by this MO procedure matches both the VB description of the molecule and the :N≡N: Lewis description.

To see how the MO approach transcends the Lewis approach (and, in this instance, the VB approach as well), consider the electronic configuration of O_2. The same MO energy-level diagram (with changes of detail) can be used because the oxygen atoms provide the same set of atomic orbitals. Now, however, there are $2 \times 6 = 12$ valence orbitals to accommodate. The first 10 electrons reproduce the configuration of N_2. The last two enter the $2\pi^*$ antibonding orbital, thereby reducing the net configuration to one σ bond and one π bond. That is, O_2 is a doubly-bonded species, in accord with the Lewis structure O=O. However, because there are two 2π orbitals and only two electrons to occupy them, the two electrons occupy different orbitals with parallel spins (recall Hund's rule). Therefore, the magnetic fields produced by the two electrons do not cancel, and O_2 is predicted to be a paramagnetic species. That is in fact the case. Such a property was completely outside the competence of Lewis' theory to predict and must be contrived in VB theory. It was an early major triumph of MO theory.

Molecular orbitals of polyatomic species. The principal qualitative difference between MO theory and VB theory becomes obvious when the objects of study are polyatomic, rather than diatomic, species. The benzene molecule is considered again but in this case from the viewpoint of its molecular orbitals. The atomic orbitals that provide the so-called basis set for the molecular orbitals (*i.e.*, the ones from which the MOs are constructed) are the carbon $2s$ and $2p$ orbitals and the hydrogen $1s$ orbitals. All these orbitals except one $2p$ orbital on each carbon atom lie in the plane of the molecule, so they naturally form two sets that are distinguished by their symmetries. This discussion concentrates on the molecular orbitals that are constructed from the six perpendicular $2p$ orbitals, which form the π orbitals of the molecule; the remaining orbitals form a framework of σ orbitals.

Six molecular orbitals, which are labeled $1a$, $1e$, $2e$, and $2a$, as shown in Figure 25, can be built from these six $2p$ orbitals. The two $1e$ orbitals and the two $2e$ orbitals each have the same energy. The six molecular orbitals are various sums and differences of the six $2p$ orbitals, and they differ in the number and position of their internuclear nodal planes (*i.e.*, areas of low electron density). As before, the greater the number of these nodal planes, the more the electrons that occupy the orbitals are excluded from the region between the nuclei, and hence the higher the energy. The resulting molecular orbital energy-level diagram is shown alongside the orbitals in the illustration. The lowest-energy $1a$ orbital has no nodal plane, so there is maximum positive overlap. The two degenerate $1e$ orbitals each have one nodal plane, the degenerate $2e$ orbitals have two nodal planes each, and the high-energy $2a$ orbital has three nodal planes. The crucial difference from the cases considered earlier is that the molecular orbitals spread over more than two atoms. That is, they are delocalized orbitals, and electrons that occupy them are delocalized over several atoms (here, as many as six atoms, as in the $1a$ orbital).

Basis set

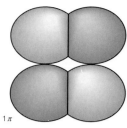

Figure 24: *The bonding and antibonding π orbitals that can be formed from overlap of $2p_x$ orbitals.*
Another pair of π orbitals perpendicular to these two orbitals are formed by overlap of $2p_y$ orbitals.

Each carbon atom supplies one electron to the π system (the other 24 valence electrons have occupied the 12 low-energy σ orbitals that are not directly of interest here). These six electrons occupy the three lowest-energy molecular orbitals. Notice that none of the net antibonding orbitals is occupied; this is a part of the explanation of the considerable stability of the benzene molecule.

The role of delocalization. In the VB description of the benzene molecule, each double bond is localized between a particular pair of atoms, but resonance spreads that character around the ring. In MO theory, there are three occupied π orbitals, and hence three contributions

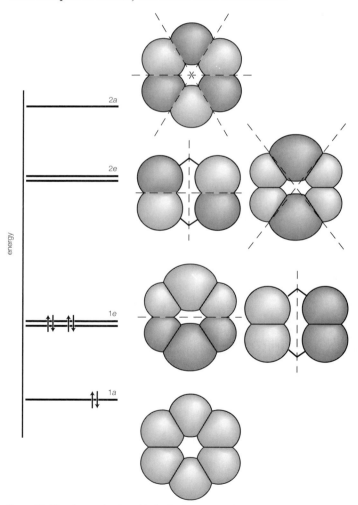

Figure 25: *The six π molecular orbitals of a benzene molecule and their relative energies.*
Only the three lowest-energy orbitals are occupied in benzene. The bonding and antibonding character of these orbitals is distributed around the ring of carbon atoms. The dashed lines represent nodal planes, and the shading reflects the two possible phases of the orbitals. Constructive interference, resulting in an area of high electron density, occurs between like phases; destructive interference, resulting in a nodal plane, occurs between unlike phases.

to double-bond character, but each electron pair is spread around the ring and helps to draw either all the atoms together (the 1*a* orbital) or several of the atoms together (the two 1*e* orbitals). Thus, delocalization distributes the bonding effect of an electron pair over the atoms of the molecule, and hence one electron pair can contribute to the bonding of more than two atoms.

Several problems that remained unsolved in the earlier discussion of Lewis structures can be unraveled. It has already been shown that one electron can contribute to bonding if it occupies a bonding orbital; therefore the problem of the existence of one-electron species is resolved.

Hypervalence is taken care of, without having to invoke octet expansion, by the distributed bonding effect of delocalized electrons. Consider SF_6, which according to Lewis' theory needs to use two of its 3*d* orbitals in addition to its four 3*s* and 3*p* orbitals to accommodate six pairs of bonding electrons. In MO theory, the four 3*s* and 3*p* orbitals of sulfur and one 2*p* orbital of each fluorine atom are used to build $1 + 3 + 6 = 10$ molecular orbitals. These 10 MOs are delocalized to varying degrees over the seven atoms of the molecule. Half of them have a net bonding character and half of them a net antibonding character between the sulfur and fluorine atoms. There are 6 sulfur valence electrons to accommodate and $6 \times 1 = 6$ fluorine electrons for a total of 12. The first 10 of these electrons occupy the net bonding orbitals; the remaining two occupy the lowest-energy antibonding orbital. In fact, this orbital is

Nonbonding orbitals

so weakly antibonding that it is best to regard it as nonbonding and as having little effect on the stability of the molecule. In any event, its weakly antibonding character is distributed over all six fluorine atoms, just as the other five pairs of electrons help to bind all six fluorine atoms to the central sulfur atom. The net effect of the 12 electrons is therefore bonding, and delocalization eliminates the need to invoke any role for *d* orbitals. The quantitative description of the forms and energies of the molecular orbitals is improved by the inclusion of 3*d* orbitals in the basis set, but only a small admixture is needed. There is certainly no need to invoke 3*d* orbitals as a necessary component of the description of bonding and no need to regard this hypervalent molecule as an example of a species with an expanded octet. Octet expansion is a rule of thumb, a correlation of an observation with the presence of available *d* orbitals, and not a valid explanation.

The other remaining outstanding problem is that of electron-deficient compounds, as typified by B_2H_6. Such molecules are classified as electron deficient because, in Lewis terms, there are fewer than two electrons available per bond. However, a consequence of delocalization is that the bonding influence of an electron pair is distributed over all the atoms in a molecule. Hence, it is easy to construct molecular orbitals that can achieve the binding of eight atoms by six electron pairs. The question to consider is not why electron-deficient compounds exist but why they are so rare. The answer lies in the smallness of the boron and hydrogen atoms, which allows them to get so close to one another that the cluster can be held together efficiently by a few delocalized pairs of electrons. Lewis was fortunate because the rules he adduced were generally applicable to larger atoms; there are more large atoms in the periodic table than there are atoms that are small enough for electron pair delocalization to be a dominant feature of their structures.

Comparison of the VB and MO theories. The language that molecular orbital theory brings to chemistry is that of bonding and antibonding orbitals and delocalization of electrons. The theory is presented here as an alternative to valence bond theory, and the formulation of the theory is quite different. However, both theories involve approximations to the actual electronic structures of molecules, and both can be improved. Valence bond theory is improved by incorporating extensive ionic-covalent resonance; molecular orbital theory is enhanced by allowing for a variety of occupation schemes for molecular orbitals (the procedure of configuration interaction). As these two improvement schemes are pursued, the wavefunctions generated by the two approaches converge on one another and the electron distributions they predict become identical.

Valence bond theory is widely used when the molecular property of interest is identifiable with the properties of individual bonds. It is therefore commonly employed in organic chemistry, where the reactions of molecules are often discussed in terms of the properties of their functional groups. The latter are small localized regions of a molecule (such as a double bond) or particular clusters of atoms (such as an OH group). Molecular orbital theory is widely used to describe properties that are most naturally discussed in terms of delocalization. Such properties include the spectroscopic properties of molecules, in which electromagnetic radiation is used to excite an electron from one molecular orbital to another and all the atoms contribute to the shift in electron density that accompanies the excitation.

Applications of VB and MO theories

Intermolecular forces

Molecules cohere even though their ability to form chemical bonds has been satisfied. The evidence for the existence of these weak intermolecular forces is the fact that gases can be liquefied, that ordinary liquids exist and need a considerable input of energy for vaporization to a gas of independent molecules, and that many molecular compounds occur as solids. The role of weak intermolecular forces in the properties of gases was first examined theoretically by the Dutch scientist Johannes van der Waals, and the term van der Waals forces is used synonymously with intermolecular forces. Under certain conditions, weakly bonded clusters of molecules (such as an argon atom in association with a hydrogen chloride molecule) can exist; such delicately bonded species are called van der Waals molecules.

There are many types of intermolecular forces; the repulsive force and four varieties of attractive force are discussed here. In general, the energy of interaction varies with distance, as shown by the graph in Figure 26. Attractive forces dominate to the distance at which the two molecules come into contact, then strong repulsive forces come into play and the potential energy of two molecules rises abruptly. The shape of the intermolecular potential energy curve shown in the illustration resembles that of the molecular potential energy curve in Figure 14. The minimum of the former is much shallower, however, showing that forces between molecules are typically much weaker than the forces responsible for chemical bonds within molecules.

Intermolecular potential energy curve

Repulsive force. The repulsive part of the intermolecu-

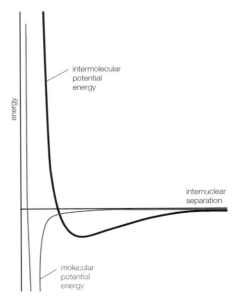

Figure 26: *An intermolecular potential energy curve.* The graph shows how the potential energy of two molecules varies with their separation. The energy minimum is much more shallow than for the formation of a chemical bond between two atoms, as depicted in Figure 14 and indicated here in gray.

lar potential is essentially a manifestation of the overlap of the wavefunctions of the two species in conjunction with the Pauli exclusion principle. It reflects the impossibility for electrons with the same spin to occupy the same region of space. More rigorously, the steep rise in energy is illustrated by the behaviour of two helium atoms and their possession of the configuration $1\sigma^2 2\sigma^2$ (see above Figure 21). The antibonding effect of the upper energy orbital dominates the bonding effect of the 1σ orbital at all separations, and the energy of the former rises more rapidly than that of the latter falls. Consequently, as the internuclear separation is decreased, the total energy rises steeply. All closed-shell species behave in a similar manner for much the same reason.

Dipole–dipole interaction. The first of the four bonding interactions discussed here is the dipole–dipole interaction between polar molecules. It will be recalled that a polar molecule has an electric dipole moment by virtue of the existence of partial charges on its atoms. Opposite partial charges attract one another, and, if two polar molecules are orientated so that the opposite partial charges on the molecules are closer together than their like charges, then there will be a net attraction between the two molecules. This type of intermolecular force contributes to the condensation of hydrogen chloride to a liquid at low temperatures. The dipole–dipole interaction also contributes to the weak interaction between molecules in gases, because, although molecules rotate, they tend to linger in relative orientations in which they have low energy—namely, the mutual orientation with opposite partial charges close to one another.

Dipole–induced-dipole interaction. The second type of attractive interaction, the dipole–induced-dipole interaction, also depends on the presence of a polar molecule. The second participating molecule need not be polar; but, if it is polar, then this interaction augments the dipole–dipole interaction described above. In the dipole–induced-dipole interaction, the presence of the partial charges of the polar molecule causes a polarization, or distortion, of the electron distribution of the other molecule. As a result of this distortion, the second molecule acquires regions of partial positive and negative charge, and thus it becomes polar. The partial charges so formed behave just like those of a permanently polar molecule and interact favourably with their counterparts in the polar molecule that originally induced them. Hence, the two molecules cohere. This interaction also contributes to the intermolecular forces that are responsible for the condensation of hydrogen chloride gas.

Dispersion interaction. The third type of interaction acts between all types of molecule, polar or not. It is also somewhat stronger than the two attractive interactions discussed thus far and is the principal force responsible for the existence of the condensed phases of certain molecular substances, such as benzene, other hydrocarbons, bromine, and the solid elements phosphorus (which consists of tetrahedral P_4 molecules) and sulfur (which consists of crown-shaped S_8 molecules). The interaction is called the dispersion interaction or, less commonly but more revealingly, the induced-dipole–induced-dipole interaction. Consider two nonpolar molecules near each other. Although there are no permanent partial charges on either molecule, the electron density can be thought of as ceaselessly fluctuating. As a result of these fluctuations, regions of equal and opposite partial charge arise in one of the molecules and give rise to a transient dipole. This transient dipole can induce a dipole in the neighbouring molecule, which then interacts with the original transient dipole (Figure 27). Although the latter continuously flickers from one direction to another (with an average of zero dipole overall), the induced dipole follows it, and the two correlated dipoles interact favourably with one another and cohere.

The hydrogen bond. The interactions described so far are not limited to molecules of any specific composition. However, there is one important intermolecular interaction specific to molecules containing an oxygen, nitrogen, or fluorine atom that is attached to a hydrogen atom. This interaction is the hydrogen bond, an interaction of the form $A—H \cdots B$, where A and B are atoms of any

Transient dipoles [left margin]

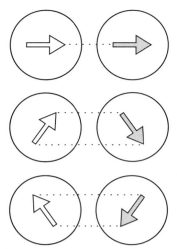

Figure 27: *Dispersion interactions.* Fluctuations in the electron distribution of a molecule can give rise to an instantaneous electric dipole. This dipole can induce an electric dipole in a neighbouring molecule, and the two electric dipoles attract one another. The resulting interaction is called a dispersion interaction.

of the three elements mentioned above and the hydrogen atom lies on a straight line between the nuclei of A and B. A hydrogen bond is about 10 times as strong as the other interactions described above, and when present it dominates all other types of intermolecular interaction. It is responsible, for example, for the existence of water as a liquid at normal temperatures; because of its low molar mass, water would be expected to be a gas. The hydrogen bond is also responsible for the existence as solids of many organic molecules containing hydroxyl groups (—OH); the sugars glucose and sucrose are examples.

Many interpretations of the hydrogen bond have been proposed. One that fits into the general scheme of this article is to think of the A—H unit as being composed of an A atomic orbital and a hydrogen $1s$ orbital and to consider a lone pair of electrons on B as occupying a B orbital. When the three atoms are aligned, these three orbitals can form three molecular orbitals: one bonding, one largely nonbonding, and one antibonding (Figure 28). There are four electrons to accommodate (two from the original A—H bond and two from the lone pair). They occupy the bonding and nonbonding orbitals, leaving the antibonding orbital vacant. Hence, the net effect is to lower the energy of the AHB grouping and thus to constitute an intermolecular bond. Once again, on encountering the hydrogen bond, one encounters a twist in the conventional attitude; the question raised by this interpretation is not why such a bond occurs but why it does not occur more generally. The explanation lies in the small size of the hydrogen atom, which enables the balance of energies in the molecular orbital scheme to be favourable to bonding.

Hydrogen bonding occurs to atoms other than nitrogen, oxygen, and fluorine if they carry a negative charge and hence are rich in readily available electrons. Thus, hydrogen bonding is one of the principal mechanisms of hydration of anions in aqueous solution (the bonding of H_2O molecules to the solute species) and hence contributes to the ability of water to act as a good solvent for ionic compounds. It also contributes to the hydration of organic compounds containing oxygen or nitrogen atoms and thus accounts for the much greater aqueous solubility of alcohols than hydrocarbons.

Hydrogen bonds are of great significance in determining the structure of biologically significant compounds, most notably proteins and deoxyribonucleic acid (DNA). An important feature of the structure of proteins (which are polypeptides, or polymers formed from amino acids) is the existence of the peptide link, the group —CO—NH—, which appears between each pair of adjacent amino acids. This link provides an NH group that can form a hy-

Effects of hydrogen bonding [right margin]

Hydrogen bonding in proteins [right margin]

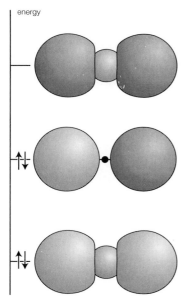

energy

Figure 28: *Molecular orbitals of a hydrogen bond.*
The formation of a hydrogen bond can be expressed in terms of molecular orbitals formed by an atomic orbital provided by an atom that has a lone pair of electrons, a hydrogen 1s orbital, and an orbital provided by an atom to which the hydrogen atom is originally attached. The four electrons of the system occupy the two lowest-energy molecular orbitals.

drogen bond to a suitable acceptor atom and an oxygen atom, which can act as a suitable receptor. Therefore, a peptide link provides the two essential ingredients of a hydrogen bond. The keying together of such peptide groups by hydrogen bonding of the type shown in Figure 29 was examined in detail by Pauling and Robert Corey, who formulated a set of rules, the Pauling-Corey rules, for its implementation. The implication of these rules is the existence of two types of structure for a polypeptide, which is either a helical form (the α helix) or a pleated sheet form (the β-pleated sheet). All polypeptides have one structure or the other and often have alternating regions of each. Since the properties and behaviour of an enzyme molecule (a particular class of polypeptides) are determined by its shape and, in particular, by the shape of the region where the molecule it acts on needs to attach, it follows that hydrogen bonds are centrally important to the functions of life.

Hydrogen bonds are also responsible for the transmission of genetic information from one generation to another, for they are responsible for the specific keying together of cytosine with guanine and thymine with adenine moieties that characterizes the structure of the DNA double helix (see the article BIOCHEMICAL COMPONENTS OF ORGANISMS: *Nucleic acids*).

Varieties of solids

Chemical bonds and intermolecular forces are jointly responsible for the existence of the solid phases of matter. This section reviews some of the types of solid that are encountered and relates them to the topics discussed earlier.

Ionic solids. The structures of ionic solids have already been described in some detail. They consist of individual ions that are stacked together in such a way that the assembly has the lowest possible energy. These ions may be monatomic (as in sodium chloride, which consists of Na^+ and Cl^- ions) or the ions may themselves be covalently bonded polyatomic species. An example of the latter is ammonium nitrate, in which the cation is NH_4^+ and the anion is NO_3^-; the N—H and N—O bonds within the ions are covalent. Ionic compounds are generally hard and brittle and have high melting points.

Molecular solids. The structures of molecular solids,

(margin note: Stacking arrangements)

which are solids composed of individual molecules, have also been touched on in the section on intermolecular forces. These molecules are held to one another by hydrogen bonds (if they can form them), dispersion forces, and other dipolar forces—in that order of decreasing importance—and the molecules stack together in a pattern that minimizes their total energy. Examples of such solids include ice, in which hydrogen bonding is of paramount importance, and polyethylene, in which dispersion forces are dominant. Unless hydrogen bonds are present (in which case molecular solids resemble ionic solids in brittleness), molecular solids are generally soft and have low melting points because the bonds between the molecules are easily overcome.

Network solids. There exists a class of solids called network solids in which the bonding is essentially due to a network of covalent bonds that extends throughout the solid. Such solids are hard and rigid and have high melting points because the crystal is like one enormous molecule. The most well-known example of a network solid is diamond, which consists of tetrahedrally bonded carbon atoms (see above Figure 10). By virtue of the rigidity of its bonding structure, diamond is the hardest substance known and also the best conductor of heat.

Some solids have a network character in certain directions and a more molecular character in other directions. Once again, carbon provides the paradigm example, for the form of carbon known as graphite consists of a stack of sheets of hexagonal rings of carbon atoms. In the plane of the sheets, the bonding is covalent (and resembles an extended version of the bonding in benzene). The sheets themselves are held together by binding that is so weak that it is sometimes referred to as a van der Waals interaction. The anisotropy of the structure of graphite accounts for the anisotropy of its electrical conductivity (which is higher in the plane of the sheets than perpendicular to them). The ability of graphite to shed sheets of carbon (a feature utilized in the manufacture of pencils) and to act as a high-temperature lubricant (because the sheets can slide over one another) appears to be consistent with this structure but in fact seems to depend on the presence of impurities between the sheets.

(margin note: The structure of graphite)

Metals. The remaining major type of solid is a metal. A metal is characterized by its lustre, the ease with which it may be deformed (rather than shattered) by hammering, and its high electrical and thermal conductivities. Metals also tend to have higher densities than other types of

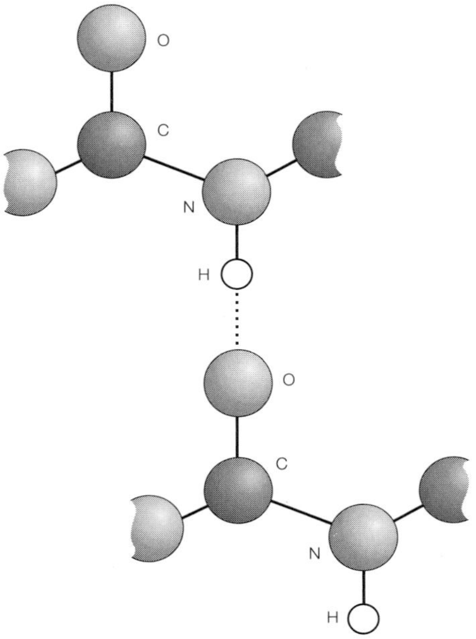

O

C

N

H

O

C

N

H

Figure 29: *The linking of atoms in two peptide links by the hydrogen bonds they can form.*
The links may be part of the same polypeptide chain that has doubled back on itself, or they may belong to different chains.

solid. The starting point for theories of the structures of metals is to regard them as consisting of cations of the metal atoms embedded in a sea formed by the discarded valence electrons. The mobility of these electrons accounts for the mechanical, optical, and electrical properties of metals. The spherical cations can pack closely together yet still give rise to locally neutral electrical assemblies. This is because of the ability of the electrons to spread between the cations and neutralize their charges regardless of how closely they are packed. The closeness of the packing of the atoms accounts for the high densities of metals.

In the context of theories of the chemical bond, a metal is one extremely large homonuclear molecule. (For an alternative point of view, see the article MATTER: *Solid state*.) If a sample of sodium metal is thought of as consisting of *n* sodium atoms where each atom has a 3*s* orbital for use in the construction of molecular orbitals and each atom supplies one electron to a common pool, then from these *n* atomic orbitals *n* molecular orbitals can be constructed. Each orbital has a characteristic energy, and the range of energies spanned by the *n* orbitals is finite, however great the value of *n*. If *n* is very large, it follows that the energy separation between neighbouring molecular orbitals is very small and approaches zero as *n* approaches infinity. The molecular orbitals then form a band of energies (Figure 30). Another similar band can be formed by the overlap of the 3*p* orbitals of the atoms, but there is a substantial band gap—*i.e.,* a region of energy in which there are no molecular orbitals—between the two bands.

Although the 3*s* band is virtually continuous, it actually consists of *n* discrete molecular orbitals, each of which, by the Pauli exclusion principle, can contain two paired electrons. It follows that the 3*s* band of sodium, which is occupied by the pool of *n* electrons, is only half full. There are empty molecular orbitals immediately above the uppermost filled orbitals, and it is easy for a perturbation, such as an applied potential difference or an oscillating electromagnetic field of incident light, to move the electrons into these unoccupied levels. Hence, the electrons are very mobile and can conduct an electric current, reflect light, transmit energy, and rapidly migrate to new locations when the cations are moved by hammering.

The full theory of the structure of metals is a highly technical subject (as are the full theories of the other topics discussed here). This brief introduction has been intended only to show that the ideas of molecular orbital theory can be naturally extended to account for the general features of the structures and properties of solids.

Advanced aspects of chemical bonding

This section treats several aspects of molecular structure that are of more specialized interest and shows how particular classes of compounds are described. Molecular orbital theory will be used as a framework for the discussion, but aspects of valence bond theory will be incorporated when it is natural (in the sense of being commonplace in chemistry) to use them.

THEORIES OF BONDING IN COMPLEXES

A particular class of compounds that once gave rise to some difficulty in the explanation of the origin of their bonding are the complexes of transition metal ions. There are numerous examples of such species; they have in common a structure in which a central metal ion is surrounded by a number of ions or molecules, called ligands, that can also exist separately. The most common complexes have six ligands arranged in an octahedron around the central ion. An example is $[Fe(H_2O)_6]^{2+}$, where Fe denotes iron. This species can essentially be regarded as an Fe^{2+} ion, with an electron configuration $[Ar]3d^6$, surrounded by six H_2O molecules linked to the metal ion through their oxygen atoms.

Complex formation is an example of a particular class of reactions known as Lewis acid-base reactions. The general form of Lewis acid-base reactions involves the formation of a covalent bond between a species that supplies an electron pair, which is called a Lewis base, and a species that can accept an electron pair, which is called a Lewis

Band theory of metals

Transition metal complexes

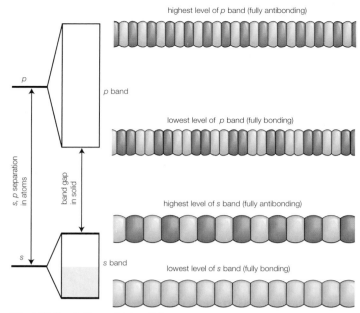

highest level of *p* band (fully antibonding)

lowest level of *p* band (fully bonding)

highest level of *s* band (fully antibonding)

lowest level of *s* band (fully bonding)

p band

s band

s, p separation in atoms

band gap in solid

Figure 30: *Bands of energies in metals.*
A band of molecular orbitals is formed when the *s* orbitals of a large number of atoms overlap; similarly, when the *p* orbitals of the atoms overlap, they form another band. The two bands may be separated by a gap. If each atom provides one electron, only the lower half of the lower band is occupied (as indicated by the shading).

acid. In complexes of the formula $[M(H_2O)_6]^{n+}$, the central metal ion acts as the Lewis acid and the ligand molecules act as the Lewis bases by virtue of a lone pair of electrons on the oxygen atom (only one of the lone pairs is in a position to act in this way). In general, a Lewis acid-base reaction is represented by the scheme $A + :B \rightarrow A—B$. Such reactions occur widely in chemistry, but the singular characteristic of metal ions is that they can act as acceptors to several ligands. The actual number of ligands that attach to a metal ion is in part controlled by the spatial problem of packing ligands together around a central ion.

Crystal field theory. Although complex formation is an example of the linking together of species by the formation of covalent (but highly polar) bonds, the first systematic approach to the explanation of the properties of complexes was based on a model in which the effect of the ligands was treated as an essentially ionic problem. In this crystal field theory, each ligand was represented by a negative point charge. (This point charge models the lone pair of electrons that is responsible for the bond formation.) There are then two contributions to the binding energy. One is the electrostatic attraction between the central cation and the negative point charges, which is largely responsible for the stability of the complex. There is also the differential effect of the array of the point charges on the energies of the *d* orbitals of the ion. Whereas in a free atom all five *d* orbitals have the same energy, in an octahedral crystal field they split into two groups (Figure 31), with three orbitals (labeled t_{2g}; the labeling is based on details of their symmetry) lower in energy than the remaining two (labeled e_g). The difference in energy between the two sets is denoted Δ and is called the crystal-field splitting energy (CFSE). This energy is the parameter that is used to correlate a variety of spectroscopic, thermodynamic, and magnetic properties of complexes.

The essential feature of crystal field theory is that there is a competition between the magnitude of the CFSE and the pairing energy, which is the energy required to accommodate two electrons in one orbital. When the pairing energy is high compared with the CFSE, the lowest-energy electron configuration is achieved with as many electrons as possible in different orbitals. The arrangement of a d^5 ion, for instance, is $t_{2g}^3 e_g^2$, with all spins parallel (as in Figure 31B). However, if the ligands give rise to a very strong crystal field, so that the CFSE is large compared with the pairing energy, then the lowest-energy electron

Crystal-field splitting energy

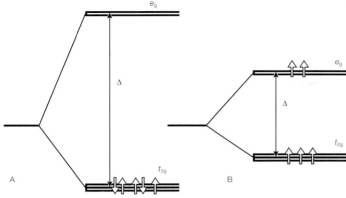

Figure 31: *Crystal field splitting.*
In an octahedral complex, the *d* orbitals of the central metal ion divide into two sets of different energies. The separation in energy is the crystal-field splitting energy, Δ. (A) When Δ is large, it is energetically more favourable for electrons to occupy the lower set of orbitals. (B) When Δ is small, it is energetically more favourable for the electrons to occupy both sets with as many parallel electron spins as possible.

configuration is that with as many electrons as possible in the lower (t_{2g}) set of orbitals. In such a case, a $3d^5$ ion would adopt the configuration t_{2g}^5, with only one unpaired spin as in Figure 31A. Thus, because magnetism arises from the presence of electron spins, it can be seen that the magnetic properties of the complex can be correlated with the size of the CFSE. The same is true of spectroscopic and thermodynamic properties. In particular it is found that ligands can be arranged in order of the strength of the crystal field that they generate, and this so-called spectro-

chemical series can be used to rationalize and predict the properties of complexes.

Ligand field theory. Crystal field theory is an artificial parameterization of the bonding in complexes, for it models the actual bonding in terms of an array of point charges. A superior theory is a modification of crystal field theory known as ligand field theory, which is more securely based in MO theory and allows for a more appropriate degree of delocalization of electrons over the metal ion and the ligands.

In essence, in ligand field theory molecular orbitals of complexes of first-transition-series (*i.e.*, period-4) metals are constructed from the five $3d$ orbitals of the central metal cation and one orbital from each of the ligand atoms that are directly attached to the metal cation. It follows that in such an octahedral complex there are $5 + 6 = 11$ molecular orbitals to accommodate the $3d$ electrons of an $[Ar]3d^n$ species and 12 electrons from the six ligand atoms, giving $12 + n$ electrons in all. The 11 MOs span a range of energies; a typical molecular orbital energy-level diagram is shown in Figure 32. Twelve of the electrons occupy the six lowest-energy MOs, which are largely ligand-atom in character. The remaining n electrons are to be accommodated in the two sets of orbitals labeled e_g and t_{2g}. The energy separation between these two sets of orbitals, the ligand-field splitting energy (LFSE), denoted Δ, is the ligand field version of the CFSE in crystal field theory, and from this point on the construction of the lowest-energy electron configuration is much the same as in crystal field theory. However, ligand field theory is less artificial, allows for electron delocalization, and is more readily extended to more complex patterns of bonding between the central metal ion and the ligands (such as the incorporation of bonds with π symmetry).

Ligand-field splitting energy

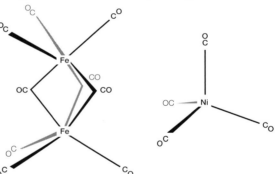

Figure 33: Two carbonyl compounds, showing the different ways (bridge or terminal) in which the carbonyl groups can attach to the metal atoms.

COMPOUNDS DISPLAYING UNIQUE BONDING

Organometallic compounds. A particular class of complexes consists of the organometallic compounds, in which there are bonds between a metal atom and a carbon atom. Among the most important of such compounds are the carbonyls, which are complexes in which one or more of the ligands is a carbon monoxide molecule, CO, either linked to one atom or bridging two (Figure 33). Another interesting class of organometallic compounds is composed of the metallocenes, informally called "sandwich compounds," in which the metal atom sits between two planar hydrocarbon rings, analogous to the meat in a sandwich. Of these, ferrocene [$Fe(C_5H_5)_2$] was among the first to be synthesized.

The stabilities of organometallic compounds follow certain empirical rules, among which the 18-electron rule is the analogue of the octet rule of main-group compounds. According to this rule, the most stable organometallic compounds are those having 18 electrons in the valence shell, a term in this context extended to include the outermost d orbitals. Nickel tetracarbonyl, $Ni(CO)_4$, a poisonous gas used in the refining of nickel, has 10 electrons provided by the neutral nickel atom and two from each of the four CO ligands, giving 18 electrons in all.

The electronic structures of organometallic compounds

The 18-electron rule

Figure 32: *Ligand field splitting.*
In ligand field theory, the atomic orbitals of the central metal ion and the ligands are combined into molecular orbitals. The properties of the complex are then determined by the filling of the orbitals in accord with the building-up principle. The shaded region corresponds to the crystal field orbitals illustrated in Figure 31.

can be expressed most effectively in MO terms, and they can be regarded as no more than a special case of ligand field theory. There are certain details that make them particularly interesting, however. To give a sense of the detail in which the structure of a metal-carbon bond may be expressed, attention will be focused here on the link between a metal atom (M) and a carbonyl group (CO): M—CO.

A CO molecule has much the same electronic structure as an N_2 molecule (see above Figure 16), because it has the same number of electrons—that is, the two species are isoelectronic. There are two important features of this structure, which differ in detail from N_2 on account of the different electronegativities of the two elements in CO. One is that the highest occupied molecular orbital, the HOMO, is largely confined to the carbon atom and can be interpreted as being a lone pair occupying an orbital with σ symmetry. This lone pair enables CO to act as a Lewis base and to link to the metal atom by forming a σ bond to it by overlap with one of the lobes of a d orbital (Figure 34). However, the lowest unfilled molecular orbital, the LUMO, has π symmetry and can accept electrons from an appropriate d orbital of the metal, and thus it can help the ligand to act as a Lewis acid. It is this ability of the ligand to act as both a Lewis base and a Lewis acid that is responsible for the stability of metal carbonyls.

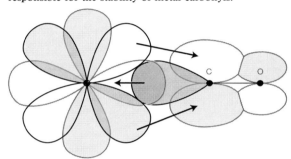

Figure 34: *The structure of the link between a metal atom and a carbon monoxide (CO) ligand.*
The light orbitals are empty in the individual species; the shaded orbitals are full. The arrows indicate the direction of electron donation.

Boranes. The electron-deficient compound diborane, B_2H_6, as noted earlier, can be regarded as a cluster of atoms held together by pairs of delocalized electrons that extend their binding influence over all electrons in the molecule. The unusual feature of diborane is the existence of B—H—B bridges as part of the cluster. Although an MO treatment of the molecule deals with it as a whole, chemists find it helpful to focus on this novel feature and to consider each B—H—B moiety as an example of a three-centre, two-electron bond (a 3c,2e bond, as shown in Figure 35). They regard diborane as three atoms held together by a pair of electrons delocalized over three atoms but are aware that this semilocalized picture is only a part of the true picture.

The three-centre, two-electron bond

The usefulness of the concept of a 3c,2e bond stems from two observations. The first is that diborane is in fact only one of a large class of compounds of boron and hydrogen, the boranes and the borohydride anions, in which the same feature is found. The second observation is that a 3c,2e bond can be formed by three boron atoms. Three examples of these species are shown in Figure 36. As can be seen, intricate networks of atoms can be formed in this way—for example, some having the form of closed frameworks (the *closo*-boranes), some looking like untidy birds' nests (the *nido*-boranes), and some resembling spiderwebs (the *arachno*-boranes). Which type of structure is obtained correlates with the number of valence electrons in the molecule, and the correlation is expressed by Wade's rules. These rules are empirical, but they can be justified by a consideration of the numbers of 3c,2e and ordinary 2c,2e bonds that are needed in each type of structure. They constitute an excellent example of how chemists utilize the concept of bond formation and deploy a mixture of valence bond and molecular orbital concepts to establish or rationalize helpful correlations between the number

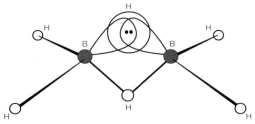

Figure 35: *The structure of the three-centre, two-electron bond in a B—H—B fragment of a diborane molecule.*
A pair of electrons in the bonding combination pulls all three atoms together.

of electrons present and the structure of the species.

Metal cluster compounds. A metal cluster compound is one in which metal atoms are linked directly to one another (Figure 37). A simple example is the ion Hg_2^{2+}, in which two mercury (Hg) ions are linked together. A slightly more elaborate version is the ion $[Re_2Cl_8]^{2-}$, in which there is a direct link between two rhenium (Re) atoms. Some metal cluster compounds have more than two metal atoms; an example is $[Re_3Cl_{12}]^{3-}$, in which there are three rhenium atoms bonded together. It is sometimes difficult to determine whether the metal atoms are indeed directly linked or merely held quite close together by a framework of bridging ligands.

Metal cluster compounds warrant a special mention here because they provide the only examples of quadruple bonds in chemistry. Apart from that, their bonding can be treated as a straightforward exercise in MO or VB theory. Indeed, a metal cluster can be regarded as an exceedingly

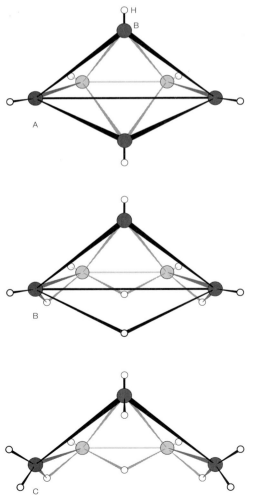

Figure 36: *Three typical borane molecules.*
(A) A *closo*-borane, (B) a *nido*-borane, and (C) an *arachno*-borane.

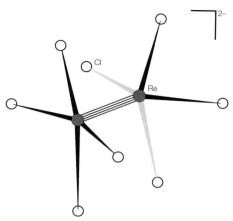

Figure 37: The $[Re_2Cl_8]^{2-}$ ion, with a metal-metal link that has quadruple-bond character.

tiny sample of metal, with insufficient atoms present for the molecular orbitals to form a continuous band. The structure of $[Re_2Cl_8]^{2-}$ is shown in Figure 37. The clue to the existence of unusual bonding is the arrangement of the two sets of chloride ligands: to minimize repulsions between the atoms, each $ReCl_4$ group might be expected to be twisted 45° relative to the next rather than being in the orientation shown. There appears to be a bonding feature between the two rhenium atoms that holds the groups as illustrated. This feature is taken to be a quadruple bond arising from the overlap of d orbitals on the two rhenium atoms.

The structure of quadruple bonds

The structure of a quadruple bond is illustrated in Figure 38. One component is a σ bond formed by the cylindrically symmetrical overlap of two d orbitals. There are also two π bonds formed by the overlap of two appropriately orientated d orbitals. The new feature is the δ bond, which is formed by the face-to-face overlap of two parallel d orbitals and has a distinctly different symmetry with respect to the internuclear axis than the other two types of bond. A quadruple bond therefore consists of a σ bond, two π bonds, and one δ bond. The reduction in bond strength that would occur if one d orbital were rotated away from its partner so that overlap is lessened accounts for the torsional rigidity of the bond and the observed shape of the species.

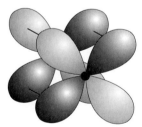

Figure 38: The δ component of a quadruple bond, shown as the outcome of the face-to-face overlap of d orbitals on neighbouring atoms.

COMPUTATIONAL APPROACHES TO MOLECULAR STRUCTURE

In conclusion, a brief introduction to the manner in which these qualitative ideas are implemented computationally follows. The computation of molecular structures by numerical solution of the Schrödinger equation is a highly developed discipline. The principal difficulty is the large number of interactions between electrons that must be taken into account; this fact makes computational quantum chemists some of the most demanding users of computers and, increasingly, of supercomputers.

There are two strands of approach to the computation of molecular structure. In the semiempirical approach, the calculation draws on a number of experimentally determined characteristics to help in the overall calculation. In the ab initio approach, the calculation proceeds from first principles (the Schrödinger equation) and makes no use of imported information. The former approach was dominant in the 1970s, but increases in computing power have led to an ascendancy of ab initio techniques since then. The latter are intrinsically more reliable because there can be no certainty that a quantity determined in one context is appropriate to a particular molecule.

The central aim of computations is to identify the lowest-energy arrangement of a given set of atoms and to identify that arrangement as the structure of the molecule. The calculational strategy adopted is to seek self-consistency in the calculation, and, for that reason, the computations are referred to as self-consistent field (SCF) procedures. Thus, a particular electronic distribution is proposed, and the distribution of the electrons is recalculated on the basis of this first approximation. The distribution is then calculated again on the basis of that improved description, and the process is continued until there is negligible change—*i.e.*, until the electron distribution has achieved self-consistency.

Self-consistent field calculations

The implementation of this basic strategy can take a number of forms, and rival techniques have given rise to a large number of acronyms, such as AM1 (Austin Method 1) and MINDO (Modified Intermediate Neglect of Differential Overlap), which are two popular semiempirical procedures.

With self-consistency established, the wavefunctions are available for detailed scrutiny. One illustration must suffice. There is certain evidence that carcinogenic or pharmacological activity correlates with certain aspects of the charge distribution in molecules. Instead of dealing with the primitive concept of partial charges, numerical wavefunctions can be used to map the details of the charge distribution and hence to screen molecules for possible activity. This approach is potentially of considerable utility for pharmaceutical products as it can help to reduce the amount of in vivo screening of novel products.

Computational procedures have advanced to the stage where the role of the environment (for example, the water around enzyme molecules) can be incorporated. They are also being applied to the demanding calculations that are needed to describe the replacement of one grouping of chemical bonds into another that takes place in the course of chemical reactions. Thus, as well as dealing with the static considerations of structure, modern treatments of the chemical bond are now confronting the dynamic problems of reactions.

BIBLIOGRAPHY. An elementary introduction to chemical bonding is found in P.W. ATKINS and J.A. BERAN, *General Chemistry*, 2nd ed. (1992). Pictorial interpretations of many of the quantum mechanical concepts mentioned in this article are available in P.W. ATKINS, *Quanta: A Handbook of Concepts*, 2nd ed. (1992). R.J. PUDDEPHATT and P.K. MONAGHAN, *The Periodic Table of the Elements*, 2nd ed. (1986), provides an introduction to the basis of chemical periodicity. DUWARD F. SHRIVER, P.W. ATKINS, and COOPER H. LANGFORD, *Inorganic Chemistry*, 2nd ed. (1994), includes descriptions of atomic structure and bonding in complexes, clusters, and electron-deficient compounds. Two authoritative monographs on bonding are LINUS PAULING, *The Nature of the Chemical Bond and the Structure of Molecules and Crystals*, 3rd ed. (1960, reissued 1989); and C.A. COULSON, *Coulson's Valence*, 3rd ed. by ROY MCWEENY (1979). A more physical view of chemical bonding than presented in this article is given by JOHN C. MORRISON *et al.*, "Electronic Structure of Atoms and Molecules," in GEORGE L. TRIGG (ed.), *Encyclopedia of Applied Physics*, vol. 6 (1993), pp. 45–98. Other accounts include ROGER L. DEKOCK and HARRY B. GRAY, *Chemical Structure and Bonding* (1980); BRIAN WEBSTER, *Chemical Bonding Theory* (1990); and AHMED ZEWAIL (ed.), *The Chemical Bond: Structure and Dynamics* (1992). Applications to pharmacologically active molecules are introduced in W.G. RICHARDS, *Quantum Pharmacology*, 2nd ed. (1983). Computational aspects of the chemical bond are described in ALAN HINCHLIFFE, *Computational Quantum Chemistry* (1988).   (P.W. Atkins)

Electronics: Principal devices and components

OPTOELECTRONIC DEVICES

Major classes of optoelectronic devices

Optoelectronic devices are devices in which the photon, the basic particle of light, is affected. Such devices can be divided into four groups: (1) photodetectors and solar cells that convert photons into electrical current, (2) light-emitting diodes and semiconductor lasers that convert an applied voltage into emitted photons, (3) optical fibres that guide light within a small plastic or glass fibre between a light source and a detector, and (4) optical-fibre amplifiers that convert the energy of an optical pump source to photons identical to an optical signal. A useful expression when dealing with optoelectronics is the conversion between the wavelength of the light, λ, in micrometres, and the energy of the photon, E, in electron volts: $\lambda = 1.24/E$.

Photodetectors and solar cells. *Photodetectors.* A photodetector is a semiconductor device that transforms light into an electrical signal. Its applications range from sensing the amount of light for control of the shutter in an automatic camera to conversion of an optical signal in an optical communication system into an electrical signal. Silicon is used for photodiodes in the 0.8- to 0.9-micrometre (μm) wavelength region, while germanium and III-V compound semiconductors are employed for those in the 1.0- to 1.6-μm wavelength region. At longer wavelengths, narrow-energy-gap compound semiconductors are used; they are cooled to the temperature of liquid nitrogen (77 K) to reduce the leakage current.

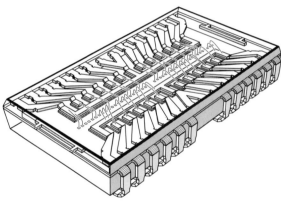

Figure 31: An integrated circuit (cutaway view) in surface-mount molded plastic package.

The absorption of light is governed by the expression $I = I_o \exp(-\alpha x)$, where I is the light intensity at the depth x, I_o is the incident light intensity, and α is the absorption coefficient at a particular photon energy. The absorption coefficients for commonly used semiconductors in the visible and near-infrared spectral region are shown in Figure 32. Photodetectors are generally intended to operate only over a narrow wavelength region of a particular optical source. The energy gap of the semiconductor should be slightly less than the photon energy.

MSM photodiode

A metal-semiconductor-metal (MSM) photodiode consists of a lightly doped photoabsorbing semiconducting layer on which a pair of interdigitized metal contacts is deposited. For gallium arsenide most of the photo-generated electron-hole pairs due to the absorption of photons with wavelengths less than about 0.9 μm are generated within 1 μm of the surface. A small voltage (5–0.5 V) is applied across the metal fingers. These photo-generated carriers are swept out by the bias electric field, giving a photocurrent. Approximately one electron flows in the external circuit for every three or four photons incident on the MSM photodiode. Attractive features of the MSM photodiode are ultrafast response, low dark current, and compatibility with processing for integration with field-effect transistors for signal amplification.

A p-n-junction photodiode absorbs photons near the p-n

From G.E. Stillman, V.M. Robbins, and N. Tabatabaie, "III-V Compound Semiconductor Devices: Optical Detectors," IEEE Transactions on Electron Devices, ED-31, 1643, © 1984 IEEE

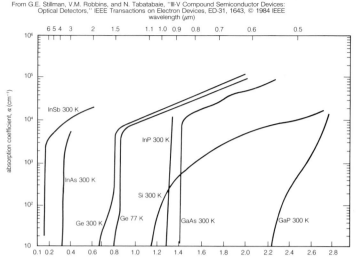

Figure 32: Absorption coefficients for silicon, germanium, and selected III-V compound semiconductors in the visible and near-infrared spectral region (see text).

junction, which generates electron-hole pairs. A schematic representation is shown in Figure 33. These photo-generated carriers result in a current through the external circuit. The photodiode can be operated in the photovoltaic mode, in which no bias voltage is applied, but the device is connected to a load resistor. The optical signal then appears as a voltage across the load resistor. The diode area is small, so that it minimizes the capacitance for better high-frequency response. An important measure of how well the device converts photons to electrons is the quantum efficiency, which is the ratio of the number of electrons flowing in the external circuit to the number of incident photons.

One of the most commonly used photodiodes is the p-i-n diode, which has a very lightly doped i region between the p and n regions. This structure can enhance the quantum efficiency, because more of the light is absorbed in the diode depletion region (between the p and n regions), where it is collected and can flow through the load resistor. Also, because the p and n regions are farther apart than in the p-n-junction photodiode, the capacitance is less and the response speed is faster.

The avalanche photodiode is designed for use at high reverse bias to provide current gain to the photo-generated hole-electron pairs. When the electric field in the depletion region of the reverse-biased p-n-junction photodiode is about 10^5 volts per centimetre, a photo-generated hole or

From S.M. Sze, Physics of Semiconductor Devices, 2nd ed. (1979); John Wiley and Sons, New York

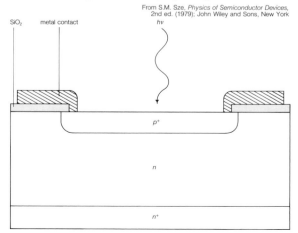

Figure 33: The p-n junction photodiode.

electron can collide with adjacent electron-bonding atoms, break the bond, and create a hole-electron pair. This process is called impact ionization. These newly created pairs can gain enough energy from the electric field to cause further impact ionization until finally an avalanche of carriers is produced. The avalanche gain can increase the signal-to-noise ratio and thus detect light signals of lower intensity than those detectable by other photodetectors. The avalanche photodiode, however, will have low noise only if either the electron or the hole (but not both) is capable of causing impact ionization. Silicon has a large difference in the ionization rates of electrons and holes, while the ionization rates for the III-V semiconductors are nearly equal. Thus, only silicon has been extensively used for avalanche photodiodes.

Solar cells. The solar cell was the first optoelectronic device developed and was demonstrated by Daryl M. Chapin, Calvin S. Fuller, and Gerald L. Pearson in 1954 with a diffused silicon *p-n* junction. The solar cell is a large-area photodiode that "detects" the solar emission spectrum rather than a specific optical signal wavelength, as do photodiodes. The solar cell is unbiased, and the load is connected directly across the two terminals of the *p-n* junction. One of the most important parameters is the conversion efficiency, which is the ratio of the maximum power output to the incident power.

The first space satellites were electrically powered by silicon solar cells, and these cells continue to be an important long-duration power source for satellites. The solar cells originally used for this purpose were made with single-crystal silicon and had conversion efficiencies of about 15 percent. The efficiency of the single-crystal silicon solar cell is limited to about 20 percent, because the long-wavelength emission is not absorbed in the silicon or is not absorbed near enough to the *p-n* junction for the photogenerated carriers to be collected by the junction. For ground applications, lower-cost solar cells have been developed by using large-grained, polycrystalline silicon with efficiencies near 16 percent instead of the more expensive single-crystal silicon. Even thin-film amorphous solar cells with efficiencies of about 12 percent have been investigated for further cost reduction. In each case, the lower cost is accompanied by reduced conversion efficiency. Other materials, such as aluminum gallium arsenide or gallium arsenide, have been used in applications where an increased conversion efficiency of more than 25 percent can justify the significantly greater cost.

The design of solar cells is influenced by the solar emission spectrum. The effect of the atmosphere on sunlight at the Earth's surface is defined by the air mass. The solar spectrum outside the atmosphere is the air mass zero (AM0). The solar spectrum at the Earth's surface for the minimum path length with the Sun directly overhead is AM1. The sunlight is attenuated by the atmosphere owing to the absorption of infrared rays by ozone and scattering by clouds and airborne particles. For the Sun at an angle of 60° from the overhead position, the spectrum is AM2. The solar spectral irradiance is given by the power per unit wavelength. These three solar spectral irradiance spectra are shown in Figure 34, together with the 5,800-K emission spectrum of a blackbody that approximates the AM0 spectrum. (A blackbody is an ideal body or surface that absorbs and reemits all radiant energy falling on it.)

The structure of a high-efficiency single-crystal solar cell with an AM0 efficiency in the range of 20–21 percent is shown in Figure 35. Top contact is made via metal stripes that cover only 0.5 percent of the top surface. The rear aluminum contact layer acts as a highly effective reflector. The inverted pyramid structure along the top surface serves to reduce the front-surface reflection and combines with the rear reflector to form an efficent light-trapping scheme.

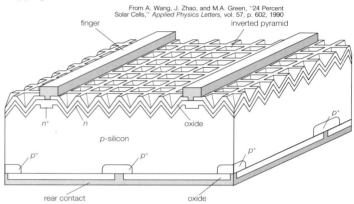

From A. Wang, J. Zhao, and M.A. Green, "24 Percent Solar Cells," *Applied Physics Letters,* vol. 57, p. 602, 1990

Figure 35: The structure of a high-efficiency, single-crystal silicon solar cell.

A more economical fabrication technology utilizing polycrystalline silicon involves cutting wafers from cast blocks. The silicon cell measures 10 centimetres square. These cells are connected in large solar panels for application on the Earth's surface to provide power at remote sites.

Light-emitting diodes and semiconductor lasers. *Light-emitting diodes.* The familiar light bulb gives off light owing to its temperature (incandescence). Luminescence, on the other hand, is the result of electronic excitation of a material. The light-emitting diode is a *p-n* junction in which an applied voltage yields a flow of current, and the recombination of the carriers injected across the junction results in the emission of light. (The process involved here is in effect electroluminescence.) The ratio of the number of emitted photons to the number of electrons crossing the *p-n* junction is the quantum efficiency. LED emission is generally in the visible part of the spectrum with wavelengths from 0.4 to 0.7 μm or in the near infrared with wavelengths between 2.0 and 0.7 μm. More than 20 billion LEDs are produced each year. Visible LEDs are used as numeric displays or indicator lamps and are sufficiently bright that a row of red LEDs are used in an automobile spoiler to replace the conventional rear-window brake light. Infrared LEDs are employed in optoisolators, in television remote controls, and as sources in optical communication systems. The applied voltage is near 2.0 volts. The current depends on the application and ranges from a few milliamperes to several hundred milliamperes.

Silicon, the most commonly used semiconductor for electronic devices and integrated circuits, is not suitable for LEDs. However, in the III-V compound semiconductors—*e.g.,* gallium arsenide (GaAs), gallium arsenide phosphide (GaAs$_{1-x}$P$_x$), aluminum gallium arsenide (Al$_x$Ga$_{1-x}$As), aluminum gallium indium phosphide [(Al$_x$Ga$_{1-x}$)$_y$In$_{1-y}$P], and gallium indium arsenide phosphide (Ga$_x$In$_{1-x}$As$_y$P$_{1-y}$)—radiative recombination can occur with ease. The peak intensity of the emission spectrum occurs at a photon energy slightly less than the semiconductor energy gap. The radiative recombination must compete with various nonradiative recombination processes, because of undesirable impurities and crystal defects, including precipitations and dislocations. Careful material processing is necessary to obtain useful LEDs.

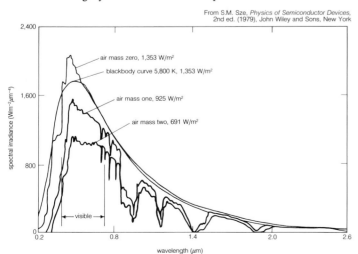

From S.M. Sze, *Physics of Semiconductor Devices,* 2nd ed. (1979), John Wiley and Sons, New York

air mass zero, 1,353 W/m²
blackbody curve 5,800 K, 1,353 W/m²
air mass one, 925 W/m²
air mass two, 691 W/m²
visible

Figure 34: Solar spectral irradiance.

In the notation used for the ternary solid solutions, the x in $Al_xGa_{1-x}As$ means that x percent of the group-III elements are aluminum and $(1 - x)$ percent of the group-III elements are gallium. For example, with $x = 0.3$, the $Al_{0.3}Ga_{0.7}As$ would have 30 percent aluminum and 70 percent gallium. For quaternary solid solutions such as $Ga_xIn_{1-x}As_yP_{1-y}$, the x represents the percent of group-III elements, while the y represents the percent of group-V elements. The energy gap, and therefore the wavelength of the emitted light, changes with the composition x or x and y. The wavelength of the emitted light can be changed by varying the semiconductor composition.

The brightness of the light observed from an LED will depend on the power emitted by the LED and the relative sensitivity of the eye at the emitted wavelength. The maximum sensitivity occurs at 0.555 μm, which is in the yellow-orange and green region.

The first visible LED with extensive applications was based on $GaAs_{1-x}P_x$ grown on GaAs substrates. The composition for maximum brightness depends on both the quantum efficiency of the LED and the sensitivity of the eye. The maximum brightness occurs near $x = 0.4$, which is an energy gap of approximately 1.9 eV. At this composition, the external quantum efficiency is about 0.2 percent.

A typical LED is illustrated in Figure 36. The clear epoxy dome in Figure 36A serves as a structural element to hold the lead frame together, as a lens to focus the light, and as a refractive index match to permit more light to escape from the chip. The LED chip, typically $250 \times 250 \times 250$ μm, is mounted in a reflecting cup formed in the lead frame. In Figure 36B the n- and p-type GaP:N layers represent nitrogen added to GaP to give green emission, the n- and p-type GaAsP:N layers represent nitrogen added to $GaAs_xP_{1-x}$ to give orange and yellow emission, and the p-type GaP:Zn,O layer represents zinc and oxygen added to GaP to give red emission. Another useful material is $Al_xGa_{1-x}As$ for red LEDs, although a more complex structure is required than for GaP:Zn,O. The $Al_xGa_{1-x}As$ light-emitting layer is confined between two larger-energy-gap $Al_yGa_{1-y}As$ layers ($x < y$); this permits the more efficient injection of carriers into the light-emitting layers and allows the confining layers to be transparent to the generated light, permitting a high light-extraction efficiency.

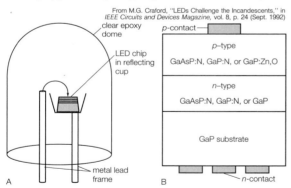

From M.G. Craford, "LEDs Challenge the Incandescents," in *IEEE Circuits and Devices Magazine*, vol. 8, p. 24 (Sept. 1992)

Figure 36: *Typical LED device and chip configuration.*
(A) Cross-sectional view of an LED lamp. (B) The LED chip.

In the early 1990s two further enhancements to LEDs were developed. One was the introduction of LEDs based on $(Al_xGa_{1-x})_yIn_{1-y}P$, which has a larger energy gap than $Al_xGa_{1-x}As$ and permits higher-efficiency LEDs throughout the spectral region from green to red-orange. The other was the commercialization of blue-emitting LEDs based on silicon carbide (SiC), although these blue LEDs are at least an order of magnitude less efficient than the other LEDs and more costly. However, blue LEDs can be combined on a cluster with other colour LEDs to give all colours, including white, for full-colour moving-message panel applications. In 1994, blue LEDs based on the III-V compound GaN were demonstrated with 2.0 percent efficiencies.

Any LED may be used as a source with a plastic or glass optical fibre for a short-range optical-fibre transmission system over a distance of less than 100 metres. For a long-range optical-fibre transmission system, the emission properties of the source are selected to match the transmission properties of the optical fibre, and the infrared LEDs are a better match than the visible LEDs. Glass optical fibres suffer much less loss than do plastic fibres, and the glass fibres have the lowest transmission loss in the infrared at wavelengths of 1.3 and 1.55 μm. To match the transmission properties of the low-loss glass fibres, the quaternary solid solution gallium indium arsenide phosphide is grown with compositions that have the same lattice constant as the indium phosphide (InP) substrate. The composition of the gallium indium arsenide phosphide may be selected to give emission at 1.3 or 1.55 μm.

Lasers. Optical devices of this kind produce a more directional light beam and a narrow wavelength band. The term laser is an acronym derived from light amplification by stimulated emission of radiation.

A photon and an electron can interact in two ways. In an absorption process, a photon with an energy slightly larger than the energy gap can interact with an electron in the valence band and raise the electron to the conduction band, creating a hole in the valence band. In a stimulated emission process, a photon with an energy slightly greater than the energy gap can interact with an electron in the conduction band and cause the electron to recombine with a hole in the valence band. The recombination process results in the emission of a photon identical to the photon that caused the recombination process, and the number of photons is increased. In absorption a photon is lost, while in stimulated emission an additional photon is created. To have a laser, it is necessary to provide a structure that will make stimulated emission more probable than absorption.

A semiconductor laser requires a p-n junction that provides light emission like an LED (*i.e.,* spontaneous emission) when a voltage is applied and current flows. This radiative recombination has to be confined along the junction plane and must be reflected by parallel, partially reflecting surfaces so as to form a cavity. These parallel mirrors are readily obtained by cleaving along the natural cleavage planes of III-V compound semiconductors. The injected electrons and the light must be confined to the same region, so that they can interact to enhance the stimulated emission.

To provide the carrier and light confinement to the region of the p-n junction and obtain continuous operation at room temperature, it is necessary to use a heterojunction—*i.e.,* the junction in a single crystal between two dissimilar semiconductors. The most significant difference is the energy gap and the refractive index. A double heterostructure made with aluminum gallium arsenide and gallium arsenide is shown in Figure 37A. The left layer is n-type $Al_xGa_{1-x}As$, the centre layer is p-type GaAs, and the right layer is p-type $Al_xGa_{1-x}As$. The centre layer of GaAs has a smaller energy gap than the two cladding layers of $Al_xGa_{1-x}As$. Typical values for x are 0.3. This gallium arsenide region with a smaller energy gap is where the light is generated owing to radiative recombination of the injected carriers; it is called the active region. With an active layer of gallium arsenide, the emission wavelength is in the infrared near 0.9 μm. Other pairs of semiconductors may be used, but all require a smaller-energy-gap active region with larger-energy-gap cladding layers.

Figure 37B shows the energy gaps of the three regions when a voltage of approximately 1.7 is applied to the heterostructure laser. Electrons are injected from the n-layer of $Al_xGa_{1-x}As$ into the potential well of GaAs formed between the two $Al_xGa_{1-x}As$ layers. The injected carriers are confined to the narrow active layer, which typically has a thickness near 0.1 μm. The refractive index profile is shown in Figure 37C. Because the $Al_xGa_{1-x}As$ layers have a smaller refractive index than the GaAs region, they form an optical waveguide that confines the light due to radiative recombination to the active layer. The light confinement is illustrated in Figure 37D. The carrier and light-confining properties of the heterojunctions permit a high density of injected electrons in the region where the light is confined, so that the photons can interact with the electrons and cause stimulated emission. The oscillation condition requires that the stimulated emission exceed the

Principles
of
operation

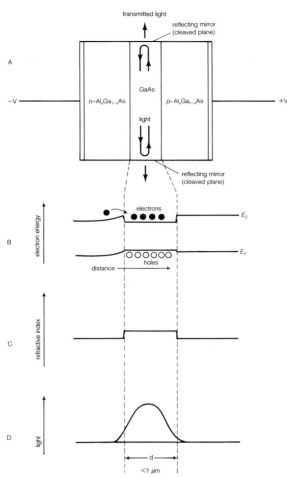

Figure 37: (A) $Al_{0.3}Ga_{0.7}As$-GaAs double heterostructure laser. (B) Energy-band diagram at forward bias. (C) Refractive-index profile. (D) Optical-field distribution.

emission, as in an LED. When the stimulated emission exceeds the internal losses and the light emitted from the cleaved facets, the laser threshold is reached and the light output rises rapidly with the current. Above the threshold current, most of the current flowing into the p-n junction results in laser emission, and the quantum efficiency is much higher than for an LED. The emission spectrum is also given in Figure 39.

Improvements have been made through other stripe-geometry structures to provide optimized properties for a particular application. Threshold currents near 1 milliampere have been obtained by reducing the active-layer thickness to 0.01 μm and the stripe width to 1 μm. These reduced-threshold lasers also permitted high-speed operation in excess of 10 gigahertz. The best match to the transmission properties of optical fibres occurs at wavelengths of 1.3 and 1.55 μm. Heterostructure lasers for emission in this wavelength region have cladding layers made of indium phosphide and active layers consisting of gallium indium arsenide phosphide, the lattice structures of which match those of indium phosphide. These lasers are used as light sources in long-distance optical-fibre communication systems. Such applications include undersea cables.

The largest-volume use of semiconductor lasers is in compact disc players. In such devices, laser light is focused on a plastic disc coated with a thin metallic film, and digital information is communicated by the presence or absence of "pits." These microscopic holes change the reflectivity of the emitted light, which is detected by a photodiode.

Other applications—such as illumination, pumping of solid-state laser media like neodymium yttrium aluminum garnet (Nd:YAG), and satellite-to-satellite and satellite-to-ground optical communication links—require multistripe, monolithic laser diode arrays with continuous-wave output power levels in the watts range. A laser array with 20-stripe lasers, each 100 μm wide, gives 38 watts of continuous wave power; it is shown in Figure 40.

Major uses of semiconductor lasers

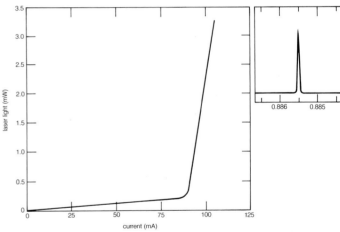

Figure 39: Light output versus the current for a heterostructure laser. The emission spectrum is shown at the upper right.

light lost through the partially reflecting facets and internal absorption.

The layers of $Al_xGa_{1-x}As$ and GaAs are grown on a GaAs substrate by a variety of epitaxial growth techniques, which include liquid-phase epitaxy, molecular-beam epitaxy, and metal-organic chemical-vapour deposition. These techniques permit the growth of the micrometre- and submicrometre-thick layers necessary for heterostructure lasers. Semiconductor lasers use a stripe geometry that restricts the current along the junction plane to a width of from 1 to 15 μm. The laser chip is mounted upside down so that the heat-generating region, the p-n junction, is close to the heat sink. Figure 38 features a stripe-geometry laser mounted on a heat sink. Figure 39 shows light output as a function of the current. At low current, the light output is small, and this emission results from spontaneous

Epitaxial growth techniques

In addition to the rectangular bar structure in Figure 38, vertical-cavity surface-emitting laser diodes (VC-SELs) were developed in the late 1980s and early 1990s for applications such as two-dimensional arrays, optical interconnections, and optical information processing. The VC-SEL structure is shown in Figure 41 with distributed Bragg reflectors of quarter-wavelength layers of differing refractive index to provide the optical cavity. These lasers have low-beam divergence and a circular beam. Individual VC-SELs typically exhibit an output power near one milliwatt, while two-dimensional arrays with one-watt output power have been demonstrated.

Vertical-cavity surface-emitting lasers

Optical fibres. Optical fibres are glass or plastic waveguides for transmitting visible or infrared signals. Since plastic fibres have high attenuation and are used only in limited applications, they will not be considered here. Glass fibres are frequently thinner than human hair and are generally used with LEDs or semiconductor lasers

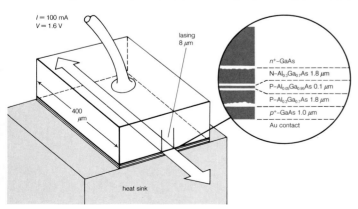

Figure 38: Stripe-geometry laser mounted on a heat sink.

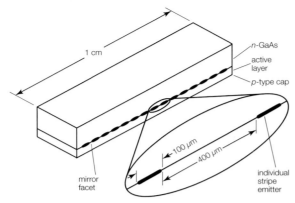

Figure 40: Schematic representation of a monolithic high-power laser structure.

From M. Sakamoto et al., "Ultrahigh Power 38 W, Continuous-Wave Monolithic Laser Diode Arrays," in *Applied Physics Letters*, vol. 52, p. 2220 (1988)

that emit in the infrared region. For wavelengths near 0.8 to 0.9 μm, gallium arsenide–aluminum gallium arsenide (GaAs–Al$_x$Ga$_{1-x}$As) sources are used, and, for those of 1.3 and 1.55 μm, indium phosphide–gallium indium arsenide phosphide (InP–Ga$_x$In$_{1-x}$As$_y$P$_{1-y}$) sources are employed. As noted earlier, optical fibres consist of a glass core region that is surrounded by glass cladding. The core region has a larger refractive index than the cladding, so that the light is confined to that region as it propagates along the fibre. Fibre core diameters range between 1 and 100 μm, while cladding diameters are between 100 and 300 μm.

Fibres with a larger core diameter are called multimode fibres, because more than one electromagnetic-field configuration can propagate through such a fibre. A single-mode fibre has a small core diameter, and the difference in refractive index between the core and cladding is smaller than for the multimode fibre. Only one electromagnetic-field configuration propagates through a single-mode fibre.

Single-mode optical fibres

From K. Tai et al., "Room Temperature Continuous-Wave Vertical-Cavity Surface Emitting Injection Lasers," in *Applied Physics Letters*, vol. 55, p. 2473 (1989)

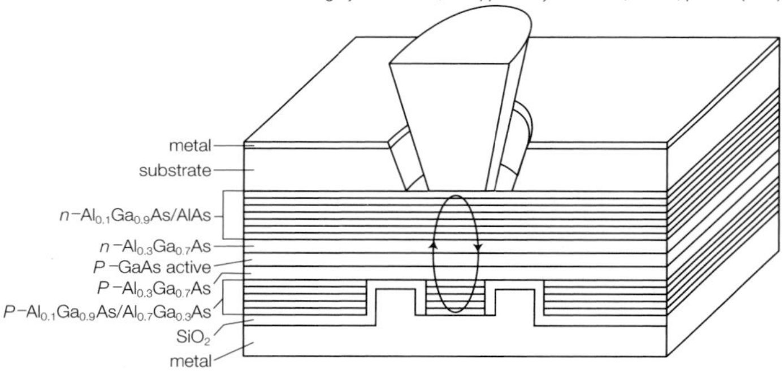

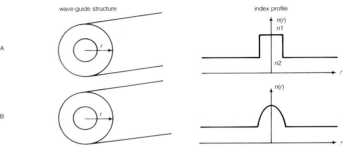

metal
substrate
n–Al$_{0.1}$Ga$_{0.9}$As/AlAs
n–Al$_{0.3}$Ga$_{0.7}$As
P–GaAs active
P–Al$_{0.3}$Ga$_{0.7}$As
P–Al$_{0.1}$Ga$_{0.9}$As/Al$_{0.7}$Ga$_{0.3}$As
SiO$_2$
metal

Figure 41: Cross-sectional representation of the vertical-cavity surface-emitting laser diode (VC-SEL).

Such fibres have the lowest losses and are the most widely used, because they permit longer transmission distances. They have a constant refractive index in the core with a diameter between 1 and 10 μm. The index in the cladding layer decreases by roughly 0.1 to 0.3 percent. This type of fibre is called a step-index fibre (see Figure 42A).

The multimode fibres may be step-index fibres with diameters between 40 and 100 μm. The refractive index step between the core and cladding is approximately 0.8 to 3 percent. In a graded-index fibre, the core refractive index varies as a function of radial distance, as shown in Figure 42B. In such a fibre, a ray in the centre of the core travels more slowly than one near the edge, because the speed of propagation v is related to refractive index n as $v = c/n$, where c is the speed of light. The ray near the edge has a longer zigzag path than the ray in the centre. The transit times of the rays are thus equalized.

Both single-mode and multimode fibres are made of silica glass. The refractive indexes of the silica are varied with dopants such as germanium dioxide (GeO$_2$), phosphoric oxide (P$_2$O$_5$), and boric oxide (B$_2$O$_3$). Vapour-phase

growth reactions are used to obtain the "preform" rod, which is then drawn into optical fibres. For example, a GeO$_2$-SiO$_2$ film may be deposited inside a silica tube. In this case, the GeO$_2$ increases the core refractive index. In another method, preforms for low-loss, single-mode fibres are made by first depositing a low-index borosilicate layer on the inner surface of the silica tube and then depositing a silica layer or inserting a pure fused silica rod before collapsing the preform. The preform is then drawn into the optical fibre and covered with a polymer coating.

There are a number of factors that contribute to attenuation in an optical fibre. Rayleigh scattering is caused by microscopic variations in the refractive index of a fibre and is proportional to λ^4. Absorption by hydroxyl (OH) ions increases the absorption as shown in Figure 43 and gives the minima in loss at 1.3 and 1.55 μm. At longer wavelengths, absorption by the atomic vibrations in the silicon-oxygen atoms rapidly increases the loss. Single-mode fibres commercially available for communications systems have losses as low as 0.2 decibel per kilometre.

wave-guide structure   index profile

A

B

Figure 42: *Optical-fibre waveguide structures and refractive index profiles.*
(A) Step-index fibre. (B) Graded-index fibre.

The low fibre loss permits increased repeater spacing and lower system cost. High-bit-rate digital systems without repeaters have been demonstrated for fibre lengths of more than 100 kilometres.

Fibre splicing techniques have been developed so that repairs can be made in the field with losses of only 0.1 to 0.3 decibel. A variety of optical connectors are used, providing both ease of use and low loss of only a few tenths of a decibel. Fibres are combined into many different kinds of cables, which can be laid both in the ground and under the sea.

Erbium-doped fibre amplifiers. In the late 1980s it was demonstrated that 6 to 10 metres of optical fibre doped with some hundreds of parts per million of the rare-earth element erbium (Er) in the core provided gain to an optical signal when pumped by an optical source. The triply ionized erbium ion (Er^{3+}) is highly absorptive at the pump

From H.T. Shang et al., "Design and Fabrication of Dispersion-Shifted Depressed-Clad Triangular-Profile (DDT) Single-Mode Fiber," in *Electronics Letters*, vol. 21, p. 202 (1985)

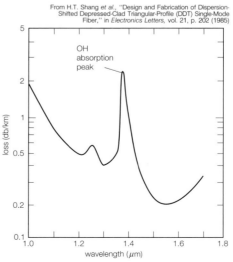

Figure 43: Low-loss, single-mode fibre attenuation plotted as a function of wavelength.

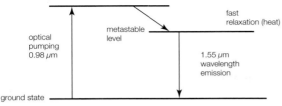

Figure 44: *Energy-level diagram for an erbium-doped optical fibre.*
The diagram illustrates pumping with the absorption of 0.98-μm-wavelength light, the decay to the metastable state, and the decay to the ground state by the generation of photons at the signal 1.55-μm wavelength.

wavelength of 0.98 μm, as shown in Figure 44. The ion decays rapidly to the metastable state, where an incoming photon at a wavelength of 1.55 μm causes decay to the ground state by the emission of a photon of identical 1.55-μm wavelength.

A low-noise erbium-doped fibre amplifier (EDFA) is illustrated in Figure 45. Optical pumping is provided by the semiconductor laser with an emission power of approximately 50–100 milliwatts at a wavelength of 0.98 μm. The low-loss wavelength division multiplexer combines the pump and signal powers, while the isolator eliminates the effects of reflections at splices. EDFAs are used to amplify the output of a signal laser source, as a preamplifier before an optical detector, and to replace optoelectronic repeaters that detect the optical signal, convert it to an electrical signal for amplification, and then drive a semiconductor laser to regenerate the optical signal. The EDFAs can amplify several different signal wavelengths near 1.55 μm, and, if the digital data rate is changed, no changes are necessary for the EDFAs. Also, the EDFAs can be used in analog optical distribution systems such as those connected to private homes. The newest transoceanic cable systems use EDFAs.　　　　　　　　　　　　　　(H.C. Casey, Jr.)

Liquid-crystal displays. Liquid crystals were discovered in 1889 when the Austrian botanist Friedrich Reinitzer observed a curious, cloudy melting behaviour in certain pure organic compounds, which he and the German physicist Otto Lehmann ascribed to a transition to a fourth, liquid-crystalline state of matter. Some organic compounds, in particular rod-shaped ones, partially melt to a liquid-crystalline phase at a precise transition temperature. In this phase, the three-dimensional crystal lattice structure disappears, and the material may flow like a liquid, yet a long-range orientational order of the molecules is retained, giving the material some crystallike properties. At a second, higher temperature this liquid-crystalline state undergoes another transition to an ordinary liquid.

Many kinds of liquid-crystal phases are known (see MATTER: *Liquid crystals* for a discussion of these phases), but generally only the nematic phase is used in liquid-crystal displays (LCDs). Averaged over time, the elongated molecules (Figure 46A) in any locality of the nematic phase all point in the same direction, which is known as the local optic axis or director (the z axis in Figure 46B). This direction can be influenced by the walls of the container or by an electric or magnetic field. The built-in direction causes certain physical properties to have one value measured parallel to the director and another measured perpendicular to it. Particularly important for LCDs are the differences, or anisotropies, in dielectric constant

The nematic phase (margin)

and refractive index measured in the two directions; for most display applications, these anisotropies should be large and positive. In this case, a potential difference of only a few volts applied across the liquid crystal is sufficient to reorient the director parallel to the electric field and away from the container walls. The refractive index anisotropy ensures that a reorientation of the liquid crystal will be accompanied by a change in the amount of light transmitted by the display.

Dynamic scattering mode displays. The first LCD, demonstrated at Radio Corporation of America (now RCA Corporation) laboratories in 1963, used an effect known as the dynamic scattering mode (DSM), which caused the liquid crystal to turn cloudy and scatter light under an applied voltage. The low power consumption of this device, which is the result of its ability to modify ambient light rather than generate light of its own, and its voltage compatibility with the newly developed integrated circuits gave this display many advantages over other flat-panel displays of the time. Although no longer used because of poor viewability and lifetime, DSM displays proved the feasibility as well as the enormous potential of LCDs.

The first LCDs (margin)

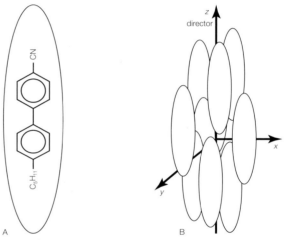

Figure 46: *Nematic liquid-crystal phase.*
The rod-shaped organic molecules (A) of nematic liquid crystals can flow as in an ordinary liquid but retain long-range orientational order (B), resulting in crystalline-like properties. The molecule shown is *p-n*-pentylcyanobiphenyl, which possesses a nematic liquid-crystal phase between 24.0° and 35.3° C.

Twisted nematic displays. The next generation of LCDs used the twisted nematic (TN) effect, developed at Hoffmann–La Roche, Inc., in 1971 and still used in watches and calculators today. The upper and lower substrate plates of a TN display (Figure 47) are separated by a narrow gap of about 8 μm and carry patterned, transparent conductive coatings of indium tin oxide on their inner surfaces. The transparent electrodes have thin polymer coatings several hundred angstroms thick that are unidirectionally rubbed to align the director of the liquid crystal at the surfaces parallel to the rub directions. The upper substrate is rubbed at right angles to the rub direction of the lower substrate, so that, when no voltage is applied (Figure 47, left), the director of the liquid crystal undergoes a continuous 90° twist in the region between the substrates. Polarizer sheets are oriented on both sides of the display in such a way that the direction of vibration of the linear polarized light is parallel to the rub direction of the adjacent alignment layer at each substrate. Linear polarized light from the upper polarizer propagates through the liquid-crystal layer and rotates its plane of polarization in step with the twisted structure. The light then emerges at the bottom of the liquid-crystal layer polarized parallel to the transmission axis of the lower polarizer, where it passes through.

Application of 3–5 volts across the upper and lower electrodes orients the optic axis in the central portion of the liquid-crystal layer predominantly parallel to the electric field and perpendicular to the plates, which untwists the structure and destroys its polarization rotating capacity

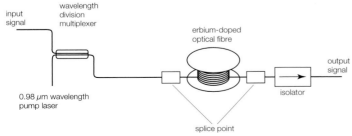

Figure 45: Low-noise erbium-doped fibre amplifier system.

(Figure 47, right). The polarized light passing through the cell now intersects the second polarizer in the "crossed" position, where it is absorbed, causing the activated portion of the display to appear dark. The display also can be operated in a reflective mode by putting a diffuse reflector behind the display; ambient light passing through the display is reflected and simply retraces its path back to the viewer.

The first TN displays were used in low-information-content watch and calculator applications, in which the digits 0 through 9 are formed by applying voltages between appropriate combinations of segmented electrodes and a common backplane. To adequately display information in the form of text, graphics, and pictures, a high-information-content dot matrix composed of many thousands of independently addressable picture elements, or pixels, is required. A VGA (Video Graphics Array) computer screen, for example, consists of an array of 640 by 480 dots resulting in 307,200 individual pixels. In the passive-matrix drive method, the pixels are defined by the overlap of transparent horizontal row electrodes and vertical column electrodes; a potential difference across any given pixel is produced by applying voltages to the appropriate row and column electrodes. To switch pixels independently in this simple matrix, the display is multiplexed by sequentially pulsing, or selecting, the row electrodes and simultaneously applying a voltage to each column electrode determined by the desired optical state of the pixel on the selected row. As the number of matrix rows increases, however, it becomes increasingly difficult to significantly affect the optical state of an individual pixel without affecting the states of the other pixels on the shared row or column electrode. With the TN effect, no more than about 20 rows can be multiplexed with good performance, and so for high-information-content displays either the drive method has to be changed or a different liquid-crystal electro-optical effect has to be used.

Thin-film transistor display. In the active-matrix drive method, developed in 1973 at the Westinghouse Electric Corporation, a thin-film transistor (TFT) is associated with each pixel. This arrangement makes it possible to apply arbitrary voltages to each individual pixel to significantly alter its optical state without affecting other pixels in the array. The TN effect is generally used with active-matrix displays. A cutaway view of a small portion of a TFT display is shown in Figure 48. Each pixel consists of a small transparent pixel electrode connected to the drain of a TFT whose source is connected to a common column data bus and whose gate is connected to a common row gate bus. During operation, the row gate bus lines

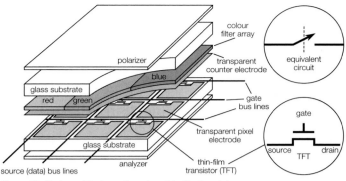

Figure 48: *Basic architecture of a colour thin-film transistor liquid-crystal display.*
A thin-film transistor is associated with each pixel to independently control the voltage on the pixel electrode and determine its optical state.

are sequentially pulsed, momentarily causing the TFTs on each pulsed row to conduct, which allows the pixels to sample the voltages on their respective data bus lines at that instant and to produce the desired optical states by appropriately reorienting the liquid crystal. After the pulse is removed from the row gate bus, the transistors in that row return to the insulating state, and the stored charge maintains the pixel at a constant optical state until the row gate pulse is cyclically reapplied one-sixtieth of a second later to update the image. Although the TN effect is innately black-and-white, full-colour operation is obtained by an additive, spatial averaging process by grouping the pixels into triads and covering them with individual red, green, and blue transparent colour filters.

TFT displays have outstanding speed, contrast, and colour saturation, which rivals that of the best-quality colour picture tubes. The disadvantages of TFT displays are their relatively high cost and limited availability, the consequences of the high capitalization costs for manufacturing, the many process steps involved, and the difficulty of obtaining flawless TFT arrays over large areas.

Supertwist nematic display. The supertwist nematic (STN) display, invented in 1983 at the Brown Boveri Research Center in Baden, Switz., made it possible to achieve a practical high-information-content display with the simpler passive-matrix drive method. In contrast to the 90° twist of the TN display, the liquid-crystal director in the STN display twists through a larger angle of about 240°, attained by appropriately rubbing the electrodes and dissolving an optically active substance into the nematic liquid crystal to induce a built-in twist. The larger twist introduces a "snap action" to the director, so that a small change in voltage makes a large change in transmission, permitting single pixels to switch independently with high contrast even when many matrix rows are multiplexed. Optical contrast is achieved by offsetting the polarizers from the rub directions to introduce two optical modes that can constructively or destructively interfere when a voltage is applied. Because the degree of interference depends on wavelength, the first STN devices were inherently coloured, but passive birefringent retardation films, introduced in 1988, compensated the cell birefringence to produce black-and-white images. Colour filters were then added for full-colour operation. Colour VGA STN panels are popular for notebook computers, and, except for the slow response that makes it difficult for them to follow a moving cursor, their performance is becoming close to that of TFT displays. The final barrier to approaching TFT performance with STN displays—namely, speed—was removed at In Focus Systems, Inc., in 1991 with the invention of Active Addressing (trademark), which made high-speed video operation possible. With this passive-matrix drive method, multiple rows are simultaneously rather than sequentially selected, and fast-responding STN displays can be used without the image fading between update intervals. (Terry J. Scheffer)

Passive-matrix drive method (margin note)

Colour capabilities of TFT displays (margin note)

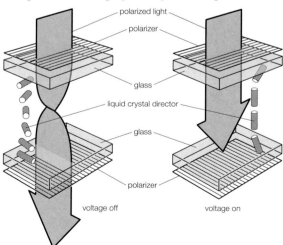

Figure 47: *The structure and operation of a twisted nematic display.*
The local optic axis undergoes a continuous 90° twist in the unactivated state (left), whereas it is predominantly parallel to the electric field in the activated state (right).

contents

THE YEAR IN SCIENCE:
AN OVERVIEW
by Robert P. Crease

If one had to select the most noteworthy event of the past year in science, it would be hard not to choose the Great Comet Crash of 1994. During six days in mid-July, fragments of the shattered comet Shoemaker-Levy 9 struck the southern hemisphere of the planet Jupiter. All large telescopes on Earth pointed toward Jupiter that week, for the crash promised literally to stir up otherwise unavailable information about the planet. Even through medium-sized telescopes, debris from the impacts could be seen as a series of tiny dark smudges—though each smudge was actually larger than the Earth. Alluding to the leading theory on the cause of a massive extinction on Earth 65 million years ago, astronomers joked, "There go Jupiter's dinosaurs!"

The Great Comet Crash was noteworthy first of all simply for its rarity. It was called a "once in a millennium" happening and "the most cataclysmic occurrence in the recorded history of the solar system." The crash was not the only event during the year that was both unique and scientifically interesting, however; as one can see in the articles that follow, a number of archaeological, paleontological, and even botanical discoveries can also be classed as truly singular. For example, in the mountains of southern France on Christmas day, in what was said to be "among the archaeological finds of the century," a cave containing hundreds of well-preserved Stone Age paintings— a veritable prehistoric gallery of pictures of such animals as bears, panthers,

and woolly rhinos—was discovered; footprints, tools, and other artifacts were also found. A shinbone unearthed in Boxgrove, England, was that of a 500,000-year-old human being—the oldest known European—while the oldest known hominid, a 4.4 million-year-old fossil of *Australopithecus ramidus,* was discovered in Ethiopia. A remarkable 75 million-year-old fossilized dinosaur embryo of an oviraptor was found in the Gobi in Mongolia, the first known embryo of a meat-eating dinosaur. In a rain forest 160 km (100 mi) west of Sydney, Australia, researchers came upon a species of pine that was thought to have died out 150 million years ago, a discovery so unlikely that it was compared to that of the prehistoric coelacanth fished out of

Stone Age paintings of woolly rhinos were among the hundreds of pictures of animals found in a cave in southern France in December 1994, a discovery regarded as "among the archaeological finds of the century."

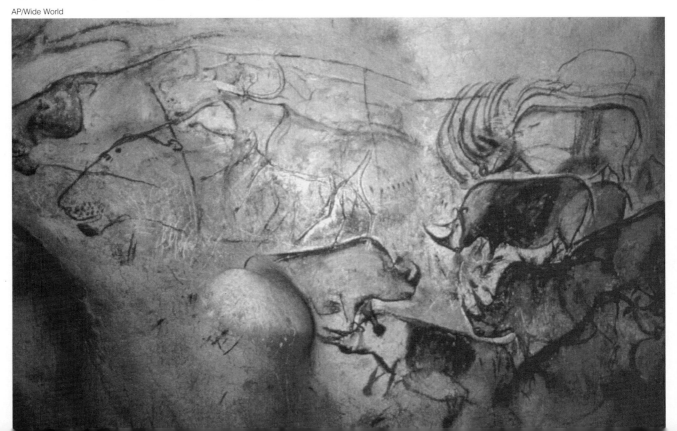

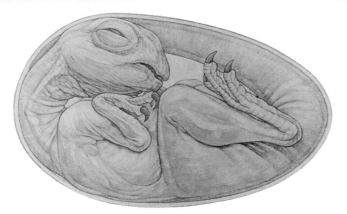

An artist's drawing depicts the fossilized embryo of an oviraptor. Found in Mongolia, it was the first embryo to be positively identified as that of a carnivorous dinosaur.

Mick Ellison—American Museum of Natural History

the waters off Madagascar in 1948. Thus, scientifically informative singular events, one may conclude, are not all that rare.

Computers

The Great Comet Crash also illustrated major changes in scientific practice from just a few years ago. Among the most important was the indispensable role of computers in the prediction and analysis of the event. Shoemaker-Levy 9 had been discovered by the team of Eugene and Carolyn Shoemaker and David Levy at the end of March 1993, and computers rapidly revealed its history and fate. The comet, it was determined, originally had orbited the Sun, but it had been captured by Jupiter and shattered into fragments by a close encounter with that planet in July 1992. It was predicted that it would actually collide with Jupiter on its next pass in 1994.

Computers also played a vital role in analyzing the data, for they were used to develop different models of the original comet and its structure and properties as well as various scenarios for the behavior of differently sized fragments as they collided with the planet and for the postimpact behavior of the Jovian atmosphere. These models vastly enhanced the speed and sophistication with which researchers could evaluate the results, and during the several postimpact conferences on the crash they were instrumental in the effort to sift through and derive meaning from the intricate series of events that had taken place.

As many of the Science Year in Review articles show, computers played an increasingly complex and important role in many fields of science, from archae-

ology to veterinary medicine. Among the unusual uses was the work of two researchers from Great Britain—one a physicist and the other a structural engineer—who used computer models to make a number of surprising discoveries about the structure of spiderwebs.

The events of 1994 also included, in the episode of the Pentium chip, a disturbing instance of the danger of over-reliance on computers. The Intel Corp. had introduced the Pentium in 1993 to drive a new central processing unit, and the power of the new chip was undisputed; in May and September 1994 a Pentium-driven computer chess program defeated reigning world chess champion Garry Kasparov (though in blitz, not tournament, chess). A few months later, however, mathematician Thomas Nicely

World chess champion Garry Kasparov (left) lost to a Pentium-driven Genius 2 computer chess program in a match limited to 25 minutes of thinking time per player.

James Morgan—The Times Newspapers Ltd.

from Lynchburg (Va.) College discovered that in certain kinds of calculations the chip made regular mistakes. Several things were troubling about the episode. One was the fact that the defect had initially gone undetected by Intel and was only accidentally discovered and revealed to the public by Nicely. Another was the

fact that Intel knew of the defect for months without informing those who had purchased the chip and while continuing to market it. Yet another was the way Intel dragged its heels in admitting and correcting the error and then in agreeing to replace the defective chips.

The Internet

During the comet crash several hundred researchers throughout the world were in constant touch with one another thanks to an Internet "exploder" in a computer at the University of Maryland astronomy department. Fast-breaking news about the collision was automatically and instantaneously copied and distributed. This allowed observers to relay their experiences with lenses, filters, and other equipment to colleagues so that they

could squeeze out the maximum amount of information from the brief viewing time. Within a matter of hours, images of the collision constructed from the data of Earthbound telescopes began appearing on the Internet.

Clearly the Internet, once a specialized tool of the scientific community, has matured into a practically indispensable feature of scientific research with ever more available on-line databases, journals, simulations, and services. Among the new on-line resources that premiered during the year was the "Visible Man," a computerized atlas of the human body comprising thousands of digitized images provided by the National Library of Medicine; the "Visible Woman" is scheduled to go on-line in the near future. Another 1994 debut was the Cybermouse, a virtual laboratory animal created by an immunologist at the Scripps Research Institute, La Jolla, Calif., and a mathematician at the University of California, San Diego, to allow computer users to explore the immune system of mice.

In 1994 the Internet was estimated to have 20 million users, and it became vastly more accessible and applicable to nonscientific uses, thanks to software such as the NCSA (National Center for Supercomputing Applications) Mosaic and World Wide Web. In January 1994 U.S. Vice Pres. Al Gore appeared

"Visible Man," an on-line resource introduced during the past year, consists of thousands of digitized images of the human body; from left to right are the muscles, internal organs, and spinal column. "Visible Woman" is scheduled to go on-line in 1995.

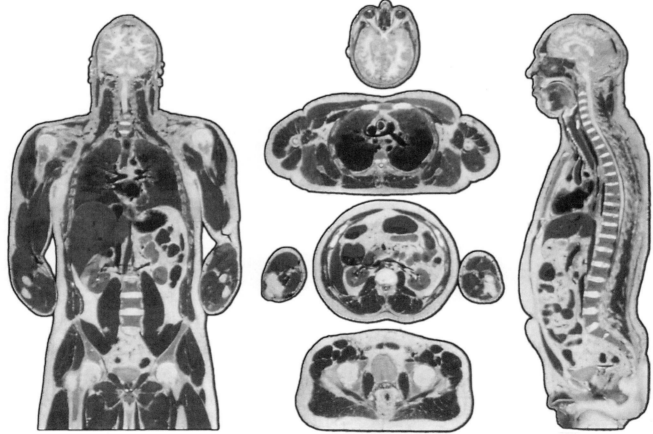

on the Internet in the first on-line White House news conference, while in November the Rolling Stones gave the first major on-line concert.

On the other hand, numerous instances of illegal intrusion, information theft, and file destruction on the Internet also revealed the difficulty in achieving both security and ease of access. According to the Computer Emergency Response Team, the number of Internet security break-ins in 1994 was 2,241, roughly double that of 1993.

Imaging

Images were another conspicuous feature of the Great Comet Crash. Though the actual collisions took place out of sight of the Earth, the impact sites rapidly rotated into view, where they were photographed in observatories around the world and in space by the Hubble Space Telescope. The best view, as it happened, was had by the Galileo spacecraft, still a full 2 billion km (1.2 billion mi) away from its Jupiter destination—and plagued by a defective antenna—yet in a position to see the event head-on.

Hubble's photo album for the year contained some spectacular pictures: a collision between two galaxies; a stellar "nursery" in Orion; a newly developing solar system around Beta Pictoris; the mysterious rings of the supernova designated SN 1987A; a storm on Saturn; and swirling disks of gas surrounding a black hole in galaxy M87. Other spacecraft turned in some equally vivid pictures: Magellan, three-dimensional images of the surface of Venus; Clementine, the Moon; Galileo, a tiny satellite orbiting asteroid 243 Ida; and Ulysses, the solar wind from above the Sun's south pole. The space shuttle *Endeavour* produced high-precision radar images of the Earth's features, including ancient streambeds, modern-day vegetation, and a remarkable slow-motion landslide taking place on the slopes of the Kilauea volcano in Hawaii.

Images can also be used as scientific tools with which to present data or the results of an investigation. A browse through the year's scientific journals, for instance, reveals a number of striking images representing data collected not by conventional cameras but by other means: the Earth's magnetosphere and the thickness of the Moon's crust; electron density in a plasma, crystal growth, and enzyme structure; and the brains of humans playing chess and of those with perfect pitch.

Extensive research into new ways of using imaging techniques was also carried out during the year. Scientists at the Fraunhofer Institute for Computer Graphics in Darmstadt, Germany, and at the University of North Carolina worked on techniques to transform ultrasound fetal data into 3-D images. An astronomer at the University of Arizona suggested a method for imaging planets around distant stars, and its possibilities were successfully tested with computer-modeling techniques. Research into how data could be more efficiently stored through the use of images was done by three Stanford University scientists, who in August reported an invention to store data in the form of holograms, shrinking the space required for storage. A computer scientist at Indiana University, with the assistance of a graduate student, developed a way to "image" the fourth dimension in three dimensions through an ingenious use of visual cues.

Image-manipulation techniques have become steadily more common in motion pictures, a striking example of which was embodied in the 1994 movie *Forrest Gump,* in which the actor (Tom Hanks) playing the title role appears to meet a succession of (deceased) U.S. presidents: Dwight D. Eisenhower, John F. Kennedy, Lyndon B. Johnson, and Richard M. Nixon. A less-innocent example of image manipulation was an arresting and no doubt newspaper-selling photo that *Newsday* ran on its front page during the winter Olympic Games showing figure skaters Tonya Harding and Nancy Kerrigan in the same frame together—a montage, caption readers discovered. A famous 60-year-old photograph allegedly of the Loch Ness monster was exposed during the year as an outright fraud by two researchers, who were able to determine that it was actually of a 30-cm (12-in) model made of plastic wood and riding on a toy submarine.

Images can also be false not for technological reasons but as a result of sheer stupidity or carelessness. An amusing instance of this was provided by *New York Times* garden columnist Anne Raver, who pointed out a number of botanical howlers in the past year's films, including the appearance of Queen Anne's lace and 1.5-m (5-ft)-high tomato plants in otherwise realistic-looking scenes supposedly taking place in Connecticut in May. "Yo, Hollywood," an aggrieved Raver complained on behalf of the nation's gardeners. Moreover, speaking of the images of 1994, it is impossible to resist mention-

A rapidly rotating disk of hot gas surrounding a black hole in the galaxy M87 was among the many remarkable images obtained during the year by the Hubble Space Telescope.

ing the revelation of a trove of 90,000 pornographic images that were stored in a computer at the Lawrence Livermore National Laboratory, Livermore, Calif.—which prompted shocked and embarrassed U.S. Department of Energy officials to order a computer audit, the cost of which could potentially run into the millions of dollars. But to put the issue in perspective, the past year also saw the rediscovery of several finger-length carved statues, dating from the Ice Age, of naked women—which suggests to at least some anthropologists that erotic imagery is an ancient concern.

Stirring up information

Astronomers no doubt would prefer to study the atmosphere of Jupiter by lowering instruments through it rather than by having to watch from a distance as a comet smashes into it. Nevertheless, the collision did provide insights into otherwise inaccessible features and behaviors of the planet. The fragments, for instance, punctured holes in the Jovian atmosphere through which plumes of gases from deeper layers shot up thousands of kilometers above the planet's clouds, where they could be seen by telescopes; moreover, the energy of the fragments heated the gases so that they were analyzable by spectroscopes. The impact also created acoustic waves whose passage around Jupiter could be charted. Even the final act of the drama, involving the dispersal of the smudges created by the impacts, revealed information about the stratospheric winds that play an important role in Jupiter's banded structure and red spot.

Astronomers are not alone in having to rely on indirect access to phenomena, however; an analogous problem is faced by high-energy physicists, who, with the demise of the Superconducting Super Collider (SSC), are cut off from being able to explore many high-energy interactions. Some access to high-energy phenomena will be provided by the Large Hadron Collider (LHC) planned at CERN, the European Organization for Nuclear Research, Geneva. But even that machine was imperiled in June by conflict between the member nations; Germany and Great Britain demanded that France and Switzerland (which benefit most from the laboratory's location) pay an increased share of the total costs of the collider. The project continued to be threatened throughout the rest of the year, but agreement was finally reached at the end of December, when the CERN council approved construction of the LHC.

The LHC is of a lower energy than the SSC, however, and may take a dozen years to build. In the meantime, some physicists have turned their attention to trying to devise inexpensive experiments that would provide narrow but reliable windows on high-energy phenomena.

In a striking example of image manipulation by computer, the title character of the 1994 movie _Forrest Gump_ (played by Tom Hanks) appears to be shaking hands with Pres. John F. Kennedy.

Media reaction

Science stories that earn major media coverage generally belong to one of the following categories: First Things (such as the origin of the universe), Scandal, Politically Hot Topics, Pseudoscience, Science Under Scrutiny, and Last Things (catastrophe and apocalypse).

The most literally cosmic of all stories involving First Things last year concerned Hubble's constant, a measure of the rate at which the universe is expanding—which, in turn, is an indication of both the age and the size of the universe. Measurements made during the year of "standard candles," stars of known brightness that are used to calibrate distances, pointed to a value for the constant that implied that the universe is younger than its oldest stars, giving rise to what astronomers called an "age problem" ("The Universe in Crisis," one headline put it). The problem provoked intense scrutiny of possible sources of error and of the various assumptions contained in the models.

Scandals of 1994 included a controversy over a book entitled *Special Tasks: The Memoirs of an Unwanted Witness—A Soviet Spymaster.* Though billed as the "autobiography" of ex-KGB agent Pavel Sudoplatov, the book was said to have been coauthored by Sudoplatov's son Anatoly and written "with" U.S. journalists Jerrold and Leona Schecter. It contained thoroughly discredited charges that Niels Bohr, Enrico Fermi, George Gamow, J. Robert Oppenheimer, and Leo Szilard spied for the Soviet Union. The ensuing controversy prompted the Federation of American Scientists to suggest that book publishers try a version of scientific peer review for historians.

By far the most controversial book of 1994 on any subject concerned the Politically Hot Topic of genes and intelligence. *The Bell Curve: Intelligence and Class Structure in American Life* by Richard Herrnstein of Harvard University and Charles Murray of the American Enterprise Institute, Washington, D.C.,

The Free Press

The book *The Bell Curve* created considerable controversy by arguing that intelligence is largely inherited and varies on average between races.

argued that intelligence is largely inherited, varies on average between races, is increasingly the basis for social stratification, and is the principal driving force of many social problems. The argument's political implications sparked a heated debate about the book's sources, assumptions, analysis, and policy suggestions that brought it to international attention.

Pseudoscience is not a purely Western phenomenon. Its popularity has been increasing in Russia, and in 1994 the Russian daily newspaper *Izvestiya,* which in years past had taken a courageous hard line against pseudoscience, gave credibility to a report that a tractor mechanic had invented a time machine. Meanwhile, the U.S. Air Force revealed that the mysterious debris found in the New Mexico desert in 1947 that has been repeatedly cited by UFO (unidentified flying object) aficionados as evidence of alien visitations to the Earth and of a government cover-up of the same, was actually the remains of a crash of a then top-secret device for detecting atomic tests. Unsurprisingly, the revelation failed to quell the conspiracy theorists, who charged that the cover-up continues.

In the category of Science Under Scrutiny, a controversy broke out over the value of science itself in connection with not one but two exhibits at the Smithsonian Institution in Washington, D.C. The first, entitled "Science in American Life," focused attention on the evils of science by dwelling on such subjects as radioactive waste and toxic pollution but did not mention such subjects as semiconductors and declining mortality rates. In November the American Physical Society charged formally that the exhibit "trivializes [scientific] accomplishments and exaggerates any negative consequences." Another controversy erupted at the Smithsonian over "The Last Act: The Atomic Bomb and the End of World War II," an exhibit concerned with what for many is the leading example of the impact of science on the modern world. The exhibit, scheduled to open in May

The *Enola Gay*, the B-29 that dropped the atomic bomb on Hiroshima, Japan, in 1945, was part of a controversial exhibit at the Smithsonian Institution.

1995, was the subject of clashes between veterans groups, professional historians, and museum officials, and the result was a substantial downsizing of the display.

Comet fever

The Great Comet Crash earned its keep as a major media story by being shoehorned into the Last Things category. "Cosmic Crash," screamed *Time* magazine on its May 23 cover; "Could it happen here on Earth? Yes . . ." The *New York Times* headlined an article "When Worlds Collide: A Threat to the Earth Is a Joke No Longer." Other headlines included "A Glimpse of Armageddon," "Doomsday Asteroids," and "Target Jupiter. Next: Us?" On Halloween CBS broadcast a made-for-television movie that used a "live" coverage format to depict asteroids striking the Earth. The movie attempted to mimic the eerie quality of Orson Welles's 1938 "War of the Worlds" radio show.

The alarm generated in many people by comet Shoemaker-Levy 9 produced an epidemic of "comet fever." The U.S. Congress instructed NASA to create a program to identify comets and asteroids with diameters larger than one kilometer (0.62 mi) that might cross the Earth's path within 10 years; NASA promptly appointed a committee, headed by Eugene Shoemaker, to come up with the plan.

Among the few who tried to address in a genuinely responsible way the subject of potential collisions between the Earth and celestial bodies were Carl Sagan and Steven Ostro in a nontechnical article that appeared in the summer issue of *Issues in Science and Technology.* There are severe dangers in embarking on a large-scale surveillance effort, the authors wrote. Maps of the 30,000 near-Earth asteroids and comets—10 times the number of stars visible on a clear night!—may paint an erroneous picture of the real danger, enhance rather than reduce public anxiety, and lead to pointless pressure to ward off nonexistent threats.

Their suggestions for an appropriate reaction to the issue—"accurate orbit es-

timation, realistic threat assessment, and effective public education"—were unlikely to excite politicians. Sagan and Ostro wrote that "our greatest concern may be a poorly informed public."

Surely a more genuine threat to human existence than killer comets and one that deserves more attention was the appearance on the international market in 1994 of samples of weapons-grade plutonium and enriched uranium thought to have been smuggled from Russia, which prompted seizures of material by police in Germany and the Czech Republic. It would be unfortunate if an expensive and bitter lesson in how a poorly informed public can lead to the squandering of limited scientific resources turned out to be the greatest impact left behind by the Great Comet Crash of 1994.

Robert P. Crease is an Associate Professor of Philosophy at the State University of New York at Stony Brook and Historian at the Brookhaven National Laboratory, Upton, N.Y.

ANTHROPOLOGY

New discoveries, DNA analyses, and restudies produced both the expected and the unexpected in anthropology during the past year. A central debate in the discipline concerned the origins of modern humans.

Human origins

During the past few years the field of physical anthropology experienced considerable ferment. Numerous debates continued unresolved as new fossils were found, old fossils restudied, and genetic studies completed. Conflicting evidence continued to raise more questions rather than provide answers.

The idea that apes and humans branched off from a common ancestor sometime after six million years ago was challenged by a new fossil from the Aramis River region of Ethiopia. Tim White, Gen Suwa, and Berhane Asfaw found bones of what may prove to be the earliest known link between African apes and modern humans. Identified as *Australopithecus ramidus,* the new fossil appeared to be the direct ancestor of *A. afarensis.* The species lived in East Africa some 4.4 million years ago, 500,000 years before *A. afarensis.* This made *A. ramidus* the oldest human ancestor ever found, living about the time of the split between apes and humans.

A. ramidus is anatomically similar to *A. afarensis* yet is sufficiently different to suggest an entirely new species. Arm bones, a canine tooth similar to *A. afarensis,* and parts of a skull were found. The configuration of the skull is consistent with upright walking. Critics of the find pointed to the thin enamel of the teeth, which seemed more in line with fossil

chimpanzees, and the ridge along the forearm, more characteristic of knuckle walking than of bipedalism.

The first complete adult skull for *A. afarensis,* found by William H. Kimbel, Donald D. Johanson, and Yoel Rak, added fuel to a number of debates, including whether *A. afarensis* had Africa to itself or shared it with others. Originally found near the Hadar site in Ethiopia in 1992, the skull appears more apelike than human but also displays traits similar to earlier hominid fossils. The skull is that of a large male, with jutting jaw, large canine teeth, tiny brain, and a thick bony ridge above the eyes and is dated at 3.8 million years, 200,000 years younger than *A. afarensis,* popularly known as Lucy. Because the skull is of an individual much larger than Lucy, some experts suggest that it could represent a separate

species, or it could mean that *A. afarensis* is not in the human ancestral line.

Redating fossils from Perning, Java, should help clarify the origins of *Homo erectus.* Carl Swisher and Garniss Curtis, using a new method of dating that measured the age of the pumice and other volcanic rock in which the fossil fragments were embedded, established that *H. erectus* migrated from Africa at least 800,000 years earlier than previously thought. The new date established the fact that there were two different populations of *H. erectus* on two different continents some two million years ago, and this appeared to contradict the previously accepted theory that *H. erectus* arose in Africa two million years ago and then ventured out to Asia and Europe about one million years ago. The new date would answer the question of

A child's jawbone may prove to be evidence of the earliest-known link between African apes and modern humans. It has been identified as belonging to *Australopithecus ramidus,* a species that lived in East Africa about 4.4 million years ago.

© Tim D. White 1994/Brill Atlanta

why the Acheulean technology has never been associated with Asian *H. erectus,* for that technology was invented in Africa well after the migration to Asia that took place two million years ago.

A restudy of *H. erectus* from the Diring-Yuriakh site in Siberia by Yury A. Mochanov and Svetlana Fedoseyeva of the Russian Academy of Sciences established a much earlier northern movement of *H. erectus* than had previously been believed. The new date, based on thermoluminescence dating, places *H. erectus* in the northern regions 500,000 years earlier than the one million years suggested by discoveries at Zhoukoudian in central China.

The debate over the origins of modern humans lost none of its fervor. Popular theories suggest either a multiregional or a single African origin for modern humans. Support for the multiregional hypothesis came with the discovery of *H. erectus* skulls in China by Chen Tiemei (Ch'en T'ieh-mei), Yang Quan (Yang Ch'üan), and Wu En. Dates for these fossils, found side by side with *H. sapiens,* clearly suggest a local evolution consistent with the multiregional theory. Support for the African hypothesis came from Anne Bowcock, who found an early genetic split in the human family between Africans and everyone else. The results of the fossil skull study completed by Diane Waddle supported Bowcock's conclusion. Seventy-four measurements, taken on 83 skulls from Europe, Asia, and Africa, were compared so that how closely the skulls were related to one another could be gauged. The results supported the single place of origin position but concluded that the place was south-

The first complete adult skull of the species *Australopithecus afarensis,* some 3.8 million years old, is so large that it might represent a separate species.

western Asia rather than Africa. Additional support for the African hypothesis came from a genetic study by Ken Kidd and Sara Tishkoff, which focused on nuclear DNA to provide a more detailed picture of a population than mitochondrial DNA because it is inherited by both sexes, whereas mitochondrial DNA is inherited only from the mother.

On the basis of a study of the thumb bones, particularly the first metacarpal, of *A. afarensis,* early *Homo* fossils, and chimpanzees, Randall Susman challenged the long-held belief that humans advanced only because of their larger brains and superior intelligence. Noting that human ancestors dating back 2.5 million years did not possess the "precision grip" suited for maneuvering tools but that all human ancestors were using tools by 2 million

years ago, Susman argued that the human thumb, providing for the "precision grip," served as a catalyst for the separation of early humans and other primates. Critics, however, pointed out the limitations of using the thumb to explain intellectual abilities and cautioned that the fossils on which the study relied could belong to the same species.

Genetic studies

Researchers from the University of Michigan Medical School, National Cancer Institute, and Russian Institute of Cytology and Genetics at Novosibirsk combined to study American Indian genes— in particular, the inherited human T-cell lymphotropic virus type II. This virus, noted in 38 American Indian groups and in Mongolia, was absent in 10 northeastern Siberian populations. Given these results, it seems possible that the first immigrants to enter and occupy the Western Hemisphere had their roots in Mongolia.

Rob Bonnichsen and Marvin Beatty obtained hair from archaeological sites by using a new technique devised for the recovery of human hair fragments from which DNA can be recovered. The method involves mixing sediments with water and sodium hexametaphosophate and then running this slurry through a flotation tub to separate organic materials. If the DNA found in the hair can be determined to be ancient rather than contemporary, the molecule could provide clues about how many related groups occupied an area, help resolve disputes about migrations, and help tie particular cultures to particular people.

The debate on the antiquity of tuberculosis in the Western Hemisphere was resolved during the past year. The finding of the DNA specific to tuberculosis in a mummy of a Peruvian who died more than 500 years before Columbus made it clear that tuberculosis was present in the New World well before European contact. The technology used to recover the ancient sample of a disease-causing organism seems certain to have a far-reaching effect on the tracking of ancient diseases and epidemics.

Molecular DNA analysis was also applied to the Tyrolean "Iceman" by a team of researchers from Germany, Great Britain, Austria, and Switzerland. Tissue samples from the 5,000-year-old mummy, discovered in the Alps in 1991, show that this man fits within the genetic variation of modern Europeans, particularly those in the central and northern areas.

Other discoveries

Two impressive Paleolithic art discoveries were made during the year. In Portugal, a 20,000-year-old site was discovered by Nelson Rebanda on the Coa River. This site was impressive because of the sheer number and variety of its rock carvings. A national debate erupted over the site because it exists in the vicinity of a dam under construction; nearly half of the carvings are already under water. Thus, in one of the poorest nations in Western Europe, the find raised the question as to whether economic development or cultural resources are more important. A second discovery, made in the mountains of southern France near Vallon-Pont-d'Arc, produced a cave art site that is being called the find of the century because of its size and variety, easily surpassing the site at Lascaux and Altamira (*see* Year in Review: ARCHAEOLOGY).

A cemetery documenting a complex Aboriginal society was discovered in Australia. Found near Lake Victoria by Colin Pardoe and Harvey Johnston, the site contains as many as 10,000 skeletons, which makes it the largest cemetery of a hunter-gatherer society ever found. The find challenges the long-held assumption that Aborigines lived only in small, scattered bands, barely surviving in a harsh environment. The actual skeletal materials were found not as in the past, disjointed and decorated with ochre, but intact and unadorned. Similarities in the bone materials strongly suggest a single population. The evidence from this site fits that of other sites in the same area, which previously had raised doubts as to the small, nomadic-band description usually associated with Aborigines.

Future prospects

The future agenda of anthropology seems certain to deal with such issues as advocacy, the ethics of sustained development, human rights, cultural relativism, and fieldwork ethics, all related to the problems of an increasingly crowded and interacting world. Of more immediate concern are the questions being raised about anthropology's work with culture, a primary focus of the discipline. Many scholars were suggesting that the concept of culture needs some reassessment as the result of migrations, modern technology, spread of the market-exchange system, and increased cultural interactions. The traditional emphasis has been on culture difference and on culture as a way of life shared by all inhabitants of a region, but people living together do not always share a uniform culture, nor are cultures always geographically bounded. Calls were being heard for a shift to a new "transnational" analysis of culture that will look at complex group interactions, particularly along borders, where people are basically "binational."

Publications of the American Anthropology Association recently made news. The efforts of Barbara and Dennis Tedlock to change the *American Anthropologist,* the premier journal of the association, pleased some and incensed others. The new editors view the new format as keeping the quarterly in the mainstream of anthropology by opening it up to new voices and approaches. Others regard the changes as straying too far from serious science. The newest publication of the association, the *General Anthropology Bulletin,* made its appearance and promises to provide timely and readable information on all the subfields of anthropology for those wishing to keep up with developments in the entire field without subscribing to all of its journals.

—Larry L. Naylor

ARCHAEOLOGY

Archaeologists made two remarkable discoveries late in 1994. In southern France a cave, apparently untouched for some 20,000 years, was found to contain some 300 Stone Age engravings and paintings of bison, reindeer, and other animals, including the first known prehistoric portrayals of a panther and an owl. Probably dating from about 20,000–17,000 BC, the paintings are comparable in quality to those found previously in caves at Lascaux, France, and Altamira, Spain.

While exploring the pyramid of the pharaoh Senusert III, south of Cairo, archaeologists discovered a collection of jewelry belonging to a queen who lived about 3,900 years ago. The treasure trove included gold brooches, necklaces of semiprecious stones, two gold lockets shaped like lions, gold pendants inlaid with cornelian, and two blue amethyst scarabs (winged beetles).

The fugitive iceman

A remarkable frozen mummy of a Bronze Age man was recovered in 1991 from high in the Ötztal Alps of northern Italy. Since that time the "Tyrolean Iceman" has been the subject of many studies. Recently, Dieter zur Nedden, Klaus Wicke, Rudolf Knapp, and several other coauthors from Austria and the U.S. published the results of their findings on the morphology and anatomy of the man,

who died between 3350 and 3120 BC. The remarkable preservation of the man's remains and belongings allowed these authors to interpret a great deal about him and his circumstances and to glimpse some aspects of the society in which he lived.

As with many modern archaeological analyses, Nedden and his colleagues. used advanced technology to study the ancient past. Computed tomography scans and X-rays of the head revealed several small bone fractures, most likely caused by glacial movement of the ice in which the man's remains were trapped. Similar studies of the thorax, however, revealed several broken ribs on the man's right side, all of which appear to have been from injuries sustained within the last two months of his life. Healed broken ribs on his left side reflect earlier traumas from which he had recovered. In addition, bones of his left foot indicate that the man suffered from severe and chronic frostbite. These physiological data combined with data from some of the man's possessions suggest that he was in flight just before he died and had entered the high mountains without proper equipment or provisions. For example, all but 2 of his 14 arrows were broken. His quiver was also broken, and one of its pieces was on his body, which suggested that he planned to repair it. The quiver belt was torn, and his bow was damaged. His clothing was sewn very carefully in patchwork fashion, but parts of it were crudely repaired with grass blades. His fur cape was torn and was repaired in places with blades of grass. His shoes were stuffed with grass leaves and were haphazardly repaired with leather sewn

with grass cords to add a protective layer against moisture above the toes. The remains of what may have been a wooden frame within a fur or leather bag were also found. Necessary provisions probably were carried in such a bag, but evidence of their presence was not found. Thus, it appears that the man entered the mountains without sufficient supplies and before he could accomplish needed repairs on much of his equipment.

The researchers proposed a rather detailed scenario regarding the man's last journey, about 5,000 years ago, over the inhospitable high Alps, as winter approached: "He had had a 'violent discussion' which caused the costal [rib] fractures on his right side. He was poorly equipped with many broken or damaged belongings because he had insufficient time to repair or replace them. The fact that the man went to such an inhospitable region, though suffering from extreme physical handicap caused by pain from his evident injuries, with such inadequate equipment, may be taken as circumstantial evidence for an escape born of desperation." Whether he sought to escape into the mountains or to cross them to comparative safety cannot be known. His luck seems to have run out high in the mountains, where he was caught by a blizzard. The snow that covered him was the first of the season but, fortunately for present-day scientists, grew into a glacier that preserved his body and secrets for 5,000 years.

Gold treasures, metalworking, and elite culture in pre-Incan Peru

Abundant masks and items of gold, silver, and other precious metals are popu-

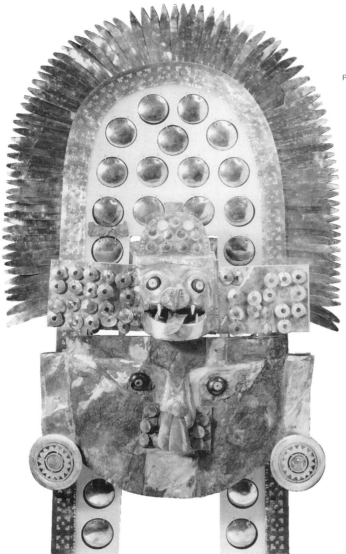

PAS/Y. Yoshii

lar symbols of ancient Peruvian cultures. Many are attributed to the highland Inca or to their lowland rivals, the Chimú cultures. Most, however, were made by the much earlier Middle Sican culture, which flourished in northern Peru between AD 900 and 1100. The reasons for the incorrect attributions are related not to the artifacts themselves but to the ways that they became known to the world. Until recently almost all of the thousands of beautiful and well-made prehistoric gold pieces known from northern Peru were in collections taken from looted tombs. Archaeologists had no way to associate specific objects or collections with their appropriate locations. Most workers and art historians merely assumed that the majority of fine gold objects were from the latest widespread prehistoric cultures of Peru. No intact contextual data, such as nonvandalized tombs, were studied by archaeologists until 1978, when Izumi Shimada discovered one during surveys of Huaca Loro, an adobe platform mound in the Batán Grande region. Shimada

Treasures found in a Peruvian tomb that dates from the Middle Sican culture (AD 900–1100) include a ceremonial headdress (above) made of hammered gold sheets, edged with 90 gold feathers and ornamented with 29 gold bangles, and (right) a hammered gold chest ornament decorated with bangles and featuring three representations of Sican lord heads.

PAS/Y. Yoshii

planned for excavations of the tomb during the next 13 years. All the necessary preparations had been made by October 1991, when Shimada led the Sican Archaeological Project in excavating the burial chamber at Huaca Loro.

Members of the project found a remarkable trove of precious treasures associated with the skeletal remains of a Middle Sican lord, accompanied by the bodies of two young women and two children. The 9-sq m (97-sq ft) burial chamber lay at the end of an 11-m (36-ft)-deep vertical shaft. It yielded approximately 1.2 tons of goods, about 75% of which comprised objects of 14–18-karat gold. Some objects, and most of the associated production scrap, were *tumbaga,* a gold-copper or gold-silver-copper alloy similar in many respects to the gold alloys in modern 10–14-karat jewelry.

The burial array was impressive. The man's body was thoroughly painted with bright red cinnabar. He had three sets of attached ear ornaments and a large gold mask over his face. A cloth mantle spread over him contained nearly 2,000 gold foil squares. Beads of sodalite, amethyst, quartz crystal, turquoise, fluorite, calcite, shell, and other materials created a 10-cm (3.9-in)-thick layer over his body. Around him were found a staff with *tumbaga* ornaments, a gold headdress, a pair of gold shin guards, a pair of *tumbaga* gloves, a gold and silver cup, a silver ceremonial knife, and six pairs of intricate gold spool-shaped earplugs. The chamber also contained nearly 500 kg (1,100 lb) of *tumbaga* scrap and 250 kg (550 lb) of bronze implements.

The richest treasures of all were found in Gold Cache 1 in the chamber's northern end. At least 60 major objects of gold sheet, silver, and *tumbaga* were found inside a rectangular box lined with woven mats. They included 5 crowns, 4 sets of parabolic headdresses that fit into slots in the crowns, 4 headbands, 14 large disks, 12 knife-shaped head ornaments, 6 sets of gold feather ornaments, and 3 *tumbaga* fans.

The chamber contained seven wall niches, and two of these also yielded metal artifacts. A pit in one niche had hundreds of bundles of uniformly shaped bronze rods called *naipes,* which may have been used as currency. The pit also contained two silver alloy knives, thousands of *tumbaga* foil squares, and 24 *tumbaga* masks similar to the large gold mask over the lord's face but smaller, of poorer craftsmanship, and with less ornamentation. Other items in the chamber included more than 50 kg (110 lb) of stone and shell beads, a carved wooden litter, and 21 ceramic vessels.

This great trove of treasure is but a minuscule portion of the precious material created during the Middle Sican period in northern Peru that has been plundered and robbed from graves during the past 200 years. With this discovery archaeologists have the first intact cache of such treasures to study in context. In addition, because the tomb was discovered by modern archaeologists, the treasure itself, while of great literal and symbolic value, is not of primary importance compared with the opportunity to understand how these objects were made and how they functioned within their societies.

The Sican Archaeological Project incorporated skilled metalsmiths into its staff to enhance the understanding of the organization of precious metal production and the meaning of such products in a society. Jo Ann Griffin, the project metallurgist, was able to elucidate much about Sican metalworking. The technology of goldworking centered on sheet production. Middle Sican metalworkers were quite skilled at creating large sheets of gold and *tumbaga*. These sheets were of various thicknesses, depending on their intended uses, but each one had a uniform thickness throughout. Most finished ornaments, masks, earplugs, and other precious artifacts were cut and shaped from these sheets. Sheets were created from gold nuggets pounded with small, carefully shaped stone hammers. Such pounding weakened the gold, and so the sheets had to be annealed regularly over fire to prevent stress fractures. The scale of sheet production is illustrated by the 500 kg of scrap found in the Huaca Loro burial chamber. Looters have found similar quantities of scrap in other tombs throughout the Batán Grande. Such scrap was saved for remelting into nuggets, and its presence in tombs, where it was not available for recycling, reflects the political power of those buried with it.

Griffin found that Middle Sican goldsmiths enhanced the appearance of *tumbaga* sheets by washing their surfaces with acid. These baths dissolved some of the base metals near the surface and created an appearance of 24-karat gold. Goldsmiths then burnished the surfaces of these sheets to provide an even more lustrous finish.

The Sican Archaeological Project showed that the production of metal objects was organized into task-specific work groups based on a nested hierarchy of master crafters, apprentices, and laborers. The scale of the production process is impressive, and precious metalworking was only one part of the overall complex of associated activities. Mining, smelting, and bronze production occurred in specialized settlements near ore deposits.

Why did the Sican people put so much effort into metalworking? Shimada and Griffin concluded that much of the aesthetic locus of the society was on gold objects because they reflected the highest standards of artistic expression. Gold objects depict the full range of Middle Sican religious icons and portray important events. Precious metal objects also marked social divisions in Sican society. Burials in Batán Grande reveal these divisions, with some people interred with no metal objects, some with bronze items, some with bronze and *tumbaga,* and a few with bronze, *tumbaga,* and gold items. It appears that gold objects were reserved for the highest elite, both as personal wealth and to reflect their social and religious importance.

Middle Sican society maintained itself for over 200 years, and Sican culture lasted well into the 14th century before it gave way to the somewhat less showy but more bureaucratic Chimú culture in northern Peru. Gold objects continued to be a mark of the highest elite, but sheet metalworking in later times did not match that developed during the Middle Sican.

A planned farming community

During the same period that Middle Sican goldsmiths were producing their dazzling wares, farming communities in western North America expanded into areas previously occupied by foragers and hunters. One such community was the focus of four years of study in eastern Nevada by archaeologists from Brigham Young University, Provo, Utah, and the U.S. Bureau of Land Management. Baker Village, near Baker, Nev., was occupied most intensively during the 13th century by farming peoples collectively called the Fremont Culture, who occupied much of the eastern Great Basin and northern Colorado Plateau from about AD 900 to 1350.

One of the most interesting aspects of Baker Village is revealed in its layout of structures and open spaces. The seven semisubterranean houses and seven small mud-walled surface storage structures are aligned along well-chosen axes. These structures surround a large central, mud-walled surface house, which seems to have been placed in its precise location so that shadows and light at solstice sunrises would be marked and noted by the site's inhabitants. In addition, structure corners and walls create sight lines to the eastern and western horizons from the large central structure and perhaps from other locations within the site so that specific times of the year can be anticipated and accurately noted. For example, sight lines and shadow edges that are cast on walls or through windows (remains of which are not present) correspond to eastern horizon landmarks that mark sunrises nearly exactly four, three, two, and one lunar months before the winter solstice. One major building axis that extends through the northeastern and southwestern diagonal of the large central house corresponds to the location of the summer solstice sunrise.

These orientation, sight-lines, and axial relations of buildings reveal a high degree of planning in the construction of the village. The occupants of Baker Village can be compared to the Hopi of northern Arizona, who were also desert farmers and who also paid very close attention to the times of year as marked by sunrises and sunsets along the eastern and western horizons.

Marking exact times by matching sunrise locations with specific times of the year allows such societies to maximize their potential to produce sufficient crops for winter sustenance. Mistakes of even a few weeks can mean crop loss and starvation. Although this timing is very important to Hopis and other Southwestern native farmers, even more important is the correct timing of important ceremonies, the most crucial of which are those centered on the winter solstice. Exact calendars are necessary for predicting accurately the number of days before this celestial event so that other ceremonies that must precede the solstice ceremony can be observed and so that important periods of preparation and religious paraphernalia construction can be finished on time. This might be a relatively easy task if ceremonies occurred on the same days of each year, as they generally do in present-day society. Hopi and other Pueblo ceremonies, however, either start or reach their peaks on the night of the full moon after a certain sunrise. Because the moon-phase cycle is 19 years long, the full moon at a given time of year, such as the winter solstice, occurs on different days each of those 19 years and oscillates between 11 days before and after the actual date of the solstice. Thus, the full moon will correspond to the actual date of the solstice only once in 19 years. The pattern is complicated by the fact that the Sun "stands still" during the solstices and does not move a noticeable amount on the horizon for about five to seven days, depending on the landmark used to measure solar movement.

Could prehistoric people in Baker Village have operated under a similar calendar? It seems highly likely that they did so. The question is, do the orientation of and the relations between the structures at Baker Village provide evidence of such a useful system? It is compelling to think so, but there may never be conclusive proof.

—James D. Wilde

ARCHITECTURE AND CIVIL ENGINEERING

Continuing their efforts to address the needs and concerns of society, architects and civil engineers during the past year focused especially on the ever increasing requirements for new transportation facilities, the preservation of historic architectural gems, and the challenges presented by the rapid growth of population in many parts of the world.

Architecture

Probably the most widely noted building of the past year was the new home of the American Center, which opened in June 1994 on the Seine River in the Bercy neighborhood of Paris. Designed by Los Angeles architect Frank O. Gehry, the center contains stage and motion-picture theaters and a variety of other performance and exhibit spaces, as well as

26 apartments for resident scholars and artists.

Gehry employed the free-form tilting, curving, and colliding shapes that made him famous, but they seem tamer than usual because of the traditional warm-toned limestone in which the entire building is clad. Many critics noted the appropriateness of the choice of Gehry, among the most innovative of contemporary U.S. architects, as designer of the American Center, which was founded in 1931 to promote French understanding of U.S. culture.

Civic buildings. Of all types of buildings, it was those designed for transportation that dominated the world of architecture in 1994. The most spectacular is in Japan—the $14 billion Kansai International Airport, which opened in September. It was built on an island cre-

ated from landfill in 18 m (59 ft) of water in Osaka Bay, connected to the mainland by a 3-km (1.85-mi)-long double-deck bridge. The building itself is 1.6 km (1 mi) long and four stories high under a single curving metal roof. The terminal's architect was Renzo Piano of Italy.

In the United States the Denver (Colo.) International Airport, the largest in the country, covers 137 sq km (53 sq mi) and includes parking for 12,000 cars. Its main terminal, roofed in Teflon-coated tensile fabric, is the world's largest tent and looks, as one critic noted, like a Sioux encampment on the plain. The team of architects included August Perez and the firm of C.W. Fentress J.H. Bradburn & Associates. Designed and built with great speed in just over four years, the airport caused frustration when it failed to open on time because nobody could figure out

Erich Koyama

Designed by Los Angeles architect Frank Gehry, the American Center on the Seine River in Paris was probably the most widely noted building of the past year.

317

A formal, symmetrical structure, the San Francisco Museum of Modern Art was designed by Swiss architect Mario Botta.

how to get its $200 million automated baggage-handling system to work. Scheduled to open in late 1993, the airport did not become operational until February 1995, causing severe cost overruns.

In Washington, D.C., a new embassy for Finland by Mikko Heikkinen and Markku Komonen is an elegant collage of glass, copper, bronze, stainless steel, polished granite, and natural wood, held together by taut nautical detailing. It faces the street with a wall of leaves and flowers—a three-story bronze trellis planted with rose and clematis vines.

Cultural buildings. A remarkable concentration of architectural energy oc-curred at Yerba Buena Gardens in San Francisco, just south of the city's downtown, where several internationally known architects created a cultural complex. Its core is the Center for the Arts, designed by Fumihiko Maki of Japan and James Stewart Polshek of New York City. Maki's building contains a film and video theater and a variety of exhibition and performance spaces and is surfaced on the outside with the architect's signature silver-toned finish. Polshek's building is a 755-seat theater. Both structures stand atop the underground portion of a 185,000-sq m (2 million-sq ft) expansion of San Francisco's main convention facility, the Moscone Center; the expansion was designed by James Ingo Freed. Also part of the complex is an oval park, the Esplanade, by MGA Partners with Romaldo Giurgola.

Across the street from Yerba Buena is a new San Francisco Museum of Modern Art by Swiss architect Mario Botta. A formal, symmetrical, blocky structure in red brick, it is topped by a huge elliptical skylight.

In Paris much attention surrounded the opening of the new Cartier building, which houses the company's headquarters as well as the Cartier Foundation for Contemporary Art. Designed by Jean Nouvel, the building contains exhibition spaces and is constructed of several transparent glass walls, one behind the other, creating elaborate depths and reflections.

In Santiago, Spain, the Galician Center of Contemporary Art was under construction. Designed by Álvaro Siza, a Portuguese architect and winner of the Pritzker Prize, it was scheduled to open

The Cartier building in Paris, designed by Jean Nouvel, houses the headquarters of the jewelry firm Cartier Monde and the Cartier Foundation for Contemporary Art.

The conical shape of the University of Wyoming's American Heritage Center, designed by Antoine Predock, reflects the center's celebration of the culture of the American Indians.

formally in 1995. The building, sited on a hillside and clad in gray granite, was to house a collection of regional art. Crisply modern, yet relaxed and angular, it was already being hailed as a masterpiece. At the University of Wyoming in Laramie, the American Heritage Center by Antoine Predock celebrated the Amerindian culture in a conical building.

In Managua, Nicaragua, a cathedral by Mexican architect Ricardo Legoretta replaced an earlier one destroyed by a 1972 earthquake. Built of raw concrete enlivened by bright colors, the cathedral is roofed by white bubblelike domes and features a 34-m (111.5-ft) bell tower.

Exhibitions. The blockbuster architectural show of 1994 was "Frank Lloyd Wright: Architect," displayed at the Museum of Modern Art in New York City from February through May 1994. It was the largest exhibit ever of the work of Wright, who lived from 1867 to 1959 and is usually regarded as the greatest U.S. architect. On view were over 450 draw-ings and photographs of famous Wright designs, from his early Prairie houses around Chicago to such later master-pieces as the vacation house "Falling-water" in Pennsylvania and the Guggen-heim Museum in New York City. The show included informative scale mod-els of several of the buildings, including some that had been demolished or that never were built.

In Montreal "Cities of Artificial Ex-cavation: The Work of Peter Eisenman, 1978–1988" was on view from March through June 1994 at the Canadian Cen-tre for Architecture. Eisenman, an avant-garde U.S. architect and teacher, de-signed the entire installation as a maze of twisting corridors and tiny rooms, which thus allowed the visitor to experience space as well as look at pictures and models of the architectural projects be-ing displayed. Both the installation and the projects gave a sense of having been carved or quarried out of the earth, layer by layer, rather than constructed.

In Paris the Pompidou Centre held an exhibit of the lifetime work of the multifaceted Italian Ettore Sottsass. In the 1960s Sottsass designed modern-clas-sic Olivetti typewriters. He later helped found an influential movement in Post-modern design that he called Memphis, and during the past year he has designed houses.

Preservation. A major controversy erupted over a proposal by the Walt Disney Co. to build a new theme park on a 1,200-ha (3,000-ac) site in Virginia near Washington, D.C. "Disney's Amer-ica" was to feature re-creations of events from U.S. history and was to be sited only 6.4 km (4 mi) from the Manassas National Battlefield Park in Virginia, a major Civil War memorial. The plan was opposed by both environmentalists and history buffs, and the Disney company abandoned the proposal.

A new concern in the field of architec-tural preservation is the fate of the dis-appearing monuments of the Industrial

Revolution, especially in the U.S. Vast steel mills along the rivers of southwestern Pennsylvania, as well as structures elsewhere such as grain elevators and bridges, attracted the interest of preservationists as those structures began to decay from abandonment. Once regarded as blighting scars on the landscape, the industrial relics are now viewed by some as powerful and haunting objects and important symbols of America's industrial past.

In 1994 several structures and districts were added to the UNESCO World Heritage List. Among them were: in China, the Mountain Resort in Chengde City, the Potala Palace in Lhasa, the Temple of Confucius, the Cemetery of Confucius, and the Kong (K'ung) Family Mansion in Qufu (Ch'ü-fu), and the ancient building complex in the Wudang Mountains; in the Czech Republic, the Pilgrimage Church of St. John of Nipomuk at Zelena Hora in Zdar nad Sazavou; in Finland, the Old Church in Petajavesi; in Germany, the Collegiate Church, castle, and Old Town of Quedlinburg and the ironworks in Volklingen; in Italy, the city of Vicenza; in Japan, the historic monuments of ancient Kyoto; in Lithuania, the Old Town of Vilnius; in Luxembourg, the city of Luxembourg: its old quarters and fortifications; in Mexico, the earliest 16th-century monasteries on the slopes of Popocatepetl; in Russia, the Church of the Ascension in Kolomenskoye; and in Turkey, the city of Safranbolu.

—Robert Campbell

Civil engineering

The most significant civil engineering developments of the recent past have occurred in the area of design for transportation, especially the Channel Tunnel (Eurotunnel) linking Britain and France and the development of the TGV (*train à grande vitesse,* or high-speed train); in the construction of long-span cable-stayed bridges; in long-range new policies designed to protect and preserve the environment; and in the response to earthquakes, especially the giant temblors that have hit two major population centers since the beginning of 1994, the Northridge quake in the Los Angeles area on Jan. 17, 1994, and the quake known as the Great Hanshin that decimated Kobe, Japan, one year later.

Transportation. The Channel Tunnel, whose absence failed to deter William of Normandy in the year 1066 but discouraged Napoleon in 1806 and Adolf Hitler in 1940, was completed in 1994 after nearly nine years of work. A labor force that at the height of construction numbered 12,000 workers dug two tunnels 50 km (31 mi) in length and 7.5 m (24.75 ft) in diameter and a smaller service tunnel at such speeds that in one celebrated week the length tunneled reached 425 m (1,400 ft). Owned by Eurotunnel and built by general contractor Transmanche-Link, the "Chunnel" is both an entrepreneurial and an engineering feat. Privately financed in its entirety, the project raised more than $13 billion in investor capital and in loans from a syndicate of 220 banks and had to obtain another $1.5 billion to cover operations until it could achieve a positive cash flow. A train, designed and built at a cost of some $38 million, began running the three-hour trip between a new terminal at London's Waterloo Station and the Gare du Nord in Paris in November 1994. Some trains also carry passenger cars and trucks.

High-speed passenger and freight trains, pioneered many years ago in Japan, are now under intense development in several other nations to counterbalance the demands for ever more highways. The French are in the vanguard, with a plan to extend TGV construction from Paris to the Atlantic and the Mediterranean; architect-engineers of the stature of Santiago Calatrava and Ove Arup & Partners' Peter Rice were used to give formal shape to the major stations, such as Lyon and Lille. In Spain the Madrid-Seville link was virtually complete. In Germany a 280-km (175-mi) magnetically levitated (maglev) train system between Berlin and Hamburg is planned.

Countries of the European Union in 1995 were contemplating a mammoth road- and rail-construction program over the next 15 years that is likely to cost $465 billion. Plans call for completion of a network of some 56,000 km (35,000 mi) of roads and 67,500 km (42,000 mi) of rail. In the U.S., Amtrak, the only entity operating intercity train service, was undertaking a $1 billion program to electrify track in the heavily traveled northeast corridor to allow for 240-km/h (150-mph) train service. Critical to these projects are innovative techniques of roadbed design and switching to accommodate the high-speed trains.

Bridges. In bridge construction two dramatic projects were completed or under way. The longest cable-stayed bridge in the world, spanning the Seine River estuary in Normandy, is ready for traffic.

The 856-m (2,808-ft) span is a combination of concrete and steel, with the first 115 m (380 ft) of the main span built in concrete and the balance in steel. Two 214-m (702-ft)-high inverted Y-shaped pylons support a 21.2-m (69.6-ft)-wide concrete deck. Steel stays as long as 450 m (1,476 ft) fan out from the pylons. Engineers for the cable-stay design are Service d'Études Techniques des Routes et Autoroutes, with Michel Virlogeux as designer.

In Japan the 1,990-m (6,500-ft) Akashi Kaikyo suspension bridge will become the world's longest span bridge upon its completion in 1998. Linking Honshu and Shikoku islands, the bridge consists of only two cables, each one made of low-alloy steel of great tensile strength. The design director of the bridge construction authority is Kazuo Tada.

Environmental policies. In the U.S. intense attention is being focused on the control and preservation of wetlands and on the principle of sustainable development by which construction of any kind must incorporate a plan to restore within a designated time span any resources consumed or likely to be consumed by the project. Also being promulgated are building codes, zoning ordinances, and development guidelines that will minimize damage to the built environment from natural catastrophes such as hurricanes, floods, and earthquakes.

One of the greatest of these catastrophes in recent years was the Northridge quake of Jan. 17, 1994. The best-known structure to suffer from the quake was the 1923 Los Angeles Coliseum, where interior columns were damaged and parts of the original structure were separated from the 1931 additions. The quake also damaged bridges and roads, approximately 25,000 houses and nearly 100,000 other structures, and several major utility lines. Among measures to guard against the impact of another quake is the proposed development of performance-based design standards for various levels of hazard in existing buildings. The Structural Engineers Association of Cal-

Peter Reina

Work has nearly been completed on the final 2.7-m (9-ft) section of the Normandy Bridge across the estuary of the Seine River. At 856 m (2,808 ft), it is the world's longest cable-stayed bridge.

ifornia has undertaken to develop such standards for new buildings by the year 2000.

The Great Hanshin earthquake, which struck the region of the industrial port city of Kobe one year after Northridge, killed more than 5,000 people and is said to have caused some $100 billion worth of damage, five times that of Northridge. Considerable damage and loss of life occurred in the widespread burning of wood dwellings caused by the rupture of gas lines. Many buildings "pancaked" owing to improper reinforcing of concrete in structures of up to 20 stories. Other damage has been traced to architectural irregularities, especially at first floors and setbacks. For example, in ground floors that are open or insufficiently braced, collapse occurs in concrete buildings; in steel buildings the result is major distortion, which makes the building unfit for use.

The author is indebted to the editors of *Architectural Record* and of *Engineering News-Record* for access to their files and to Christopher Arnold for his on-site report from Kobe, Japan, two weeks after the Great Hanshin earthquake.

—Stephen A. Kliment

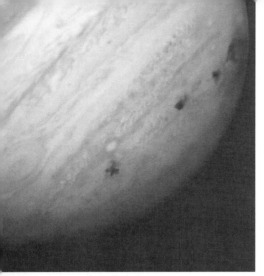

Hubble Space Telescope Comet Team/NASA

An image of Jupiter obtained by the Hubble Space Telescope reveals sites (dark spots) where fragments of Comet Shoemaker-Levy 9 struck the planet.

ASTRONOMY

The most significant discoveries in astronomy during the past year were made possible by one event, the repair of the Hubble Space Telescope (HST). During five space walks in December 1993, astronauts Tom Akers, Jeffrey Hoffman, Story Musgrave, and Kathy Thornton installed corrective optical systems and replaced faulty gyroscopes and solar panels. What followed was an exciting year for astronomers.

Solar system

In July 1994 nearly every telescope on Earth was pointing toward Jupiter to watch the impact on that planet of Comet Shoemaker-Levy 9. This comet had been captured by Jupiter's gravity and had fallen into an orbit around the planet. Less than a year before the comet's discovery, its motion in orbit had carried it to within 21,000 km (1 km = about 0.62 mi) of the planet's cloud tops, where it was broken into about 21 major fragments by the tidal forces of Jupiter's gravity. The orbital trajectory was such that on July 16–22 the comet fragments hit the planet. At a speed of 60 km per second at impact, the largest fragments, estimated at about four kilometers across, unleashed an energy comparable to several million megatons of TNT per fragment. Astronomers did not know what to expect; the comet fragments might break up high in the Jovian atmosphere and disperse the impact energy over a large area, or they might penetrate so deeply into the cloud layers that they would disappear from view. From the Earth the impact sites were out of view just around the planet's limb, but Jupiter's rapid rotation carried these regions into view a few minutes after the impacts.

The first collision produced a plume of hot gas that rose at least 3,000 km high, which made it visible from the Earth above Jupiter's limb. When the impact site became visible a few minutes later, a large dark spot surrounded by a dark ring with a diameter twice that of the Earth was seen. These dark features were unexpected. Ground-based infrared telescopes, observing at wavelengths of one–three micrometers, recorded not dark spots but bright ones. At infrared wavelengths these sites were the brightest places on the planet because of the heat of the impacts. Most of the other fragments struck Jupiter with similar results. In visible light the planet developed a dark band of "bruises" that were easily seen even by amateur astronomers with small telescopes. The Galileo spacecraft, en route to Jupiter, observed bright flashes of light from the impacts.

The dark markings appear to be composed of dust or soot that came from the cometary fragments. Spectra of the hot impacts recorded by the HST showed the presence of ammonia, sulfur, and hydrogen sulfide. This indicates that the impacts penetrated and expelled material from the upper two cloud layers of Jupiter. Surprisingly very little water was detected, which indicates that this comet contained little or no water, although comets are usually composed largely of water. Furthermore, other spectral observations indicated the presence of magnesium, carbon, silicon, and iron in the fragments—also elements not usually expected in great abundance in a comet. Some astronomers suggested that Shoemaker-Levy 9 was really an asteroid.

The Earth, too, is vulnerable to collisions from space. In 1994 two small asteroids nearly hit the Earth. On March 15 an asteroid estimated to be 10 m (1 m = 3.28 ft) in diameter, missed the Earth by 160,000 km. Designated 1994 ES$_1$, this asteroid had been discovered just two days earlier by David Rabinowitz and James Scotti as a faint moving, starlike object. In December Scotti discovered another asteroid just 14 hours before it passed the Earth at a distance of 100,-000 km. This object, now designated as 1994 XM$_1$, was estimated to be 6–14 m

C. Burrows/ESA/STScI/NASA

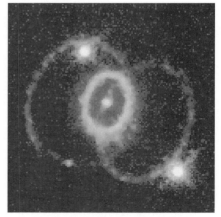

A bright ring of glowing gases surrounds an exploding star, and two other rings are offset from it. No such astronomical structure had ever been seen before.

in diameter. There are surely many small asteroids that pass the Earth undetected. An actual collision with an asteroid of this small size might not be catastrophic. Depending on its composition, it might break up into smaller objects that would be vaporized by friction with the atmosphere. Even if the asteroid remained intact, it would most likely strike in (or vaporize above) the ocean because water covers two-thirds of the Earth's surface. Such an event was recorded in February 1994 in the Pacific Ocean near the Micronesian island of Kosrae. A flash nearly as bright as the Sun was recorded by a network of Earth satellites designed to detect nuclear detonations. The asteroid exploded at an altitude of 20 km and released the energy equivalent of 11,000 tons of TNT, comparable in strength to a small atomic bomb. This asteroid is estimated to have been 7 m across.

It is now widely believed that a collision with one or more asteroids 65 million years ago contributed to the extinction of the dinosaurs. By comparison, such asteroids would have been some 10 km across. Celestial objects of that size are far less common, of course, and collisions with them are rare.

Because of the asteroids' distance from Earth, little detail is usually visible through telescopes. They appear only as moving starlike objects. In March 1994 the Jet Propulsion Laboratory released close-up pictures of one asteroid, 243 Ida, taken by the Galileo spacecraft from a distance of less than 100 km. Ida is an oblong rock 56 km long. Like the Earth's Moon, Ida's surface is marked by many impact craters. Ida appears similar to Gaspra, the only other asteroid ever

observed in detail, also by Galileo. The images of Ida also showed something surprising: Ida has a moon. A small asteroid 1.6 km in diameter, now called Dactyl, orbits Ida. There had been previous suggestions of binary asteroids, but this was controversial until the photographs of Dactyl. (*See* Feature Article: ASTEROIDS: SECRETS LOCKED IN STONE.)

Stars

In February 1987 a star was seen to explode violently in the Large Magellanic Cloud, a nearby galaxy. This event, a supernova, marks the end of the life of a massive supergiant star. In the explosion the outer layers of the star are blasted into space at speeds of thousands of kilometers per second, producing an expanding debris cloud. The core of the star collapses to form a dense neutron star. Even though the 1987 supernova was very close to the Earth by astronomical standards (160,000 light-years), by early 1995 the debris cloud had not yet become large enough to be resolved with ground-based optical telescopes. The remnant stellar core and the expanding debris still appeared starlike. An image obtained from the HST before it was repaired showed a bright ring, about one light-year across, surrounding the explosion site. This ring is believed to be stellar material ejected into space by the strong stellar wind that existed in the supergiant prior to the explosion. The ring material could not have come from the supernova blast because there has not been enough time for it to expand that far. The reasons for the ring shape remain uncertain.

The sharper vision of the repaired HST revealed two additional fainter and larger

rings, each offset from the star. These rings are about two light-years across. It is suspected that they lie in different planes. The star itself is offset from the rings in that it does not lie along a line connecting the centers of the rings.

No structure like this has been seen before in any astronomical object. Christopher Burrows, the discoverer of the rings, suggested that the star is surrounded by a large bubble of cool, transparent gas that was puffed out by the stellar wind when the star was a supergiant. The rings are gas within the bubble that is excited into fluorescence when struck by oppositely directed jets of radiation from the central star. The source of the jets is precessing like a wobbling top, causing the jets to trace circular patterns on the inside of the bubble.

Astronomers have long wondered whether stars other than the Sun have planets. Planets around other stars are difficult to detect because they appear too small and faint with ground-based telescopes and the image of the planets and the star they orbit cannot be resolved. In recent years, however, astronomers have found indirect evidence for the existence of planets outside our solar system. The Orion Nebula is a large interstellar cloud that is known to be a location of star formation. A star is formed when a region of the nebula collapses under its own gravitational attraction. As the region collapses, it spins and the outer regions flatten into a disk. The compression heats the center, which eventually ignites hydrogen fusion to become a star. The material in the surrounding disk then condenses to form planets. If this scheme is correct, then the existence of planets

Young stars in the Orion Nebula are surrounded by disks of dust and gas, which astronomers believe may condense to form planets.

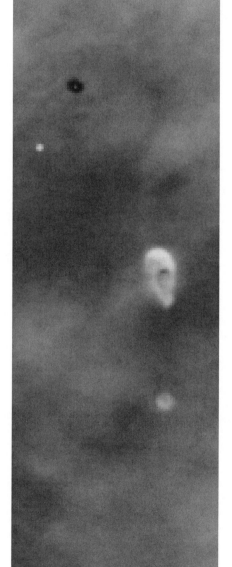

C.R. O'Dell/Rice University/NASA

around stars should be very common.

Because of the Earth's turbulent atmosphere, ground-based telescopes have been unable to detect these protoplanetary disks around young stars. (The one exception is Beta Pictoris, which is discussed below.) Prior to its repair the HST photographed young stars in the Orion Nebula that seemed to have circumstellar material. Because of the telescope's optical flaws, it was not possible to discern if this material was disk-shaped as expected. Clearer images taken by C. Robert O'Dell and Zheng Wen with the repaired telescope revealed disks of dust and gas around 56 of the 110 young stars they surveyed. If they are sufficiently heated by the central star, these disks are bright; otherwise, they are seen in dark silhouette against the glowing background of the Orion Nebula. These observations support the concepts about star formation and the idea that the formation of planets is a common process in the universe.

In 1984 the bright star Beta Pictoris was shown to be surrounded by an extended disk of dust. This disk extends 1,000 astronomical units from the star. (An astronomical unit is 150 million km, the mean distance between the Earth and the Sun). While this disk was widely believed to be a solar system in the making, there was no evidence that any planets had actually begun to form. Recent observations of Beta Pictoris by Pierre-Olivier Lagage and Eric Pantin supplied that evidence. They studied the inner 100 astronomical units of the disk at infrared wavelengths and found evidence that the density of the disk material is by a factor of 100 lower than it is in the outer disk.

Normally, the density of the disk would be expected to increase toward the center. They proposed that the density is lower because the dust has been swept up to make planets.

In one case astronomers are confident they have detected planets—but it is in the last place they expected to find them. The planets are orbiting a neutron star, the remnant of a supernova explosion. In 1990 Alexander Wolszczan began studying a radio pulsar in the constellation Virgo. Pulsars are neutron stars that are only 10 km across and have a mass of two to three times that of the Sun. A neutron star is formed when the collapse of a stellar core triggers a supernova explosion. Neutron stars rotate rapidly because angular momentum is conserved as the core collapses. As beams of radiation from spots on the neutron star are swept across our line of sight by the rotation, pulses are produced. Pulsars are known to be extremely regular in their pulse periods. In this particular pulsar, however, Wolszczan noted that there was a repeating pattern in which the pulses seemed to change from arriving early to arriving late. He interpreted this as due to motion of the neutron star. There are times when the star is moving toward the Earth, which causes the pulses to arrive a bit early, and times when it is moving away, causing the pulse to arrive a bit later. These motions, he concluded, are due to the gravitational pull of planets that are orbiting the neutron star.

Some astronomers were skeptical of this interpretation, suggesting that the pulse variations might be due to some variation in the pulsar itself. Also, the supernova that produced the neutron star would be expected to destroy any nearby planets. Wolszczan predicted that, in time, the gravitational interaction of the planets themselves would produce an observable signature in the pulse-arrival pattern. During the past year that signature was seen, indicating the presence of three planets. They have masses that are 3.4, 2.8, and 0.015 times the mass of the Earth and orbit the pulsar at 0.36, 0.47, and 0.19 astronomical units, respectively. It has been suggested that they formed from the supernova debris. In this way the death of a star gave birth to both a neutron star and new planets.

Galactic astronomy

For many decades astronomers have been aware that most of the mass of the Milky Way and other galaxies is unseen. This is evident from the orbital motions of stars within galaxies and galaxies within clusters, which indicate the presence of 10 times more mass than can be seen directly. One of the more conservative explanations for this unseen matter is that it exists in the form of numerous low-mass red dwarf stars and brown dwarfs (stars not massive enough to ignite nuclear fusion). Such stars are intrinsically very faint and difficult to see.

Star-formation theory predicts an abundance of low-mass stars. This has been difficult to test with ground-based telescopes because the blurring effects of the Earth's atmosphere make it difficult to distinguish between very faint stars and very distant galaxies. Two recent studies using much sharper images from the HST cast doubt on the existence of a large population of faint, low-mass stars. The first study, by John Bahcall and Andrew Gould, used images of two locations along the Milky Way made with the upgraded Hubble Wide Field Planetary Camera 2. They found many fewer faint red stars than expected. In a similar study Francesco Paresce studied a region of a globular star cluster. There, too, the number of red dwarf stars was far fewer than expected. Though these studies sampled a very small fraction of the sky and require confirmation, they suggest that star-formation theory and the prevailing ideas about unseen matter may require modification.

On a clear, dark night one can see the plane of the disk-shaped Milky Way galaxy as a hazy band of light extending across the sky. Other, external galaxies are found throughout the sky in great abundance except along this band. Near the plane of the Milky Way, astronomers' vision is severely limited by interstellar dust. For this reason astronomers have long known that there could be some nearby galaxies that have not been detected in visible light. Because infrared and radio waves penetrate this interstellar dust much better than visible light, an international team of astronomers led by Renée Kraan-Korteweg used the 25-m-diameter radio dish in Dwingeloo, Neth., to search for radio emissions from external galaxies in the direction of the Milky Way plane. Spiral galaxies contain large amounts of cold hydrogen gas that radiate energy at a wavelength of 21 cm (8 in). These waves penetrate the dust of the Milky Way, making the galaxy detectable, but it is necessary to disentangle this emission from the foreground hydrogen emission in the Milky Way. The researchers relied on the fact that the background galaxies would be rotating and thereby cause the radio emission to show a different Doppler shift on the side rotating toward the observer compared with the side rotating away. Their search turned up a pair of interacting galaxies at a distance of about 10 million light-years from Earth. These have been dubbed Dwingeloo 1 and 2 and are estimated to have masses of a quarter and a tenth of the Milky Way, respectively. Since its discovery Dwingeloo 1 has been imaged with an infrared camera, which revealed its form as a barred spiral.

A similar search found the closest galaxy to the Milky Way. It was discovered by Rodrigo Ibata, Gerry Gilmore, and Mike Irwin. Only 50,000 light-years from the Milky Way's core, the new galaxy was discovered because the apparent motions of its brightest stars are different from those of the foreground stars of the Milky Way. It most likely belongs to a class of dwarf galaxies that typically contain a few million stars and are 1,000 light-years across. In time, gravity will cause this galaxy to merge with the Milky Way.

Extragalactic astronomy

When we look into the sky, we are looking back in time. Even for the closest stars, we are looking decades to centuries into the past because of the travel time of the light to the Earth. When we look at distant galaxies, we are looking back millions and sometimes billions of years. Therefore, images of distant galaxies should reveal how they appeared when the universe was young and possibly would show galaxy formation. Unfortunately, the most distant galaxies appear the faintest and the smallest, and the blurring effects of the Earth's atmosphere prevent ground-based telescopes from seeing much detail. The HST, however, has now provided the first clear views of infant galaxies. Mark Dickinson and his colleagues used the HST to take an 18-hour exposure of galaxies at an estimated distance of 9 billion light-years. The image shows a collection of galaxies unlike any previously seen. The elliptical galaxies appear well-formed, which implies that they formed soon after the Big Bang. Spiral galaxies are mostly absent. Instead, there are many misshapen objects. Their blue color indicates that they are fragments of spiral galaxies that are undergoing vigorous star formation. These fragments either have been produced by interactions between adjacent galaxies or are in the process of combining to form spiral galaxies.

Astronomers have long suspected that the centers of many galaxies contain massive black holes. The galaxy M87 in the heart of the Virgo Cluster of galaxies has been a prime candidate. The core of this galaxy is the source of strong radio emission, and oppositely directed jets of gas shoot thousands of light-years into space. The event horizon (the region from which nothing can escape) of the massive black hole is believed to be surrounded by a disk of gas that is spiraling inward. The disk material would come from interstellar clouds and stars that were shredded by the intense gravitational field. It is the release of energy by the disk material that makes the black hole detectable.

Unfortunately, ground-based telescopes have never been able to see the core of M87 with enough clarity to determine if such a disk is really there. Even the repaired HST is unable to see the event horizon, which is only the size of our solar system, but it has detected the larger disk. Holland Ford and Richard Harms obtained an image that shows a disk of gas 500 light-years across in the center of M87. Furthermore, they were able to isolate the light on either side of the disk and measure the rotational speed by means of the Doppler effect. At distances of 60 light-years from the galaxy's center, the disk has a speed of 550 km per second. A mass two billion to three billion times that of the Sun in the center of M87 is required for supplying the gravity to prevent gas that is moving at such speeds from escaping. Historians may record that 1994 was the year that the existence of a massive black hole was finally proved.

Astronomers have long known that the distances between galaxies and galaxy clusters is increasing with time. This expansion, which began with the Big Bang, implies that the universe was once much denser and hotter. Everything would have been compressed within a small volume. Astronomers can estimate the age of the universe by calculating the time taken for the galaxies to reach their present positions. This requires a measurement of the expansion rate and the distances to galaxies. The most reliable method of finding distances is to identify a type of star, known as a Cepheid variable, in the galaxies. These stars have known intrinsic luminosities (total amounts of radiation emitted over a specified range of wavelengths). By comparison of these with their apparent brightness and then application of the inverse-square law for light, their distances can be found. (The inverse-square law states that a physical quantity varies with distance from a source inversely as the square of that distance.) These also equal the distance to the galaxy in which the stars are embedded.

For getting the best possible estimate of the expansion rate, distance measurements to the farthest galaxies are required. Unfortunately, the blurring effects of the Earth's atmosphere make it difficult to distinguish individual stars in all but the closest galaxies. This limitation was recently overcome in two different ways. First, Michael Pierce and collaborators used a ground-based telescope with adaptive optics that compensate for some of the atmosphere's effects. Second, Wendy Freedman and collaborators used the Hubble Space Telescope, which orbits above the Earth's atmosphere. In both cases the distance to the galaxy M100 in the Virgo cluster of galaxies was found. This allowed the researchers to estimate distances to even more distant galaxies on the basis of brightnesses and eventually resulted in a better estimate of the expansion rate. The conclusion is that the universe is 7 billion to 14 billion years old. Unfortunately, the latter figure is at least two billion years younger than the known ages of the stars in our Galaxy. Clearly, the stars cannot be older than the universe. Because the ages of the stars are considered firmly established, astronomers are working hard to understand why this method of establishing the age of the universe has apparently failed.

—Ronald H. Kaitchuck

CHEMISTRY

Unusual achievements in chemistry during the past year included the detection of buckminsterfullerene in a microscopic meteorite crater on a satellite retrieved from space, the development of a new family of low-calorie fats based on natural ingredients found in foods, and the finding that even fairly small clusters of some metal atoms behave remarkably like the metal in bulk. In other highlights a team of German researchers announced the discovery of two new synthetic elements, while two teams of American chemists reported the total synthesis of the important anticancer compound taxol.

INORGANIC AND PHYSICAL CHEMISTRY

The past year saw the discovery of two new elements amid a fight over the naming of several others. Scientists reported synthesizing a family of materials that contract rather than expand when heated. The question of how small a metal particle can be before it no longer behaves like a metal was clarified for several elements. Experiments with ultrafast lasers helped unravel some of the mystery surrounding the mechanism of vision, resolved the disputed reality of an intermediate molecular structure in an important class of organic chemical reactions, and furthered scientists' understanding of the interaction of water molecules with dissolved molecules.

New elements and lingering disputes

A team of German scientists headed by Peter Armbruster at the GSI (Society for Heavy-Ion Research), Darmstadt, Germany, together with guest scientists from Russia, Slovakia, and Finland announced the discovery of element 110 in November 1994. They bombarded a target of lead-208 with a beam of nickel-62 atoms and produced a small number of atoms of the superheavy element, specifically an isotope having an atomic mass of 269. Even though the atoms of element 110 had a half-life of only 0.17 millisecond (ms; a thousandth of a second), they could be positively identified by the manner in which they radioactively decayed. In subsequent experiments using nickel-64 as the projectiles, the researchers created atoms of another isotope of element 110, one with a mass of 271 and a half-life of 1.4 ms. The following month Armbruster's team added a second new element to the periodic table with the announcement that they had made three atoms of element 111 by bombarding a bismuth-209 target with projectiles of nickel-64. The isotope had an atomic mass of 272 and a half-life of 1.5 ms. Encouraged by their success, the GSI team expressed optimism that they would create element 112 by early 1996 and eventually elements 113 and 114.

The discovery of the elements 110 and 111 came in the midst of a dispute over the naming of the elements 104–109. These elements, which like elements 110 and 111 are unstable and synthetic, had all been made at GSI, the Lawrence Berkeley (Calif.) Laboratory, or the Joint Institute for Nuclear Research, Dubna, Russia. They long had gone without official names because of conflicting claims of discovery and the need for experimental confirmation—problems that were recently resolved. Scientists who discover a new element traditionally have the right to name it, but in the case of the elements in question, the delays in their official naming opened the way for the use of logical but unpronounceable temporary names, such as unnilquadium for element 104.

In late 1994 the arguments over names became more heated when an independent panel of chemists sponsored by the International Union of Pure and Applied Chemistry (IUPAC)—the body normally involved with nomenclature issues in chemistry—recommended a list of names that were at odds with most of the names proposed by the discovery teams. For elements 104–109 the panel offered the following names and symbols: 104, dubnium (Db); 105, joliotium (Jl); 106, rutherfordium (Rf); 107, bohrium (Bh); 108, hahnium (Hn); and 109, meitnerium (Mt). In the U.S. there was particular anger over the recommendation to call element 106 rutherfordium after New Zealander Ernest Rutherford, the discoverer of the atomic nucleus. The American discoverers of the element had wanted to call it seaborgium (Sg) after Glenn T. Seaborg, a codiscoverer of plutonium and eight other heavy elements. (See *1995 Yearbook of Science and the Future* Year in Review: CHEMISTRY: *Inorganic Chemistry*.) The IUPAC panel eliminated his name on the grounds that elements are not named after living scientists. Nevertheless, the name seaborgium had been greeted warmly since its suggestion and had already appeared in periodic tables and encyclopedias. It seemed likely that resolution of the dispute would depend on the actions of learned societies and journals. The American Chemical Society already was on record as supporting the names proposed by the discoverers, so a rapid resolution of the affair seemed unlikely.

Smaller when hot

Most solid materials expand when heated, as their chemical bonds lengthen and their atoms move farther apart. The tendency to expand creates serious problems for solids used in optics, electronics, and other applications. Even slight expansion of materials in telescope mirrors and lasers, for instance, can result in distortion and poor performance. Heat-related expansion is a major cause of premature failure of circuit boards in computers and other electronic devices.

Arthur Sleight and co-workers of Oregon State University announced discovery of a unique family of solid materials that could help solve such problems. The materials—typified by $ZrVPO_4$, an oxide of zirconium (Zr), vanadium (V), and phosphorus (P)—contract steadily when heated between about 200° and 800° C (390° and 1,470° F). Sleight suggested that the unusual behavior of the materials is due to their crystal structure, in which atoms of vanadium and phosphorus bond not to each other but to an intermediate atom of oxygen. When such a material is heated, the oxygen atom vibrates in a fashion that tends to pull the other atoms physically closer together. The behavior differs from that of existing materials that resist expansion, such as those used in heat-resistant cookware. Those materials are made of small particles that, when heated, expand in some directions and contract in others, resulting in little net change in volume. But existing materials have disadvantages that limit their use in other applications. Compounds such as $ZrVPO_4$ might be used as components in new polymer, graphite, or ceramic composites that would be more versatile yet highly resistant to heat-related failure.

When is a metal not a metal?

The familiar properties of metals include their shiny luster, high electrical conductivity, and, in some cases, magnetism. The ability to conduct electricity or act as a magnet are cooperative effects involving many atoms rather than the property of any one atom. It thus is reasonable to ask how small a cluster of metal atoms can become before it loses these metallic properties.

L. Jos de Jongh, Fokko M. Mulder, Timeke A. Steginck, and Roger C. Thiel at Leiden University, The Netherlands, investigated the question using platinum clusters prepared by Günter Schmid of the University of Essen, Germany. The researchers transmuted some of the platinum atoms in the clusters to unstable gold isotopes by neutron irradiation. The gamma rays given off by the gold atoms as they decayed allowed the scientists to probe the electron charge density in the cluster by means of a technique known as Mössbauer spectroscopy. They found the charge density in a cluster containing as few as 147 platinum atoms to be very similar to that of the bulk metal, whereas the charge density for a 13-atom cluster showed significant differences. Pinning down just at what point between a 13- and a 147-atom cluster the differences cease clearly needs more investigation, but even a 147-atom cluster is still a remarkably small unit to show such metallic behavior.

In a second example of this type of investigation, Isabelle M.L. Billas, A. Châtelain, and Walt A. de Heer of the Federal Polytechnic Institute, Lausanne, Switz., studied the development of magnetism in clusters of iron, cobalt, and nickel atoms. They determined the magnetic character of particular-sized clusters by deflecting them with a magnet and, in so doing, discerned a gradual evolution of magnetic properties with cluster size. For nickel, a cluster of only about 150 atoms behaves magnetically like bulk nickel metal. For cobalt and iron, the cluster has to be about 450 and 550 atoms in size, respectively.

Snapshots of vision

The operation of the human eye still provides many mysteries. It has been known for some time that rhodopsin is the main molecule in the retina that detects light and converts it into a signal that can be processed by the brain. The exact manner in which that process occurs, however, remains unclear. During the past year ultrafast-laser experiments by Qing Wang and Charles V. Shank of the Lawrence Berkeley Laboratory provided snapshots of the very first events that occur when light strikes the rhodopsin molecule. In an extremely short time, about 200 femtoseconds (fs; one quadrillionth of a second, or 10^{-15} second), after light strikes the molecule, the latter twists into a new shape in a manner similar to the release of a compressed spring. The experiments showed that vision depends in its earliest stages on extremely fast changes in the shape of rhodopsin and may point the way to designing artificial eyes that can convert light into information.

Water as a solvent

Water is the most familiar solvent that people encounter, yet the details of the way that water molecules react to the presence of solutes, or dissolved substances, are not well understood. Two new laser experiments shed light on the fundamental process of solvation.

The first was carried out by R. Nathaniel Pribble and Timothy S. Zwier of Purdue University, West Lafayette, Ind. Using powerful, tunable infrared lasers, they made direct measurements of infrared absorption by a beam of molecular clusters of water and benzene (C_6H_6) and compared them with measurements made on molecular clusters of pure water. Depending on the conditions used to generate the beam, the size of the clusters can vary from several to hundreds of molecules. In the past such measurements had been plagued by an inability to separate the absorption signals from clusters of different sizes. Pribble and Zwier devised a method to overcome the problem, allowing them to correlate infrared spectral features with specific clusters of the type C_6H_6-$(H_2O)_n$ in which *n,* the number of water molecules in the cluster, ranged from 1 to 7. Their results showed that water clusters are little affected by the presence of a benzene molecule. Effectively the two substances are immiscible on the molecular level just as they are in bulk liquid form. One can think of the benzene molecule as being adsorbed on the surface of a cluster of water molecules. For the smaller clusters (in which *n* ranges from 3 to 5) an unusual type of bond is formed between the electrons in the benzene ring and a "free" OH group of a water molecule that is not bonded to other water molecules in the cluster (*see* 1).

Other ultrafast-laser experiments performed by Ralph Jimenez and Graham Fleming of the University of Chicago and P.V. Kumar and Mark Maroncelli of Pennsylvania State University looked at a different facet of solution behavior.

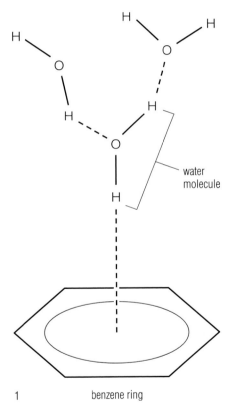

1   benzene ring

Their investigations probed the speed with which water molecules react to a redistribution of electric charge in a dissolved solute molecule. Many chemical reactions proceed via the formation of an intermediate molecular state in which such a charge shift has occurred. Electrostatic interactions between the reaction intermediate and molecules of the solvent in which the reaction is taking place can affect the reaction rate. The chemists' measurements, which were done on dye molecules dissolved in water, confirmed theoretical predictions of James T. Hynes of the University of Colorado that the response of water to a charge shift in the solute molecule occurs on two very different time scales. There is an initial ultrafast response in which the surrounding water molecules perform correcting oscillatory motions in less than 50 fs. Then there is a diffusion of water molecules to and from the solute molecule, a much slower type of process. The fast response of the water molecules constitutes a kind of solvent "friction" that can slow down the rate at which an charge-shifted intermediate can form products.

Found: a reaction intermediate

Organic chemists have known for a century that the thermal decomposition of many organic molecules proceeds by the breaking of a carbon-carbon covalent bond. Still, despite a plethora of experimental and theoretical investigations, there remains much dispute as to the mechanism by which this occurs. The well-known ring-opening reaction of cyclobutane (C_4H_8) is a good example (*see* 2 on page 330). The reaction can be thought to proceed smoothly in one step (route a) via a "transition state," a useful construct that has no physical existence. Alternately, it may occur as a two-step process (route b) in which a diradical intermediate with an unpaired electron on each of two carbon atoms is formed. The distinction is important in that such an intermediate exists for a finite time

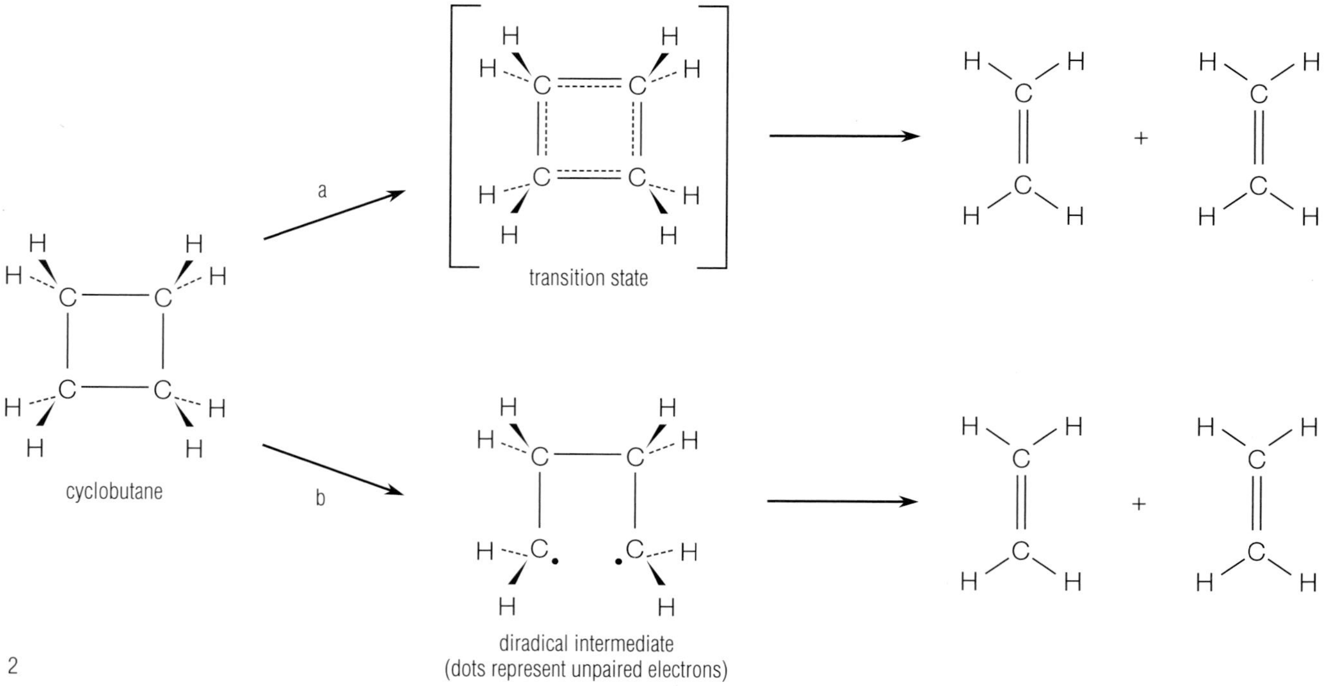

transition state

cyclobutane

diradical intermediate
(dots represent unpaired electrons)

2

(though the time may be very short) and, in principle, can be detected. Using ultrafast lasers, S. Pedersen, J.L. Herek, and A.H. Zewail of the California Institute of Technology were able to "freeze out" a definite diradical intermediate in the cyclobutane reaction even though it existed only for some hundreds of femtoseconds. Such experiments, which can directly probe structural changes and molecular motions at such short time scales, promise to solve many long-standing mechanistic questions in organic chemistry.
—Philip R. Watson and Michael Woods

ORGANIC CHEMISTRY
Every scientific discipline experiences evolutionary pressures due to a complex interplay of forces stemming from chance discovery blended with political and economic change. Organic chemistry is no exception. During the past year the computer revolution continued to transform the discipline, influencing not only how research was carried out but also, owing to a new wave of fledgling electronic-publishing technologies, how results were disseminated to the scientific community. There was also an extraordinary increase in efforts to make chemistry and the chemical industry more environmentally friendly. A particularly strong emphasis was being placed on the development of new chemical technologies to reduce the production of chemical waste. Although many subdisciplines within chemistry were expanding at a substantial pace, biological chemistry and materials-based chemistry appeared to be especially strong. More to the point, the demarcations between the various subdisciplines were growing increasingly blurry and arbitrary as chemistry became more interdisciplinary.

Unusual molecules with unusual properties
Buckminsterfullerene (C_{60}), a spherical, cagelike molecule made of 60 carbon atoms bonded into a geometry reminiscent of architect Buckminster Fuller's geodesic domes and akin to the pattern found on a soccer ball (*see* 1), continued to catch the attention and imagination of chemists around the globe. Development of practical uses for C_{60} and its larger and smaller all-carbon relatives—collectively called fullerenes—hinged upon finding new methods for inducing the molecules to participate in

chemical reactions and characterizing the products. Research groups led by John Fischer of the University of Pennsylvania and Yoshihiro Iwasa of the University of Tokyo successfully strung series of fullerenes together like a pearl necklace to study the interesting optical properties of the resultant structures. Collaborative groups led by Martin Saunders of Yale University and Frank A.L. Anet of the University of California, Los Angeles, incorporated helium-3, an isotope of helium, inside fullerene molecules, allowing them to use nuclear magnetic resonance (NMR) spectroscopy to study flows of electronic charges (ring currents) characteristic of certain molecules containing delocalized electron clouds (so-called aromatic compounds). Theodore Bunch and co-workers of NASA discovered fullerenes in a tiny meteorite crater on the hull of a satellite that had been retrieved from Earth orbit by a U.S. space shuttle in 1990. Although their analyses suggested that the molecules originated in the meteorite, the possibility that they were created in the impact could not be ruled out.

Three decades of the chemistry of cubanes offered an excellent illustration of the logical progression from basic research to technological development. Cubane, a hydrocarbon molecule whose eight carbon atoms occupy the corners of a cube (see 2), was synthesized in 1964 by Philip E. Eaton and co-workers of the University of Chicago. Their work was motivated entirely by curiosity about the properties that such a strained molecule might exhibit. Later, in the 1980s, research at the U.S. Army Armament Research, Development, and Engineering Center, Picatinny Arsenal, New Jersey, led to improvements in large-scale preparation of cubane and various nitrogen-containing derivatives for use as explosives. Later still, in 1994, A. Bashir-Hashemi and co-workers of Geo-Centers, Inc., Lake Hopatcong, N.J., reported that the military-inspired technology for preparing a wide variety of substituted cubanes (cubanes with attached molecular groups) had led to an extensive screening program for detecting pharmacologically active cubanes as part of the fight against AIDS.

Synthesis of complex molecules

The development of techniques for the total synthesis of the anticancer compound taxol (see 3 on page 333), certainly one of the more important achievements in natural-product synthesis in recent years, was reported by the research groups of Robert A. Holton of Florida State University and K.C. Nicolaou of Scripps Research Institute, La Jolla, Calif. Taxol, originally isolated in

2   cubane

trace quantities from the bark of the Pacific yew tree, shows potent inhibitory activity against ovarian, breast, and lung cancer. At first, obtaining the compound in quantity had been expected to require the cutting of thousands of trees, raising concerns about the widespread destruction of yew forests. Later, chemists developed tree-sparing semisynthetic methods for making taxollike compounds from chemical precursors that can be extracted from needles and twigs rather than bark. The most active form of the compound, a semisynthetic taxol analog to be marketed by Bristol-Myers Squibb, was made available as the result of work carried out at Florida State.

A major task confronted in the synthesis of complex molecules is imposition of control over the spatial orientation of groups of atoms such that only one of two possible mirror-image forms (enantiomers) of the molecule is made. Molecules that can exist as either of two nonsuperimposable mirror images, are said to be chiral. In view of the growing

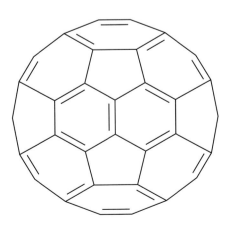

1   buckminsterfullerene (C$_{60}$)

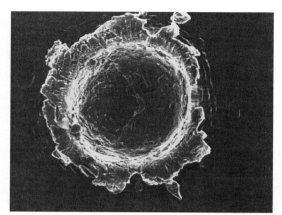

(Top) photos, F. Radicati di Brozolo, T.E. Bunch, R.H. Fleming, and J. Macklin; (bottom) NASA

Traces of the fullerenes C$_{60}$ and C$_{70}$—all-carbon molecules containing 60 and 70 carbon atoms, respectively—were detected in a meteorite crater (above and, after flattening, right) less than 0.2 mm (0.008 in) across in an aluminum panel on a satellite retrieved from space. The ropey mass in the crater consists of impact-melted aluminum and material from the carbon-bearing meteorite. The satellite, the Long Duration Exposure Facility, orbited Earth for nearly six years before being recovered by a U.S. space shuttle in 1990 (below).

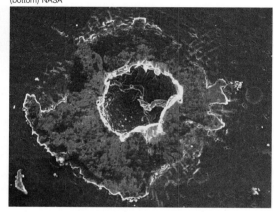

number of pharmaceutically important compounds that display such handedness and the well-documented differences in biological activity between pairs of enantiomers, methods to prepare enantiomerically pure compounds have assumed a central importance. For example, a research team at Merck & Co., Inc., Rahway, N.J., headed by Paul J. Reider developed the synthesis of a promising new drug currently known only as L-735,-524 for the fight against AIDS (see 4). The economic feasibility of the synthesis relied on an enantiomerically highly selective reaction called the Jacobsen epoxidation, named after its originator, Eric Jacobsen of the University of Illinois.

In an ironic twist, concurrent with the push for more highly selective syntheses of medicinally important molecules, there exists an emerging interest in developing syntheses that generate random mixtures of potential drug candidates. Historically, organic chemists have approached drug development by using an iterative protocol requiring synthesis of a target drug candidate, biological testing, and subsequent redesign of the drug candidate for more testing. While successful, the strategy is extremely labor-intensive and costly. To offset these drawbacks, chemists have been taking a new approach called combinatorial synthesis, in which an enormous number, or "library," of compounds are synthesized at one time. The strategy relies on the development of analytic methods to sort through the libraries, detect important biological activity, and determine which substance is responsible for it. The sorting problem can be staggering in cases in which literally millions of substances are synthesized and tested at one time. Just one of many clever examples was reported by Clark W. Still and graduate student Allen Borchardt of Columbia University, New York City. Using a special split-synthesis technique, they prepared tiny plastic beads containing molecular chains made of different sequences of 20 amino-

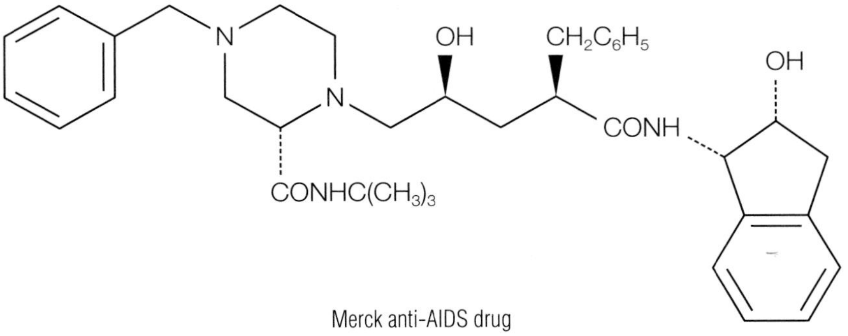

4   Merck anti-AIDS drug

acid building blocks—117,649 different sequences in all. The library of amino-acid chains, or polypeptides, then was searched for variants that functioned as synthetic receptors, characterized by their binding to biological compounds of interest. Binding by a polypeptide receptor was monitored by a color change of the bead, with the intensity of the color proportional to the degree of binding. The most highly colored beads could then be analyzed for their content by means of highly sensitive analytic techniques.

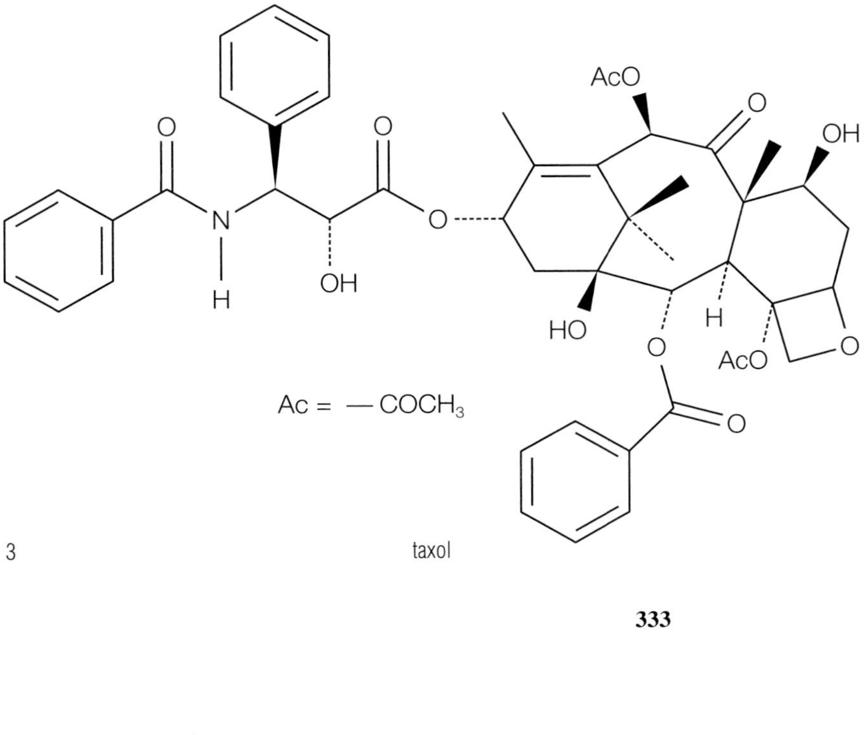

Bioorganic chemistry

In the 1980s the research groups of Peter G. Schultz at the University of Califor-

3   taxol

Ac = — COCH$_3$

nia, Berkeley, and Richard A. Lerner at Scripps Research Institute used monoclonal antibody technology, a technique for producing populations of antibodies of a single type, to develop a new class of catalysts called catalytic antibodies. By eliciting the production of antibodies to judiciously chosen analogs of transitional molecular structures that form during chemical reactions, the researchers turned the natural binding properties of antibodies, which are central to the body's immune response, to an "unnatural" use as catalysts for promoting specific chemical reactions.

In the past year a research group headed by Thomas Scanlan and Robert Fletterick of the University of California, San Francisco, reported X-ray crystallographic evidence that the binding site of a catalytic antibody having certain chemical-bond–breaking (hydrolytic) abilities similar to those observed for natural enzyme catalysts called proteases also has a remarkable structural similarity to some natural serine proteases. This observation suggested that the chemical mechanisms used by at least some catalytic antibodies resemble those that evolved naturally in enzymes. Meanwhile, Lerner's group reported the development of a catalytic antibody that promotes a molecular-ring formation of a type found in the biological synthesis of steroids and terpenes. Further studies of catalytic antibodies may unravel some of the many mysteries underlying natural enzyme-catalyzed reactions. Lerner and Schultz shared the 1994 Wolf Prize in Chemistry, a prestigious Israeli prize that in the past has often foreshadowed receipt of a Nobel Prize.

5   electrooptic material

Schultz and co-workers also reported making RNA molecules 165 nucleotide building blocks long that can catalyze a structural change in a molecule called biphenyl. The work has interesting implications in view of the suggestion that RNA molecules were the key biological catalysts in the prebiotic environment of Earth several billion years ago. Although the RNA-catalyzed reaction studied by Schultz has no obvious relationship to normal catalyzed biological processes, it did represent the successful outcome of an attempt to mimic billions of years of evolution by screening a library of a quadrillion (10^{15}) different RNA molecules by means of a combinatorial strategy similar to that described above.

Polymers and materials

In recent years polymer chemistry has experienced a renaissance. One particular area in which polymer chemists have made substantial inroads is in the development of materials for biomedical applications. For example, Ulrich Suter and Peter Neuenschwander of the Swiss Federal Institute of Technology, Zürich, developed a polymer designed to kill tumors. The solubility of the polymer was carefully engineered such that when a solution of it enters body tissue, dilution in aqueous biological fluids causes the polymer to precipitate as a solid. Iodine atoms present on the polymer's side chains allow visualization of polymer deposition in the tissue by means of X-ray technology available in standard medical clinics. For service as an anticancer agent, the polymer solution would be injected into the tumor, where its precipitation would restrict the blood supply and thus kill the tumor cells.

The revolution in biochemistry has been accompanied by a huge demand for efficient synthesis of the key biological polymers central to all living systems. Laboratory-scale syntheses of polypeptides (long chains of amino acids that make up enzymes and other proteins) and polynucleotides (long chains of nucleotides that make up DNA and RNA) became feasible only with the advent of automated processes relying on polymer supports to anchor the growing chain. A research team lead by Chi-Huey Wong at Scripps Research Institute and James Pauson of Cytel reported that polymer-supported synthesis methods can be extended to prepare polysaccharides, naturally occurring polymers comprising sugar subunits. The process appeared promising both for the preparation of laboratory-scale quantities of specific polysaccharides and for the development of combinatorial libraries of polysaccharides containing random distributions of sugar subunits.

Researchers at the University of Leicester, England, discovered a potentially important organic material displaying interesting electrooptic properties. Andrew Abbott, Paul Jenkins, and Nadia Khan synthesized a semiconducting organometallic salt (*see* 5) that visibly darkens on application of an electrical potential. They found that the electrooptic effects are due to a physical rather than a chemical change in the material and are reversible upon warming. The authors speculate that automobile window glass containing such a material may someday allow a driver to tint the windshield against glare at the flip of a switch on the dashboard. A similar application may allow an optical sensor to regulate automatically the amount of sunlight entering the windows of a room much the way that a thermostat regulates the temperature.

Milestones

The 1994 Nobel Prize for Chemistry was awarded to George A. Olah (*see* Scientists of the Year) of the University of Southern California for his pioneering studies of organic molecules known as carbocations. These short-lived, highly reactive species, which bear a positive charge on their carbon atoms, are important in the chemistry of hydrocarbons, yet they proved to be notoriously challenging to study. Among his many outstanding achievements, Olah succeeded in preparing stable solutions of carbocations and in characterizing them by means of NMR spectroscopy.

The past year also saw the passing of Linus Pauling (*see* Scientists of the Year) at the age of 93. Pauling will be remembered as one of the most influential scientists of all time. During his tenure at the California Institute of Technology, his ideas and research influenced scientific thinking on an enormous number of topics throughout physics, chemistry,

U.S. chemist Linus Pauling, a monumental figure in the chemistry, biochemistry, and physics communities, died Aug. 19, 1994, at the age of 93.

and biochemistry. In the 1920s Pauling assumed a leadership role in the application of X-ray crystallography to the structural determination of molecules. During a seminal lecture series given at Cornell University, Ithaca, N.Y., in 1936, he laid the foundations for the current understanding of chemical bonding. He also played a central role in the structural characterization of DNA. His extraordi-

nary scientific accomplishments won him the Nobel Prize for Chemistry in 1954, and his tireless efforts to stop nuclear proliferation won him a second Nobel, for peace, in 1962.

—David B. Collum

APPLIED CHEMISTRY

During the past year research in applied chemistry led to developments in battery designs, food products, biodegradable films, methods for clarifying wine, and the synthesis of proteins. Chemists also sought ways of making production processes in the chemical industry more environmentally friendly.

Advances in batteries

Cellular telephones, camcorders, and laptop computers, known collectively as the three C's, are among the leading electronic consumer items, but their usefulness is restricted by the batteries that power them and render them portable. Conventional nickel-cadmium batteries are heavy, require recharging after only a few hours, and can leak toxic cadmium after the battery has been discarded. To avoid those problems, scientists have been pursuing development of lightweight high-energy-density rechargeable batteries containing lithium, the third lightest element (see *1995 Yearbook of Science and the Future* Year in Review: Chemistry: *Applied Chemistry*). Use of such batteries for electric vehicles, however, has been prohibited by high cost and by the possibility of intense smoke or fire, caused by reaction of metallic lithium with the nonaqueous organic electrolytes used in some versions, if the batteries reach temperatures above 120° C (250° F).

Jeffery R. Dahn and Wu Li of Simon Fraser University, Burnaby, B.C., and David S. Wainwright of Moli Energy, Ltd., Maple Ridge, B.C., developed a rechargeable lithium-ion (rather than lithium-metal) battery with an aqueous electrolyte containing a lithium salt. According to the researchers, their cells, which use lithium manganese dioxide ($LiMn_2O_4$) and vanadium dioxide (VO_2) as electrodes and a solution of lithium nitrate ($LiNO_3$) as the electrolyte, "provide a fundamentally safe and cost-effective technology that can compete [as an electric-vehicle battery] with nickel-cadmium and lead-acid batteries on the basis of stored energy per unit of weight." Their test cells, 12 mm (0.5 in) in diameter and 2.5 mm (0.1 in) in thickness, were estimated to possess an energy density of 55 w-hr/kg (25 w-hr/lb), compared with lead-acid batteries (about 30 w-hr/kg [14 w-hr/lb]) and nickel-cadmium batteries (about 50 w-hr/kg [23 w-hr/lb]).

A test dummy is entangled in "sticky foam," a lightweight, tenaciously adhesive material created at Sandia National Laboratories, Albuquerque, N.M., as part of a program to develop nonlethal weaponry for such uses as riot control. When sprayed as a liquid stream from a dispenser, the material expands up to 50 times its original size with the help of a gas and is capable of immobilizing humans or sticking them to walls or floors.

Sandia National
Laboratories

Another promising development in lightweight high-energy lithium batteries was the use of a new carbon material that stores lithium by an electrochemical mechanism. Kenji Sato and co-workers of Honda Research & Development Co., Saitama, Japan, and Morinobu Endo of Shinshu University, Nagano, Japan, prepared the material, which contains structural irregularities such as extensive branching and cross-linking, by heating the polymer poly(p-phenylene). Unlike previously explored intercalation compounds, in which lithium atoms are stored between ordered graphite sheets, lithium is stored electrochemically in the new disordered carbon material and may be present as molecules of Li_2 in additional covalent storage sites.

Food products

Because fats in foods are high in calories and may result in deposits that can clog arteries and lead to heart disease, researchers have been seeking to produce low-calorie, low-cholesterol fat substitutes to fill a market niche that could be worth billions of dollars annually. In 1993 low-fat items amounted to almost 7% of newly introduced processed foods. Unfortunately, fats appear to be crucial in making some foods taste good. Rather than relying on a single fat substitute, manufacturers have usually looked to modified starches, gums, and fragments of proteins to reproduce the satisfying feel of fats in the mouth. One of the earliest "fake" fats was Simplesse, a whey-protein concentrate discovered in 1979 and manufactured by NutraSweet, Deerfield, Ill. It received approval from the U.S. Food and Drug Administration

(FDA) in 1989. Olestra, a no-calorie, no-cholesterol sucrose polyester announced by Proctor & Gamble Co., Cincinnati, Ohio, in 1987, was still awaiting FDA approval as a food additive eight years later. (See *1989* and *1990 Yearbook of Science and the Future* Year in Review: CHEMISTRY: *Applied Chemistry*.)

Instead of producing new fatlike substances, some researchers were modifying the cholesterol and calorie content of existing fats. In mid-1994 RJR Nabisco Foods Group, East Hanover, N.J., announced a new family of low-calorie fats called Salatrim, which were intended to replace conventional fats, first in chocolate and eventually in a variety of foods such as cheese, cookies, crackers, snacks, ice cream, puddings, yogurt, margarine, and baked goods. Like most fats in food, Salatrim consists of three fatty acids bonded to a molecule of glycerol. However, it contains the long-chain stearic acid, which is poorly absorbed by the body and does not interfere with the body's cholesterol-removing ability, unlike other saturated fatty acids. It also contains short-chain acetic, propionic, or butyric acids, which have fewer calories than other fatty acids. Animal studies show that the new product has five calories per gram, compared with nine calories per gram for ordinary fat, but the comparison may not be accurate for humans, who are better absorbers of fat than are the laboratory animals used in the studies.

Because Salatrim is made from ingredients already in use (vegetables oils and other foods), the FDA did not consider it a new synthetic food additive when RJR Nabisco requested in a 40,000-page petition that it be included on the FDA's list of substances "generally recognized as safe," an approval process that requires less review than does a new additive. The FDA's decision allowed RJR Nabisco and its partner, Pfizer, Inc., to begin selling Salatrim while awaiting final approval, which is expected to require less than a year. According to RJR Nabisco Foods Group spokesman Hank Sandbach, "By mid-1995 consumers can expect to see it in products." Still, consumers will probably buy foods containing Salatrim only if they are convinced that the products are more healthful than others. According to J. Bruce German of the University of California, Davis, "I don't believe the FDA would permit [a company] to suggest [a person's] diet would be healthier with this in it."

Since table salt (sodium chloride) can raise blood pressure, many persons are advised to restrict their salt intake. Unsalted foods, however, like foods without fat, can be unappetizing, and potassium- or ammonium-based salt substitutes are often bitter or sour. Eldon Lee and John Tandy of Nestlé SA, New Milford, Conn., claimed to have made lightly salted foods taste saltier by mixing the sodium chloride with ammonium salts, which are obtained as by-products of vegetable-oil manufacture. The ammonium salts, contained in the residue from the extraction of oil from corn, wheat, or soybeans, are purified, degasified, and encapsulated in maltodextrin, gum arabic, or gelatinized cereal starch to make granules containing 15–25% solid ammonium salt. The researchers claimed that foods seasoned

The Dow Chemical Company, Midland, Mich.

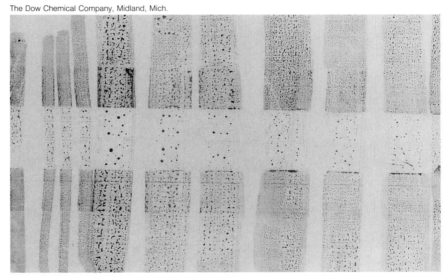

Ink from felt-tip markers beads up on sheet material coated with a fluorocarbon-based polymer (horizontal stripe) from Dow Chemical Co. researchers. The Teflon-like material, which can be applied with a brush or spray gun and cured at a fairly low temperature, may find use, for example, as a wallpaper finish or an anti-barnacle coating for ships.

with 0.3–0.6% of the material need only half the usual amount of sodium chloride to provide the same taste.

Biodegradable films

Researchers in various countries have been trying to prepare packaging films from food-derived starch and various other biodegradable materials. Peter Weigel, Hans-Peter Fink, and co-workers of the Fraunhofer Institute for Applied Polymer Research, Teltow, Germany, a country with stringent recycling regulations, have been working with starches from corn, peas, and potatoes. During the past year they prepared a transparent product that looks like plastic film but, unlike synthetic films, is completely biodegradable. They heated the starch to break down the starch granules and then extruded it through a slit-shaped aperture. Each kind of starch required a different set of pressure and temperature conditions for the process. To produce homogeneous materials, various amounts of additives such as plasticizers were required. The films, 30–50 micrometers (0.0012–0.0020 in) thick, possess mechanical properties similar to those of common packaging materials and are strong enough for commercial applications. The films dissolve on contact with food, but the researchers were attempting to make them water-resistant.

Clearer wines

The international wine industry spends hundreds of millions of dollars annually to prevent unsightly haze in white and sparkling wines. The haze, which is not harmful to health and has no effect on wine flavor, is due to the heat instabil-

Coaster-sized wafers made of thin-film diamond (above, highly magnified) are being developed for computer circuit boards. Diamond's excellent thermal conductivity and heat resistance may allow electronic components to be packed more closely on diamond boards to boost computer speed.

ity of naturally occurring wine proteins, which do not remain soluble indefinitely and thus aggregate to form suspended particles and sediments. Producers traditionally clarify wines with filtering clays such as bentonite, which absorb these proteins and deposit them in the fermentation tank bottom before bottling, but their removal causes loss of flavor in some wines. Research carried out in Australia and France by Elizabeth Waters of the Australian Wine Research Institute, Adelaide, raised the possibility of developing a new generation of natural protein-stabilization techniques in wine making.

Waters separated, identified, and purified two of the major proteins causing wine haze and identified two polysaccharide fractions that seemed to decrease haze formation. One is a mannoprotein similar to that found in the cell wall of the yeast used in fermentation, and the other is an arabinogalactan protein that seems to be derived from grapes. As the concentration in wine of these polysaccharide fractions increases, the particle size—and thus the visibility of the haze—decreases, even though the concentration and types of the flavor-contributing proteins remain the same. By enriching wine in polysaccharides derived from yeast or grapes either by prolonged aging or by adding them during production, Waters claimed to have found "a much better solution than using bentonite because the proteins don't have to be removed so there would be no loss of flavor. The component is already present in a wine, and it's natural."

"Green" chemical production

John Wesley Frost, currently of Michigan State University, used glucose, the most common sugar and a component of cane sugar (sucrose), to replace more expensive and more toxic substances such as benzene in the production of industrial chemicals. His process, which he claimed "will allow the chemical industry to adopt a more environmentally friendly approach to manufacturing chemicals," used genetically engineered microbes to digest glucose to form nontoxic quinic acid, which, in turn, can be converted at near-ambient temperatures into various industrially important chemicals such as benzoquinone and hydroquinone. Frost also used other microbes to convert glucose into adipic acid or catechol for manufacturing nylon or pharmaceuticals.

Glucose is produced from renewable, cheap materials such as corn or as a by-product of the processing of agricultural products. On the other hand, benzene, one of the most widely used starting materials in organic chemistry, not only is carcinogenic but also is derived from non-renewable fossil fuels such as petroleum. Adipic acid, for example, is currently produced from benzene by reaction in organic solvents at high temperatures, which results in toxic nitric oxide gas as a by-product. According to Frost, his new process "avoids the use of toxins such as benzene and does not generate noxious gases."

Protein synthesis

Proteins are high-molecular-mass polymer compounds composed of a variety of amino acids joined by distinctive chemical linkages called peptide bonds. They are the building blocks of life, and their synthesis provides considerable insight into the nature of biological processes. Yet, according to Michael H. Hecht of Princeton University, "To design and build a protein de novo is the ultimate test of our understanding of how proteins work. If we can learn to build these molecular machines, make them to order, and tailor them to our specifications, then we don't have to rely only on the [proteins] that nature provides." Another researcher in the field, Thomas P. Quinn of the University of Missouri, observed that "trying to build proteins is a very humbling experience." Nevertheless, during 1994 researchers continued to make progress in this extremely complicated field.

Keith Rose of the University of Geneva Medical Center reported a technique for preparing synthetic proteins of unprecedented size and weight. Rose synthesized an artificial protein with a molecular mass of 20,000 daltons (atomic mass units; the hydrogen atom has an atomic mass of one dalton) that would seem to be, in his words, "the largest artificial protein ever made, in pure form [and] in good yield, by controlled total synthesis." The technique is one of several recently developed to connect up peptides (short chains of linked amino acids) chemically or enzymatically into larger structures in hopes of designing proteins de novo and modifying versions of natural proteins.

In Rose's technique multiple copies of a small peptide spontaneously self-assemble on a template molecule, with linkage occurring by formation of a certain kind of chemical bond called an oxime bond between groups on the peptide and the template. According to Rose, "We can put eight 23-residue [23-amino-acid-long] unprotected peptides in with a template molecule, and the whole structure self-assembles." Because natural proteins contain peptide bonds rather than oxime bonds, the technique constitutes a new way of putting together proteins that has promising applications. Stephen B.H. Kent of the Scripps Research Institute, La Jolla, Calif., stated that Rose's technique "opens proteins to the whole world of organic chemistry. . . . Good ways of making proteins and proteinlike entities—and the oxime ligation technology is the best so far—are going to allow us to approach proteins of any size by total chemical synthesis."

The technique can be used not only to link peptides to a template but also to attach reporters (easily detectable chemical groups), lipophilic anchors (those with a strong affinity for fatty molecules), and reactive groups, possibly leading to products that are monitored easily and in which the synthetic proteins are coupled to other large molecules, to surfaces, or to themselves. Other possible applications include the creation of new types of vaccines, biosensors, and libraries (large collections) of various peptides that can be used to identify biologically active substances. A U.S. patent application for the technique was filed, and Abiotic Pharmaceutical Technologies, a San Francisco Bay Area company, was formed to market it.

Scripps researchers Kent, Philip E. Dawson, and Tom W. Muir, together with Ian Clark-Lewis of the University of British Columbia, reported the synthesis of proteins by means of a technique in which the peptide bonds linking the pro-

The year 1994 marked the 200th anniversary of the death by guillotine of the French chemist Antoine-Laurent Lavoisier, the founder of modern chemistry and a powerful advocate for the application of science in the public service. In the 1788 painting by Jacques-Louis David, Lavoisier is pictured with his wife and assistant, Marie.

The Bettmann Archive

Anniversaries

The year 1994 marked several anniversaries related to applied chemistry. On May 8, 1794, 200 years earlier, Antoine-Laurent Lavoisier, the founder of modern chemistry, who devoted himself to applied research on street lighting, water analysis, and gunpowder and agricultural manufacture on behalf of his native France, was guillotined during the Reign of Terror. The widely circulated remark—"The Republic has no need of scientists; let justice take its course!"—attributed to Jean Coffinhal, president of the Tribunal, is apocryphal, but the comment made the following day by the mathematician Joseph-Louis Lagrange is authentic—"It took them only an instant to cut off that head, and a hundred years may not produce another like it."

In 1844, 150 years earlier, American inventor Charles Goodyear, who worked and died in poverty and realized little from his work, prepared the first pair of vulcanized rubber shoes, five years after he had serendipitously discovered the vulcanization process. In the same year, John Mercer, a calico printer in Lancashire, England, invented the process of mercerizing cotton yarns and fabrics, thereby improving their strength, luster, and affinity for dyes. In 1919, 75 years earlier, the Nobel Prize for Chemistry for 1918 was awarded to German chemist Fritz Haber for his synthesis of ammonia from its elements, an industrial process that revolutionized the production of fertilizers and explosives.

—George B. Kauffman

See also Feature Articles: AEROGELS: THE LIGHTEST SOLIDS; DAYS OF WINE AND SCIENCE.

tein's amino-acid components resemble those found in natural proteins, a method that they called native chemical ligation. Because synthesizing large peptides or proteins is difficult if done one amino acid at a time, the researchers linked two long peptides—one with 33 amino acids and one with 39 amino acids—to yield an exact replica of human interleukin-8, an immune-system protein with 72 amino acids. According to Dawson, "In this paper, we showed how to connect two pep-

tides, but in theory this technique can join four or five peptides in series, which would allow someone to make larger proteins. . . . So the next step is to generalize this work and apply it to many kinds of biological problems to learn more about how enzymes work." Muir also stated, "There are things that this method can do that DNA recombination technology can't do and vice versa. So the two techniques complement, rather than compete with, each other."

DEFENSE RESEARCH

Consolidation swept the worldwide defense industry in 1994 as the last vestiges of the Cold War receded. The evolving international climate produced a dual effect on defense research: sharp declines in overall governmental support of military projects and a shift from the previous focus on strategic weapons systems to a new stress on tactical systems. Instead of creating weapons for the superpower

Lockheed Corp. bought General Dynamics' fighter aircraft business for $1.5 billion. Then the two companies merged to create a new firm called Lockheed Martin Corp., which became the nation's second largest defense supplier (after Boeing Co.). Loral Corp., meanwhile, bought the aerospace division of Ford Motor Co. for $750 million and the federal systems operations of IBM Corp. for $1.5 bil-

expected. Some analysts predicted that 80 of the top 100 defense suppliers would no longer be in the business by the end of the decade.

The situation was similar in Europe, where it was apparent that no company—or even country—could afford the huge expenses of developing the complex weapons systems of the future. Four countries had teamed to create the

A Eurofighter 2000 prototype takes off in England. Being built for the air forces of Britain, Germany, Italy, and Spain, the planes are scheduled to go into service in 2000.

confrontation between the United States and the former Soviet Union, defense research was reoriented toward countering any recurrence of localized conflicts such as the 1991 Persian Gulf War.

Accordingly, a wave of mergers and acquisitions occurred in the U.S. defense industry during the year. Martin Marietta Corp. acquired General Electric's aerospace subsidiary for $3 billion, and

lion. Such smaller defense firms as Litton Industries Inc. and Control Data Corp. spun off their defense operations as separate subsidiaries for possible future sale to one of the larger companies. The net result was to cut defense industry employment in the U.S., which once totaled more than three million, to a level below one million for the first time since the Cold War began. Further declines were

Eurofighter consortium based in Munich, Germany, to build the next-generation fighter aircraft: Deutsche Aerospace (33%), British Aerospace (33%), Alenia of Italy (21%), and CASA of Spain (13%). These four plus Aérospatiale of France later joined to create Euroflag, a consortium based in Rome, to develop a new military cargo jet to be known as the Future Large Aircraft. In addition to having the usual problems of coordinating the efforts of the different countries, which resulted in cost overruns and schedule slippages, the aircraft-development programs faced an uncertain market as demand for new weapons declined.

In the United States, federal funding of military research and development and procurement of advanced weapons systems, after growing at a steady rate of 2–4% per year since the early 1960s, peaked in 1986 and had since declined at a rate of 4% per year. The consulting firm Booz Allen & Hamilton estimated that real spending on these categories fell from approximately $150 billion (in 1993 dollars) in 1986 to a little more than $80 billion in 1994. As a percentage of gross domestic product, furthermore, the company projected that defense spending would drop from 6.5% in 1986 to 3.2% by 1997—the largest decline since the period between World War I and World War II.

The U.S. congressional elections in November 1994, in which the Republicans swept to power in both the House of Representatives and the Senate, offered scant hope for a reversal of this trend. Although Ronald Reagan, a Republican, had increased defense budgets during his presidency, the reduction in spending had actually begun earlier under Democrat Jimmy Carter, and it continued more sharply under Republican George Bush. Furthermore, the new Republican majority in Congress served notice that it intended to cut federal expenditures across the board and that defense research would not be exempted.

John Gibbons, Pres. Bill Clinton's science adviser, defended the administration's research policies during congressional testimony in January 1995: "Most things this country values—long-term economic growth, good jobs, high-quality health care, environmental protection, top-notch education and worker training, and a strong national defense—all depend on sustaining our world leadership in science and technology."

Upgraded electronics

New technology, particularly rapid advances in electronics, also shifted the focus of defense research away from such traditional weapons systems as ships, aircraft, and ground vehicles, which increasingly became mere "platforms" to carry the advanced electronic warfare systems and precision guided munitions. Instead, defense research concentrated on upgrading the electronic subsystems to achieve greater military effectiveness for existing weapons platforms and to extend their useful lifetime.

An example was the applications-specific electronic module (ASEM) research program launched by the U.S. Department of Defense in 1993, which began to reach fruition in 1994. According to Nicholas J. Naclerio, ASEM program manager at the Defense Department's Advanced Research Projects Agency (ARPA), ASEMs were poised for widespread use in the coming generation of electronic products. Like their predecessors, applications-specific integrated circuits, ASEMs represented an increasing integration of electronic functions resulting in corresponding reductions in costs and product cycle times and improved reliability.

Among the applications of ASEM technology that got under way in 1994 were the following: an advanced data-transfer module built by IBM to download data into the avionics subsystem of the air force's F-111 fighter aircraft; a processor module developed by McDonnell Douglas Corp. for an infrared and video sight that would be mounted on top of the army's OH-58D helicopter; and a miniature receiver using chips from Motorola Corp. to receive signals from the Global Positioning System navigation satellites, under a development program managed by the Mayo Foundation in Rochester, Minn.

ARPA-sponsored research also continued in 1994 to create new military displays capable of winning what the Defense Department called the "information war." The goal was to augment current centralized, crew-served information systems with smaller, lighter, and more capable individual systems that could be deployed far forward on the battlefield. New capabilities in signal processing and computing, using mobile, low-power, battery-operated devices, were being developed to meet those needs at the small-unit level. These devices would collect, analyze, and disseminate a wide range of tactical, administrative, and logistic information. Individual soldiers operating these new products would be tomorrow's combat "force multipliers" as they rapidly processed and communicated (both horizontally and vertically) critical information on the battlefield. This trend toward greater availability of information was expected to enhance the situational awareness of small units, enabling them to seize the initiative in dynamic battlefield conditions. Using their individual information systems, soldiers and teams cut off from their units could continue to fight.

Given the anticipated decline in defense budgets, ARPA accelerated its efforts in 1994 to advance "dual-use" technologies beneficial to both military and commercial users. This approach was applied to both products, such as individual microchips, and processes, such as computer-aided design methods capable of producing both military and commercial parts. The argument advanced in favor of dual-use technologies was that the end products were required for national defense purposes but the U.S. could not afford two complete separate technology bases.

Electric vehicles

Another emerging area of defense research with commercial implications was technology to support electric vehicles (EVs). Specifically, the research was aimed at developing better batteries (and better ways to charge the batteries), improving the vehicles' performance (particularly range), and reducing the costs of the vehicles to the level where enough motorists could afford them.

Among the military applications for which EV technologies were being considered were the M-939 five-ton trucks, the High Mobility Multipurpose Wheeled Vehicle (HUM-V; general-purpose transport vehicles), and 25-ton tracked vehicles. In each case the goal was to achieve ranges of 480 km (300 mi) by using hybrid electronic vehicle (HEV) systems and 16–32 km (10–20 mi) on batteries while maintaining current speed,

acceleration, and other performance requirements. Also, by reducing their heat production and by operating silently on battery power, the electrically powered vehicles were expected to be less vulnerable to detection in combat situations.

The government efforts that began in 1994 built on earlier attempts by the automobile industry. Since 1990 General Motors Corp. had been working on the experimental two-seat Impact, which used 395 kg (870 lb) of standard lead-acid batteries to achieve a top speed of 120 km/h (75 mph) and range of 160 km (100 mi). Initial cost to consumers was projected to be at least $25,000. Ford, meanwhile, adapted the European version of its Escort van, called the Ecostar, for battery use at a cost of $100,000 each to fleet operators. Chrysler Corp. had a battery-powered version of its minivan priced at $120,000 (of which $50,000 was for the more advanced nickel-iron batteries). Both had speeds and ranges comparable to GM's Impact.

Previous government attempts to develop EV technology in the 1960s and '70s (particularly attempts to respond to the energy crises of the latter decade) ended in failure, but a new impetus arose from efforts to curb pollution. The turning point was the 1990 decision by the California Air Resources Board that 2% of all new-car sales in that state in the 1998 model year had to be zero-emission vehicles—rising to 10% by 2000. Five eastern states (Maine, Maryland, Massachusetts, New Jersey, and New York) soon followed suit. Since zero emission can be achieved only by electric vehicles, the Washington, D.C.-based Electric Transportation Coalition estimated

that in order for the stringent standards to be met, 65,364 new electrics would have to be sold in California and the five eastern states in 1998. And just for those six states, the number would have to rise to 352,320 by 2003. (California alone accounted for two million new-car sales each year.)

This requirement put pressure on the automakers to extend the range of the EVs and make at least a start in driving down their costs. Of the two, costs were considered the more difficult task. Studies conducted by GM found that 84% of drivers drove under 120 km (75 mi) a day, which was considered well within the capability of the currently proposed EVs. Furthermore, by using standard 220-v household current, the batteries could be fully charged in two or three hours at home overnight. Other possibilities included installation of recharging stations in shopping malls and at restaurants around interstate highway exits. The Boston subway system began investigating preferential parking spaces for EVs at a commuter parking garage, where they could be recharged by using solar-cell arrays.

Future costs of EVs depended on two factors: increased volume to enable manufacturers to achieve economies of scale, and development of the necessary underlying technologies. The auto industry began taking some technological steps, such as the formation of the United States Advanced Battery consortium by GM, Ford, and Chrysler in 1991, but the magnitude of this challenge demanded increasing federal involvement. Among the federal agencies that began sponsoring research on EVs and HEVs that use turbine power plants were the U.S. Departments of Defense, Energy, Transportation, and Commerce; the National Aeronautics and Space Administration; the National Science Foundation; and the Environmental Protection Agency. Basic research focused on four clusters of technology: (1) energy storage, including advanced batteries, capacitors, ultrahigh-speed carbon composite flywheels, and high-pressure, high-capacity fuel tanks; (2) power generation, including environmentally compatible fuel cells, natural gas turbines, and clean fuel engines; (3) system control, including advanced motor/controller designs, onboard sensors, information management and decision aids, and automated test and diagnostic capability; and (4) vehicle structures, including lightweight, high-strength composites and other materials, and real-time process control.

Like the U.S. Postal Service and other federal agencies, the Department of Defense was a major operator of fleets of vehicles and therefore could benefit from improved efficiencies made possible by EV/HEV technologies. The department also had a national defense mission that dictated uniquely military capabilities for the advanced vehicles. Current operating experience made it evident that future tactical ground, sea, and air vehicles would require even greater amounts of electrical power to operate their onboard weapons, communications, navigation, command and control, sensor, and other systems. These increasing demands for electrical power in the past had been met by the addition of auxiliary power units, but future military vehicles were expected to require two to three times

more electrical power to operate the onboard systems than the power to move the vehicle. Rather than generating electrical power as a by-product of moving the vehicle, as contemporary military and civilian vehicles did, the military-sponsored research envisioned central power sources capable of providing both movement and the necessary electrical power to operate the electronics systems. For EVs this would be a battery; HEVs would use a natural gas turbine or other power source such as fuel cells.

EV or HEV power plants developed for classes of military vehicle should be readily transferable to their civilian counterparts. Manufacturing methods that allow both military and commercial components to be manufactured in a common production system were expected to yield economies of scale that should benefit both sectors. Furthermore, reducing the current dependence by both military and civilian vehicles on foreign sources of petroleum should also contribute to national security.

—John Rhea

EARTH SCIENCES

Strong and destructive earthquakes, bitterly cold weather in North America and Europe, and extensive flooding after heavy rainfall in California and northwestern Europe were among the major events of the past year of interest to the Earth sciences. Significant advances in research were noted in a wide range of subjects, including climate change, the ozone hole, dinosaurs and their extinction, contamination of groundwater, and the rise and fall of sea levels.

ATMOSPHERIC SCIENCES

Significant progress has been reported in recent months by atmospheric scientists concerned with weather and climate problems. Promising new field programs for the study of the atmosphere were launched, and important new observational systems came on line. Especially exciting was the field of climate change, where attention turned from greenhouse gases and chlorofluorocarbons to focus more on the human impact on long-term weather patterns.

A broad upper-level trough of low pressure over the central and eastern United States during January and early February 1994 brought bitterly cold conditions to those parts of the country. The temperature plunged to −37.8° C (−36° F) as far south as Indiana, and several locations across the Ohio Valley and central Appalachians established new all-time record-low readings. In sharp contrast, abnormally mild and dry weather prevailed across the Far West during the 1993–94 wet season, with some areas receiving less than 50% of their average precipitation. Beginning in late October 1994, however, the Far West experienced above-average precipitation, culminating in very heavy rainfall in January 1995 in parts of northern, central, and southern California. Rivers overflowed, and extensive mud slides closed highways. The storms, steered toward California by a jet stream flowing from Hawaii, caused at least 11 deaths and about $300 million in damage.

Frequent storms, heavy snows, and bitter cold afflicted much of Europe during January and February 1994, and heavy rains—600–850% of average—drenched the Middle East in March and early April. In January 1995 heavy rainfall and melting snow caused the highest river levels in northwestern Europe since 1926. Thousands of people fled their homes, and 29 died as flooding rivers submerged towns and farm fields in Germany, France, Belgium, and The Netherlands. In Germany much of downtown Cologne was under 2 m (6 ft) of water from the Rhine River, which crested at 10.7 m (35.1 ft).

Observational systems

Great strides were made during the year in monitoring the atmosphere. In particular, warning systems for tornadoes and severe thunderstorms—as well as the low-level wind shear that is dangerous to aircraft—were markedly improved with the opening in February 1994 of the first WSR-88 (NEXRAD; Next Generation Weather Radar) Doppler weather radar at Twin Lakes, Okla. This technology makes use of the Doppler shift of an echo due to relative motion of a radar target within a several-hundred-kilometer radius of the site. This information provides accurate measurements of rainfall and snowfall as well as the exact speed and direction of the wind.

Answers to questions about the chemical composition of the lower stratosphere (altitudes of 6–17 km [4–11 mi]) were being sought by the U.S. National Center for Atmospheric Research (NCAR) in Boulder, Colo., which began using a WB-57F reconnaissance jet airplane obtained from the U.S. Air Force for these purposes. Meanwhile, in late 1994 NASA began using its remotely piloted Perseus aircraft to collect weather data at even higher altitudes, up to 27 km (17 mi).

On December 30 the U.S. National Oceanic and Atmospheric Administration (NOAA) launched the polar-orbiting satellite NOAA 14 into an 864-km (537-mi)-high orbit. Its 1,180-kg (2,600-lb) payload included a solar backscatter ultraviolet scanner to monitor ozone levels and a very high-spatial-resolution radiometer to measure landscape changes and atmospheric temperature and humidity. NOAA 14 replaced NOAA 11, which was launched in September 1988 and failed in September 1994. Geostationary Operational Environmental Satellite 8, the orbit of which was fixed over the Equator at longitude 90° W, was launched in April 1994. Compared with its predecessor geostationary satellites, it provides improved resolution of the atmosphere, including vertical soundings at eight-kilometer (five-mile) horizontal intervals. At the end of January 1994, the European geostationary weather satellite Meteosat 6 became operational over the Equator at longitude 0°.

By early 1995 Earth's automated surface observing system (ASOS) had been installed at more than 378 stations in 47 states of the U.S. Working nonstop 24 hours a day, ASOS provides such information on weather as precipitation type and intensity, wind, and visibility. Located on airport runway touchdown zones, the stations were intended to improve airplane flight safety and to reduce manpower needs in collecting weather data. Installation began in 1991.

In April the space shuttle *Endeavour* launched into orbit an imaging radar satellite that monitors at high spatial resolution such quantities as soil and vegetation moisture and the type and amount of

NEXRAD image, Earth Satellite Corporation; radar data provided by Unisys Corporation

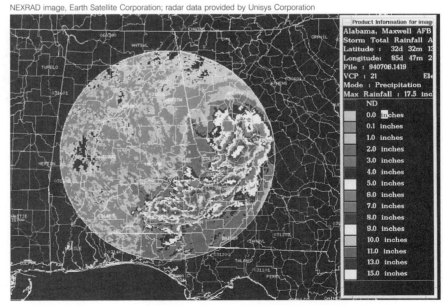

NEXRAD (Next Generation Weather Radar) data are overlaid on a map of Alabama and Georgia to produce total precipitation estimates for the area from Tropical Storm Alberto.

Flooding in Laguna Beach, Calif., in January 1995 was the result of very heavy rainfall produced by a jet stream flowing from Hawaii to California.

vegetation. A cooperative effort between NASA, the German Space Agency, and the Italian Space Agency, a 10-day data-collection mission of the satellite sought to develop an improved understanding of the influence of the land surface on weather. The satellite operates at three frequencies (3 cm, 6 cm, and 24 cm) and has capabilities that allow it to obtain detailed characterization of the Earth's surface.

Field programs

In Manitoba and Saskatchewan the Boreal Ecosystem-Atmosphere Study, a joint U.S.-Canadian project initiated by Piers Sellers and Forrest Hall of NASA, investigated the interaction of the northern forest with the atmosphere before and during the growing season. In the higher latitudes and altitudes of the Northern Hemisphere, the multinational Second European Stratospheric Arctic and Midlatitude Experiment investigated the cause of loss of some of the ozone layer over the midlatitudes and determined that it was due to either the mixing of polar air with midlatitude air, processes entirely within the midlatitudes, or a combination of both.

The focus of the Observations at Several Interacting Scales project in New South Wales, Australia, was the biosphere-atmosphere exchanges of energy, water, carbon dioxide, other trace gases, and stable isotopes in an area of spatially variable vegetation on scales ranging from a leaf to a region. The MacKenzie GEWEX (Global Energy and Water Cycle Experiment) Study organized research on water and energy balances of the Canadian Arctic in order to assess the potential impact of climate variability and change on water resources. GEWEX, is a component of the World Climate Research Program, which was designed to coordinate and direct international studies of climate change.

Red and blue flashes and gamma rays radiating upward from thunderstorms attracted researchers' attention. Such electromagnetic discharges, which are incompletely understood, are of concern to space shuttle pilots because they might affect the spacecraft. David Sentman and Eugene Wescott of the Geophysical Institute of the University of Alaska observed hundreds of these light flashes extending upward to 60 km (37 mi) above thunderstorms over Oklahoma. The relationship between the very high-energy gamma rays and the optical flashes is especially puzzling, and Walter Lyons of Mission Research Corp. used low-light-intensity video-monitoring cameras to document this geophysical effect in Colorado.

Ozone hole

The annual occurrence of very low levels of ozone in the Antarctic polar stratosphere in the Southern Hemisphere spring has been observed for more than 10 years. The explanation for the ozone hole includes the isolation of the Antarctic stratosphere from the lower-latitude atmosphere, which prevents dilution of the ozone hole until late in the spring, and the chemical depletion of ozone as a result of the interaction of chlorofluorocarbons (CFCs) with ozone. Experiments to monitor the ozone hole and the chemical composition of the Arctic stratosphere continued in 1994. In the Southern Hemisphere spring of 1993, ozone levels over Antarctica were the lowest ever recorded. In the Weddell Sea of Antarctica, scientists aboard the research vessel *Nathaniel B. Palmer* estimated that the increased ultraviolet radiation that reaches the surface because it is not absorbed by ozone has reduced the productivity of ocean phytoplankton by 6–12%. Ultraviolet radiation could also increase skin cancers, although so far the reduction in ozone has been observed in high latitudes, where solar radiation is weak.

Chemical replacements for the ozone-damaging CFCs have been introduced, but there were concerns that these chemicals might create other types of environmental hazards. Hydrochlorofluorocarbons and hydrofluorocarbons, for instance, were being investigated by the U.S. National Science Foundation's Long Term Ecological Research sites as possible dangers to plants.

Changing climate

Scientists from Moss Landing Marine Laboratories in California and other institutions confirmed that the uptake (absorption and incorporation) of carbon dioxide by plant growth in large areas of the ocean is limited by available iron. Reducing the amount of carbon dioxide, a greenhouse gas, in the atmosphere would help prevent potential global warming (see *Oceanography,* below).

Using data from the satellite-based Earth Radiation Budget Experiment, Tom Vonder Haar and David Randel of the Cooperative Institute for Research in the Atmosphere in Colorado concluded that the effect of the increase in the level of greenhouse gases caused by human activities on the Earth's radiation cannot be separated from natural variations in this budget associated with clouds. That there has been no definitive evidence of global greenhouse gas warming is therefore not surprising.

Land-use patterns may cause climate change—at least at a regional level. David Smith of NCAR reported on water-diversion projects in the Aral Sea basin of Central Asia. They have resulted in a drastic shrinking of the sea, which in turn has caused hotter summers and colder winters in the region. Jeff Copeland of Colorado State University reported that 60% of the landscape in the U.S. (excluding Alaska and Hawaii) has been changed from its natural state to such an extent that regional climate change could be expected there as well.

Studying the biological effects of climate change, Peter K. Van de Water and Steven W. Leavitt of the University of Arizona and Julio Betancourt of the U.S. Geological Survey reported that a 30% increase in atmospheric carbon dioxide in the U.S. Southwest between 12,000 and 15,000 years ago produced a 17% decrease in the density of plant stomata (minute openings in the epidermis of a plant organ [as a leaf]) and a 15% increase in water-use efficiency in limber pine needles.

Changes in the circulation of North Atlantic Ocean waters over time scales of decades, as discussed by Uwe Mikolajewicz and colleagues at the Max Planck Institute for Meteorology, Hamburg, Germany, were found to influence surface temperatures. Changes in the heating of the atmosphere over the North Atlantic as a result of these temperature changes could in turn influence weather over western Europe. Basing their research on pollen records in sediments, Brian Huntley and colleagues at the Environmental Research Centre at the University of Durham, England, determined that substantial climate fluctuations were common in past climates.

Weather prediction

Notable success in the prediction of weather on a seasonal basis was associated with the El Niño-Southern Oscillation (ENSO) cycle. Mark Cane and Gidon Eskel of Columbia University's Lamont-Doherty Earth Observatory in Palisades, N.Y., and R.W. Buckland of the Southern African Development Community reported in *Nature* that whether an El Niño (a pronounced warming in the central and eastern Pacific Ocean) occurred the previous year determines whether there will be a good corn harvest in Zimbabwe (see *Oceanography,* below). According to J. Michael Hall of NOAA's Office of Global Programs, wet crops (rice) or dry crops (corn and wheat) are planted in Peru on the basis of ENSO predictions. Bill Gray of Colorado State University uses El Niño conditions as one of his statistical predictors in his Atlantic tropical cyclone forecasting. He and his colleagues successfully forecast the relatively inactive tropical cyclone season in the Atlantic in 1994.

In recognition of the heightened interest of longer-term forecasts, the Climate Analysis Center of the U.S. National Meteorological Center was renamed the Climate Prediction Center, with a task of providing forecasts of the weather a year or more in advance. NOAA and other U.S. government agencies also proposed the establishment of an international seasonal-to-yearly weather-prediction program.

Education

The American Red Cross, in cooperation with the U.S. National Hurricane Center, increased its efforts to correct public misconceptions of proper procedures for reducing damage to life and property during severe weather. Taping windows to reduce damage, for example, does not stop breakage but results in larger broken pieces. The recommended procedure is to board up windows with plywood or other coverings. Similarly, opening windows, supposedly to equalize pressure in a house as a tornado approaches, is also useless. It is not the pressure differential between the inside and the outside that destroys a building; rather, it is the lifting of the roof by the extreme winds and the impacts on buildings by airborne debris.
— Roger A. Pielke

GEOLOGIC SCIENCES

By 1995 most geologists and geophysicists accepted the idea that a large body of extraterrestrial origin struck the Earth at the end of the Cretaceous Period 65 million years ago. They further agreed that the Chicxulub impact structure, located on the Yucatán Peninsula in Mexico and on the adjacent continental shelf, is the best candidate for the site of the impact. There are, however, many unresolved problems surrounding this catastrophic event, some of which were aired at a conference in Houston, Texas, in February 1994. One significant issue is the effect of the impact upon plants and

animals living at the time. The hypothesis that it was a principal factor in the extinction of the dinosaurs has been widely publicized. Jan Smit of the Free University of Amsterdam noted, however, that extinction of some organisms was not sudden but began before the time of the impact event, which is clearly marked in many places by a stratigraphic layer rich in iridium (a trace element rare in asteroids and meteorites but even rarer on the Earth). Other organisms, however, appear to have suffered a sudden and dramatic decrease in abundance at exactly the time of the impact.

Geology and geochemistry

A study by Rodolfo Coccioni and Simone Galeotti of the Institute of Geology at the University of Urbino, Italy, revealed a complex history of deepwater foraminiferans (microorganisms with a perforated shell through which amoeba-like pseudopodia emerge) during the transition from the Cretaceous to the Tertiary Period. Their research, based upon a section of this layer from southeastern Spain, suggested that during that transition there was a dramatic decrease in the diversity of deepwater foraminiferans and a marked increase in forms that fed on dead organisms in the bottom layers of the ocean and could tolerate low levels of oxygen. They attributed this change to a large influx of nutrients derived from the rapid accumulation of "nutrient soup" produced by the mass mortality at the time of the impact event.

On the basis of a section of marine sediments exposed on Seymour Island just off the coast of the Antarctic Peninsula, D.H. Elliot of Ohio State University and

his colleagues concluded that the Cretaceous-Tertiary (K-T) impact did not cause a mass extinction of species there. The section contains an abundant assemblage of marine microfossils and a single layer of iridium-rich sand. A study of the distribution of organisms within the section revealed that with few exceptions the species exhibit gradual trends of first and last appearances across the K-T boundary rather than an abrupt extinction, which supports earlier suggestions that the impact event had a diminished effect upon organisms living at high latitudes.

Ancient climates. Although geologists are accustomed to studying the Earth's history in terms of events separated by millions, or at best hundreds of thousands, of years, it is sometimes possible to achieve a much finer temporal resolution. For example, dendrochronologists established an uninterrupted record of annual growth of the bristlecone pine extending back 8,000 years. Xiahong Feng and Samuel Epstein of the California Institute of Technology took advantage of this record in an attempt to establish the climatic conditions prevailing during the lives of trees from the White Mountains of southeastern California. The comparative quantities of stable carbon isotopes in the cellulose of precisely dated tree rings can be related to the temperature of rainwater ingested at the time of the ring's formation. On this basis the authors concluded that although there have been significant short-term fluctuations, the general trend has been a continuous cooling of the Earth's climate since a postglacial high was reached 6,800 years ago. This finding suggested that the climatic change has been worldwide.

Using a radically different technique, G.A. Zielinski of the University of New Hampshire and his colleagues arrived at a conclusion consistent with that reached by Feng and Epstein. They examined ice cores from Greenland and found high concentrations of sulfates at various levels, indicating the presence of fallout from volcanic eruptions. Many of these inferred eruptions can be matched with eruptions already known from other evidence. The authors attached particular significance to the fact that there were three times as many eruptions between 5000 and 7000 BC as there have been during the last 2,000 years. This suggests that the consequent greater volume of volcanic material in the atmosphere during the earlier period may have been a contributing factor in global cooling.

In another study of a Greenland ice core, Sungmin Hong of the Glaciology and Environmental Geophysics Laboratory, Grenoble, France, and his coworkers detected evidence of industrial pollution of the atmosphere dating back to antiquity. In a core covering the period from 3,000 to 500 years ago, they found that during the period from 2,500 to 1,700 years ago—between 500 BC and 300 AD—concentrations of lead that were four times as great as would have been expected on the basis of natural processes. The authors suggested that Greek and Roman mining and smelting during that period were sufficient to raise the concentration of lead in the atmosphere on a hemispheric scale to a level as high as 15% of that caused by the use of lead additives in gasoline since the 1930s. Evidence of mining and smelting during medieval times was also detected.

Such precise resolution is not confined to the more recent events of geologic history. It is sometimes possible to establish precise time scales for very ancient events. The ebb and flow of tides, for example, may leave a characteristic sedimentary signature and thus provide a scale of daily, monthly, semiannual, and annual resolution. E.P. Kvale of the Indiana Geological Survey and his coauthors reported that in a record of tidal sedimentation preserved in cores taken from Pennsylvanian period rocks in south-central Indiana, they found semiannual and annual deviations from expectations that were based on tidal theory alone. They attributed these deviations to seasonal fluctuations in rainfall that produced corresponding variations in the accumulation of sediments derived from a nearby shore, providing evidence that seasonal climates existed during Pennsylvanian time (about 300 million years ago) in this region.

A wholly unexpected interaction of atmosphere and lithosphere (the outer part of the solid Earth) was suggested by L.G. Mastin of the U.S. Geological Survey in Vancouver, Wash. Between Aug. 24, 1989, and June 18, 1991, at least 28 explosion-like seismic events occurred at Mt. St. Helens in Washington. Six of them were accompanied by the violent ejection of rock fragments, some to a distance of one kilometer (0.6 mi) from the vent. Calculations revealed a statistically significant correlation between the six ejections and storms that had occurred 2–15 days earlier. Mastin suggested that the storms may have caused the explosions by releasing gas trapped within the mountain's dome, but he also concluded that the storms may just have triggered events that would have occurred later without them.

Paleontology. Until recently the presence of dinosaurs in the fossil record was considered indicative of a tropical climate because they were presumed to be, like living reptiles, ectothermic (cold-blooded) organisms whose body temperature was largely determined by the temperature of the environment in which they lived. Many paleontologists now maintain, however, that dinosaurs were endothermic (warm-blooded) and were thus able to maintain, by the action of internal regulating mechanisms, a nearly constant body temperature in the face of widely varying external temperatures.

Employing an ingenious procedure, R.E. Barrick of North Carolina State University and his colleague W.J. Showers lent support to the view that dinosaurs were endothermic. They determined the ratios of stable oxygen isotopes in bone phosphate in a well-preserved specimen of *Tyrannosaurus rex*. Oxygen-isotope ratios in vertebrate bone are related to the body temperature at which the bone was formed. Because, unlike the bone of living reptiles, their specimen did not reveal large intrabone and interbone differences in oxygen-isotope composition, the investigators concluded that the bones were formed in relatively constant temperatures maintained by a controlled metabolic rate.

There is, however, a difficulty that plagues all isotope determinations in paleobiology. Most fossil remains have been altered chemically to such an extent that the possibility that the original organic material has been changed or removed

Andrew Starenko

Based on fossils found in Antarctica, an artist's depiction re-creates a species of crested theropod dinosaur from the early Jurassic Period (about 200 million years ago).

is always present. Yehoshua Kolodny of the Hebrew University of Jerusalem was, for that reason, skeptical of Barrick and Showers' conclusion.

W.R. Hammer of Augustana College, Rock Island, Ill., and his colleague W.J. Hickerson described a crested theropod dinosaur recovered from the early Jurassic Period (about 200 million years ago) Falla Formation exposed in the Central Transantarctic Mountains about 650 km (400 mi) from the geographic South Pole. They noted that this specimen was one of the few reasonably complete Jurassic carnivorous dinosaur remains to be discovered in any of the continents (Africa, South America, Australia, and Antarctica, along with peninsular India) that had their origin in the ancient continent of Gondwanaland. Hammer and Hickerson concluded that the occurrence of this dinosaur and associated fossils that are similar to early Jurassic assemblages from other continents indicates the existence of conditions that were at least reasonably mild but not necessarily tropical in that part of Gondwanaland during the early Jurassic.

Charles Darwin believed that although the record of past life, like any historical record, would never be complete, some gaps would be filled as the search for fossils extended beyond Europe and North America. This expectation has been abundantly fulfilled, and a discovery reported in 1994 reveals that the search is still yielding important new material. Dinosaur remains from the southern continents have been scarce compared with the abundant fossil faunas from North America, Europe, and Asia. Thus, the discovery of the remains of both theropod and sauropod dinosaurs from the lower Cretaceous beds of the southern Sahara, reported by Paul Sereno of the University of Chicago and his coauthors, assumed special significance.

Darwin, who believed that the continents had been fixed in the present relative positions throughout geologic history, could not have anticipated that little more than a century after the publication of *On the Origin of Species by Means of Natural Selection* in 1859, ideas about continents would change in such a way as to revolutionize the study of biogeog-

raphy. When the dinosaurs whose remains were described by Sereno and his colleagues were alive, about 130 million years ago, what was to become the continent of Africa was just beginning to be differentiated from Gondwanaland. The authors concluded that their study does not support the existence of a distinct Gondwanaland dinosaur fauna in the early Cretaceous and thus suggests that a land bridge with Europe persisted until late Jurassic time, about 150 million years ago. With the loss of that connection and the fragmentation of Gondwanaland to form the separate southern continents, distinct dinosaur faunas emerged later in the Cretaceous.

A dramatic development in dinosaur biology was the announcement by S.R. Woodward of Brigham Young University, Provo, Utah, and his associates that they succeeded in extracting DNA from a fragment of bone recovered from the Upper Cretaceous Blackhawk Formation exposed in the roof of an underground coal mine in eastern Utah. Because the nine DNA sequences obtained from the extract do not reveal a closer affinity to birds (which are believed to have descended from dinosaurs) than to mammals (which are held to be only distantly related to them), the results were met with skepticism. The fact that tests showed that the sequences do not resemble those of living bacteria or of humans seemed to eliminate the possibility of contamination by a modern source, but it was suggested that contamination may have resulted from the presence of some ancient bacterial source hidden in the bone. Despite the enormous technical difficulties surrounding the effort to extract DNA from fossils, this practice will, given the possibility of exciting results, no doubt continue.

With so much attention being devoted to dinosaurs, both by the scientific community and by the media, it is easy to overlook other significant recent work in paleontology. In the April 28, 1994, issue of *Nature,* Michael Novacek reviewed recent contributions concerning the evolution of whales. It has long been recognized that there is an affinity between land mammals and whales and dolphins. With the acceptance of evolutionary theory, it was supposed that this affinity grew out of an ancestral-descendant relationship, it being generally agreed that the progenitors of the order Cetacea (the whales and dolphins) lay somewhere among the ungulates (hoofed mammals). Until quite recently, however, the gap between terrestrial four-limbed mammals and cetaceans, with their drastically reduced hind limbs and their highly modified front limbs, remained very wide. Two recently discovered specimens have, however, gone a long way toward. filling this gap. J.G.M. Thewissen and his colleagues described a fossil from the Eocene beds of Pakistan (52 million years ago), which, although clearly recognizable as a whale on the basis of its cranial anatomy, has front and hind limbs so little specialized for swimming as to suggest that it represented the remains of an amphibious mammal. The authors assigned the generic name *Rodhocetus* to it. The somewhat more recent *Ambulocetus,* described by P.D. Gingerich and his colleagues, was clearly not amphibious, but was less specialized for swimming than are living whales.

A recent discovery was expected to help solve a problem that has puzzled paleontologists for more than a century. Conodonts are small toothlike structures found in sediments dating from late Ordovician time (450 million years ago) to late Triassic time (215 million years ago). Although they have been extensively studied because of their value as stratigraphic markers, their biological affinities have remained a matter for debate. Many paleontologists have maintained that they represent the partial remains, indeed the teeth, of some primitive vertebrate. A principal objection to this view has been that conodonts do not contain in their structure the hard, dense material called dentine that is characteristic of all vertebrate teeth. Ivan Sansom and M. Paul Smith of the University of Birmingham, England, and Moya Smith of the United Medical and Dental Schools of Guy's and St. Thomas's Hospital in London reported that studies of conodonts from the Upper Ordovician Harding Sandstone Formation of Colorado have revealed the unmistakable presence of dentine. The authors maintained that their study provides additional and conclusive evidence for the vertebrate nature of conodonts.
—David B. Kitts

Geophysics

The highlight of the past year for geophysicists occurred in June 1994, when the largest deep-focus earthquake on record struck 630 km (1 km = 0.62 mi) beneath Bolivia. Data from the quake, recorded by dozens of seismographs throughout the world, will help seismologists refine models of the Earth's deep structure and study the cause of deep earthquakes, one

of the most important unanswered questions in geophysics.

In January 1995, one year after the magnitude-6.6 Northridge earthquake struck southern California, a magnitude-7.2 quake ravaged Kobe, Japan, shaking that nation's confidence in its earthquake preparedness and causing researchers to redouble their studies of urban earthquake hazards. While scientists, builders, and emergency planners in earthquake-prone regions are sometimes obsessed with the anticipated "big one," Northridge and Kobe reminded them that the hazard can be far greater from smaller, more frequent earthquakes that are close to populated areas.

Noteworthy volcanic eruptions during the past year occurred in Indonesia, Italy, Alaska, Colombia, Chile, Mexico, Hawaii, Nicaragua, Russia, Papua New Guinea, Guatemala, and China. Llaima Volcano in Chile erupted in May 1994, accompanied by heavy lava flows, mud flows, and a 4,000–5,000-m (1 m = 3.3 ft) ash plume. Ongoing activity at Láscar Volcano in Chile peaked in July, when several strong eruptions produced ash plumes as high as 10,000 m. A major eruption at Klyuchevskaya Volcano on the Kamchatka Peninsula, Russia, began on September 8 and continued for weeks, generating a 15-km-high ash plume, 900-m-high lava fountains, and 1,500-m-long lava flows. On September 18 a magnitude-5.1 earthquake beneath the Rabaul caldera in Papua New Guinea presaged major eruptions that began the next day at Vulcan and Tavurvur volcanoes. Up to 50 cm of volcanic ash fell on the town of Rabaul. At least five people died, but early evacuations saved many more lives. Also in September, 23 people were killed by ash and mud slides when a volcanic lake overflowed after heavy rains on the slope of Mt. Pinatubo in the Philippines.

Destructive earthquakes occurred in Indonesia, Uganda, Iran, Mexico, Colombia, Bolivia, New Zealand, California, China, Russia, and Japan. On Feb. 15, 1994, a magnitude-7.2 earthquake, accompanied by destructive landslides and fires, struck southern Sumatra in Indonesia, killing at least 215 people. A magnitude-7.7 earthquake off the southern coast of Java in Indonesia on June 2 generated 6-m-high waves that swept as far inland as 0.5 km, killing at least 250 people and destroying 400 houses and over 250 boats. On June 6 a magnitude-6.4 earthquake, accompanied by destructive landslides, shook southern Colombia, killing more than 250 people. A magnitude-8.2 earthquake on October 4 in the Pacific Ocean off the Kuril Islands in Russia killed at least 16 people, generated a 3.5-m-high tsunami (sea wave), and caused damage as far away as the east coast of Hokkaido Island in Japan.

Deep-focus earthquakes. Very large, very deep earthquakes beneath Fiji and Bolivia in 1994 captured the attention of scientists who are trying to understand the structure and dynamics of the Earth's interior. The deepest-known earthquakes occur in the Earth's mantle at depths approaching 700 km, generally beneath areas of active subduction (areas where the edge of one of the Earth's crustal plates is descending below the edge of another). The physical mechanism of deep-focus earthquakes, rare and enigmatic compared with their well-recorded and

well-studied crustal cousins, remains one of the most important unanswered questions in geophysics, but a clearer picture is beginning to emerge as researchers study recent laboratory results and new seismic data from modern networks of broadband digital seismographs.

Except for one recent study suggesting that deep earthquakes have shorter faulting durations than shallow earthquakes of similar size, the mechanisms of deep earthquakes (the pattern of energy release, inferred from the direction, amplitude, and duration of recorded seismic waves) tend to be similar to those of crustal earthquakes. This is remarkable, because scientists know from high-pressure, high-temperature laboratory experiments that mantle materials must respond to stress by ductile flow rather than brittle fracture; mantle materials cannot support "typical" earthquakes. (Thus, it might even be misleading to use the term *faulting* when discussing deep-focus earthquakes, although for convenience it will be used here.) Thermal modeling and seismic imaging reveal, however, that a cold 80-km-thick slab of subducting lithosphere (the outer part of the solid Earth), although eroded and thinned during its descent, might maintain its identity (and brittleness) to depths below 700 km before being completely absorbed into the mantle. (In seismic imaging the structure of the Earth is computed from differences in the travel times of seismic waves along many different ray paths.)

This evidence points to an intrinsic relationship between deep earthquakes and subducted lithosphere. According to this hypothesis, at typical subduction rates of a few centimeters per year, the deepest

earthquakes would be related to pieces of lithosphere that began to subduct more than 20 million years ago. Minerals in the descending lithosphere dehydrate as they adjust to increasing temperature and pressure, and the water lost must play a role in intermediate-focus earthquakes (depths of approximately 75–300 km), increasing the pore pressure (the stress transmitted through the interstitial fluid of a soil or rock mass) and lubricating the faults.

The role of water at greater depths is controversial, however, and some kind of sudden transformation from unstable-to-stable mineral phase seems a more plausible mechanism to some researchers. Olivine, a complex silicate of magnesium and iron that is abundant and stable in the lithosphere, transforms to a denser phase in the laboratory at simulated depths of 300–400 km, which makes it the leading candidate in the transformational-faulting hypothesis. In a fast-descending slab, olivine might persist to a great depth, but some models show that the surviving wedge of olivine at 700 km would be no more than 5 km thick, a volume that is not large enough to cause a great earthquake through pure transformation alone. Furthermore, the simple transformation of a volume of olivine would radiate seismic energy isotropically (in all directions with equal intensity), which is the wrong radiation pattern for a large earthquake. To address these questions, researchers are searching for a kind of cracklike, propagating transformation that might also involve other mechanisms, such as melting.

In this context the June 9 deep earthquake in Bolivia was particularly interesting for seismologists. It was the largest deep-focus earthquake ever recorded, with a depth of 630 km and a magnitude of 8.2. Within minutes of the quake (the fastest seismic waves travel 8–10 kilometers per second in the mantle above 700 km and 6–7 kilometers per second in the crust), shaking was felt throughout central South America. Fortunately, damage and injuries were minor because the energy was released at great depth. Remarkably, 10–20 minutes later shaking was felt at locations in North America as far away as Seattle, Wash.; Minneapolis, Minn.; and Toronto—by far the largest area over which an earthquake had been felt in recorded history. (For comparison, the next largest deep-focus quake, a magnitude-8.2 earthquake in Colombia in 1970, was felt only as far north as Mexico City.)

Abundant seismic data from the Bolivian quake are providing the best test yet of deep-earthquake models, and preliminary results do not support the transformational-faulting theory. Seismologists agree that the earthquake occurred on a horizontal plane with a fault that is at least 40 km long. Geometrically, if faulting was confined to a subducted olivine layer no more than five kilometers thick, the subducted slab would have to be horizontal. Most independent evidence, however, suggests that subducting slabs dip steeply into the mantle. If so, the Bolivia earthquake fault must have cut through the slab at a high angle and involved the surrounding mantle materials, jeopardizing the transformational-faulting hypothesis. These questions will be answered only when seismologists can image the slab itself.

The Kobe earthquake. A major earthquake struck southwestern Honshu Island in Japan on Jan. 17, 1995. The magnitude-7.2 Hyogo prefecture earthquake was centered 25 km southwest of Kobe and 50 km west of Osaka. Kobe, a city of 1.5 million people and Japan's second largest port, was hardest hit. The quake left more than 5,100 dead, about 25,000 injured, and over 45,000 buildings destroyed or badly damaged. Although modern structures generally remained intact, many older structures suffered damage from shaking. Wood-frame houses with heavy tile roofs behaved like inverted pendulums, which amplified the shaking. Much of the damage was due to fires caused by ruptured natural gas lines, and firefighting efforts were hampered by damage to the water-supply system—an all-too-common scenario in urban earthquakes. Five elevated sections of the Hanshin Expressway, a major traffic artery between Kobe and Osaka, collapsed, and one 0.5-km section toppled over virtually intact when concrete columns broke at their bases. Kobe's port facilities were heavily damaged. Several train derailments occurred, and officials estimated that the high-speed Shinkansen "bullet" train would be out of service for several months while repairs were made to more than 80 km of track. Shaking intensity (a somewhat subjective measure of a quake's strength based on damage) reached six on the seven-point Japanese scale.

Japan lies near the intersection of three active tectonic plates, and the Japanese expect large earthquakes. From the amplitude and polarity of the radiated seismic waves and the area of aftershock ac-

tivity, seismologists know that the quake occurred southwest of Kobe on a near-vertical fault trending northeast–southwest. Rupture began at a depth near 20 km and then propagated upward to the surface and horizontally for 40–50 km. Faulting was predominately right-lateral strike slip, with the northwestern crustal block sliding approximately two meters northeastward relative to the southeastern block. Afterward, scientists observed one–two meters of predominantly right-lateral strike-slip faulting on a nine-kilometer-long segment of the Nojima Fault, which crops out along the northwestern coast of Awaji Island near the earthquake's epicenter. (Elsewhere, faulting either did not reach the surface or was hidden underwater, and so these direct observations are consistent with the seismological data.) Reports of surface faulting within Kobe could not be confirmed. The earthquake was not predicted.

This was the most destructive earthquake in Japan since 1923, when the great Kanto quake near Tokyo killed 140,000 and destroyed more than 500,000 buildings. As with the predawn Northridge quake in southern California, which preceded it by almost exactly one year, casualties in the Kobe earthquake would have been much greater if it had occurred during commuting or business hours. As it was, more than 300,000 people were still living in temporary shelters two weeks after the earthquake, and government officials found themselves on the defensive when emergency services were quickly overwhelmed. Preliminary analyses of data from strong-motion accelerographs revealed that ground shaking in Kobe was average for a magnitude-

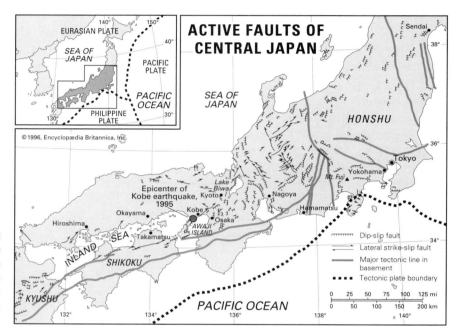

ACTIVE FAULTS OF CENTRAL JAPAN

© 1996, Encyclopædia Britannica, Inc.

A powerful earthquake in January 1995 caused severe damage in the Japanese port city of Kobe (below and below right). More than 5,100 people were killed, and over 45,000 buildings were destroyed. Because of Japan's location near the intersection of three tectonic plates (right), there are many active faults throughout the region.

(Above)Vladimir Sichov—Sipa; (right) © Patrick Robert—Sygma

7.2 earthquake. Given the severity of the damage and the similarity of building codes in California and Japan, data from the Kobe earthquake will provide lessons for emergency planners and engineers throughout the world for years to come.

Seismic performance of steel-frame buildings. In the aftermath of the January 1994 Northridge earthquake, a remarkable story came to light concerning the seismic performance of steel-frame buildings. Because of its flexibility, welded steel was long thought to be among the safest materials for construction in earthquake areas. At first, Northridge seemed to confirm the conventional wisdom; most of the damaged buildings were made of wood, concrete, or brick. Then engineers discovered cracks at main column-beam welded joints in two unfinished steel-frame buildings in Los Angeles. Inspection of other buildings in the Northridge area (exacting work that involves removing walls and insulation and may cost as much as $2 million for a 20-story building) revealed similar damage to dozens of structures. By mid-1994 the California Seismic Safety Commission had taken the extraordinary step of recommending suspension of current building codes for steel construction throughout the western U.S.

Unfortunately, there was no consensus on improved guidelines for either new construction or repairs of weakened existing buildings—especially after traditional modifications were found inadequate in laboratory tests that simulated the shaking in a magnitude-7 quake. A new building code must now await new research results, forcing builders in the meantime to justify current and future designs on a costly case-by-case basis. Fortunately, Northridge provided an early warning without destroying any steel-frame build-

An elevated expressway in Kobe, Japan, collapsed as a result of the earthquake of January 1995, the most destructive in Japan since 1923. Many Japanese had believed that their recently built structures were quakeproof, and they also had considered Kobe to be in an area relatively safe from earthquakes.

© Noboru Hashimoto—Sygma

355

ings. Builders, engineers, the steel industry, and governmental officials all agree that the danger is much greater than previously thought, especially from a large earthquake with high-amplitude and/or long-duration shaking.

—Charles S. Mueller

HYDROLOGIC SCIENCES

Hydrologic investigations at the Walnut Gulch experimental watershed in southeastern Arizona provided new insight concerning the reliability of flash-flood predictions and led to improved capabilities for monitoring water and energy balances at the ground surface by using remote-sensing data. A study examining the usefulness of current regulatory standards for the remediation of sites with contaminated groundwater was released by the U.S. National Research Council. Data from a satellite were helping oceanographers gain a better understanding of the rise and fall of sea levels.

Hydrology

The reliability of predictions of peak streamflow from rainfall measurements is an important issue in flood forecasting. In regions subject to high-intensity thunderstorms, there is considerable interest in developing the capability for a real-time flash-flood-warning system. The hydrologic simulation models on which these predictions are based require estimates of the areal and temporal distribution of rainfall across a watershed. These estimates must be derived from a limited number of measurement sites within a watershed. Errors in estimations (rainfall-sampling errors) result in errors in predictions of peak streamflow.

Streamflow studies. Writing in the journal *Water Resources Research*, Jene Diane Michaud and Soroosh Sorooshian at the University of Arizona investigated the effect on streamflow prediction of rainfall-sampling errors associated with localized thunderstorms in a semiarid watershed. Their study area, covering 150 sq km (58 sq mi), was in the Walnut Gulch watershed, a gently rolling rangeland with brush and grass vegetation. Stream channels are sandy and normally dry. Virtually all of the storm runoff is produced by rainfall rates that exceed the infiltration capacity of the surface soils.

Of particular interest to Michaud and Sorooshian was the evaluation of a rainfall-sampling scheme having the density of rain gauges used in the ALERT (Automated Local Evaluation in Real Time)-type flash-flood-warning systems (one gauge per 20 sq km; [7.7 sq mi]) and a sampling scheme with an areal resolution similar to that of the NEXRAD system. (The NEXRAD system gives digital precipitation estimates that represent an average value for an area 4 × 4 km [2.5 × 2.5 mi]).

By analyzing data from 10 convective storms that caused large runoff events, Michaud and Sorooshian found that inadequate rain-gauge densities resulted in predicted runoff that on average was only 58% of the actual peak flow. They attributed approximately one-half of that percentage to rainfall-sampling error. Spatial averaging equivalent to the NEXRAD weather system led to predictions in the peak flow that were smaller by 50% than the observed flows. The spatial resolution of these measurement systems was too coarse to capture the

effects of small, high-intensity thunderstorms. Michaud and Sorooshian concluded that for localized thunderstorms the current spatial resolution of ALERT-type precipitation measurements and the NEXRAD precipitation estimates may not be sufficient to produce reliable peak-flow forecasts in midsize watersheds in the southwestern U.S.

Monsoon '90. The Walnut Gulch watershed was also the site of an important multidisciplinary experiment to evaluate the use of remotely sensed data in estimating the magnitude of components of the hydrologic cycle and the energy balance at the Earth's surface (the net radiation, the soil heat flux, and the sensible and latent heat fluxes). The experiment, entitled Monsoon '90, involved the integration over a wide range of resolutions of remote-sensing observations from ground-, aircraft-, and satellite-based systems. Results were reported in a series of papers compiled in the May 1994 issue of *Water Resources Research*.

Studies in Monsoon '90 were organized along three lines: those concerned with the correction and interpretation of remotely sensed data, those investigating the potential for inferring geophysical and biophysical properties of the ground surface from remote-sensing information, and those that applied remote-sensing data in modeling the hydrologic and surface-energy fluxes. In one study Tom Schmugge and his coauthors correlated airborne radiometer measurements of microwave brightness temperature (thermal emission from the soil at the longer microwave lengths) to soil moisture content. They found that changes in microwave brightness temperature after a rainfall were highly correlated to the amount of rainfall.

In a second study, David Goodrich and his coauthors obtained results suggesting that satellite-based microwave systems that suffer from low resolution may provide acceptable prestorm soil-moisture data for computing runoff in a semiarid rangeland.

Goundwater contamination. Industrialized countries throughout the world struggled with the issue of how best to deal with groundwater-contamination problems. In the U.S., for example, estimates of the total number of sites where groundwater and soil may be contaminated were as high as 400,000. Contaminants are of many different types and include chemical solvents, metals, and radionuclides. Estimates of the total cost of cleaning up those sites over the next 30 years approached $750 billion.

The most common approach to cleaning groundwater is a pump-and-treat system; wells are installed in and around the zone of contamination, and contaminated groundwater is pumped to the surface for treatment. By early 1995 there were more than 3,000 pump-and-treat systems in operation at contaminated sites within the U.S. Since 1990 evidence has been accumulating that this approach is seldom effective in restoring groundwater quality to drinking-water standards and that pumping may be required for decades or even centuries to comply with current standards for groundwater cleanup. While groundwater pump-and-treat systems are effective in containing the migration of contaminated water through the subsurface, they have not proved to be successful in removing contami-

nant mass. The concern has arisen that countries may be wasting large sums of money on a technology that can seldom achieve its goal.

The U.S. National Research Council (NRC) released a report in late 1994 entitled *Alternatives for Groundwater Cleanup.* It concluded that at many sites where groundwater cleanup has been mandated by regulatory agencies, some areas will remain contaminated above drinking-water standards for the foreseeable future, even if the best available technologies are used. In a survey of 77 sites where conventional pump-and-treat systems were operating, the committee found that at 69 of them cleanup goals had not been achieved, although it was deemed possible that they would be reached at some of those sites in the future. The success at eight of the sites in the survey suggested to the committee that only under special circumstances would the cleanup of contaminated groundwater be possible in less than 10 years of pumping.

Technical reasons underlying the difficulty in groundwater cleanup include the physical heterogeneity of the subsurface environment, the migration of contaminants into fine-grained sediments that are not easily flushed by groundwater pumping, the presence of organic contaminants such as chlorinated hydrocarbons that become trapped in the pore spaces and then dissolve only slowly into the groundwater, the transfer of contaminants from the water to the sediment surface, and the inherent difficulties in characterizing a complex subsurface environment.

Researchers have developed many new, innovative technologies with the potential to improve the efficiency of groundwater

cleanup, but the NRC committee found that their use had been limited by technical, institutional, and economic barriers. Examples of such barriers include the difficulty of pinpointing liability if a technology fails, the lack of testing facilities, and the requirement to construct a pump-and-treat system if the innovative technology fails to achieve the cleanup goal.

Given the difficulty in groundwater cleanup, the NRC committee addressed the need to reevaluate the goal underlying this effort. Regulations in 1995 often required that the contaminated groundwater be restored to drinking-water standards. As noted above, technical evidence now suggests that this goal may not be reached within a reasonable time at many sites. Less-stringent goals, such as cleaning up areas containing dissolved contaminants and installing containment systems around areas that contain organic liquids trapped in the pore spaces, may, however, be possible at many sites.

Those who argued that cleanup goals should be maintained at the drinking-water standard did so for two general purposes: to provide incentive against further pollution and to encourage the development of improved cleanup technologies. Alternatives to a health-based standard include cleanup to the capabilities of the best available technology, cleanup to a level allowing for uses other than drinking, such as irrigation, and ongoing containment of the contaminant plume. Unfortunately, for each of those strategies, there was a high degree of uncertainty in quantifying the risks and benefits. The NRC committee concluded that because existing groundwater-cleanup goals cannot be attained within a reasonable time at many sites, regulators should set short-term objectives for those sites based on the capabilities of current technology. They argued that interim objectives are needed to acknowledge current technological limitations.

Many countries facing the task of remediating sites with contaminated groundwater are reporting experiences similar to those encountered in the U.S. It seems likely that they will be faced with the same management issues as those tackled by the NRC panel.

—Leslie Smith

Oceanography

In 1992 U.S. and French scientists collaborated in launching TOPEX/Poseidon, a satellite capable of making extremely precise measurements of the ocean surface height. During the past year they began reaping the benefits of this satellite by making important discoveries about the ocean. Several research groups used data from the satellite to monitor the rate of sea-level rise, a matter of concern because swelling ocean heights threaten coastal regions and island nations. The satellite measurements revealed that global sea level climbed faster between 1992 and 1994 than it had during previous decades. Researchers reported that the average global height rose three millimeters per year during the two-year span, about twice the rate previously measured.

Oceanographers believe that sea levels have been creeping upward during the past century because of rising atmospheric temperatures. As the air warms, it melts mountain glaciers, which drain into the ocean. Warmer air also heats

the ocean, causing it to expand. Scientists expect that sea levels will rise faster in the future because of continued global warming due to the greenhouse effect.

Although the recent findings from TOPEX/Poseidon appeared to match the greenhouse warming predictions, scientists cautioned that they remained unsure as to why sea levels rose quickly between 1992 and 1994. Over a short time span, such as two years, natural fluctuations may cause ocean height to rise and fall for reasons unrelated to greenhouse warming. Scientists concluded that they needed to continue monitoring ocean levels for many years in order to assess whether carbon dioxide and other greenhouse gases are causing a rapid rise in sea heights.

Indeed, humans can cause sea levels to edge upward for reasons unrelated to global warming. A study of water habits on land revealed that as much as a third of the current sea-level rise might result from activities such as chopping down forests and pumping groundwater from subsurface aquifers. Pulling water out of the ground contributes to the problem because some of the water brought to the surface eventually makes its way into the ocean. For instance, groundwater used for irrigation can flow into the sea via rivers, or it can evaporate and then fall as rain into the oceans. Deforestation boosts sea levels because much of the water locked up in trees escapes into the atmosphere when those trees are burned or undergo decomposition.

El Niño. Other measurements from the TOPEX/Poseidon satellite helped oceanographers discover new aspects of the climate phenomenon known as El

Niño. The name El Niño describes a pronounced warming in the central and eastern Pacific Ocean, which recurs irregularly at about four- to seven-year intervals. When an El Niño brews, it upsets weather around much of the world. By comparing data from the TOPEX/Poseidon satellite with measurements from earlier satellites, scientists discovered that an ocean current in the northwestern Pacific had been displaced northward in the early 1990s. They attributed the shift to extremely long-lived waves generated by an El Niño in 1982–83.

During a typical El Niño, broad waves (undetectable to passing ships) travel from the west to east and then reflect off the coast of South America and North America. Although some of the reflected wave energy heads northwest, scientists had believed that the waves would die out long before they reached far into the midlatitudes. The satellite measurements, in combination with computer simulations, indicated, however, that the waves continued for more than a decade into the far reaches of the North Pacific. By displacing the position of major Pacific ocean currents, such waves may alter weather conditions in the U.S., according to some researchers.

In another discovery tied to El Niño, scientists from the U.S. and Zimbabwe found a strong connection between weather in the Pacific and corn (maize) harvests in southern Africa, halfway around the world. Data collected since 1970 revealed that crop yields in Zimbabwe suffered most when El Niño warmings raised sea-surface temperatures in the Pacific. When Pacific temperatures dropped, Zimbabwe received plentiful rains and the corn crops flourished. The link proved devastating at times. During the 1991–92 El Niño, southern Africa suffered its worst drought of the century, and harvests of cereal crops fell 50%.

The researchers suggested that Zimbabwe could use information about temperatures in the Pacific to forecast crop yields. Climate experts were learning how to predict El Niño warmings up to a year in advance. If an El Niño appeared to be developing, farmers in Zimbabwe could compensate by planting drought-resistant species. Governments in the area could accumulate sufficient grain reserves to handle a drought.

Climate researchers have long known that El Niño warmings can shift rainfall patterns and alter weather around the world. Australia, Peru, and other countries routinely use El Niño forecasts in agricultural projections. The Zimbabwe study was the first to suggest that African nations might benefit from these forecasts, however.

Clues to the Africa-Pacific connection might arise out of studies of the Indian Ocean. Scientists who analyzed sea-surface and subsurface temperature records found that the Indian Ocean produces its own version of El Niño. In the Pacific Ocean an El Niño starts when warmth shifts from the western end of the ocean into the central and eastern regions. According to measurements made between 1979 and 1991, warmth in the Indian Ocean followed a similar pattern, moving from a position near the African coast toward the center of the ocean. The relocation of warm water in the Indian Ocean occurred at the same time as the movement in the Pacific.

As the heat moved, so did the position of thunderstorms, which carry energy from the ocean into the atmosphere. The events in the Indian Ocean may help explain why El Niño warmings in the Pacific can have such dramatic effects on parts of Africa, India, and other regions far removed from the central Pacific.

Iron, plankton, and global warming. In a much-heralded experiment with ramifications for greenhouse-warming policy, a team of scientists poured a half ton of iron into the Pacific Ocean 270 nautical miles south of the Galápagos Islands. The team wanted to test a theory that iron would fertilize plankton growth in areas of the ocean that contain abundant nutrients but little plant life. Scientists had long debated why the Antarctic Ocean and other nutrient-rich waters do not support thriving communities of floating plants. In 1990 some oceanographers suggested that iron deficiencies in the water may be the answer. They further surmised that adding iron to stimulate plant growth could help avert global greenhouse warming because ocean plants absorb carbon dioxide from the atmosphere.

As a test, oceanographers from the U.S. and U.K. released iron into an area of about 42 sq km (16 sq mi) and then mea-

Netherlands Institute for Sea Research/Alfred Wegener Institute for Polar and Marine Research; photo, Cornelis Veth

Researchers sample ocean water near a large iceberg for evidence of dissolved iron. Iron-rich water, it is believed, promotes plankton growth.

sured chemical and biological changes in the water. During the next nine days, they found a significant increase in the growth of floating plants. The concentration of the photosynthetic pigment chlorophyll tripled, and the amount of biological material in the surface waters doubled. Such results verified the hypothesis that iron deficiencies limit plant growth in these nutrient-rich waters.

The experiment did not, however, support the idea that adding iron to ocean water would help slow global warming. The oceanographers found that the ocean waters absorbed relatively little carbon dioxide, which makes this an inefficient way to reduce atmospheric carbon dioxide concentrations.

Atlantic warming. In the Atlantic Ocean, ships that retraced Columbus' route from Europe to America detected a substantial warming in subtropical waters. Temperatures at certain depths had climbed by as much as 0.32° C (0.58° F) since the late 1950s, an amount that is roughly consistent with predictions based on global greenhouse warming. In order to collect these measurements, a team of oceanographers sailed aboard a Spanish naval ship that followed the latitude line of 24° N as part of a celebration of Columbus' voyage of discovery in 1492. Temperature measurements along this course had been taken previously in 1957 and 1981.

Between 1957 and 1981 the western portion of the Atlantic warmed considerably, while the central and eastern regions changed little. From 1981 to 1992 the central and eastern Atlantic warmed, which resulted in a temperature increase across the entire ocean. The warming was most pronounced between 700 m (2,300 ft) and 2,500 m (8,200 ft) in depth. By contrast, conditions close to the surface had changed little since the late 1950s.

From the limited measurements available, oceanographers could not determine what caused the warming trend. Either increased concentrations of greenhouse gases in the atmosphere or natural fluctuations in oceanic conditions could be the answer. Scientists noted that the observed changes resemble, in part, the predictions made by computer climate models of how the oceans should respond to atmospheric greenhouse warming. The match between observations and predictions was not exact, however, because the models forecast a warming in the surface waters as well as in the deeper ocean. The researchers suggested making future measurements along the same course in order to resolve the cause of the temperature increases.

Ice age. The most recent ice age gripped the globe from 115,000 to 10,-000 years ago. Although the term *ice age* suggests a period of perpetual cold, temperatures actually rose and fell quite often during that time. New evidence culled from the seafloor and from the Greenland ice cap revealed that the ice-age Earth suffered a case of fevers and chills even more severe than previously thought.

At least six times during the last ice age, huge numbers of glaciers poured into the North Atlantic during major cold snaps. These iceberg armadas left telltale signs on the seafloor because they dropped grains of rock as they melted, pieces of evidence that scientists could use to trace the origin of the icebergs.

When they first discovered hints of the iceberg inundations, scientists thought all the ice came from the thick glacial sheet that covered much of North America during the last ice age. But results later revealed that the small ice sheet on Iceland disgorged icebergs at the same time as the North American ice sheet. Other researchers also found signs of major cooling in the Southern Hemisphere that was taking place at the same time as the iceberg events in the North Atlantic. This combination of findings suggested that the entire globe behaved erratically, swinging from cold to warm and back again. The cause of such planetary shivers remained a mystery.

Scientists were also unable to determine whether the current climate is at risk. Researchers once thought that warm periods between ice ages—such as the last 10,000 years—do not suffer from the types of climatic flip-flops that wracked the globe during the last ice age. They started to question that assumption in 1993, though, on the basis of evidence collected from far below the surface of the Greenland ice cap. When European researchers drilled through this deep ice, they found evidence that the climate was unstable during the warm period prior to the last ice age. Such results suggested that the current climate might also jump up and down erratically.

U.S. researchers countered such claims during the past year, however, when they analyzed records from their own ice-drilling project. They found evidence that the deepest ice layers in Greenland were folded and therefore were unreliable as a climatic record.

—Richard Monastersky

ELECTRONICS AND INFORMATION SCIENCES

Major developments in electronics and the information sciences during the past year included the introduction of a powerful new central processing unit (CPU) for personal computers, the discovery of a flaw in a CPU introduced in 1993, and the decoding of a 129-digit message that had remained unsolved since its creation in 1977. Internet, the worldwide "network of networks," continued to grow in size and frequency of use, and cellular radio (cellular phones) was enlisting some 14,000 new subscribers each day in the United States alone.

COMMUNICATIONS SYSTEMS

Advances in communications technologies during the past year had less to do with their introduction than with their application. Though there were advances in such areas as cellular radio and fiber optics, they were less significant than the acceptance of the technologies by the major firms in the communications industry and, certainly, by the public at large.

Cellular radio

The most significant changes in the past year took place in wireless communications. Cellular radio, in 1995 just 12 years old, continued to experience explosive growth. In the U.S. alone there were more than 20 million subscribers by the end of 1994.

There was, however, still no "standard" method of transmission between cell sites and vehicles. The system first used, and still the most popular, was called AMPS (Advanced Mobile Phone Service). Though this analog (one in which data are represented by continu-ously variable physical quantities) system performed the job effectively, the unanticipated demand for cellular phones made it necessary to continue to expand and install cell sites—and cell sites were expensive. Consequently, the development of a digital transmission scheme, which would require only one-third as many cell sites, was attractive. This scheme (called TDMA—Time Division Multiple Access) was accepted in the United States as a second standard. A similar system, Global System for Mobile Communications, was adopted in Europe and in much of Asia.

A third system, one that utilized a complex coding scheme, was developed. Called CDMA (Code Division Multiple Access), it was derived from military operations and provided a user with several advantages, one of the greatest being a 10-fold increase in the capacity of a cell site.

The major challenge of these systems was how to incorporate all of them, or at least some of them, into a cellular telephone. Subscribers wanted their phones to work beyond their home region; thus, these phones had to be compatible with whatever system was being used in a distant city.

By 1995 it seemed clear that new systems would employ either TDMA or CDMA schemes. Neither appeared to be a clear winner, and it was likely that both would continue to be used.

The explosive growth of wireless communications did not go unnoticed by entrepreneurs. They sought approval of a third, or even a fourth, cellular carrier in each area (as of early 1995 the U.S. Federal Communications Commis-sion [FCC] allowed only two). They also envisioned a wireless system for pedestrians, incorporating smaller cells and smaller telephones, designed for slower (nonvehicular) speeds.

This thinking led to a demand for more space on the electromagnetic spectrum, an increasingly scarce commodity. In the U.S. the FCC recently made such space available, and by 1995 much of it was being auctioned. The auction was taking place over a protracted period of time and was being done electronically, with each participant using a computer as a bidding device.

It was quite likely that in the not too distant future, each telephone subscriber would be assigned a telephone number at an early age. He or she would use this number with the standard wired telephone system at home, and it would automatically shift to a small cell-site system when a person left the home, to a typical cellular radio system when he or she traveled by vehicle, and even to a nonwired system in a person's office, allowing the user to be free to move up and down the office aisles without missing a call. It was no wonder that this overall scheme was called a Personal Communications Service, since telephone calls would for the first time be placed to a person rather than to a place where a person was expected to be.

Another wireless system that received considerable attention during the past year was a low-Earth-orbit (LEO) satellite system. This was a communications satellite system in which the satellites orbited the Earth at an altitude of approximately 800 km (500 mi). (See *Satellite systems,* below.)

Telemedicine, a combination of video and communications technology, allows a patient to be treated for hand pains by a physician many kilometers away.

Fiber optics

Wireless communications was not the only area where changes were taking place. Equally as significant was the explosive growth of the capacity to transmit vast amounts of information rapidly between two points. The medium for this was fiber optics, hair-thin strands of glass that transmit information in the form of light rather than electricity. It had long been known that the frequency, and therefore the bandwidth, of light is orders of magnitude greater than that of the electricity used in conventional telecommunications, but the significance of this fact was not at first fully appreciated.

Massive transmission speeds cannot be achieved and implemented without set standards, however. SONET (Synchronous Optical Network) was one accepted standard. As such, it set transmission speeds, which ranged from a low of 51.84 Mbps (mega, or million of, bits per second) to a high of 9.9 Gbps (giga, or billion of, bits per second). SONET was, essentially, the highway over which data would travel in the Information Age.

But there had to be a vehicle to carry the information. This vehicle, which gained increased prominence in 1994, is called Asynchronous Transfer Mode (ATM—not to be confused with the automated teller machines). ATM puts all data into same-sized "boxes" that can be easily handled by computers. Each box is 53 bytes long (one byte = eight bits).

ATM in 1995 was available at speeds of 622 Mbps, but 2.4 Gbps was expected to be available soon. Even at the slower speed, however, the transmission capability of ATM, riding on SONET, was remarkable. For instance, the entire set of the *Encyclopædia Britannica* could be transmitted in 2½ days at the (now) relatively slow speed of 2,400 bits per second. At a speed of 622 Mbps, utilizing ATM, this transmission time would be reduced to less than one second.

These phenomenal speeds were not just dreams. In 1995 the computers at the University of Wisconsin at Madison were connected to those at the University of Illinois at Urbana-Champaign using ATM at a speed of 622 Mbps.

Networks

The transmission of information between far-flung sites was, indeed, a trend with vast implications. It would not be incorrect to say that the network is a computer and that computers themselves are simply nodes.

Magic Link, developed by the Sony Corp., is a 0.45-kg unit that allows users to send voice messages over E-mail.

The networks were used, or soon would be used, for many applications. Among them were:

1. Distance learning. Expert teachers from any location would teach classes to hundreds or thousands of remotely located students.

2. Telecommuting. Workers would eliminate the challenge of braving the expressways by working at home and transmitting information.

3. Telemedicine. Physicians skilled at reading electrocardiograms and X-rays would be able to do so without incurring delays.

4. Simple communications. Internet, the interconnection of thousands of presently existing networks, enabled librarians at any library to have access to virtually any book in the world. University professors could gather data from any other university's databases. Computer buffs could communicate with other computer buffs via electronic mail.

Late in 1994 Sony Corp. introduced Magic Link, a 0.45-kg (1-lb) unit that allowed users to send voice messages throughout AT&T's national E-mail (electronic mail) network. Equipped with one megabyte of memory and a fax modem, Magic Link needed to connect with phone lines to communicate unless the customer bought a pager card that slipped into its side.

—Robert E. Stoffels

COMPUTERS AND COMPUTER SCIENCE

During the past year a group of volunteers demonstrated that it was possible to break a data-encryption (encoding) scheme that was thought to be secure. The team decoded a message that had remained sealed for 17 years and thus proved that computers have become powerful enough to make some existing encryption schemes inadequate. Two companies that had been rivals in the personal computer (PC) market—IBM and Apple—cooperated to design a new, breakthrough processor for PCs. Both will build operating systems for the new computer, which will make it possible for a customer to use an operating system from one company with a computer built by the other. Also during the year both hardware and software manufacturers encountered difficulties in building large, complex systems. Customers with PCs discovered a problem in Intel's popular Pentium microprocessor that caused PCs that contain the chip to perform some complex arithmetic problems incorrectly. Software manufacturer Microsoft faced legal difficulties during the year and encountered problems with its new operating environment that caused the company to delay shipping the system.

Data encryption

When information is stored in a computer, copied onto a disk, or sent across a network, it must be protected against both theft and tampering. For example, a corporation that uses a computer to store documents describing the company's plans for new products or services must protect files against theft because a copy of the files could be sold to competitors. In addition to protecting data against theft, an organization usually needs to ensure that information stored in a computer cannot be altered by unauthorized personnel. Keeping information secure is important because the correct and efficient operation of many companies depends on information integrity.

To guarantee that information cannot be stolen or modified, computer systems use encryption. A person who owns a file for a computer can encode it so that it cannot be read without a password. The best encryption programs use complex methods that scramble information so well that it cannot be unscrambled without the password, even with the help of a fast computer. Furthermore, because someone trying to break an encoded message can program a computer to try all words in a dictionary, the best passwords consist of long strings of characters chosen at random instead of common words.

In 1977 three scientists—Ronald Rivest, Adi Shamir, and Leonard Adleman—devised an encryption technique known as the Rivest-Shamir-Adleman, or RSA, cryptoalgorithm. The technique uses the mathematical concept of prime numbers to encrypt data. (A prime is any integer other than 0 or ±1 that is not divisible without remainder by any other integers except ±1 and ± the integer itself.) In the RSA scheme the password needed to decrypt a message is not a character string at all. Instead, each secret password is a prime number that contains 50 or more digits. Using numbers and complex mathematical functions to encrypt a document or a picture works well on a computer because a computer stores all information, including video and voice, digitally. That is, documents, pictures, spreadsheets, and sound recordings are all stored as a sequence of numbers.

When Rivest, Shamir, and Adleman devised the RSA encryption technique, they were so certain it could not be broken that they offered a demonstration. They chose a long random password and used it to encrypt a sample message. The scientists then published the encrypted message and challenged anyone to decrypt it without knowing the password. The puzzle became known as RSA 129 because it contained 129 digits. With the computing power available in 1977, some mathematicians estimated that it would take centuries for a computer to decrypt RSA 129 without the secret password.

In 1994 an international team surprised the world. They were able to break RSA 129 and decrypt the message without knowing the password. Led by Arjen Lenstra at Bell Communications Research, Inc. (Bellcore), the team included approximately 600 volunteers in 24 countries on five continents. The group used the Internet, a global computer network, to communicate and coordinate their activity. The volunteers created computer software and divided the possible solutions among themselves. Most used their own computers to help go through the list of possible solutions and check each one. Others helped manage the effort by assigning work and then collecting and organizing the results.

When the team correctly decoded the message after only eight months of work, many were surprised at the contents: "The magic words are squeamish ossifrage." Although the sentence is composed of valid English words (an ossifrage is a bird of prey) and is syntactically correct, it seems to be nonsense. In fact, the message has no real meaning. The scientists who devised the puzzle chose some of the words at random because they wanted to avoid using a common phrase.

Most experts agreed that finding a way to decrypt the RSA 129 message does not mean that the entire RSA encryption method is invalid or that any encrypted message can be decrypted instantly. In essence, the work enabled the volunteers to figure out one password; an equal amount of work will be required for reading a message that has been encrypted with another password. The breakthrough is significant, however, because it shows that computers have become so powerful that a group of enthusiasts can cooperate to unscramble an encrypted message. The consequences are especially important because encryption methods that employ prime numbers, including the RSA algorithm, are used to protect military secrets, data in banks, and the security systems of nuclear power stations. In France a scheme similar to RSA is used in telephone "smart cards." Although such security systems will not be changed immediately, the demonstration made everyone aware that modern computers have made encryption vulnerable to attacks that were impossible a few years ago. Even the RSA schemes that use prime numbers of as many as 500 digits could eventually be decrypted.

The national standard proposed by U.S. Pres. Bill Clinton's administration for the encryption of data and voice transfers by telephone lines was attacked by privacy advocates and the information processing industry during the year. The proposed Clipper encryption chip would contain a "key" that would give U.S. government agencies the ability to decrypt private data sent over public phone lines. The Clipper project was temporarily shelved. The Clinton administration has also been criticized by many in the computer software industry for ignoring its call for the freedom to export encryption programs.

Hardware developments

In the marketplace a war was under way over which central processing unit (CPU) would dominate as the brains of the latest generation of PCs. The battle involved some surprising alignments. On one side were former rivals Apple Computer, Inc., and IBM Corp., which in 1994 introduced the new PowerPC family of microprocessors, high-speed CPU silicon chips developed jointly with Motorola, Inc. On the other side were Intel Corp., once IBM's chief supplier of PC microprocessors, and Microsoft Corp., the world's largest producer of PC software and the supplier of both MS-DOS—the major Intel-based disk-operating system (DOS)—and the popular Windows operating environment. Intel's fastest chip, the Pentium, which was introduced in 1993, competed directly with PowerPC, but it did not have the speed edge of PowerPC's reduced instruction set computing (RISC) architecture. Intel competitors announced that they would produce their own cheaper Pentium-class chips.

Meanwhile, Digital Equipment Corp. (DEC), which had developed a RISC CPU known as Alpha, released faster versions of it. DEC's new Alpha operated at a clock speed of 275 MHz (megahertz—million cycles per second), which means it could perform 275 million operations per second. Most IBM-compatible PCs used a CPU that operated at 33 or 66 MHz. DEC and other companies, notably Carrera Computers, Inc., announced that they would use Alpha chips in new, faster computers that would run the same software as existing PCs but would operate almost 3.5 times faster than most current models.

In March 1994 Apple released the first PowerPC-based hardware, the Power Macintosh (Power Mac) line of computers (with clock speeds of up to 100 MHz). Although the Power Macs used Apple's proprietary graphic operating system, Mac OS, they were capable of running both Apple- and Windows-compatible software. They were also able to run older, less-sophisticated Macintosh software. In November Apple, IBM, and Motorola disclosed plans for the joint development of a universal PowerPC capable of running operating systems made by different companies. It was expected to be available in 1996.

PowerPC microprocessors, high-speed silicon chips developed jointly by IBM Corp., Apple Computer, Inc., and Motorola, Inc., were introduced in 1994.

Jeffrey Macmillan—Los Angeles Times Photo

Late in the year Intel encountered difficulties with its new microprocessor. Although the Pentium CPU fits on a silicon chip less than 2.5 cm (1 in) square, it is among the most complex devices made. Internally, it contains 3.1 million transistors, organized into circuits that perform operations such as addition and subtraction. In 1994 a major problem was discovered in the Pentium circuitry. An error in the wiring of one transistor caused some arithmetic operations to be computed incorrectly. At first Intel stonewalled, insisting that problems would occur only once in 27,000 years of normal use. On December 19, however, IBM, claiming that the error could appear as often as once every 24 days, suspended sales of its PCs that contained the Pentium chip. Intel, prompted by IBM's action and a precipitous drop in its stock price, acknowledged its public relations blunder and offered free replacement of faulty chips. In February 1995 Intel unveiled the P6, a new generation of microprocessors that incorporates 5.5 million transistors and is expected to challenge the speed of the RISC-based PowerPC.

A battle was also shaping up in a new line of consumer hardware. In August 1993 Apple introduced Newton, the first personal digital assistant (PDA), a pocket-size computer with a write-on screen instead of a keyboard. Newton was immediately criticized for its poor handwriting recognition, and only about 80,000 units were sold. In 1994, however, the company introduced a new Newton with triple the memory and a lower price tag. More important, Apple said that it had persuaded 2,400 software developers to write programs for Newton, something

the machine had sorely lacked. Competition increased, however, as other manufacturers began to release new PDAs.

Software developments

The PC microprocessor war also sparked a battle over operating systems. In 1993 Microsoft announced Windows NT, which included features not found in earlier Windows, including support for computer networking. Microsoft's as-yet-unreleased Windows 95 (formerly code-named Chicago) faced IBM's new operating system, OS/2 Warp, and a new Mac OS, both of which could run several tasks at once. Windows 95 was expected to take advantage of the Pentium's speed and to eliminate the need for DOS by incorporating an operating system with the graphic interface. Windows 95, however, would require earlier Windows programs to be rewritten in order to take advantage of its increased capabilities. While Microsoft originally announced its new system for early 1994, the company later delayed its debut.

In a major break with the past, Apple celebrated the 10th birthday of the Macintosh computer by announcing that it was licensing the Mac OS to other companies (mainly in Europe and Japan) and thus was making possible the first Macintosh clones ever. The move was a strategy by Apple's new president and CEO, Michael H. Spindler, to increase the demand for Macintosh software and thereby boost the variety of software available and the sale of all kinds of Mac-compatible computers. Some experts expected the move to boost Apple's market share in desktop computers from 10% to 30% in the next three years.

In June a U.S. judge ruled that Microsoft had infringed two patents on data-compression technology held by Stac Electronics, Inc. Microsoft appealed the ruling, which could affect millions of computers, as well as the $120 million judgment. A month later the U.S. Justice Department settled an 11-month antitrust investigation of Microsoft by imposing minimal conditions on the company. The conditions would end Microsoft's practice of requiring PC makers to pay for one copy of MS-DOS for each computer that was shipped regardless of whether it was actually installed in the PC. The department, though, took no action regarding competitors' claims that Microsoft kept to itself special features in MS-DOS and its best-selling Windows, allowing only its own programmers to exploit them. Nor did it require Microsoft to pay damages to competitors or even admit guilt. On Feb. 14, 1995, a federal judge rejected the agreement as too narrow because it failed to take into account competitors' complaints about these other practices and because it did not ensure that Microsoft would not institute similar practices in the future, notably in regard to the company's plans to incorporate access to a new on-line service directly into Windows 95. The Justice Department immediately appealed the judge's ruling.

—Douglas E. Comer,
Melinda C. Shepherd,
and Edward S. Warner

ELECTRONICS

Contrary to the predictions of many economic experts, the United States in 1994 outproduced both Germany and Japan in computer chips. Statistics show that from 1982 to 1987 Japan held a 14% share and Germany a 12% share of the chip market. The U.S. share was approximately 11%. By 1993, however, the market share of the United States had increased to almost 16%, while the Japanese and German shares had declined to 12% and 8%, respectively.

The Compaq Computer Corp. exemplified the changes in the relative position of the U.S. versus its nearest competitors. In 1990 that company was experiencing declining sales and profits. Since 1991, however, sales had tripled to the $10 billion level, while profits increased from $131 million to $432 million in just the first six months of 1994. Two reasons accounted for the company's success. First, it shifted its manufacturing strategy from large mainframe computers to the popular personal computers. Second, an effective reduction of production costs enabled the company to slash the price of its computers by an average of 30% during 1994. By the end of that year, Compaq occupied the position of the world's largest personal computer manufacturer.

Similar success stories were enjoyed by the Intel Corp. and the Electronid Corp. Over the last eight years, Intel turned a $203 million loss into a $2 billion profit. During 1994 the company became the largest producer of semiconductors. Electronid was awarded the overhaul and management of Inland Revenue, the British government's main tax-collection agency. This 10-year contract was valued at $1.5 billion. It was that company's ability to specialize in a particular field of high technology that led to the award of the lucrative contract.

Chips

It seemed in early 1995 that the world's semiconductor chip industry could look forward to a boost of its production during the coming year and continued growth for the remainder of the decade. The primary reason for this optimistic forecast was the economic recovery in Europe and the consequent growth of the electronic industry there. On that basis Jean-Philippe Dauvin of SGS-Thomson Microelectronics foresaw a jump of the semiconductor market from $50 billion to $100 billion by the end of 1995 and to $200 billion by the year 2000.

During November 1994 rumors of a flaw in Intel's Pentium™ chip began to circulate. Since that chip was the electronic brain for four million personal computers sold during that year, there was widespread concern about its alleged imperfection. This imperfection manifested itself in division problems involving many digits, which proved to be of special concern in cases where both a high degree of accuracy and a large repetition of calculations were required.

While IBM and Intel debated the nature and the seriousness of the problem, many customers who had either bought or planned to buy a Pentium-based computer system were angered by Intel's assertion that a mistake would happen once in about 27,000 years at most; on this basis Intel argued that there was no need for the company to replace the defective chip. What further irritated customers was that Intel had known of the flaw in the Pentium chip and yet had continued to market it. The company refused to replace the chip unless a consumer could prove that computational problems would be encountered because of the chip. Under continued pressure from customers, however, Intel eventually eased its hardline approach and agreed to replace the chip for those customers who requested it. The company then began to sell its corrected model.

European developments

For Europe the projected growth rate in the sale of personal computers was expected to remain in the double digits until at least 1998. Some sectors were expected to grow faster than others. Portable computers would replace the larger desktop units at an increasing rate, and high-powered PCs were replacing minicomputers as network servers.

France was considering postponing the creation of its information superhighway. A cost analysis showed that it might cost more than $100 billion over the next 20 years. The French government, which commissioned the study, was shocked by its findings and concluded that such expenditure could not be justified.

The Nokia Oy company of Helsinki, Fin., developed what it claimed to be the lightest and smallest digital handset anywhere in the world. It measured 148 × 56 × 25 mm (25.4 mm = 1 in). The set, named the Nokia 2000, could communicate data over two separate lines and was fully programmable. It used a liquid display and a set of cursor controls. Its keypad was designed for both alphabetic text and for telephone numbers. The set could send short messages to printers that would make hard copies, to digital phones, and to facsimile receivers. Its initial cost in the U.S. was expected to be $1,000.

The Deutsche Bundespost Telekom put the first segment of the Trans-Europe Line into operation. It was a 140 megabits-per-second fiber-optic cable communication system. The cable started at its westernmost terminus in Frankfurt, Germany, and proceeded to extend for 3,700 km (2,300 mi) to Warsaw. On the way there it branched off to Prague and Budapest. A southern cable, also starting at Frankfurt, connected Austria, Slovenia, and Croatia. Further expansion was planned to connect Lithuania, Belarus, Ukraine, Romania, Bulgaria, and Moldova. System links to Moscow and to Helsinki were also projected. Each network operator in the various countries constructed, operated, and owned its segment of the network. Frankfurt was thus positioned as the major telecommunications hub connecting Eastern and Western Europe. In December AT&T won a $1.2 billion contract to lay a cable extending from the U.K. to Japan.

The Italian computer market was showing signs of recovery after three years of sales declines. First-quarter sales during 1994 increased by 1.6% to 20.7 trillion lira ($12.8 billion) compared with the same period of the previous year. The firm IDC Italia reported a 4.7% increase in services and a 3.3% increase in software sales over 1993. Despite the upswing of the market, the relative smallness of that increase was blamed on the unwillingness of the major industrial firms and the government to invest in new computer equipment.

Developments in Asia and India

China planned to spend $52 billion on its telephone system between 1995 and 2000. This figure doubled the previous estimate by Western manufacturers. China expected to have 110 million lines installed by 2000. This would serve about 35% of city dwellers and about 5% of those living in rural areas. To support this expansion, China needed 22,500 km (14,000 mi) of optical cables and 16,-000 km (10,000 mi) of digital microwave lines.

Japan was experiencing a banner year for the sales of personal computers. Every major computer company during 1994 revised its projection for the sale of PCs upward to a growth rate between 30% and 40%. Fujitsu Ltd. expected to sell 420,000 workstations for 1994, a 35% increase over 1993. Seiko Epson Corp. doubled its sales forecast to 280,000 units for the year, a 40% increase over 1993. NEC Corp. revised its sales forecast from 1,520,000 to 1.8 million units, a 31% increase over the previous year.

As of 1995 India had seven million telephone lines, not even one per 1,000 people. The worldwide average was 10.5 lines per 1,000 people. That country in 1995 was beginning to relax the strict regulations governing its telecommunications industry. In the past India had refused to permit the use of any technology that did not meet its standards. The newly appointed head of Indian Telecom, Nagarajan Vittal, decided to stimulate foreign investment by liberalizing rules governing the operation of telephone networks. Consequently, the U.S. company U.S. West was allowed to start trials of a pilot project. The company planned to build its first network around the town of Tiripur in southern India. In its initial phase it would install 430,000 local lines. The company said that it was prepared to invest more than $90 million in the project. An eventual investment of $176 million was foreseen. The network would provide data services, cable television, and basic telephone services.

New technologies

The Philips Dictation Systems of Vienna exhibited its new speech-recognition software in September at San Francisco. It allowed voice control of PCs and speech-to-text applications. The software model, based on phonemes (distinctive sounds in a language), ran on Microsoft Windows. Speech-recognition users trained the system to recognize samples of their phonemes by speaking them into it. Each sample was then applied to the 30,000-word dictionary of the software. The system included a microphone with record, playback, rewind, and fast-forward controls. A prototype of this system was being used in Germany and Austria in medical applications.

If one did not like to talk to one's computer, maybe one could wink at it to send a message. Pete Olivieri, a computer scientist at Boston College, developed a system by which a human operator could control a computer with a mere glance. Electrodes attached to the skin around the eyes reacted to any muscle movement and in response produced tiny electrical signals that were detected, amplified, and interpreted by the system. It next decided at which place on the screen, filled with symbols such as letters and numbers, the user was looking. The system then positioned a cursor into that area to capture the symbol. A user could then glance sequentially at different letters of the al-

Naohiro Kimura—Time Magazine

A woman tests a Macintosh computer in a store in Japan. Sales of personal computers in that nation rose rapidly in 1994.

phabet to compose phrases just by looking at the screen. Such a system would be of enormous benefit to people who had lost the use of their hands and arms. A wearable, or even implanted, computer could soon follow.

Automotive applications

Delco Electronics Corp. designed a radar system to warn a driver of a potential danger when changing driving lanes. The technology was borrowed from the air-traffic-control system of the F-15 fighter jet. In a car equipped with the system, a transmitter mounted out of sight behind the front wheels sent out a continuous signal. Another car moving within 6 m (20 ft) of the first one would cause an echo that would be picked up by a receiver situated near the transmitter. If the receiver detected an echo, indicator lights on the sideview mirrors would be turned on. If the driver then activated the

car's directional signals, an audio alarm would sound. As of 1995 only some luxury cars were equipped with this feature. The price for such a system, should a mass market develop, would be about $100.

Lojack, an electronic system designed to recover stolen vehicles, was introduced during the year to New York City. A radio transceiver (transmitter-receiver) the size of a chalkboard eraser was installed in a hidden place in an owner's car. A five-letter code was paired with a vehicle-identification number at police computers. When a Lojack car was stolen, the owner notified the local police department, which then entered the vehicle-identification number into its computer. This started a broadcast system that sent out a radio signal to turn on the Lojack unit in the stolen car. A specially equipped police cruiser picked up the signal within a maximum area of 52 sq km (20 sq mi). An electronic compass pointed in the direction of the stolen vehicle, and a signal-strength meter revealed the distance between the stolen car and the police cruiser. The price of the system was about $600, and a monthly maintenance fee ranging from $8 to $15 was charged.

Solar energy and electronics

The conversion efficiency of solar energy to electricity was by 1995 approaching the 20% mark, about twice the previous conversion rate. This increased efficiency was achieved by means of devising better ways to capture the electrons liberated from the solar panel's silicon chips as they were torn loose from their atoms by the Sun's energy. Connectors to the solar panel were placed so that they did not cast a shadow on the panels themselves and thereby reduce the efficiency of the conversion process.

Such a system was built by Amonix Inc. During the year its engineers installed a 20-kw system, a power level sufficient to supply the needed electricity to a cluster of about 10 houses. Industry observers

Designed to recover stolen vehicles, Lojack is a radio transmitter-receiver (transceiver) that is installed in a hidden place in an owner's car. Its five-letter code is paired with a vehicle-identification number in police computers, and when a Lojack car is stolen, this system can be used to send a radio signal to turn on the Lojack unit in the car.

expected that the Amonix silicon chips could be produced cheaply by the same process that produced computer chips. Thus, once a mass market developed, solar energy production would become more economical. As of early 1995 the total installed solar capacity in the U.S. was about 20 MW. To put that figure into perspective, the daily power consumption in New York City in 1995 was about 8,000 MW.

New products

While investigating possible tampering of magnetic tapes, Ronald Indeck of Washington University, St. Louis, Mo., discovered that every magnetic tape had a unique magnetic "fingerprint." Such a tape was made up of many tiny bits of magnetic oxides that aligned themselves in a random pattern. This pattern remained largely intact even when information was recorded on the tape, thereby providing a means of identifying the tape. Indeck devised a simple process that could be used to authenticate any recorded tape by comparison of its magnetic fingerprint to that of the unrecorded tape. This was bad news for thieves who obtained a credit card number and then created a magnetic strip on a duplicate card. A card reader in a store equipped with magnetic fingerprinting technology would reject the counterfeit card.

A danger that police officers and owners of guns faced was the unauthorized use of their weapons. To counter this possibility, two companies designed handguns that could be used only by authorized persons. The Sandia National Laboratories developed a handgun that could be fired only by its owner. The de-

sign of this gun used sophisticated technologies, including some originally developed to safeguard nuclear weapons. The gun could communicate via radio signals, acoustic waves, lasers, and infrared or ultraviolet light with a tag worn by the gun owner. The Fulton Arms Co. developed a .357 revolver that would fire only when its custom-fitted handgrip came close to a magnetic ring worn by its owner. The gun was to go on sale shortly and would cost about $1,000. It was projected that such "smart guns" eventually would find their way into private homes, where they could effectively prevent accidental shootings.

For those parents who dreaded having to listen to yet another choppy rendition of "Chopsticks" by their not necessarily musically gifted offspring while having to maintain an encouraging demeanor,

A noiseless piano, developed by Yamaha Corp., can be played the same way as a standard instrument, but when a foot pedal is depressed, it loses its sound.

help was on the way. The Yamaha Corp. designed a noiseless piano. The piano had 88 keys just like the standard instrument, and it could be played the same way as a piano. When one depressed a footpedal, however, it lost its voice and noise. Instead of a hammer striking a set of strings, an optical sensor read the movement of the hammer and compared its movement with a digital library of such movements collected from the notes played on a concert grand piano. A transducer then converted the identified hammer movement into sound. The player, and a teacher, could then plug in headphones to listen. The price of the piano was $8,000.

—Franz J. Monssen

INFORMATION SYSTEMS AND SERVICES

U.S. Vice Pres. Al Gore, a leading proponent of the information superhighway, during the past year advocated a "network of networks," a global information infrastructure (GII) that would transmit messages and images at the speed of light across every continent. The GII, he stated, would promote democracy by enhancing the participation of citizens in decision making and would provide the information needed to improve the quality of life around the world. By linking clinics and hospitals, the GII would ensure that physicians had access to the best possible information on the diagnosis and treatment of diseases. Used as an early-warning device for natural disasters such as volcanic eruptions, floods, and earthquakes, the GII could save thousands of lives and help people work together to solve local and regional problems.

Information and communications networks require the use of multimedia technologies by means of which information in the form of text, images, and audio and video recordings could be processed, stored, retrieved, and disseminated. The development of such technologies promoted a new relationship between people and computers and influenced the way individuals organized workplaces, shared activities with colleagues in distant locations, and purchased goods and services. Just as television was widely influential during the last half of the 20th century, so the global information infrastructure with its multimedia capabilities would influence life in the 21st century.

U.S. information systems

The National Science Board, the policy-making body of the National Science Foundation, examined the role of the federal government in basic research and concluded, "Basic research is one of many forces that contribute to the nation's economic development. Its benefits will be achieved only in connection with other parts of the nation's scientific and technological enterprise, including applied research, education, technology transfer and development, innovation and manufacturing. . . . Providing requisite support for this process is a matter of strategic national importance."

The U.S. Department of Defense opened a computerized public-access information system called CPR (Cooperative Programs for Reinvestment) in order to provide information on government assistance programs to industries affected by cutbacks in defense spending. Firms were encouraged to use CPR,

available through the Internet, to identify government programs that assisted in developing new technologies, improving manufacturing processes, increasing exports, and enhancing employee skills.

The National Library of Medicine (NLM), the world's largest library of health sciences, eliminated all on-line charges for searching its three AIDS databases and an on-line directory of related information sources. The action resulted from recommendations by community organizations that made it clear that even moderate fees inhibited access to this needed information. As a result, the 75,000 members of the NLM international network could search AIDSLINE, a database with more than 90,000 AIDS-related journal articles, books, audiovisual materials, and conference abstracts, and other related databases without access charges.

Having recognized that electronic information had become the preferred medium for preserving and accessing library materials, the National Agricultural Library (NAL) made a commitment to becoming, according to Pamela Andre, its acting director, "truly a library without walls, where our magnificent collection can be accessed by computer by anyone, anywhere and at any time." To achieve that goal, the NAL embarked on a systematic program of managing electronic data and establishing strategies for collecting, storing, and distributing U.S. agricultural information in electronic form.

Project Gutenberg was established by Edward McGrath of Walnut Creek, Calif., to encourage the creation and distribution of English-language electronic texts, called "etexts," on CD-ROM. The project was to provide a collection of 10,000 of the world's most important books, transcribed in electronic form and recorded on CD-ROM, by the year 2001 and to make those works available to more than 100 million readers. As of 1995 the etexts available on CD-ROM included classical literature such as *Aesop's Fables, Alice in Wonderland, Moby Dick,* and *Paradise Lost;* historical documents such as the Declaration of Independence, the U.S. Constitution, and the Magna Carta, and many reference works, such as *Roget's Thesaurus,* almanacs, and census data.

Chemical Abstracts Service (CAS) recorded the 13 millionth chemical substance in its computer-based Chemical Registry. The substance, a polymer, was assigned CAS Registry Number 155827-99-9. The Registry system was developed to provide a means for determining whether a chemical substance reported in the scientific literature had been indexed previously in *Chemical Abstracts.* The Registry was begun in 1957, and more than 700,000 new substances were added to it each year.

Anthropological Literature, a database at Harvard University's Tozzer Library of more than 83,000 citations to journal articles and monographs, was published on CD-ROM by G.K. Hall & Co. It contained materials in many languages, with English translations of titles when necessary, and covered the whole spectrum of anthropology, including cultural and social anthropology, archaeology, folklore, linguistics, and much more. New literary entries and citations supplied through a conversion project at the Tozzer Library were added quarterly. Cited documents,

requested through interlibrary loan, could be obtained from the library.

The Encyclopedia of U.S. Postage Stamps, published by ZCI Publishing Co. on a CD-ROM, incorporated a narrated introduction to stamp collecting, more than 2,500 pictures of stamps, and stories about the stamps. For the advanced col-

Historic Vatican Apostolic Library manuscripts could soon be available to be called up onto computer screens via the Internet. More than 10,000 pages will be scanned into a database.

lector the disc included information on misprints, imperfections, and errors, plus alphabetical, chronological, and topical indexes.

InterActive Publishing Corp. recorded Beethoven's *Symphony No. 5* on CD-ROM. Included on the disc were the complete musical score of the symphony performed by the Zagreb (Croatia) Philharmonic Orchestra and recorded in

high-fidelity, 16-bit stereo sound. A click of the mouse provided in-depth commentary explaining the theme and meaning of each movement. Another click displayed a detailed biographical time line that brought to life the events and people that influenced Beethoven. The CD-ROM also contained three games that challenged players to name a tune, match a tune to a name, and answer trivia questions.

International information systems

Following the publication of the European Commission's White Paper *Growth, Competitiveness, Employment,* the Directorate-General XIII focused on three main activities: (1) telecommunications, networks, and postal services, including communication security; (2) research and development programs in the areas of advanced communications and telematics and the exploitation of these results; and (3) support for the establishment of a European single market for electronic information creation, storage, and retrieval. Each of these activities emphasized multimedia technologies and the creation of tools to manipulate, display, and store multimedia information.

The Federation of Information and Documentation (FID), based in The Hague, established a special interest group on archives and records management (FID/ARM). This group's task was to study actions, policies, and information about the incorporation of archives and records as part of an overall information-management strategy. In addition to monitoring relevant activities and resolutions of governments and organizations, FID/ARM was mandated to disseminate such information to the worldwide membership of FID and to provide a forum for the exchange of knowledge and expertise relating to archives and records management.

The Canadian Center for Occupational Health and Safety released an enhanced version of its *Safe Use of Chemicals* publication on CD-ROM. This multimedia training package used animation, audio, full-color graphics, quizzes, and checklists to increase user interaction and improve knowledge retention. The disc's contents focused on many of the common types of hazardous chemicals found in the workplace, such as corrosives, flammables, and toxic materials, and identified good practices for handling each type of chemical product.

English-language profiles of Japanese companies, made available on-line through Investext, offered easy access to Japanese business information that had previously been difficult to obtain. The initial Investext database consisted of approximately 3,000 Japanese company profiles and was expected to grow to almost 200,000. These records provided a current source of intelligence on both large and small, publicly listed and privately held, Japanese corporations. Each profile contained details about the company's chief executive officer, address, telephone number, number of employees, and shareholders. In addition, the reports contained vital financial data about income, sales, profits, and dividends, calculated in both yen and U.S. dollars.

EPAT (European Patents), produced by the French National Patent Office, increased its updating schedule and enlarged its coverage by adding abstracts

of new patents to the previously provided standard bibliographical information—patent name, application number, assignee, and inventor. These additions and improvements provided users with better retrieval and faster access to the contents of European Patents.

A multimedia CD-ROM edition of the *Viking Opera Guide* was introduced by ATTICA Cybernetics and Penguin Books. The guide contained the full text of the book together with more than four hours of music extracted from some of the finest operatic works and provided different ways of accessing the information through voice and location maps. Other features on the multimedia disc were a 12-minute audio introduction by Nicholas Kenyon, head of BBC Radio 3; a 1,200-word pronunciation guide for composers' names, opera titles, and technical terms; and a chart showing composers and operas associated with different geographic areas and a time line displaying a composer's life span and operatic works.

Research and development

Drexel University's College of Information Studies, Philadelphia, received a three-year $750,000 grant from the Alfred P. Sloan Foundation to study whether college students learn better and faster when their courses are taught over a computer network. The project marked the first time that a combination of mainstream technologies had been used in teaching information systems and software engineering courses. Richard Lytle, the dean of the college, stated, "This project will help us better understand how to teach using today's powerful hardware and software, and how the learning

process is affected by having students and teachers interact over a computer network."

An agreement was signed between IVI Publishing Co. and Glencoe, a division of Macmillan/McGraw-Hill School Publishing Co., to develop a series of health-related education titles in an interactive CD-ROM format. The first title, *Mayo Clinic: The Total Heart,* provided a comprehensive look at the heart, using text, 48 animation and video sequences, 145 illustrations, and 60 minutes of audio. The animations illustrated three different techniques that could be used for angioplasty, while the video clip showed an echocardiogram, how the heart works, and what happens when it does not. The disc also contained information on ways to keep the heart healthy and explained the risks of a sedentary lifestyle and the pros and cons of taking aspirin and of drinking alcohol.

The Washington Department of Wildlife contracted with WLN Multimedia Services to create and catalog a multimedia CD-ROM database of 350 scanned images of documents about various aspects of Washington's wildlife species plus over 50,000 bibliographic citations and some 1,400 pages of text, maps, photographs, and charts. The specially designed search software allowed for keyword, browse, and exact-word searches of author names, titles, and subjects and provided potential users throughout the Pacific Northwest with convenient access to the material.

The state of Illinois, the Abraham Lincoln Association, and a group of history scholars undertook a project, called Lincoln Legal Papers, to locate every document involved in Lincoln's legal career. The project required a file-by-file search of practically all of the Illinois county courthouses plus the records in thousands of major research libraries and manuscript collections throughout the country. Persistent research and hard work uncovered more than 71,000 documents relating to the 5,000 cases Lincoln personally handled during his career. Included were 143 priceless documents handwritten by Lincoln himself. On completion of the collection, Illinois awarded the Media Conversion Corp. with a contract to index the Lincoln Legal Papers and to transfer them to CD-ROM so that they could be replicated and made available to libraries and Lincoln experts throughout the world.

—Harold Borko

SATELLITE SYSTEMS

Earth applications satellites consist of three broad classes: communications, Earth observation, and navigation. These automated civil and military spacecraft are built and operated by nations, groups of nations, and commercial firms.

Communications satellites

This largest class of commercial satellites continued to grow in number, complexity, and performance during the year. By early 1995 virtually every country in the world relied on such satellites for domestic, regional, and global links and for defense communications, direct-broadcast services, and mobile communications.

The International Telecommunications Satellite Organization (Intelsat), the major provider of global transoceanic telephone and television services, operated 22 satellites positioned in Clarke (geosyn-

chronous) orbits. (In a geosynchronous, or geostationary, orbit at an altitude of approximately 35,900 km [22,300 mi], a satellite travels west to east at the same speed as the Earth's peripheral velocity of rotation and remains fixed in a given spot above the Equator.) During the year

Intelsat operated two of its new small but high-powered Intelsat VII satellites and leased several transponders to television organizations for regional direct-broadcast satellite (DBS) service.

Both Intelsat and the International Maritime Satellite Organization (In-

The Intelsat VII, a small but powerful communications satellite, is used to provide transoceanic telephone and television service.

marsat), composed of agencies from 134 and 75 member countries, respectively, evaluated arrangements that would convert them to privately held stock companies. Inmarsat, in particular, moved to create a commercial structure for its new 12-satellite land mobile system, featuring handheld transceivers. (A land mobile system consists of base and mobile communications stations operating within the geographic limits of a country or a continent.) An investment of $2.6 billion was sought to finance this new activity, called Project 21 P. Immediate privatization of the project was judged necessary because of objections by many nations that Inmarsat's regular maritime and aeronautical services could improperly subsidize the new land mobile system.

The U.S. Federal Communications Commission (FCC) licensed the Orbital Sciences Corp.'s low-altitude Earth-orbit communications messaging system, known as ORBCOM, to launch 48 satellites. A first launch of this system was scheduled for early 1995. First launches also were scheduled in 1995 for the American Mobile Satellite Corp.'s geosynchronous satellite system and a parallel system for Canadian services, the Telesat Mobile Incorporated (TMI) network.

Other low- and medium-altitude Earth-orbit satellite communications systems also moved ahead during the year. In particular, the FCC awarded a 5-MHz allocation to the 66-satellite Motorola Iridium system and an 11-MHz allocation to the remaining proposed voice- and data-based systems, namely Aries, Odyssey, Globalstar, and Ellipso.

Perhaps the most important event in the U.S. during the past year involved

RCA

The RCA Digital Satellite System, a direct broadcast satellite service, provides access to more than 150 television channels for consumers in the continental U.S.

the full deployment and marketing of DBS services. The Primestar system provided services via leased capacity on GE American Communications Inc. satellites employing Earth terminal receiver dishes one meter (39.3 in) in diameter. The Hughes DirecTV satellite system used digital compression technology to provide 150 television channels to 46-cm (18-in)-diameter receiver dishes. The Hubbard United States Satellite Broadcasting (USSB) system also provided DBS service by leasing capacity on the Hughes DBS satellites. Sales of satellite communications ground hardware, especially very small-aperture terminals (VSATs), soared during 1994. Some 500,000 VSAT units were sold in the U.S. alone.

The FCC authorized GE American Communications Inc. to purchase the GTE Spacenet Satellite System, which, after the merger, brought to GE an operating network of 15 satellites. The AT&T Telstar 402 satellite, launched in September 1994 as an intended replacement for Telstar 302, ceased operating soon after reaching orbit. NASA continued an active experimental program with the Advanced Communications Technology Satellite (ACTS), which tested mobile Earth terminals, broadband video, switched networking, and onboard data processing.

In Asia EchoStar obtained U.S. permission to transfer to China two of its DBS satellites being built by Martin Marietta Corp. Under the approved export license these satellites could be launched in 1995 and 1996 to provide domestic services for that country. Japan launched its Experimental Test Satellite (ETS-6) on August 28 to test millimeter-wave operation (wavelengths between one millimeter and one centimeter) and onboard optical communications and data processing. A launcher malfunction placed the satellite in a medium-altitude elliptical orbit instead of the intended Clarke geosynchronous orbit. The unplanned orbit would, however, permit some experimental communications tests.

Earth-observation satellites

This category includes meteorological (weather), Earth-survey, and military early-warning surveillance and reconnaissance satellites.

Weather satellites. Continuous global weather observations were obtained during the past year from U.S., European,

Russian, and Japanese weather satellites in Clarke geosynchronous orbits and from U.S., Russian, and Chinese satellites stationed in lower-altitude polar or near-polar Earth orbits. Images and other meteorological data transmitted by these satellites greatly benefit such economic sectors as energy, construction, agriculture, fishing, and the transport and service industries.

Europe's Meteosat weather satellite system (Eumetsat) maintained complete weather coverage over the continent with three operational Meteosats positioned in Clarke orbits as Europe's contribution to the World Meteorological Organization's (WMO's) World Weather Watch Global Observation System. (Other participants were the U.S., Russia, and Japan.) Russia's long-awaited addition to this system, the 2,500-kg (5,500-lb) Elektro weather satellite, launched on October 31 into a Clarke orbit, was positioned over the Indian Ocean at longitude 76° E. Elektro began providing much-needed meteorological imaging of this region, which previously had represented a major gap in global coverage. The five-satellite worldwide system was thus completed, with a European Meteosat at longitude 0°, one U.S. Geostationary Operational Environmental Satellite (GOES) spacecraft at 75° W and another at 135° W, a Japanese Geostationary Meteorological Satellite at 140° E, and Elektro at 76° E. These satellites had a direct broadcast capability and allowed international users to access the data directly.

The U.S. National Oceanic and Atmospheric Administration (NOAA) operated its two GOES in Clarke orbits above North America and at least two operational weather satellites in low-altitude polar orbits. GOES 8, the first of four new NOAA geosynchronous satellites with improved cameras and more sophisticated scientific instruments, was launched on April 13, 1994, replacing a Meteosat previously leased from Eumetsat.

During the year the U.S. acted to consolidate all of its low-altitude polar-orbiting military meteorological satellites with their NOAA civil counterparts and with satellites of NASA's Earth Observing System into a single Earth-observing constellation. After the launch of weather satellites already under construction, the new consolidated Earth-survey system would begin operations in 2005.

Earth-survey satellites. This class of remote-sensing spacecraft, normally placed in low-altitude polar orbits around the Earth, observe the Earth and transmit images in various spectral bands. Among other applications they provide information on changes in the physical, chemical, and biological processes in the Earth's ecosystem and the influence of human activity on those systems. Increasingly, to save costs, their instruments were being combined with those of the low-altitude polar orbiting meteorological satellites.

The Franco-American (CNES-NASA) TOPEX/Poseidon oceanographic polar-orbiting satellite continued its ocean-mapping mission and assay of activity in the seas. This effort had proved valuable for understanding the circulation of currents and heat transport (the process by which heat is carried past a fixed point) in the oceans. It was scheduled to conclude in 1995 unless NASA approved a two-year extension.

Other Earth-observing satellites equipped with imaging scanners, such as the French SPOT (Satellite Pour l'Observation de la Terre) and U.S. Landsat vehicles, furnished imagery of significant commercial value during the year. European authorities continued operating SPOT 2 and SPOT 3 spacecraft, with SPOT 1 held in reserve. U.S. authorities successfully tested an Earth-monitoring Synthetic Aperture Radar in flight on board the space shuttle *Endeavour.* Meanwhile, the European Space Agency (ESA), to save costs, canceled funds to operate its radar-equipped Earth-observing satellite, ERS-1, and instead planned to rely on its twin, ERS-2, scheduled for launch in early 1995. Almost 10% of ESA's budget was committed to the fabrication and launch of its Artemis telecommunications-data-relay satellite, which would be placed in a Clarke orbit to process, store, and route the immense amounts of data generated by Europe's low-altitude civil and military satellites when they were beyond the line of sight of ground stations.

Elsewhere, the Indian Space Research Organization (ISRO) launched a second remote-sensing satellite, IRS-P2, into polar orbit in the first successful flight of its four-stage Polar Satellite Launch Vehicle (PSLV) from the Sriharikota Launch Center. (A first PSLV launch of IRS-1E failed in 1993.) IRS-P2 imagery would be marketed by India's National Remote Sensing Agency and would be under license by the U.S. Earth Observation Satellite Corp. (EOSAT).

Military reconnaissance/surveillance satellites. Reconnaissance satellites provide high-quality optical and radar images of the Earth and monitor electronic emissions of terrestrial and airborne communications and radar systems. Early-warning surveillance satellites equipped with infrared sensors detect missiles within moments of their launch from land or sea, while other sensors record nuclear explosions above ground or in space. In a peacekeeping role, these U.S. and Russian spacecraft monitor compliance with international treaties and furnish warning of imminent hostilities. Reconnaissance/surveillance spacecraft normally operate around the Earth in low-altitude polar orbits, highly elliptical Molniya (Northern Hemisphere-loitering) orbits, and Clarke geosynchronous orbits.

Both Russia and the U.S. continued to operate all forms of instrumented reconnaissance and surveillance satellites. With the end of the Cold War, however, these programs were reduced in size and scope. Western European governments, on the other hand, expanded their efforts to develop and acquire information by using reconnaissance satellites. In keeping with the 1993 Western European Union (WEU) reconnaissance satellite agreement, France completed its first Helios 2.5-metric ton optical imaging satellite and planned to launch it, along with a 50-kg (110-lb) Cerise experimental satellite to detect electronic emissions, in 1995. Helios 2 was scheduled for launch in 1996. The WEU also explored with Russian officials the possibility of purchasing Russian spy-satellite images.

In Asia the Japanese Defense Agency began to consider including reconnaissance satellites in its National Defense Outline, despite a national policy against using space for military purposes. Japan's National Space Development Agency al-

ready had launched 24 satellites, including the JERS 1 Earth-observing radar satellite, which had an imaging resolution sufficient for military reconnaissance.

In the U.S., after prolonged debate, plans moved ahead to replace the current constellation of four missile-detection and early-warning satellites in Clarke orbits, known as the Defense Support Program, with an advanced "multilayer" satellite system called the space-based infrared (SBIR) early-warning system. It would consist of four satellites in Clarke orbits, two satellites in highly elliptical Molniya orbits, and, added later, several satellites in high-inclination low-altitude Earth orbits. Work on the SBIR was scheduled to begin in 1995.

Navigation satellites

Both the U.S. and Russia continued to operate navigation satellites in high-altitude Earth orbits. Signals from these military satellites permitted anyone with receivers on the Earth to determine their geographic position, altitude, and velocity with a high degree of accuracy. Near-identical twins, the U.S. Global Positioning System (GPS) and Russia's Global Navigation Satellite System (Glonass) both consisted of 24 satellites. Because of the enormous commercial benefit that signals from these vehicles provided to terrestrial surveying and air and surface transportation, numerous civil organizations utilized these military satellite systems.

Although signals from the GPS satellites were encrypted to prevent their accurate use by potential U.S. adversaries, commercial users demanded the more precise unencrypted signals. Therefore,

to avoid maritime and aeronautical accidents, the U.S. Coast Guard and Federal Aviation Administration (FAA) continued to rebroadcast differentially "corrected" GPS signals in selected areas. The rebroadcasting allowed users to determine their locations or to track vehicles to within a few meters of their actual positions by using a combination of signals from GPS satellites and local FM radio stations. During the year the FAA scrapped plans to expand its ground-based navigation system in favor of using GPS satellite technology. This decision opened an estimated $1 billion aviation market for GPS receiver manufacturers.

Other companies continued to test products that offered vehicle drivers the ability to navigate city streets and country highways by using navigation satellites. A new vehicle mobile navigation technology developed by the Sony Corp. began to be sold in the U.S. General Motors Corp. also began selling a satellite-aided navigation system called GuideStar in its Oldsmobile cars that featured digital maps and hotel and restaurant locations. Similar automobile-navigation systems using GPS satellites were on the market in Japan. Finally, the U.S. Army began field-testing a device that used encrypted GPS signals to improve the aim of field artillery. The device directed accurate fire within one mil in the artillery's range (one mil is an angular measurement equal to $1/6400$ of the circumference of a circle.) Current systems using laser range finders typically resulted in a pointing error of 5–10 mils.

—F.C. Durant III; R. Cargill Hall
See also Feature Article: SCIENCE AND THE INTERNET.

ENERGY

The past year brought few surprises in the energy industry. Certainly there were no developments even remotely as striking as the oil crises of the 1970s, which inspired major, rapid shifts not only in the world oil markets but in other energy sectors as well. Nor were there major accidents that would inspire a rethinking of current technologies, as did the nuclear power plant accidents at Chernobyl in the Soviet Union in 1986 and at Three Mile Island in Pennsylvania in 1979.

Nonetheless, though there were no outstanding developments, a broad array of changes were occurring in the energy industry, largely as continuations of trends of the past several years. These trends included continuing advances in a wide range of energy technologies, from advanced nuclear power plants to automobile-propulsion systems to natural-gas-exploration methods. Perhaps as important in determining the long-term outlook for energy, the year brought continued attention to energy-related institutional efforts such as restructuring the electric power industry and addressing the environmental effects of energy production and use.

Energy and the environment

As with many industrial activities, energy production and use can cause major environmental impacts. During the past year a number of environmental issues continued to draw intense attention in the energy industry. Although many of these concerns, such as the effects of oil spills or the need to dispose of radioactive waste from nuclear power plants, are local or regional in scope, they are found in many parts of the world.

One environmental concern that transcends national boundaries and has broad implications for all aspects of energy supply and use is global climate change. At the Earth Summit in Rio de Janeiro in June 1992, most of the world's nations agreed to try to limit emissions of carbon dioxide (CO_2)—produced by the combustion of fossil fuels and considered the major contributor to potential climate change—to the levels of 1990 by the year 2000. Many nations during the past year continued to grapple with how best to meet that goal and, in addition, looked beyond to the next steps. U.S. efforts were focused on implementing the "climate change action plan" announced in 1993 by Pres. Bill Clinton. That plan included a variety of initiatives spurring private-sector adoption of energy-efficient technologies, encouraging the use of natural gas (a fuel that emits less carbon dioxide per unit of energy than either oil or coal), assisting electric utilities in developing methods to reduce emissions of greenhouse gases (those that contribute to global warming), accelerating commercial deployment of renewable energy sources, and reducing emissions of natural gas (the second most significant greenhouse gas, after carbon dioxide) from distribution systems and coal mines. However, reflecting concern about the rapid increase in spending that would be necessary, coupled with the already large national budget deficits, the U.S. Congress provided only partial funding for the plan. Options for controlling CO_2 emissions in other countries ranged from improving energy efficiency to accelerating the development of nuclear power, and several nations considered (but did not adopt) taxes on carbon emissions. Overall, progress was slow, and in many countries there was a growing concern that the year 2000 goal may not be met.

Electric power

Worldwide consumption of electricity, with its ease of use and versatility, has grown rapidly during the past decade. Consumption in North America and Western Europe, although both were already heavily electrified, increased by about one-third between 1982 and 1991. Consumption grew even more rapidly in the less developed countries during this same period. For example, consumption nearly doubled in India and China and grew by about 50% in Central and South America and Africa.

As the pace of electricity development continued, fossil fuels, led by coal, remained the dominant power-plant sources. For example, in the U.S. coal accounted for about 55% of electric power generation, with natural gas and petroleum supplying another 12%. Worldwide, fossil fuels accounted for more than 60% of electric power generation. Nearly all the remaining electric power was generated by hydroelectric or nuclear means. The dominance of coal, nuclear, hydroelectric, oil, and natural gas was expected to continue for many years.

Research, development, and commercialization continued on a broad range of electricity technologies during the year. While there were a number of interesting and useful developments holding both near- and long-term promise, there were no unanticipated breakthroughs in basic research or demonstrations of new

377

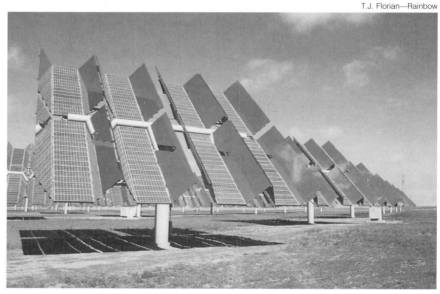

In an application of photovoltaic technology, rows of rectangular dark panels on white metal posts are tilted toward the Sun to collect solar energy.

technologies likely to revolutionize the energy industry. There was, rather, continuing progress leading to cleaner, more efficient production. At the same time, work continued on developing new technologies for generating electricity, such as nuclear fusion, that ultimately could revolutionize energy industries in terms of virtually unlimited resource availability and potentially limited environmental degradation.

The nuclear industry continued preparing new designs for a next generation of light-water reactors in the U.S. despite a two-decade gap in orders for new nuclear power plants and the cancellation in 1994 of two of the last three nuclear power plants remaining under construction. The U.S. Nuclear Regulatory Commission (NRC) in 1994 approved the design of the first of a new generation of advanced nuclear reactors created by the General Electric Co. Other reactor designs were awaiting NRC certification. The new nuclear plants were expected to make use of a variety of technical advances, including digital control systems and simpler designs that require fewer pumps, valves, and motors than were currently used in U.S. nuclear power plants.

Nuclear power development outside the U.S. also had slowed greatly over the past decade, but some orders for new plants were announced in 1994, including one in Indonesia. These new plants generally incorporated many of the advanced features noted above. During the past year China opened one new nuclear power plant and announced plans to build 14 others within the next three decades. France, India, South Korea, and Japan continued large nuclear power

plant construction programs, with a total of more than 40 units under construction. Efforts to improve the safety and overall performance of troubled nuclear power plants in Central and Eastern Europe accelerated in 1994 with government and private-sector agreements to provide a range of Western technologies.

Gains in photovoltaics (PVs) technology and markets continued during the year. (Photovoltaics technology is based on the generation of voltage that occurs when radiant energy falls in the boundary between dissimilar substances, such as two different semiconductors.) Shipments of PV devices in the United States have increased steadily since the early 1980s, averaging 13% annual growth since 1988. Typically, these devices have been used for special-purpose applications (such as remote power needs) rather than as sources for utility systems. A record 15.6 MW of PVs were shipped in the U.S. in 1992, most of which were for export

markets, whereas installed generating capacity in the U.S. totaled about 700,000 MW. While special-purpose markets continued to grow, research was under way to lower the cost and improve the performance of PV devices; if successful, PVs could become economically competitive for supplying electricity on a large scale to utility systems. Among the developments in 1994, an international partnership cofunded by the U.S. Department of Energy (DOE) announced plans to build a $30 million manufacturing facility to produce PVs by using an extremely thin silicon alloy that could cut the cost of PV power by half. And researchers from the University of New South Wales, Sydney, Australia, announced a breakthrough in using lower-quality, less-expensive silicon that they anticipate could reduce PV costs by about 80%. One newly formed partnership between a major oil company subsidiary (Amoco Corp.'s Solarex) and a large gas-pipeline company (Enron

Corp.) announced plans to mass produce photovoltaic panels and during the next two years develop a large (100-MW) photovoltaic power plant in Nevada at the DOE's nuclear weapons test site.

As in past years several nations continued to devote substantial funds to researching the distant but potentially revolutionary prospect of generating power by nuclear fusion. In the U.S. alone federal funding of fusion research during the past decades has totaled billions of dollars, with more than $300 million added in 1994. Continued progress was made with a successful experiment at the Tokamak Fusion Test Reactor at the Princeton University Plasma Physics Laboratory that used a mixture of deuterium and tritium to fuel a brief fusion reaction producing more than 10 MW. The goal of commercial fusion power remained a few decades in the future at best, however, with many more scientific and technical challenges to be met. Among them were the fundamental challenges of creating a reaction energetic enough to be self-sustaining and to produce more energy than was consumed in starting it and, if that was accomplished, developing an economically attractive design for a commercial plant. Engineering design work continued on the proposed International Thermonuclear Experimental Reactor, proposed to be the first fusion device to demonstrate self-sustaining fusion reactions. Because of the high cost of fusion research, international collaboration involving the U.S., Japan, the European Union, and Russia was required for this reactor and was increasingly viewed as a necessity in the long-term effort to develop commercial fusion power.

Considerable progress continued to be made in improving the efficiency of electricity-consuming devices and appliances. These ranged from compact fluorescent lamps that were lighter, brighter, and less expensive than their earlier counterparts to integrated steelmaking processes that greatly reduced the need for coking coal. In 1994 the first "Golden Carrot" refrigerator was installed in the president's private kitchen in the White House. The Golden Carrot was a $30 million award established by a group of utilities for a refrigerator design that would use 25% less energy than mandated by U.S. energy-efficiency standards. Also, reflecting the diversity of more efficient technologies currently available for residential appliances, the DOE developed standards for products ranging from water heaters to air conditioners to ovens that it predicted could ultimately reduce those items' energy consumption by another 15%.

Perhaps the most dramatic developments in the electric power industry during the past few years were institutional rather than technical. In 1994 an ongoing shift in the ownership, planning, and development of electric power systems continued in many parts of the world. One aspect of the change was the continued growth of nonutility organizations that design, build, and/or operate power plants, eroding the traditional monopoly of electric utilities. In the U.S. the development of such competition was spurred by the Public Utility Regulatory Policies Act of 1978 and further boosted by the Comprehensive National Energy Policy Act of 1992. As the nonutility generation market grew, electric utilities increasingly became the purchasers of this competitively supplied power, which they then sold to retail consumers. Large industrial consumers increasingly sought direct access to nonutility supplies through utility transmission networks, however, and made some limited advances in this regard during the year. Long-term prospects for such "retail wheeling" received a substantial boost in 1994 when California announced plans to restructure the power industry. Some other states also began pursuing less extensive but ultimately quite significant retail wheeling programs.

Another structural change was occurring in many nations with government-owned utilities. Efforts to increase private-sector involvement in the electric power industry accelerated recently in many of these countries, beginning with the 1990 privatization of the state-owned Central Electricity Generating Board in the United Kingdom and continuing with the 1992 sale of Argentina's state-owned utility. Among the most significant decisions in 1994, an influential government panel in Japan recommended a series of sweeping changes. They included establishing a bidding system that required utilities to purchase power from others and providing transmission access to power producers wanting to sell electricity in other areas.

One environmental concern specific to the electric power industry that continued to draw great attention during the year was the disposal of radioactive wastes from nuclear power plants. Efforts to find suitable sites and develop facilities continued to proceed far more slowly than originally anticipated owing to a combination of political, economic, institutional, and technical challenges. For example, the DOE, which in the U.S. is to be responsible for the permanent disposal of commercial spent nuclear fuel beginning no later than 1998, planned to spend the next several years evaluating whether Yucca Mountain in Nevada is a suitable site for a permanent repository. If the evaluation is favorable, the DOE intends to construct the facility by 2010. However, many experts viewed the DOE's schedule as optimistic. Expressing concern with the pace of development, 20 states in 1994 filed a lawsuit against the DOE, demanding accelerated efforts to develop options for either temporary storage or ultimate disposal of nuclear waste.

Oil

Petroleum remained the leading commodity in international trade. During the year the flow of crude oil between nations averaged nearly 30 MBD (million barrels per day). World petroleum production in 1994 remained at about the same level as the all-time high of more than 60 MBD reached in the late 1970s. The relative stability in total world crude oil consumption masked substantial underlying regional changes, including a 10% decline among industrialized nations over the past 15 years and a drop in the former Soviet Union since 1989, which together countered the large increase in the less developed countries.

In contrast to the relative stability of total consumption, world oil prices had fluctuated greatly during the past two decades. Adjusted for inflation, 1994 prices, which by the year's end increased about 15% from 1993 levels, remained at about half of their 1990 levels and at only about one-third of the highs reached in the early 1980s.

While the amount of oil produced by OPEC increased slightly during the past decade, at about 26 MBD it remained well below the maximum production of more than 31 MBD in 1978. Despite the intensive exploration efforts throughout the world, OPEC nations continued to hold the great majority of the nearly one trillion barrels of world crude oil reserves, with Saudi Arabia alone accounting for over one-quarter of the total.

Until its dissolution in 1991, the Soviet Union had been the world's largest oil producer. Output declined sharply, however, from the highs of about 12 MBD in 1987 and 1988. By 1993 poor management of oil resources in the former Soviet Union, including lack of exploration, a shortage of spare parts, and a decline in the amount of drilling had reduced production to about 7 MBD. This collapse was accompanied by similar drops in consumption in the former Soviet Union and in Central and Eastern Europe. With the decline in oil production in the former Soviet Union came international efforts to revive the industry. For example, oil companies and industry suppliers continued to announce new plans to invest billions of dollars in oil production in the former Soviet Union during the next several years, both for new development and to help return to production some of the 35,000 idle wells.

Some major oil spills occurred during the year, the largest of which resulted from a ruptured pipeline in the Russian Arctic. In that spill, the second of two in the region during the year, an esti-mated 300 million liters (80 million gal, or nearly 2 million barrels) were released, roughly eight times the amount in the *Exxon Valdez* spill of 1989. The accident highlighted growing concerns that much of Russia's energy infrastructure did not meet international standards. And for the *Exxon Valdez* spill, in Alaska's Prince William Sound, a federal jury in 1994 ordered the Exxon Corp. to pay $5 billion in punitive damages.

Automotive transportation remained the leading use of oil, accounting for more than 40% of the total consumption in the U.S. Although automobile technology had improved greatly over the past decades, a race was on worldwide to boost dramatically the efficiency and environmental performance of cars. Between the early 1970s and the mid-1980s, the average fuel economy of new automobiles in the U.S. doubled from 14 to 28 mi per gal, as mandated by Federal Corporate Average Fuel Economy standards, and it had since remained constant. Longer-term efforts in the U.S. continued under the banner of a joint industry-government effort intended to promote a tripling of fuel efficiency during the next decade.

Natural gas

With its relative abundance, favorable emissions characteristics, and well-established technologies for production and delivery, natural gas remained a widely used fuel. Worldwide consumption had soared in the past two decades, from about 43 tcf (trillion cubic feet) in 1973 to about 75 tcf in 1992. As with oil, consumption totals masked dramatic shifts in regional production. For example, in the

U.S. fluctuating prices had had a strong impact on natural gas consumption since the 1970s. Owing to rapid price increases in the 1970s and early 1980s, consumption dropped from 22 tcf in 1972 to 16 tcf in 1986. Since 1984, however, inflation-adjusted prices at the wellhead had fallen to about half their peak, with a corresponding increase in demand to 20 tcf in 1993.

Natural gas reserves were primarily in the former Soviet Union, rather than in the Middle East, as was the case with petroleum. For example, Saudi Arabia held more than 25% of the world's oil reserves but less than 5% of natural gas reserves. In contrast, the former Soviet Union held about 6% of world oil reserves and about 40% of natural gas reserves. Another difference between oil and natural gas reserves was their relative magnitude, with natural gas far more abundant. For example, at current consumption rates world oil reserves represented about 16 years of consumption compared to 60 years for natural gas.

Despite the relative maturity of natural gas technologies, a variety of new developments held considerable promise for both consumption and supply. Among the most dramatic trends in recent years was an increase in estimated remaining resources as a result of better information and technology. For both oil and natural gas, changing economics, recovery technology, and exploration all could add to the estimated reserves. Technologies enabling more economic deeper wells, horizontal drilling, in-field development, and wells farther offshore continued to be developed; all of these could increase reserves. Exploration efficiency also continued to improve, aided by such improved analytic techniques as three-dimensional seismic evaluations. Technological advances were also increasing the efficiency of gas-consuming equipment such as furnaces, heat pumps, and advanced aeroderivative turbines for electric power system use.

—Robin K. Roy

ENVIRONMENT

During the past year many environmental scientists discussed a wide spectrum of policy matters. One of the most comprehensive discussions, by C.S. Holling at the University of Florida, focused on the key elements of five policy positions. The first position perceives economic and human population growth as exponential and upward indefinitely. There are no limits, because human ingenuity will always invent substitutes for resources that are becoming too expensive. The second position perceives collapse and decrease as inevitable following a period of expansion that excessively strains the world's limited resources. The third predicts growth of human population and economic activity to plateaus in about a half century; the policy challenge is to navigate a nonturbulent ascent to those plateaus. The fourth position is a view of nested cycles organized by fundamentally discontinuous events and processes. For example, some business-cycle economists are interested in "long waves" of economic fluctuations ranging in length from 7 to 60 years. The fifth view has gained increasing visibility during the past few years. It is evolutionary, focusing attention on the adaptive potential of complex systems. Strongly influenced by the concept of nonlinear equations, it has much

Two men on a raft work to clean up thick black oil on the Kolva River in the Russian Arctic, the result of a 300 million-liter spill caused by a ruptured pipeline.

Sovfoto/Eastfoto

to say about such issues as complexity and order and the value of focusing on the pattern created by data sets rather than on the minute details of the data themselves.

These five positions have profound implications for public policy in all fields. Some of these views must be wrong, however, because they are based on assumptions incompatible with assumptions underlying the other views.

The object of the most discussion during the year was the third position. This view is politically attractive, because it basically argues that humankind can have its cake and eat it too (a sustainable environment and economic growth). The problems of Third World countries, according to this position, are problems not of overpopulation but of poverty. The way to overcome all environmental, so-

cial, and economic problems is for the less developed countries to use economic growth to escape from poverty. With the arrival of affluence, the population will be less likely to degrade its environment, as when the very poor of tropical countries destroy forests and other vegetation for fuel and for food for goats and cattle. Much of the most interesting research reported during the year was concerned with detailed analyses to determine if this simultaneous attainment of a viable, safe environment and considerable growth was possible.

The fifth position was being promulgated by the Santa Fe (N.M.) Institute, particularly by one of its most visible members, the Nobel Prize-winning physicist Murray Gell-Mann. His ideas on these themes were made accessible to the public during the year in *The Quark and*

The Jaguar. This book contains a number of powerful ideas concerning the predicament of humankind. Gell-Mann regards the appearance of great complexity in the real world as an illusion. He believes, instead, that complex phenomena can be understood in terms of a small number of powerful general principles that create the impression of complexity because they operate at all times and places and at all levels of organization, from atoms to societies.

Gell-Mann sees many types of systems as being "complex adaptive systems," which compete with other, similar systems (as when nations compete) by trying to do the best possible job of constructing a "scheme," or mental model, that accurately reflects the forces producing the stream of data impinging on people's conscious minds. The data stream, in turn, has components that are causally determined but are also random. The trick in formulating a realistic and winning schema is to avoid the confusion that results from trying to make sense out of the genuinely random components. The solution to that problem, Gell-Mann concludes, is to focus on data at the right level of aggregation, or scale.

This point about viewing environmental problems at the appropriate scale of space and time was made repeatedly during the year. Indeed, the most recent symposium volume of the British Ecological Society was devoted to the issue of spatial scale. Gell-Mann's ideas about the potential of fundamental, generalizable principles for simplifying the complex appearance of phenomena was supported by analytic work on environmental phenomena.

Marchers protest Proposition 187, a California law that prohibits illegal aliens from attending public schools and receiving public social services and nonemergency health care.

Michael Newman—Photo Edit

An Amtrak train departs from Seattle, Wash. Amtrak service was cut 21% during the past year.

Several of the major events and discoveries of the past year could be viewed from the perspectives of the five positions. Emigration from poor to rich countries, and particularly illegal immigration into the U.S., became a major issue in 1994. California voters approved Proposition 187, which forbids educational, social, and nonemergency medical health care to illegal immigrants. This was one of the most striking shows of political support by a large electorate for the second position mentioned above. The reasoning is that there is a limit to the amount of tax revenue available from U.S. citizens and legal immigrants to also pay the costs of illegal immigrants. Basic to this vote was the idea of inherent limitations on resources.

A little-noticed incident of great import for the future was the decision by the U.S. passenger rail company Amtrak to cut back 21% on service. This move, a reflection of the first position, was forced on the company by the U.S. government, which was providing inadequate support for rail relative to the subsidies to automobile and air transport. This is of great interest because it is a signal that the U.S. is going in a policy direction opposite to that of most other countries, which are committed to supporting rail use for passenger traffic. It also is astonishing given the U.S. crude oil position; according to the most recent government statistics, proven domestic reserves and domestic production are the lowest ever.

Quite apart from energy considerations, the lack of support for railroads in the U.S. is illogical; far more passengers can be moved down a transportation corridor per hour in fully loaded high-speed trains than in cars or minivans, 90% of which are occupied by one person. A commitment to cars and minivans overlooks the fact that space for transportation corridors in metropolitan areas is limited. Transportation systems other than rail saturate the available space at much lower traffic densities, which leads to long delays because of congestion and to high mortality and injury rates because of the small distances between vehicles.

Ecological economics

An interesting book published during the year by Faye Duchin and Glenn-Marie Lange of the Institute for Economic Analysis of New York University was *The Future of the Environment: Ecological Economics and Technological Change.* It is a model of how to do research to assess the realism of public policy proposals put forth in the political arena. The authors noted that the Brundtland Report—otherwise known as the report of the 1987 UN World Commission on Environment and Development, an important statement of the third position referred to above—defined "sustainable development" as humanity's ability to "ensure that it meets the needs of the present without compromising the ability of future generations to meet their own needs." The proposed means of achieving these twin goals was to "speed up world growth while respecting the environmental constraints." In an effort to assess whether that is possible, Duchin and Lange set out to model and track not only monetary measures of performance but also flows of energy and materials. Their model split the world into 16 geographic regions, each described in terms of about 50 interacting activity sectors, such as transportation, construction, paper, and electronics.

After completing their analyses, Duchin and Lange concluded that "it appears that the economic and environmental objectives of the Bruntland Report cannot simultaneously be achieved." The reason is that if the world economy grew enough to elevate the economic well-being of Third World inhabitants, the increased levels of carbon dioxide, sulfur oxides, and nitrogen oxides would rise to dangerously high levels. The data generated by their computer model projected that by 2020 in rich, developed economies, nitrogen oxide emissions would actually decline to about 90% of the 1980 level. In less developed countries, however, they would increase fivefold from 1980 to 2020.

Duchin and Lange suggested two routes out of this problem. One is to adopt bold technological and social changes. For example, they proposed that a large portion of the stock of private automobiles in developed countries be replaced by practical, convenient systems of public transport. The fact that the U.S. is currently headed in the opposite direction was noted above in connection with the Amtrak cutback. Heavy concentration on high-technology rail systems instead of cars for passenger transportation should probably be the appropriate path for evolution of transportation systems in Third World countries also. The other approach they suggested was large-scale, region-specific reliance on renewable sources for energy and materials.

Another innovative research program in ecological economics during the year was based on the notion of "the ecological footprint" of the human populations living in metropolitan regions. William Rees and Mathis Wackernagel of the School of Community and Regional Planning, University of British Columbia, devised an ingenious approach to computing the actual land requirements of people living in a city. They noted that for most types of material or energy consumption, a measurable area of land or water is required for providing the resources consumed in cities. For each of the various categories of requirements by urban inhabitants, they used government and other statistics to compute the totals needed per person per year. Then they added up all the categories of area requirements per person, multiplied them by the number of people in the city, and thus discovered how large this "ecological footprint" of the city is relative to the actual land area occupied by the city. To illustrate the results, the Vancouver, B.C., region appropriates from nature the ecological production of an area 22 times larger than the metropolitan area itself. For The Netherlands the corresponding factor is 14 times.

Extrapolation from such findings leads to revealing insights. If the entire world population of 5.6 billion used resources at the same rate as the inhabitants of greater Vancouver, the total area required would be 28.5 billion ha (1 ha = 2.47 ac). In fact, the total land area of the Earth is only 13 billion ha, of which only 8.8 billion is productive. The ultimate conclusion is similar to that of Duchin and Lange: "There may simply not be enough natural capital around to satisfy current development assumptions."

Another study that raised warning flags about global economic growth was by Edward Barbier of the University of York, England. His research demonstrated a linkage between economic and environmental problems for Third World countries. For most of those countries, the export of raw commodities makes an extremely large contribution to the total revenue from exports—frequently 85–99%. Thus, the long-run economic fate of those nations is critically dependent on the status of the resource base used to produce those commodities. Typically, a single commodity makes up more than 50% of export income.

Barbier also established a linkage between economic, environmental, and social problems. For example, in Malawi a large percentage of the poorest households are headed by women. These families are often unable to purchase fertilizer, to rotate crops, or to undertake soil conservation. Consequently, such households generally face declining soil fertility and lower crop yields, further deepening their poverty and increasing their dependence on the land.

Water in crisis

Another large study full of interesting insights was called "Water in Crisis." Developed by an international team based at the Pacific Institute for Studies in Development, Environment, and Security, Oakland, Calif., and at the Stockholm Environment Institute, it provides a revealing overview of the freshwater status of a nation or region. The researchers plotted graphs in which the horizontal axis is water availability per person in cubic meters per person per year and the vertical axis is water demand expressed in the same units. Of most interest are the regions where stress will materialize shortly. The graph exposes three large areas as impending trouble spots. One is the dry Middle Eastern and North African countries with rapidly growing populations: Egypt, The Sudan, Saudi Arabia, and many others. The two others

are in the U.S.: the basins of the Rio Grande and lower Colorado River.

One especially interesting aspect of this research was the difficulties looming for large metropolitan regions in Third World countries. For example, in 1982 Mexico City had to pump water from a distance of 100 km (60 mi) and from 1,000 m (3,300 ft) below the city. By the 1990s rapid population growth required the city to draw additional water from 200 km away and from wells 2,000 m deep. The costs of satisfying this increasing water demand are equal to roughly half of Mexico's annual interest payments on its external debt.

Conclusions

Progress has been made in understanding economic problems when more than monetary measures of variables are used. The full situation is exposed when statistics on human populations, energy and materials flows and storages, patterns of land use, and changes in all of these are also explored.

The findings of the year also bring to mind a Canadian experimental physicist, Ursula Franklin, who has won 13 honorary doctorates for her penetrating insights into science and technology. She explains that the findings of modern science and scholarship are as much a product of the methods used to arrive at the findings as they are a reflection of the real world. To quote Franklin, "One has to keep in mind how much the technology of doing something defines the activity itself, and, by doing so, precludes the emergence of other ways of doing 'it,' whatever 'it' might be. This has been so historically but it is even more so today,

because so many activities are technologically structured."

Our world view and the choices we make are largely determined by the ways we think about and measure things. We choose cars instead of high-speed rail for commuting because if we use only money measures, the initial capital cost of building an extensive high-speed rail network is overwhelming. However, if human time lost to congestion delays or the number of years of useful life lost to traffic accidents were factored in, we would arrive at a different answer.

Much recent research allows one to make a prognosis about the fate of the five policy positions mentioned at the outset. The first and third views appear correct only because they view the world largely in terms of monetary measures. Within that framework either indefinitely continuing growth or a great deal of further growth is possible because there is no inherent thermodynamic or other limit on the amount of money available. The money supply depends only on the willingness of people to take on debt and the willingness of central banking authorities to foster the creation of more money. However, by considering factors other than monetary cost, the second, fourth, and fifth positions each supply essential ingredients for a realistic view of the future for humankind that the other two positions lack. Therefore, a synthesis of these three appears to be the world view that should prevail.

—Kenneth E.F. Watt

Air pollution

Results of a study commissioned by the Swedish NGO Secretariat on Acid Rain identified 100 installations responsible for about 43% of Europe's sulfur dioxide emissions. Of the offenders, 95 were power plants, 11 of them in Britain. The biggest offender was the Maritsa plant in Bulgaria, which released 350,000 tons of sulfur dioxide a year. Three installations were metal smelters, two of them in the Russian Arctic; one was an oil refinery; and one was a blast furnace producing pig iron. European Union (EU) figures released in May showed that in 1993 unleaded gasoline accounted for nearly 90% of sales in Germany, more than 75% in The Netherlands and Denmark, 52.6% in the U.K., and 20.9% in Portugal. The EU average was 53.3%. Results of a study of Antarctic snow, published in May, showed that lead concentrations fell during the 1930s, declined overall between about 1920 and 1950, doubled by 1980 to six parts per billion, and declined again to five by 1986, probably because of the use of unleaded fuels in Brazil.

In March 1994, estimates by Joel Schwartz, an epidemiologist at the Environmental Protection Agency (EPA), suggested that microscopic particulate emissions called PM10s, the major source of which is vehicle emissions, could be causing up to 10,000 deaths a year in England and Wales. This idea found support at a meeting on urban air pollution and public health held in London in September, at which Jon Ayres of the Chest Research Institute at Birmingham (England) Heartlands Hospital reported that asthma attacks increased with rises in PM10 levels. Douglas Dockery of the Harvard School of Public Health said evidence that linked an increase of PM10s with a slight increase in deaths from heart attacks, respiratory illness, and asthma attacks was growing. He said these trends had been detected in 10 U.S. cities and in São Paulo, Brazil. Although PM10s were not known to be toxic, it was suspected that they might carry toxins on their surfaces into the lungs. Medical researchers also found a link with gaseous pollutants. Ayres reported that patients with mild asthma caused by an allergy to house-dust mites had more severe symptoms if they inhaled nitrogen dioxide, which acted as a potentiating agent that made the respiratory tract more sensitive to allergens. Jagdish Devalia of St. Bartholomew's Hospital, London, reported studies that found that nitrogen dioxide could inflame cells lining airways, preventing them from expelling allergens. Increased asthma was therefore linked to rising numbers of house mites, which thrive in centrally heated homes, and to rising emissions of nitrogen dioxide from vehicles and gas fires.

For four days in June, an experiment in traffic control brought a marked improvement in air quality to Heilbronn, Germany. Cars were prevented from entering the town unless they had been fitted with three-way catalytic converters, and trucks were barred unless they had the most efficient diesel engines. At the same time, a 60-km/h (37-mph) speed limit was imposed on the nearby autobahn. Traffic within the town was reduced by 40%, and use of public transport increased 50%. Urban concentrations of nitrogen oxides decreased by 40%, and in the town center benzene concentrations were halved. Results on the autobahn were inconclusive, although there was a reduction in traffic noise. In late July the state of Hessen introduced a 90-km/h (58-mph) speed limit on autobahns and an 80-km/h (50-mph) limit on other roads in an attempt to curb tropospheric ozone levels, which reached record levels during a long spell of hot weather in Central Europe.

In June the U.S. government announced that alcohol made by fermentation of corn (maize) had to be added to gasoline sold in several cities in an effort to reduce carbon monoxide emissions. The decision required that by 1996, 30% of the oxygen content in reformulated gasoline would have to come from renewable sources, mainly ethanol, which was made from corn. The remaining 70% would continue to come from methyl tertiary-butyl ether, made from methanol, which is derived from natural gas.

Marine pollution

On Nov. 12, 1993, the International Maritime Organization (IMO)—by a 37–0 vote with 5 abstentions (Belgium, the U.K., France, China, and Russia)—modified the London Dumping Convention by replacing the 10-year moratorium imposed in 1983 with a worldwide ban on the dumping of radioactive wastes at sea. Two weeks earlier Russian authorities had dumped 900 tons of radioactive cooling and cleaning water from submarine reactors into the Sea of Japan about 500 km (310 mi) from the Japanese coast. Following the outcry, Russia suspended plans to dump an additional 800 tons, and Japan abandoned its support for dumping radioactive waste. The IMO ban also covered the dumping of industrial waste and the incineration of industrial waste at sea.

A report by the North Sea Task Force, published in April 1994, said that pollution levels were falling in some parts of the sea but increasing in others, especially in inshore waters in the south. High cadmium and mercury levels were found in the kidneys and livers of seals and porpoises, cadmium in the livers of fish in the Dogger Bank, and lead on the coast of northeastern England and in the Dogger Bank and the Norwegian Trench. Nutrients carried by rivers were causing algal blooms on Dogger and off Norway and Sweden, killing stock in fish nursery areas.

Toxic wastes

On March 25, 1994, member countries of the Basel Convention on Hazardous Wastes—which had already prohibited dumping—agreed to ban from the end of 1997 all exports of toxic waste to less developed countries for recycling. In the U.S. on September 13, the EPA issued a draft of a report, to be finalized in September 1995, on the findings of a three-year review of the health effects of dioxins. The six-volume, 2,000-page report by more than 100 scientists affirmed a link between dioxins and cancer, a reduction in male sperm count, damage to fetuses and the immune system, and diminished IQ in children. The EPA concluded that there is no safe threshold for exposure. The main source of dioxins was found to be waste incinerators, which accounted for at least 95% of known emissions, and contaminated food and drink were the principal route by which humans encountered them. No immediate new controls were planned.

—Michael Allaby

FOOD AND AGRICULTURE

Agriculture, especially in the United States, was expected to be a major beneficiary of global trade accords and rebounding economies in the European Union and Asia. It was predicted that major advances in animal genome mapping and textile research would give agribusiness yet another boost. Consumers also were expected to benefit from these trade and research activities in the form of lower prices and increased food safety. The role of diet in the development of coronary heart disease was the subject of considerable research, with particular attention paid to the healthful qualities of fruits, vegetables, and whole grains.

AGRICULTURE

The release of the world's first "maps" of the genetic composition of cattle and swine, by U.S. Meat Animal Research Center (MARC) scientists at Clay Center, Neb., in April 1994, signaled a possible new era of rapid progress in farm animal breeding. Since that time MARC, by means of interactive databases, has communicated its findings with scientists throughout the world.

Maps of the cow and swine genome promise an acceleration of traditional breeding techniques in the short term and spectacular advances through gene manipulation in the future. Scientists expect to be able to develop animals resistant to disease, parasites, and foodborne pathogens and provide to consumers safer and higher-quality animal-based food products. As the cow and swine maps were being refined, MARC scientists expected to release genome maps of sheep in 1995.

To construct such maps, scientists must

At the U.S. Meat Animal Research Center in Nebraska, a technician reads animal DNA sequences. Knowledge of the genetic composition of livestock may result in an era of rapid progress in farm-animal breeding.

extract DNA from cells—often blood or semen—from a group of animals of specific and defined families. Then they use a process called polymerase chain reaction to amplify very small amounts of a genetic marker (a usually dominant gene that serves especially to identify genes linked with it) and a process called electrophoresis to separate it into its alleles (different forms). When they identified the alleles most closely associated with the inheritance of a particular trait, the researchers found that a gene or genes controlling the trait lie in or near the allele. Because marker patterns—allelic variations—are inherited, they are useful in identifying or selecting animals for breeding. Ultimately, identification of the locations of genes or groups of genes that regulate such characteristics as meat quality, reproductive efficiency, and disease resistance will allow efficient selection of animals possessing those traits.

Research in this area promises to increase milk production significantly while reducing the numbers of cows needed to produce that milk. The improved ability of cattle genetically engineered to digest forages is expected to reduce the amount of feed required for producing a pound of meat or quart of milk. Genetic manipulation allowing the control of sex and offspring should increase the efficiency of production.

Textiles

Scientists at the U.S. Department of Agriculture's Southern Regional Research Center in New Orleans, La., developed a new durable press treatment for cotton that does not contain formaldehyde. The center's scientists also developed treatments for cotton textiles that can fight disease-causing and odor-producing bacteria.

Currently, chemical agents used by the textile industry to impart permanent-press properties into cotton fabrics generally contain formaldehyde. Though there is no harm to consumers wearing fabrics containing formaldehyde, several federal regulatory agencies control exposure to it in the workplace because of its possible harmful effects to workers—it is especially irritating to mucous membranes. Butanetetracarboxylic acid (BTCA) has been identified as the most effective chemical replacement for formaldehyde in imparting permanent-press properties to cotton fabrics. Mixtures of BTCA

with citric acid have proved effective and economical.

Medical usage of cotton fabrics received a boost from research that uses compounds containing peroxides to impart bacteria-fighting properties to fabrics. The compounds' effects in fighting disease- and odor-causing bacteria last through laundering.

Food safety

One in 10 people in the U.S. develops a foodborne illness each year. An estimated 9,000 persons die from those illnesses, about 90% of which are caused by bacteria. At the same time, consumer concern about food safety is at an all-time high, and many have unrealistic expectations that fresh meat and poultry should be completely free of pathogens. This poses a special challenge for agricultural researchers.

Realizing that the quality of food cannot be improved after the food has been produced, scientists at the state agricultural experiment stations in the U.S. pioneered the development of effective critical control points in food production and processing. Included among them are devices developed by University of Georgia researchers that can detect *Escherichia coli* bacteria in food as much as 6–10 times faster than previous techniques. The new test involves an antibody

Chris Steel—Magnum

A genetically engineered giant cabbage is displayed in a greenhouse. Some genetically engineered foods are now available in grocery stores.

388

specific for 0157:H7, the lethal form of *E. coli.*

Ohio Agricultural Research and Development Center researchers determined that whey, a natural by-product of cheese production, is a natural preservative that could eventually eliminate risk from food-borne pathogens, including those that cause botulism poisoning. Whey is fermented with microbes that transform it into a natural food preservative.

The millions of lactic-acid bacteria found in yogurt and other dairy products produce bacteriocins that kill harmful bacteria in food. One, ricin, has been cleared for this purpose by the U.S. Food and Drug Administration, and university researchers have identified at least 50 more. Food scientists at Purdue University, West Lafayette, Ind., who found the bacteria *Listeria monocytogenes* in hot dogs said that soon manufacturers will add cultured whey or cultured milk to the hot-dog-production process in order to prevent growth of the bacteria. Iowa State University researchers developed a simple method of harvesting bacteriocins from their bacteria that will speed commercial use of bacteriocins.

Bacteria also are benefiting chicken. More than half of the poultry sold each year for consumption in the U.S. is contaminated by the *Campylobacter* pathogen. University of Georgia researchers identified beneficial bacteria that can be fed to chicks and reduce their carriage of the pathogen by 40–100%.

Food irradiation eliminates pathogens such as *E. coli* in ground beef without killing the food's taste, according to University of Georgia researchers. Irradiation does not harm food, but Louisiana State University scientists found that store managers are much less willing to stock irradiated food products than consumers are to buy them.

Other developments

In August a crop of genetically engineered wheat was harvested in the U.K. Created by the insertion into wheat cells of microscopic gold balls coated with DNA, the wheat contained genetic markers that were of no commercial significance but proved that the DNA can be passed predictably from one generation of plants to another. For example, some of the plants contained a red pigment gene taken from wild corn in Peru. When these plants were harvested, their grains had red spots, unlike any wheat previously grown.

Scientists from the International Rice Research Institute in the Philippines announced in October that they had developed a new variety of rice that they believed would increase harvests by 20–25%. After studying rice plants on computers, the researchers concluded that the best way to increase production is to direct most of the plant's energy to developing panicles (flower clusters) by reducing the energy devoted to producing tillers (stalks). One newly developed variety produced a panicle filled with almost 200 grains, double the usual amount.

—John Patrick Jordan; Patricia Brazeel Lewis

NUTRITION

As is usually the case, progress in nutrition during the past year underscored the need to move slowly and conservatively in making dietary recommendations to improve health. Also, as always, evidence was obtained that reinforced the time-honored recommendations of variety and moderation.

Extensive research supports the notion that consumption of fruits, vegetables, whole grains, and synthetic antioxidant vitamins (C, E, and beta-carotene) is effective in slowing the development of coronary heart disease by strengthening the resistance of low-density lipoprotein (LDL) to oxidation by active oxygen species. Such species cause chemical reactions that degrade first the antioxidants protecting LDL and then the polyunsaturated fatty acids and the cholesterol of LDL. The end result is the accumulation of degradation products of polyunsaturated fats and cholesterol—lipid-oxidation products—many of which are toxic to cells lining the inside layer of arteries (angiotoxicity). This cellular injury is likely the first step in atherosclerosis, the development of fatty deposits in the inner layer of the arteries.

Other detrimental changes in LDL are seen if lipid-oxidation products accumulate. Elevated plasma LDL is a risk factor for coronary heart disease, and this seems to be consistent with its important function of delivering cholesterol to cells; unfortunately, high plasma LDL levels, it was hypothesized, delivered too much cholesterol to certain cells of the blood vessel, causing them to become "foam" (fat-filled) cells, the hallmark of atherosclerosis and the main constituent of plaque. It was found, however, that LDL could produce foam cells only after it was modified by lipid oxidation. Scientists now hypothesize that enrichment of LDL and cells of the body with antioxidants strengthens LDL's resistance to oxidation and slows atherosclerosis.

Heated oils and coronary heart disease

Rancidity is one of the most difficult problems in foods, often causing the loss of valuable polyunsaturated fatty acids and vitamins and resulting in the development of unpleasant odors and flavors. Recently it has become possible to quantify the large number of fatty acid and cholesterol degradation products in rancid foods. It turns out that these are the same as are seen in oxidized LDL. This area of research thus raised the question as to whether the consumption of rancid foods is a risk factor for coronary heart disease.

Martin Grootveld and co-workers at London Hospital Medical College may have provided some answers to this question. Using a sensitive and sophisticated technique, high-field proton nuclear magnetic resonance spectroscopy, these researchers studied in detail the end products of heating of both polyunsaturated oils and saturate fats. Polyunsaturated cooking oils, such as corn oil, safflower oil, and sunflower oil, rapidly accumulated lipid-oxidation products, many of which had been shown to be toxic to cells. Many of them were the same as are formed in LDL during oxidation. Studies also demonstrated that the toxic compounds of oxidized oils are absorbed into the bloodstream and therefore could cause the damage to arterial cells that is the early stage of atherosclerosis. Given the widespread popularity of deep-fried foods cooked in such oils and the variations from country to country with regard

to government regulations covering the degree of degradation of the cooking oils (the U.S. has none, and some European countries are quite rigid), these issues are of great importance and deserve more attention and research.

One of the fascinating corollaries to the findings on lipid-oxidation products is that saturated fats such as butter, palm kernel oil, and coconut oil do have one indisputable advantage in the diet. They are much more stable than the polyunsaturates and thus are much less likely to break down to form toxic chemical products.

Fatty acids are not the only lipids that undergo oxidative degradation. Cholesterol, although more stable than polyunsaturated fatty acids, will exhibit chemical deterioration if stressed by heat or stored in a dehydrated food for a long period of time with inadequate antioxidant protection. Evidence that has accumulated during the past two decades indicates that many studies used to link cholesterol to coronary heart disease were flawed because the cholesterol that was fed to the research subjects was an impure mixture of cholesterol and cholesterol-oxidation products. Studies comparing the angiotoxicity of cholesterol with that of cholesterol-oxidation products consistently showed harmful effects of the latter but no such effects associated with purified cholesterol.

Health effects of *trans* fatty acids

Most oils used in the deep-frying process are hydrogenated. In this process hydrogen molecules are added to polyunsaturated fatty acids to convert a liquid oil to a semisolid form, producing mar-

garines and shortenings. These tend to be solid at room temperature, contain fewer polyunsaturates and more saturates than nonhydrogenated oils, and would appear to be a partial answer to the problem of the susceptibility of polyunsaturates to oxidation. In the hydrogenation process, which requires elevated temperatures and pressures, however, "unnatural" forms of unsaturated fatty acids are produced. These *trans* fatty acids are unusual in their shape compared with the natural form, the *cis* fatty acid. Long suspected of having harmful effects in biological systems, the *trans* fatty acids have been studied continuously since the early years of hydrogenation. Though there was much controversy, the evidence indicated that *trans* fatty acids were safe. The publication in 1993 by Walter C. Willet and co-workers at Harvard University in the British journal *The Lancet* of an epidemiological study of some 85,000 nurses caused reconsideration of the issue.

It must be recognized that such studies establish only a statistical relationship, not a cause-and-effect relationship, between two factors under study. In the Harvard study the consumption of *trans* fatty acids was divided into five levels (quintiles), and the risk of coronary heart disease was calculated for all five. Coronary heart disease was defined as nonfatal and fatal myocardial infarction (heart attack). The probability of disease in the highest quintile, the heaviest users of *trans* fatty acids, was 1.5 times that in the quintile with the lowest consumption of the acids. Such strong relationships are rarely found. Red meat consumption did not increase the risk of coronary heart disease in this study.

These results rekindled the debate about animal versus vegetable fats in the diet. The epidemiological data need laboratory and clinical evidence to support the hypothesis on *trans* fatty acids. In a paper published during the past year, Artemis P. Simopoulos observed that in developed countries the incidence of obesity, diabetes, and coronary heart disease has increased at the same time that consumption of saturated fats, *trans* fats, and linoleic acid has also increased and that of long-chain polyunsaturated fatty acids, especially from fish, has declined. (The main source of the increased intake of saturated fats in the U.S. has been the hydrogenated vegetable shortenings. Animal-fat consumption has been on the decline for decades.) As a result of this increase in consumption, muscle metabolism can be adversely affected because of alterations of fatty acids in the membrane (sheath or covering) of muscle cells. Insulin is necessary for movement of the sugar glucose into the muscle cell, and glucose is necessary for the normal metabolism of fat for energy. In the case of abnormal fatty acid content of the membrane, however, the action of insulin is interfered with and the normal metabolism of muscle is disrupted. This is called insulin resistance and is characterized by elevated levels of blood insulin because the body must produce more insulin to get the same level of glucose into the cell. These problems occur in genetically susceptible individuals, illustrating that both inheritance and environment may be factors in precipitation of a clinical case. Fatty acids alone are not the entire story. Increases in body weight, decreases in physical exercise, and increases in alcohol intake also can contribute to insulin resistance and, ultimately, to diabetes.

The controversial issue of *trans* fats in the diet will be vigorously debated and intensively studied for the foreseeable future. There are a number of uncertainties associated with the databases used in studying fatty acid intake, vitamin E intake, and other factors that might favorably or unfavorably affect the risk of coronary heart disease. It could be that in the study from Harvard the consumption of saturated fats and *trans* fats was high in those persons who consumed low levels of "protective foods," such as whole grains, fruits, vegetables, and antioxidants; sometimes it is difficult to obtain adequate information on food and nutrient consumption.

Variety and moderation

Given the foregoing discussion, how can the consumer develop a prudent approach to dietary fats? The following analysis of "Which spread should I use on my toast?" might help. Basically there are three choices: butter, a hard margarine, or a soft margarine—one made with less hydrogenation and low levels of *trans* fats but with higher levels of polyunsaturates. Butter is high in saturates and cholesterol, both disadvantages, but is stable and is not likely to contain lipid-oxidation products. In cooking, if not at high heat for a long time, butter is stable. Soft margarines have the advantages of being low in saturates and containing essential fatty acids but suffers from the stability standpoint. Long-term storage and any significantly extended heating could cause the formation of lipid-oxidation products. In between these two in stability is hard margarine, but this product has lost much of the essential fatty acids of the vegetable oil and contains larger amounts of *trans* fats than the soft margarine. It also has more saturates than oils or soft margarines but is less stable upon heating than butter.

Application of the time-honored nutritional principles of variety and moderation in this case would be simple, although the reasoning, as has been seen, is complex. One should choose all three but do so in moderation.

Other developments

A new Japanese production method called single-cell technology involves using an enzyme to break down vegetables and fruits into cell units in order to produce liquid and powder ingredients of foods and beverages. A Japanese company, Single Cell Foods, has begun using the technology, which has gained approval by the U.S. Food and Drug Administration.

By altering the structure of a natural enzyme used in cheese manufacture, two Japanese companies, NEC Corp. and Yakult Honsha, jointly developed an artificial enzyme potentially able to produce new types of food. Tetra Laval of Sweden launched Ovotherm, a system for processing and packaging liquid egg products that eliminates *Salmonella* and *Listeria* bacteria and reduces bacterial count to a level unattainable by other methods.

—Paul Bradley Addis

See also Feature Articles: DAYS OF WINE AND SCIENCE; THE GODDESS AND THE GREEN REVOLUTION.

LIFE SCIENCES

A new species of large mammal, a Cambrian Period monster thought to be capable of crushing an animal the size of a large cat, the isolation of DNA from bacteria found in extinct insects preserved in amber, the elucidation of mechanisms used by cells to repair damaged DNA, and the use of molecular genetics to manipulate specific plant genes were among the major discoveries and achievements of the past year in the life sciences.

BOTANY

The techniques of molecular genetics by means of which specific genes can be manipulated in several powerful ways (isolated, transferred from one plant to another, their structure determined, tested for function, etc.) are being widely applied in many of the plant sciences, especially those dealing with plant pathology, plant physiology, and agriculture. Hundreds, perhaps thousands, of papers reporting studies of this type were published during 1994, with some describing significant breakthroughs. Also of great concern are the problems that loom on the horizon as human activities continue to have a negative impact on the environment.

Molecular genetics

Although many species are used in genetic engineering, *Arabidopsis thaliana* (mouse-ear cress, in the mustard family, but commonly referred to by the genus name *Arabidopsis*) has been widely used because it is tiny and can be grown through a complete life cycle in about 30 days. Yeast has also been widely used in such studies. Much is now known about the genetic constitution of *Arabidopsis* and yeast.

Although other examples are presented below, the following illustrates some of the complexities as well as the possibilities of the techniques of genetic engineering. Alan M. Lloyd, Mark Schena, Virginia Walbot, and Ronald W. Davis of Stanford University worked with an *Arabidopsis* mutant that lacks epidermal hairs (trichomes) and pigments called anthocyanins. The gene that regulates the production of these features is apparently defective in this mutant. A similar gene in corn (maize) plants has a similar function, and when the corn regulatory gene is transferred into the *Arabidopsis* mutant, trichomes and anthocyanins appear. The researchers combined the gene from corn with a gene from rats that has a receptor site that responds to a steroid hormone and apparently occurs only in animals. (While steroids are known in plants, they are not known to act with receptors such as that on the rat gene—a glucocorticoid receptor.) When this created gene from corn and from rats (and two other essential parts as well) was inserted into the *Arabidopsis* mutant, it became possible to cause that mutant to produce both trichomes and anthocyanins by treating the plants with a suitable steroid at extremely low concentrations. The mutant without the inserted gene did not respond to the steroid. For many decades the most important unsolved mystery in biology has concerned development: why some cells develop only in certain ways at certain times and places even though all genes controlling all development are present in virtually all cells of any given organism. The Stanford researchers applied the steroid at different times during the development of the *Arabidopsis*

plants, turning on trichome and anthocyanin formation at will. They noted that after cells have achieved a certain level of maturity, they no longer respond to the steroid.

A productive area for the techniques of molecular genetics is the field of plant pathology. For many decades plant breeders have dealt with genes that were known to confer resistance to specific diseases upon otherwise susceptible crop plants. Indeed, breeding for disease resistance has been one of the most important tools used to increase agricultural yields and quality during this century. Plant breeders faced some formidable obstacles, however. Conferring resistance typically required a breeding program that lasted a decade. In the course of such work, breeders were able to locate the positions of many resistance genes on the chromosomes of the plants being studied, but they had no way of understanding what the genes were really doing.

By applying the techniques of molecular genetics during the past two years, researchers have isolated resistance genes that act against several pathogens, including fungi, viruses, and bacteria. The sequences of nucleotides in these genes (which consist of DNA) have been determined, and from these the sequences of amino acids in the proteins controlled by the genes can be deduced. This is a much greater achievement than researchers just a few years ago thought would be possible. During the past year, for example, Brian Staskawicz of the University of California, Berkeley, and his colleagues described a gene from *Arabidopsis* that confers resistance to a bacterial pathogen. Fred Ausubel and his colleagues at Har-

Photos, Visuals Unlimited; (top) K.G. Murti

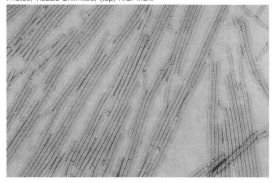

The tobacco mosaic virus (above left) causes elevated dark green blotches on the leaves of tobacco plants (left). During the past year researchers discovered a gene that defends against the virus.

vard University described the same gene. Barbara Baker and her colleagues at the University of California, Berkeley, along with colleagues at the U.S. Department of Agriculture Plant Gene Expression Center, Albany, Calif., were the first to characterize a plant gene that defends against tobacco mosaic virus. Jonathan Jones and colleagues at the Sainsbury Laboratory, Norwich, England, described a gene from tomato that confers resistance to infection by varieties of the fungus *Cladosporium fulvum*.

These three genes—even though they confer resistance to different bacterial, viral, and fungal pathogens—have common sequence patterns. This was a surprise because the relationship between a pathogen and its host is typically highly specific. The possibility of underlying mechanisms common to many plants and acting against different pathogens in ways that are not yet understood is an exciting one.

Photosynthesis

Techniques of molecular biology have been applied to aid in the understanding of the import machinery of chloroplasts,

the green bodies in plant cells that carry out photosynthesis. Many of the photosynthetic proteins in chloroplasts are actually synthesized in the cytosol (the liquid in which chloroplasts and other cellular organelles are suspended). Protein molecules are large compared with the many small solute molecules that cross membranes, and the chloroplasts are enclosed in a double membrane system that controls passage of substances in and out of these green bodies. Thus, some kind of special molecular machinery is required for moving specific proteins from the cytosol into the chloroplasts.

Danny J. Schnell and Hitesh A. Patel at Rutgers University, New Brunswick, N.J., and Felix Kessler and Günter Blobel at Rockefeller University, New York City, identified components of the chloroplast protein import machinery. Based on the sequence of amino acids that constitute the proteins, they suggested that channels can be opened in the chloroplast membranes that would allow the cytosol proteins to move into the chloroplast by a kind of ratchet mechanism, permitting movement in only one direction. Stephan Hirsch, Eva Muckel, Frank Heemeyer,

and Jürgen Soll at the University of Kiel, Germany, and Gunnar von Heijne at the Karolinska Institute Center for Structural Biochemistry, Huddinge, Sweden, also studied the movement of cytosol proteins into chloroplasts. Their results indicate that there are different pathways for different proteins moving into the chloroplasts.

The different groups of photosynthesizing plants contain different pigments that absorb light. Red algae, for example, have chlorophyll *a* and other pigments called phycobiliproteins, and the cyanobacteria (blue-green algae) also have phycobiliproteins. Green algae and higher plants, however, have chlorophylls *a* and *b* plus carotenoids but no phycobiliproteins. Diatoms and brown algae have chlorophylls *a* and *c* plus fucoxanthin. Because of the different pigments, it was suggested that these different groups of algae had separate origins; that is, that photosynthesis originated independently more than once. However, Greg R. Wolfe, Francis X. Cunningham, and Elisabeth Gantt at the University of Maryland and Dion Durnford and Beverly R. Green at the University of British Columbia demonstrated, again by using techniques of molecular biology (in this case immunology), that the proteins associated with the pigments in these different systems have amino acid sequences that are closely related. This ties together the organisms from the different groups and supports the idea that all chloroplasts had a common ancestor.

Plant hormones

Since the early 1900s plant scientists have been enamored with the study of plant hormones. By 1995 six broad classes of hormones had been generally recognized, and a few others were waiting in the wings for such recognition. The auxins and gibberellins cause stem elongation and several other responses; abscisic acid (ABA) and ethylene also cause several responses, some of which concern how plants react to stress; the cytokinins are involved in cell division and other responses; and salicylic acid, which has been recognized as a plant hormone only during the past few years, is involved in plant responses to pathogens and also controls the metabolism that produces heat in the developing flowers of arum lilies (such as the voodoo lily). Although plant physiologists have studied these responses for several decades, only recently has it been possible for them to begin studies of how these substances might act at the molecular level.

To be effective, each plant hormone must react with something in the cell, a something that plant physiologists refer to as a receptor. Thanks again to advances in molecular biology, receptors were identified during 1993 for salicylic acid, ethylene, auxin, and blue light (not a hormone but requiring a receptor). In 1994 Knut Meyer, Martin Leube, and Erwin Grill of the Swiss Federal Institute of Technology, Zürich, studied a mutant of *Arabidopsis* that was insensitive to ABA. Applying a complex series of molecular-genetic steps, the workers were able to isolate the mutant gene, combine it with certain genetic markers, and reintroduce it into *Arabidopsis* plants. Seeds from those plants germinated in the presence of very small amounts of ABA, which normally inhibits their germination. This response demonstrated that the gene had been transferred. Further complex manipulations revealed the unmutated gene, which was then sequenced. Its protein product has 434 amino acids, and much of its structure is identical to that of protein phosphatases from animals (enzymes that remove phosphate from proteins); however, there is also a binding site for calcium ions (Ca^{2+}) that is not present in other known phosphatases. This discovery should open the door to a much better understanding of how ABA functions in plant growth.

Plants in their environment

Human activities are having profound effects upon the planet. Carbon dioxide (CO_2) is increasing in the atmosphere, and this may lead to increases in temperature (if it has not done so already—*see* below) unless increasing pollution reflects more sunlight, which would lead to a decrease in temperature. Numerous studies have been carried out to determine how plants respond to increasing amounts of CO_2 and to higher temperatures. It has been demonstrated that virtually all plants increase their rate of photosynthesis when CO_2 is increased as much as two to three times the present atmospheric concentrations. But most of those studies have been done with individual leaves, individual plants, or in some cases a canopy of plants in a growth chamber. Many of the studies were relatively short-term, limited to only a portion of a plant's life cycle.

A group of 10 researchers with Walter C. Oechel as senior author reported on a three-year study of tundra plants in northern Alaska. Transparent chambers 1.2 m (4 ft) square and 0.5 m (1.6 ft) high were placed over natural tundra vegetation. Temperatures and CO_2 concentrations in three of the chambers were the same as those outside. CO_2 was elevated to twice the outside level (340 raised to 680 parts per million) in three chambers, but the temperatures remained the same as those outside. In three more chambers CO_2 was elevated and temperatures were raised 4 °C (7.2 °F). At first, more CO_2 was absorbed than was lost by the ecosystem in the chambers with elevated CO_2. By the end of the three years, however, about as much CO_2 was being lost as was being absorbed in the chambers with elevated CO_2 and with the temperature the same as outdoors; however, plants in the chambers with elevated CO_2 and a higher temperature were still absorbing more CO_2 than was being lost to the atmosphere.

The study clearly demonstrates the complexities of predicting what will happen as CO_2 continues to increase. In the tundra some observed effects may be accounted for by consideration of the rate of breakdown of organic matter and of its release of nutrients to the plants. In any case, results are likely to vary from ecosystem to ecosystem.

John W.H. Dacey, Bert G. Drake, and Michael J. Klug of, respectively, Woods Hole (Mass.) Oceanographic Institution, Smithsonian Environmental Research Center, Edgewater, Md., and the Kellogg Biological Station, Hickory Corners, Mich., reported on similar studies that suggest even further complications. In an outdoor study somewhat similar to that in Alaska, researchers placed enclosures, open at the top, around plants in a

Chesapeake Bay marsh. Carbon dioxide was introduced into these enclosures and monitored to maintain its level at twice that in today's atmosphere. Net primary productivity (the amount of new organic matter produced by photosynthesis) increased in the marsh in response to CO_2 fertilization, but so did the emission of methane, which, like CO_2, can act as a greenhouse gas, trapping the Sun's energy and potentially leading to global warming. So far, however, the effects of methane have been relatively minor compared with those of CO_2.

Georg Grabherr, Michael Gottfried, and Harald Pauli of the University of Vienna studied the species richness (weighted numbers of species) of 26 mountain peaks above 3,000 m (9,842 ft) in western Austria and eastern Switzerland. They compared current species richness with information collected about 70–90 years ago from the same locations. They found that at a given elevation and especially at the lower elevations, species richness increased significantly over that time span. They suggest that this may have been caused by the slight increase in average annual temperature of approximately 0.7 °C (1.3 °F), which would cause the flora from lower altitudes to migrate up the mountain. It is possible that rising temperatures will drive species toward the mountaintops, and in many cases, the researchers suggest, such species may then have nowhere to go and will thus become extinct.

P.K. Van de Water, S.W. Leavitt, and J.L. Betancourt of the University of Arizona and the Desert Laboratory, Tucson, Ariz., studied needles from limber pine found in rat middens in the western U.S.

dating back 30,000 years (radiocarbon dating). They examined ratios of carbon isotopes and distribution of stomata (the surface pores through which CO_2 and other gases enter the leaf). During the interglacial period, when CO_2 increased 30% in the atmosphere according to measurements of bubbles in polar ice, the stomatal densities decreased markedly as expected (known from laboratory studies that control CO_2), and plants used water more efficiently. This study confirms plant responses to atmospheric CO_2 in prehistoric times.

It seemed reasonable that productivity of an ecosystem would depend upon the primary producers: the plants that absorb sunlight and convert its energy into the food required by herbivores that eat the plants and carnivores that eat the herbivores. B.E. McLaren and R.O. Peterson of the Michigan Technological University have, however, documented an important complication to this simple picture. For 35 years the animal populations of Isle Royale National Park in Michigan have been carefully monitored. A population of wolves has increased and decreased, probably as the animals died off because of disease. The moose population was controlled by the wolves; when there were many wolves, there were fewer moose. The Michigan researchers examined the growth of balsam fir trees over this same period by measuring the thickness of annual growth rings. Thin rings indicate reduced growth of the trees. They discovered a clear correlation between the growth of the trees and the moose and wolf populations. When there were many wolves and few moose, the trees, which were fodder for the moose, grew more.

Thus, in this rather simple ecosystem with its three steps in the food chain, the control seems to be exercised from the top down (the wolves) rather than from the bottom up (the trees). This may well be relevant to the reintroduction of wolves into Yellowstone National Park and central Idaho, which took place in early 1995.

In assessing the future of the Earth as human influences continue to affect its atmosphere, biosphere, and hydrosphere, it is important to estimate the activities of single-celled plants, called phytoplankton, in the Earth's oceans. In most of the open oceans, phytoplankton populations are very sparse. This is thought to be because as organisms die, they slowly sink to the bottom, taking mineral nutrients with them. The result is that the oceans have become "nutrient deserts," limited in photosynthetic activity not by light or water but by unavailable nutrients. In the equatorial Pacific, however, concentrations of nitrate and phosphate, necessary nutrients of phytoplankton, are unusually high although phytoplankton remain low in numbers. Seeking to resolve this apparent inconsistency, Zbigniew S. Kolber of Brookhaven National Laboratory, Upton, N.Y., and his colleagues obtained evidence that the low phytoplankton populations in the equatorial Pacific are caused by a lack of iron. This had been suggested by earlier researchers, but Kolber's team used a sensitive fluorescence method to follow changes in photosynthetic activity of the natural phytoplankton community both before and after the addition of iron to a small area (7.5 × 7.5 km [4.7 × 4.7 mi]). As predicted by the iron hypothesis, phytoplankton chlorophyll (which depends upon iron for its synthesis) increased sharply after the addition of iron, which strongly supports the hypothesis.

Kevin R. Arrigo and Charles R. Mc-Clain of the NASA Goddard Space Flight Center, Greenbelt, Md., used satellite images to examine phytoplankton populations in the Ross Sea near Antarctica. They discovered an intense phytoplankton bloom that occurred in early December, developing inside the Ross Sea polynya (open water surrounded by ice). These values were three to four times greater than those previously reported for the western Ross Sea.

Genetic engineering and agriculture

Much activity in the field of genetic engineering is directed toward possible human applications. For example, it is possible to transfer a gene into *Arabidopsis* so that the plant makes a low grade of plastic. Twenty percent of the dried plant consists of the plastic, according to Chris Somerville of the Carnegie Institution of Washington at Stanford University and his colleagues.

The U.S. Food and Drug Administration granted permission during the past year for large-scale field trials of a genetically engineered tomato. Maarten Chrispeels of the University of California, San Diego, T.J. Higgins of Canberra, Australia, and Larry Murdock of Purdue University, West Lafayette, Ind., used genetic engineering techniques to create a strain of garden pea that resists attack by two weevil species that damage stored crops.

—Frank B. Salisbury

MICROBIOLOGY

The isolation of dinosaur DNA from mosquitoes preserved in amber is the basis for the novel and movie *Jurassic Park*. The mosquito species most commonly found in amber, however, are not the bloodsucking species in the book and movie but are sapsucking species that do not feed on animals. Occasionally these mosquitoes and other sapsucking insects become trapped in the sticky sap, and they can become preserved if the sap becomes transformed into amber.

Although the isolation of dinosaur DNA from insects embedded in amber is a remote possibility at best, Raul Cano and his associates at California Polytechnic State University have studied DNA from bacteria that lived in the abdominal cavities of extinct insect species preserved in amber. (Bacteria that live in beneficial association with other organisms are called symbionts.) In the Dominican Republic there are amber mines located 15–30 m (50–100 ft) underground, where the temperature is maintained at a stable level and the DNA is protected from

the Sun's ultraviolet radiation. The amber is 25 million to 40 million years old, but DNA in amber's dehydrated environment is protected from denaturation (change in the molecular structure) and hydrolysis (alteration by water). Though the DNA has deteriorated so that all that are left are gene-sized fragments of 100–1,000 base pairs, it is possible to extract and study specific genes. The amber is first decontaminated to remove present-day bacteria living on its surface. It is then fractured to expose an insect, and DNA is extracted from the abdomen. Then the polymerase chain reaction (PCR) is used to amplify, or massively replicate, the DNA taken from symbionts associated with the bees. Starting from a few molecules that serve as templates, PCR can amplify specific segments of DNA millions of times. Specific primers (molecules whose presence is required for the formation of other molecules) are chosen so as to amplify a 530-base-pair portion of the 16S ribosomal RNA (rRNA) gene, a gene that is found in all bacteria and is known to evolve very

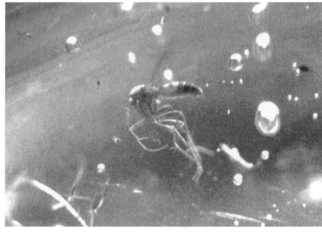

Preserved in amber is an extinct insect species. DNA from bacteria that lived in the stomachs of the insects has been extracted and amplified for further study.

Raul J. Cano, California Polytechnic State University, San Luis Obispo slowly with time. Finally, the nucleotide sequence of the PCR-amplified rRNA gene is determined and compared with that of present-day relatives.

DNA from the rRNA genes of bacteria found in the abdominal cavities of the extinct stingless bee *Proplebeia dominicana* was similar to rRNA sequences from the present-day symbionts *Bacillus circulans, B. firmus,* and *B. pumilus.* These results argue that the symbiotic associations observed in modern insects were already in place millions of years ago. Perhaps by observing these ancient symbiotic associations, scientists can learn more about present-day host-microbe interactions.

The myxobacterium *Myxococcus xanthus* typically feeds on other microorganisms by releasing enzymes that hydrolyze the cell wall; this gives it access to the protein fractions of the microorganisms, which it also hydrolyzes to amino acids for use as carbon and energy sources. *M. xanthus* cells move by gliding on solid surfaces at rates of 2–20 μm/min (micrometers [millionths of a meter] per minute) and have little trouble feeding on stationary prey. *Escherichia coli* cells, however, move at rates of 900–1,200 μm/min, 50–200 times faster than *M. xanthus,* which makes it unlikely that *M. xanthus* could capture *E. coli* cells. Wenyuan Shi and David Zusman at the University of California, Berkeley, however, discovered that *M. xanthus* cells are able to lure faster prey to them. *M. xanthus* cells release chemical attractants, most likely amino acids, that cause the *E. coli* cells to swim toward them. Once the *M. xanthus* cells have established contact with their prey, they rupture them with the hydrolytic enzymes. Hydrolysis

of the protein fraction of the *E. coli* cells produces additional amino acids to lure more *E. coli* cells into the area. The process of luring prey is common to many animals, but this is the first report of such a behavior in bacteria.

During the past year the smallest eukaryotic organism was discovered, a green alga named *Ostreococcus tauri.* (A eukaryote is a cell with a definitive nucleus.) It was found in the picoplankton (cell size less than two micrometers) of a marine community that previously had been thought to be exclusively prokaryotic (without a definitive cell nucleus). When examined by transmission electron microscopy, *O. tauri* cells were found to be extremely compact and to have the features typical of eukaryotic cells. They contain a nucleus, one plastid (a structure containing pigments of protein materials) with a starch granule, one mitochondrion (a minute structure responsible for generating energy), and one Golgi apparatus (a part of the membrane system external to the nucleus). *O. tauri* is the main component of the phytoplankton from the Thau lagoon in the Mediterranean Sea off the coast of France; cell abundance during the year ranges between 10^7 and 2×10^8 cells per liter, which averages to about 86% of the total number of phytoplankton cells. In the summer, when *O. tauri* cells are most abundant, their carbon assimilation is 1.3 to 5.4 times greater than that of larger species (more than two micrometers in diameter). Therefore, they are extremely efficient in producing new organic matter by photosynthesis.

The reasons why this species is so abundant in the lagoon are not clear.

One possibility is that *O. tauri* cells are more resistant to radiation from the Sun owing to their unusually high production of a photoprotective pigment known as violaxanthin. Another possibility is that they are more compatible with the lagoon's large oyster population. Oysters, which are filter feeders, preferentially retain cells larger than two micrometers in diameter and thus encourage the growth of smaller cells. Furthermore, oysters excrete large amounts of ammonium ions, which favor the growth of picoplankton over large varieties. Other coastal waters are now being examined for this organism to determine whether it represents a substantial but overlooked contribution to marine production of organic matter.

Since the 1950s it has been known that people with blood type O are 1.5 to 2 times more likely to have ulcers than people with other blood types. This appears to be due to the association of a bacterium with the epithelial cells lining the stomachs of people with type O blood. *Helicobacter pylori* is a bacterium that causes a number of stomach ailments, including gastritis, gastric and duodenal ulcers, a common form of stomach cancer referred to as gastric adenocarcinoma, and a rare form of cancer referred to as non-Hodgkin's lymphoma of the stomach. The first step in the infection process is the attachment of *H. pylori* to specific molecules (receptors) on the surface of the epithelial cells. The surface of type O red blood cells contains a specific carbohydrate molecule that differs from that found on the surface of A, B, or AB red blood cells. This molecule is also found on the surface of the epithelial cells that line the stomachs of people with type

O blood, where it serves as the receptor for *H. pylori* attachment; it is found in much smaller numbers in individuals with A, B, or AB blood. As a result, people with type A, B, or AB blood have reduced chances of colonization by *H. pylori*.

Once *H. pylori* has attached to the epithelial cells, it is transported into them and can cause a chronic infection that leads to ulcers and, eventually, cancer. If *H. pylori* is unable to attach to the cells, it passes through the digestive tract without causing any harm.

Less than 20 years ago it was believed that living organisms could be divided into two groups, prokaryotes and eukaryotes, on the basis of simple examinations of their structures. For example, unlike eukaryotes, prokaryotes have no membrane surrounding their genetic material. This was a satisfactory distinction based on the understanding of the cells at that time. Then in the late 1970s Carl Woese at the University of Illinois discovered that prokaryotes can be divided into two very different groups on the basis of the structure and sequence of their 16S ribosomal RNA genes. These two groups, now often referred to as Bacteria and Archae, are extremely different from each other when examined closely, even though both are prokaryotes. The Archae appear to be much more closely related to eukaryotes than are the Bacteria. In 1990 Wolfram Zillig and his associates at the Max Planck Institute for Biochemistry, Martinsried, Germany, and Michael Thomm at the University of Regensburg, Germany, found a transcriptional regulatory sequence known as the TATA box in DNA from Archae; this sequence was previously observed to be present in eukaryotes but not in Bacteria. This nucleotide sequence binds a regulatory protein, TATA binding protein (TBP), that activates transcription of eukaryotic cells. (Transcription is the process by which RNA is formed from DNA.) During the past year TBP was discovered in Archae by Gary Olsen and his colleagues at the University of Illinois and by Stephen Jackson and his colleagues at the University of Cambridge. The Archae and eukaryotic proteins are 40% identical in the binding region, which leaves little doubt that they shared a common ancestral protein. These results argue that the Archae and eukaryote lineages shared a common ancestor much more recently than the eukaryotes did with the Bacteria lineage. The Archae may provide important clues as to the nature of the first eukaryotic cell.

About 330,000 patients undergo coronary angioplasty in the United States every year to open clogged arteries and restore normal blood flow to the heart. In about one-third of these patients, the arteries quickly clog again owing to excessive proliferation of the smooth muscle cells in the blood vessel walls, a condition referred to as coronary restenosis. During the past year Edith Speir and Stephen Epstein of the U.S. National Heart, Lung, and Blood Institute suggested that restenosis is triggered by the activation of a latent cytomegalovirus (CMV) that usually produces asymptomatic infections in adults. A key element in the process is p53, a protein in smooth muscle cells that activates transcription of certain target genes that ultimately inhibits the growth of muscle cells. Inactivation of p53 is believed to cause some types of malignant tumors by permitting uncontrolled cell proliferation. With this in mind, Speir and Epstein proposed that CMV inactivates p53, which leads to increased growth of muscle cells in the blood vessels. Their hypothesis is based on the finding that about 38% of the restenosis lesions they observed contained high amounts of p53 and CMV. Furthermore, one CMV protein known as IE84 binds to p53 and renders it unable to activate transcription of the p53-dependent target genes. These results predict that administering antiviral drugs to patients undergoing coronary angioplasty will reduce the incidence of restenosis by inhibiting CMV proliferation.

During the past 50 years disease-causing bacteria have slowly developed resistance to the antibiotics that have been used to treat infected individuals. As scientists exhaust the supply of known antibiotics, they must turn elsewhere for the protection of the human population against infections. In this connection an important discovery by a research team led by Harriet Robinson of the University of Massachusetts that promises to hold significant advantages over current vaccine therapy is a novel type of vaccine composed of DNA. Influenza-virus DNA was injected into mouse cells by means of a "gun" that shoots gold beads coated with DNA from an influenza virus gene directly into skin cells. The skin cells then manufacture the influenza protein that the DNA directs them to make. This viral protein in turn activates the mouse immune system.

Direct injection of genetic material offers several advantages. First, immunization with DNA mimics an actual infection in that the viral proteins are made inside the cell, where the virus would make them. As a result, the vaccine stimulates both an antibody response (the production of antibodies against the foreign proteins) and a cellular response (production of killer T cells to destroy the infected cells). A traditional vaccine, composed of an inactivated virus particle or a viral protein injected into the muscle, provides an antibody response but not a cellular response. Thus, the DNA vaccine provides a more natural type of protection. Second, because DNA is stable at room temperature, these vaccines would not have to be refrigerated, as do vaccines containing viruses. Third, vaccine manufacturing could be much cheaper because it would no longer be necessary to cultivate large amounts of the virus in tissue culture. All that is necessary is production of all or part of the viral genetic material in another organism where DNA can be produced and extracted.

—Lawrence J. Shimkets

MOLECULAR BIOLOGY

It is convenient to think of the molecular biology of the cell in terms of trinities: the three master classes of macromolecules—DNA, RNA, and protein—or the three major processes of replication (DNA copying), transcription (DNA to RNA), and translation (RNA to protein). During the past year the explosion of information based on the three-dimensional structures of the proteins that carry out those processes continued. The significance of such detailed structural information lies in its ability to show how the protein enzymes that cat-

alyze the chemical reactions involved in the synthesis of DNA, RNA, and protein actually work. Progress also was significant in areas slightly removed from this major axis. Cellular processes that repair damage to DNA, without which human beings would all succumb to cancer almost immediately, and the structure and mechanism of proteins involved in the proper folding of other proteins were the focus of major efforts brought to fruition.

DNA repair

Damage to DNA is regularly repaired by systems of enzymes operating in all forms of cells, from bacterial to human. The building blocks of DNA consist of repeating units called nucleotides, each comprising a purine or pyrimidine base attached to a sugar molecule called deoxyribose, which in turn is attached to a phosphate group. The helical backbone of each DNA strand consists of the sugar deoxyribose alternating with the covalently attached phosphate groups. The bases, abbreviated A, G, C, and T (for adenine, guanine, cytosine, and thymine), are paired across the two strands of the double helix in a complementary fashion, A always pairing with T, and G with C. A nucleotide damaged by chemical reaction with, for example, a chemical carcinogen or by absorption of energy from sunlight or from a radioactive source can be fixed by a system called excision repair. This process involves the recognition and cutting of the damaged DNA strand and removal of a short stretch of it, followed by resynthesis of an undamaged version of the stretch just removed. Other types of errors that occur during DNA replication can be corrected by another system

called mismatch repair. Although these two systems have been known and studied for many years, only recently have the enzymes responsible for repairs in human cells been identified and purified. The way they work turns out to be very similar to the mechanisms used by bacteria.

Imagine a bacterial DNA double helix with a damaged base, no longer capable of pairing correctly with its partner across the helix. A system of enzymes called excision repair proteins recognize this lesion, bind to it, and then in a series of reactions make two incisions in the sugar-phosphate backbone of the damaged strand, one five nucleotides away on one side of the lesion, the other eight nucleotides away on the other side. The 14-nucleotide fragment, containing the damaged nucleotide, is then released from the double helix, leaving an exposed (and healthy) single strand to serve as template for resynthesis of the damaged strand.

In bacteria, three proteins are required to recognize the lesion, bind to the DNA, and make the two incisions. (*See* Figure 1 on page 400.) Another protein releases the 14-nucleotide fragment, leaving a strange structure containing a single-stranded region of 14 nucleotides on one strand and a gap on the other strand. The enzyme DNA polymerase is needed for the repair synthesis that fills in the gap, using the correct sequence on the remaining strand as template. In humans the reactions have been found to be basically the same, except that 17 proteins are required and the incision enzyme clips out a 29-nucleotide fragment rather than a 14-nucleotide one. In

Figure 1

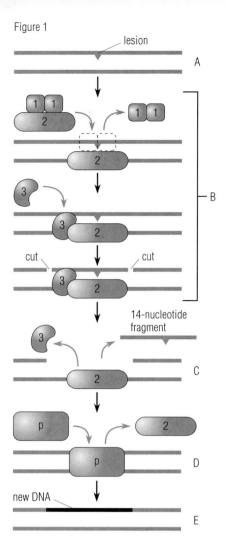

lesion

A

cut   cut

14-nucleotide
fragment

C

p   2

p

D

new DNA

E

DNA EXCISION REPAIR IN *E. COLI*

A. Double strand of DNA contains damaged base.

B. Three kinds of proteins (1, 2, and 3) participate in recognizing damage, binding to DNA, and making necessary incisions in DNA strand.

C. Another protein (not shown) releases the excised fragment and protein 3.

D. DNA polymerase (p) displaces protein 2 and uses sequence on intact strand to synthesize repair.

E. Double strand is repaired with 14-nucleotide patch.

the first recognition and binding step, a huge protein complex called TFIIH unwinds the damaged region of the double helix, two separate proteins make the incisions, and several more proteins recruit DNA polymerase to the site for the last synthesis step. Totally unexpected, given what was known of the bacterial system, were the discoveries that three of the proteins required for the recognition and resynthesis steps are components of the normal DNA replication machinery and that TFIIH is a six-protein complex that normally functions in transcription by RNA polymerase II, the enzyme responsible for synthesizing messenger RNA from a DNA strand. These observations integrate the repair processes into the fundamental life of the cell.

Excision repair takes care of damage to cellular DNA due to environmental insults. However, in cells that divide often, such as epithelial cells or liver cells, there is another prevalent source of DNA "damage": errors in DNA replication. In order to produce two new strands of DNA, the two parental strands are used as templates for synthesis of the new strands, with each new nucleotide selected according to the complementary pairing rules, A with T and G with C. The enzyme that replicates DNA, DNA polymerase, moves along a parental strand and synthesizes the new strand by adding nucleotide units one at a time. Mistakes are made in this process, such as the insertion of an A where the pairing rule calls for a G, but most such mistakes are caught immediately by the "editing" function of DNA polymerase, which backs up, removes the mispaired nucleotide, inserts the correct

one, and moves on. Nevertheless, a few errors escape the editing function. Left unchecked, these errors can lead to mutation; the improper nucleotide will encode either a wrong amino acid at that particular place in the protein or no amino acid at all. In either case, the protein may not function properly and the cell in which that error occurs can either die or grow uncontrolled. Most of these errors are caught, as well, by a backup system called mismatch repair. The mismatch repair system of bacteria has been studied for a long time and in great detail, but last year it moved to center stage owing to, once again, recognition that a parallel system exists in humans. Moreover, as might be expected, defects in the human mismatch repair system lead to cancer.

During the past 10 years detailed information has been obtained for the mismatch repair system in the bacterium *Escherichia coli*. Mismatch refers to a base pair in which one of the bases is not the complement of the other. The repair system must be able to tell the parental DNA strand from the new one; correction of the wrong strand would lead to permanent establishment of the wrong base pair and permanent mutation. In *E. coli* the specific nucleotide sequence GATC, which occurs in DNA on average once every 300 base pairs, is recognized by a methylase, an enzyme that adds a methyl group to the adenine base (A). This modification does not change the base-pairing properties of the adenine, but it protrudes into one groove of the DNA helix, where the methyl group can be recognized by a protein sliding along the groove. When DNA has just been replicated, there is a brief period when

addition, some of the proteins that take part in the human repair system turn out to be part of the retinue of proteins that participate in normal DNA replication and transcription processes.

Progress in the study of excision repair in human cells began with the discovery in the mid-1960s that the inherited disease xeroderma pigmentosum (XP), which results in sunlight-induced skin cancer, is due to the absence of one or more excision repair proteins. Scientists used XP cells to discover the genes that code for the missing enzymes, which allowed their subsequent purification and characterization. Much of this work was done over the past few years in the laboratory of Aziz Sancar at the University of North Carolina School of Medicine. The human repair reactions follow, in general, the bacterial reactions described above, except that four proteins are required for

Figure 2

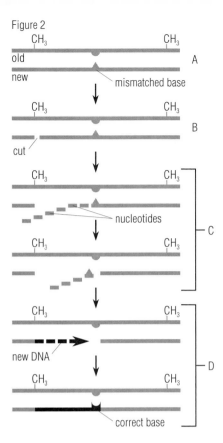

A. Mismatch error occurs in new DNA strand, on which methyl groups (CH₃) are not yet present.

B. Several proteins participate in binding to the mismatch and cutting the new strand at nearest unmethylated site.

C. Nucleotides are removed from strand one at a time until mismatched base is reached.

D. Removed nucleotides are restored, including correct base at site of former mismatch. Strand ends are connected.

the new DNA strand has not yet been methylated at its GATC sequences. During this interval the mismatch repair system can tell the old—and correct—DNA strand from the new one by the presence or absence of the methyl groups.

Repair is begun by the binding of a protein, called MutS, to the mismatch region. (_See_ Figure 2.) What follows is incredible in terms of the sophistication and elegance of the biochemical reactions used to replace the wrong base. Several more proteins bind to MutS, one of which is a specific enzyme that cuts the unmethylated DNA strand (the new one with the error) at the nearest unmethylated GATC sequence, which can be as far away from the error as 300 nucleotides. This cut is followed by removal of nucleotides from the unmethylated strand, one at a time, until the mispaired base is removed. Then removal stops and new synthesis begins, in which all the missing nucleotides are restored. Finally, a reconnection is made between the free end of the repair and the cut end created at the original incision. In all, 10 proteins are required for this process in bacteria.

For some years scientists had noticed a correlation between defects in mismatch repair and the frequency of certain cancers. During the past year, however, compelling evidence for a direct connection was obtained, principally from the laboratory of Paul Modrich at Duke University, Durham, N.C. One of the most common forms of colon cancer is hereditary nonpolyposis colorectal cancer (HNPCC). Earlier research had associated four chromosomal regions with HNPCC, and in 1994 it was shown that all four regions possess genes that encode proteins corresponding to bacterial Mut proteins—MutS and a second protein called MutL. When normal cells from a person with HNPCC were studied in the laboratory, they were found to have low mutation rates in their DNA synthesis and to be competent for mismatch repair. On the other hand, cancer cells from the same individual showed high mutation rates and had lost their ability to repair mismatches. An individual who is affected with HNPCC must have inherited one good copy of a gene for a Mut protein and one defective one. In the individual's normal cells the good copy is functioning as it should. In the cancer cells the good copy has been lost or has become mutated itself, leaving the cells prone to unrepaired mismatches, further mutation at high frequency, and uncontrolled growth.

Protein folding

A freshly minted protein is a polypeptide, or chain of amino acids, without a distinctive, unique three-dimensional structure. Early conjectures about the path taken by polypeptides to achieve the folded structure that characterizes native proteins included the possibility that folding was an enzyme-catalyzed process. This idea was set aside, first for the logical reason that if each protein needed another protein to fold it up, there would be no end to the number needed to sustain life. Later came an elegant demonstration, using the protein ribonuclease, that a completely denatured (unfolded) form of the protein could refold perfectly in the test tube, with no accessory proteins and no information other than the amino acid sequence of the polypeptide to guide the process. This reasoning and demonstration pushed the pendulum to the extreme, leading to the belief that all proteins take up their three-dimensional structures unaided.

This dogma has since been shown to be wrong. For example, some 40% of the proteins in _E. coli_ require the services of a large protein complex called a chaperonin in order to achieve their correct structures. This is not to say that the chaperonin imparts folding information to its "clients"; _i.e._, its substrates. It seems instead that the chaperonin works by binding to unfolded forms of its substrates, preventing them from aggregating irreversibly with one another. It then releases the unfolded protein, which has a brief period in which to fold correctly. If it succeeds, the job is done. If not, it is rebound by another chaperonin, then released and allowed another chance to fold. The process is repeated until all the newly made molecules are folded correctly. A curious aspect of the process is that a single kind of chaperonin serves this function for all the proteins, more than 1,000, that need it.

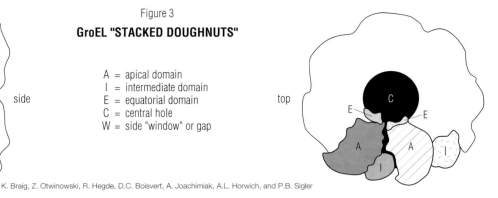

Figure 3

GroEL "STACKED DOUGHNUTS"

A = apical domain
I = intermediate domain
E = equatorial domain
C = central hole
W = side "window" or gap

side

top

K. Braig, Z. Otwinowski, R. Hegde, D.C. Boisvert, A. Joachimiak, A.L. Horwich, and P.B. Sigler

The chaperonin of *E. coli* was discovered in the 1970s in a very indirect way. The story begins with the fact that bacteria can be infected by viruses called bacteriophages. A bacterial virus infection starts with the attachment of the virus to a protein on the surface of the bacterium. Each type of virus has its own mechanism for inserting its genetic material, usually a single molecule of DNA, into the bacterial cell's cytoplasm. There the viral DNA is transcribed into RNA, and the RNA is translated into proteins. The proteins include enzymes for replicating the viral DNA and others that make up the coat of the virus. Where there was one virus particle infecting the cell, in a short time there can be hundreds of identical particles containing newly made DNA and protein.

It was in studies of the bacterial genes required for the propagation of viruses that the chaperonin of *E. coli* was found. Mutants of *E. coli* were being sought in which the propagation of the bacteriophage known as lambda was blocked at a stage later than viral attachment and injection of DNA. Such mutants were found. Then, variants of the virus that could still propagate in these uncooperative hosts were isolated. The virus mutations that permitted propagation were found to occur in a gene called *E,* which encodes the major coat protein of the virus. Further study of the original bacterial mutation revealed that it was defective in the production of a bacterial protein that the nonmutant virus needed to assemble its E protein. This requirement was bypassed by the mutation in the viral *E* gene, which allowed the mutant virus to make its E protein unassisted by

the bacterial protein. The bacterial mutant was called GroE, and its defect was assigned to a gene called *groE,* which turned out to encode the chaperonin discussed above. The chaperonin actually consists of two proteins, GroEL and GroES, both of which are needed for chaperonin function. Similar and related proteins have been found everywhere in the living world, from microorganisms and cell organelles like chloroplasts and mitochondria to the cytoplasm of all eukaryotic cells (cells of living organisms other than bacteria) that have been examined for them.

The general structure of GroEL has been known for some time, based on electron micrographs. It consists of two rings of seven subunits each, joined face to face like two stacked doughnuts, with a large hole running through the doughnuts. GroES is a ring of seven much smaller subunits, capable of stacking on either end of the GroEL cylinder at the appropriate time. During the past year X-ray crystallographic studies provided a high-resolution picture of the structure of GroEL, which furnished considerable insight into how the chaperonin works.

The architecture of GroEL was determined in the laboratory of Paul Sigler at Yale University. (*See* Figure 3.) Each of its 14 subunits has the same structure, folded into three domains: apical, intermediate, and equatorial. The equatorial domains form a flat surface at which the two seven-subunit rings come in contact, yielding a cylinder whose top and bottom halves are mirror images of each other. The apical domains are at each end of the cylinder, and they define the central cavity, the hole in the doughnut. The

beauty of the detailed structure lies in the identification of the amino acids that line the central cavity.

The entire GroEL protein contains 548 amino acids. In the laboratory of Arthur Horwich, also at Yale University, individual amino acids in GroEL were replaced one by one (by changing nucleotides in the cloned *groEL* gene), and then the biochemical properties of these genetically engineered variants were determined. The detailed X-ray structure guided the choice of amino acids to be replaced. The results of this extensive study included the finding that side chains containing such hydrophobic (water-avoiding) amino acids as leucine, valine, phenylalanine, and tyrosine are required to form a site in the apical domain that faces the central cavity where both the unfolded substrate polypeptide and the accessory protein GroES bind. Release of the substrate polypeptide was shown to require both GroES and an input of energy, which GroEL acquires by binding a molecule of ATP (adenosine triphosphate), the energy carrier of the cell, and breaking its energy-rich bond (a process called ATP hydrolysis). The sites for ATP binding and hydrolysis are deeper within the interior of the GroEL cylinder, involving amino acids in both the intermediate and the equatorial domains. In the laboratory studies, amino acid replacements that prevented either ATP hydrolysis or GroES binding also prevented the release of the polypeptide substrate.

The GroE chaperonin is required in bacteria not only for the assembly of proteins under normal growth conditions. It is also a major heat-shock protein, meaning that its synthesis is abundantly provoked by an abrupt rise in the temperature to which the cells are exposed. The role of GroE in the heat-shock response is thought to be one of preventing the aggregation of cellular proteins that have been partially unfolded at the elevated temperature. This would be a "repair" function, separate from its normal role in assisting the folding of newly made proteins. This function also has been detected in eukaryotic cells from yeast, fruit flies (*Drosophila*), and human beings. Eukaryotic cells, in response to heat shock, produce several proteins that aid their survival; one protein, hsp60, which is found in both yeast and humans, corresponds to GroEL in bacteria. How they actually work to protect the cell remains to be learned, but the detailed structure of GroEL provides the essential base for such studies.

—Robert Haselkorn

ZOOLOGY

Highlights of the past year in zoology included the first coral reef studies to document a high rate of coral degradation, deep-sea measurements of the fastest-growing invertebrate, and the identification of a 2-m (6.5-ft) Cambrian Period monster capable of crushing organisms as large as a large cat. One new species of large mammal was discovered. Tim Flannery of the Australian Museum, Sydney, and a team of Australian and Indonesian colleagues found on a remote forested mountainside in New Guinea a tree kangaroo previously unknown to science. About as large as a medium-sized dog, the marsupial is thickly furred with unique black-and-white patterns.

Coral reef degradation

The Caribbean island of Jamaica has the greatest coral diversity in the Atlantic Ocean and its marginal seas. Unfortunately, its reefs have suffered extensive damage from human activities, and that damage has caused a dramatic change in the structure of the reef community.

Terence P. Hughes of James Cook University, Queensland, Australia, has gathered information from the most comprehensive reef-monitoring program conducted in the Caribbean Sea and perhaps

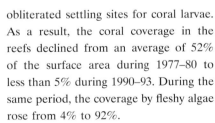

Lobophora algae smother coral on a reef in the Caribbean Sea. Such fleshy algae have flourished because of overfishing of plant-eating fish and a die-off of sea urchins.

Terence P. Hughes

the world. This has involved 17 years of annual censuses of 9 coral communities containing 60 species of coral and encompassing 300 km (186 mi) of the Jamaican coastline. The study found that the major reasons for the decline of the coral coverage of the reefs are chronic overfishing, the decline of sea urchins, and the rapid growth of algal cover. Chronic overfishing reduced herbivorous fish by as much as 80% in biomass and virtually eliminated such predatory species as sharks, groupers, snappers, jacks, and triggerfish. The lack of fish herbivores allowed al-

gae to flourish. At first the large spiny sea urchin *Diadema antillarum* controlled the algae and increased dramatically in population. From 1982 to 1984, however, the sea urchin population suffered a 99% die-off from a species-specific pathogen, which allowed the fleshy algae, notably *Sargassum, Lobophora, Dictyota,* and *Halimeda* to grow uninhibited and to form mats up to 10–15 cm (4–6 in) thick that covered the reefs. This coverage created a tremendous hindrance to the feeding and growth of the coral colonies and obliterated settling sites for coral larvae. As a result, the coral coverage in the reefs declined from an average of 52% of the surface area during 1977–80 to less than 5% during 1990–93. During the same period, the coverage by fleshy algae rose from 4% to 92%.

Suggestions for coral recovery include the reduction of overfishing and the revitalization of the *Diadema* population. Unless planned management of the reefs is implemented, their future is gloomy and will affect the ecology, tourism, and general welfare of the area.

Fast-growing tube worms

Scientists using the Deep Submergence Vehicle *Alvin* have had the amazing good fortune to examine a deep-sea eruption area and to observe the reestablishment of hydrothermal vent communities that include the tube worms *Tevnia jericho-nana* and *Riftia pachyptila,* the dominant and most conspicuous members of the vent areas. Richard A. Lutz and Timothy M. Shank of the Institute of Marine and Coastal Sciences at Rutgers University, New Brunswick, N.J., along with five other scientists studied the developing community of a deep-sea hydrothermal vent area three separate times between 1991 and 1993. The area is located between latitudes 9° 45′ and 9° 52′ N along the crest of the Pacific Rise off the southwestern coast of Mexico at a depth of approximately 2,500 m (1.55 mi).

The erupted area was first visited in April 1991, at which time devastation of vent communities by lava flow less than two weeks earlier was noted, particularly the charred remains of the tube worms. At that time no large animals characteristic of the vent area (tube worms, crabs) were observed, although extensive bacterial mats up to five centimeters (two inches) thick were noted. In March 1992, however, extensive populations of the tube worm *T. jerichonana* were found. These worms had rapidly colonized the numerous fissure vents and possessed tubes measuring approximately 30 cm (12 in) in length. At that time no specimens of the giant tube worm *R. pachyptila* were discovered, but on revisiting the same area in December 1993, the scientists found massive colonies of *R. pachyp-tila* with some individuals having tubes

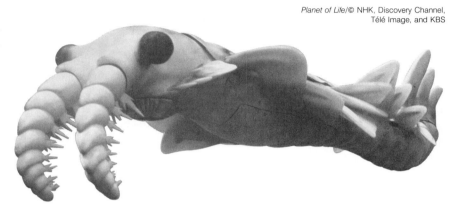

Planet of Life/© NHK, Discovery Channel, Télé Image, and KBS

One of the world's earliest predators, *Anomalocaris,* roamed the world's oceans in the early Cambrian Period more than 500 million years ago. The model shown above is based on fossils found in southern China.

measuring 1.5 m (5 ft) in length. These worms were also observed spawning.

On the basis of the two observation periods, the *R. pachyptila* growth rate was documented as more than 85 cm (33.5 in) per year, the fastest growth rate recorded for tube worms or, for that matter, any marine invertebrate. Such observations suggest that the biological processes (metabolism, growth, reproduction, larval settlement) may proceed rapidly in the dangerous and unstable vent environment.

Earliest giant predators

Discovered in rocks of the early Cambrian Period, more than 500 million years ago, are fossils of anomalocaridids, invertebrate animals that are the oldest known large predators. Chen Junyuan and Zhou Guiqing of the Nanjing (Nanking, China) Institute of Geology and Paleontology and Lars Ramsköld of the Museum of Paleontology at Uppsala (Sweden) University described three specimens of anomalocaridids, including *Anomalocaris canadensis,* a new species

from the Early Cambrian Chengjiang (Ch'eng-chiang) fossil beds near Yunnan in southern China. On the basis of jaws only, another specimen was estimated to have been a 2-m (6.5-ft)-long predator capable of crushing and consuming an organism as large as a human head.

Although other specimens of anomalocaridids had been described by scientists, the Chinese specimens are 10 million years older (about 525 million to 530 million years ago) and include fossil body parts never before seen, particularly the structures of the posterior region. With the new information, the researchers concluded that *A. canadensis* had a flattened elongated body with two appendages extending from the head that were lined with sharp teeth used to grasp prey. The animal also had flaps on each side that could be moved like an underwater wing to aid in locomotion. The tail end was flattened and had two trailing spinelike structures. Two large eyes were located above the appendages. This predator probably detected motion and captured prey with the two appendages.

The grinding circular jaws made a fast meal of small animals.

A squirt-gun defense

Larvae of the beetle *Blepharida* chew only on the leaves of the succulent desert shrub *Bursera schlechtendalii* in the arid Tehuacán Desert in Mexico. When the leaves of some of these shrubs are damaged, they are stimulated to spray resins a distance of 5–150 cm (2–60 in) or to secrete a resin coating on the leaf. Beetle larvae caught in the spray or the coating can suffocate or have their mouth parts glued together. The resins (primarily terpenes) are found in channels running through the plant leaves and are stored under pressure.

Judith X. Becerra of the University of Arizona compared the behavior of *Blepharida* larvae feeding on leaves of high-responsive plants (those spraying resins) with larvae feeding on leaves of low-responsive plants (either little or no spraying). For the former, the larvae that survived the initial spraying or coating were observed to vacate the leaves and then on later approaches to sever or trench the channels that transport resins from the stem into the leaves; this allowed the larvae to feed and to survive presumably undisturbed.

From all appearances this insect has mastered the defense mechanisms of the plant. As observed by Becerra, however, the larvae have paid a price because in the process of severing the channels they are exposed for a longer time to predators and have a decreased growth rate and higher mortality compared with larvae that devour leaves on low-responsive plants.

The nearest living relative to vertebrates

Amphioxus, a wormlike invertebrate 3.8 cm (1.5 in) long, feeds on algae and lives half buried in the sands of shallow seas in temperate and tropical areas. It is a member of the subphylum Cephalochordata in the phylum Chordata, which also includes the subphylum Vertebrata (the vertebrates). The two subphyla have similarities in physical structure, and some scientists have suspected that amphioxus is similar to an ancestral vertebrate. On the basis of an extensive genetic study of amphioxus, this relationship was confirmed. Jordi García-Fernández of the University of Barcelona, Spain, and Peter W.H. Holland of the University of Reading, England, examined amphioxus for the presence and arrangement of Hox genes, which in mice and other vertebrates control the spatial arrangement of the body during development. In vertebrates the Hox genes appear in four clusters, each on a different chromosome.

The scientists were eager to search for a possible origin of the vertebrate Hox gene clusters and chose the amphioxus. Their investigations of amphioxus DNA fragments revealed that the amphioxus Hox genes were clustered on one chromosome, as is found in many invertebrates; however, the cluster had a linear organization similar to that of the vertebrate Hox gene clusters. In fact, 10 of the 13 Hox genes found in mammals were found in the amphioxus genome.

On the basis of their findings, the authors suggested that the first vertebrate had a single cluster of Hox genes similar to that found in amphioxus. The four Hox gene clusters in modern vertebrates represent gene duplications of the ancestral Hox cluster. These duplications may have provided genetic diversity during the early evolution of vertebrates.

Extraordinary salmon growth

The technology for forming transgenic (genes from at least two species) animals has progressed at a rapid pace. Stimulating the rapid growth of fish would be a way to reduce the long production cycle in nature and in hatcheries. One means of accomplishing this is the insertion in an early stage of development of a promoter gene that stimulates the production of growth hormones.

Previous attempts of insertion have involved promoter genes constructed from a mouse. This produced a transgenic fish (one with a mouse gene) but resulted in little or no growth. Robert H. Devlin, Timothy Y. Yesaki, Carlo A. Biagi, and Edward M. Donaldson from the Canadian Department of Fisheries and Oceans in British Columbia and two other colleagues, Penny Swanson from the Northwest Fisheries Science Center in Seattle, Wash., and Woon-Khlong Chan of the National University of Singapore, circumvented these problems, however, by successfully constructing a promoter gene from sockeye salmon *Oncorhynchus gorbusha*. They injected this gene into the embryo-forming region of coho salmon *O. kisuth* eggs and then observed and compared growth rates of treated and untreated salmon over a 14-month period. For 3,000 eggs that were injected, 6.2% possessed the promoter gene in their tissues after that time. The average growth rate for these transgenic salmon was 11 times faster than for untreated

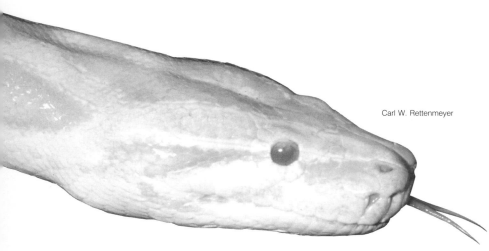

Carl W. Rettenmeyer

An albino Burmese python reveals its forked tongue. Recent research by a scientist at the University of Connecticut has led him to conclude that snakes and their relatives possess forked tongues to follow pheromone trails of prey or mates.

salmon that were used as a control group. One individual was 37 times larger than the untreated fish. Most of the transgenic salmon also underwent smoltification, a morphological and physiological preadaptation for the spring migration from fresh water to the marine environment, earlier than the control group.

Sea turtle navigation

The hatchlings of loggerhead sea turtles *Caretta caretta* emerge from nests late at night on Florida and Caribbean beaches, sense the moonlight bouncing off the ocean, enter the water, and navigate east to the Gulf Stream. They are then carried in first a northeasterly and then an easterly direction, reaching the Azores islands about halfway across the North Atlantic, where they turn south into the mid-Atlantic Sargasso Sea. There they feed and grow, returning to their birthplace in six or more years either to mate or to lay eggs.

The mechanisms by which these animals migrate such great distances and return have been studied by Kenneth J. Lohmann and Catherine M. Fittinghoff Lohmann of the University of North Carolina. Believing that magnetic directional preference is developed early by the hatchlings, the Lohmanns experimented with newly hatched turtles that had been

removed from buried nests without being exposed to light. The turtles were placed in a harness attached to a swivel arm in the center of an upended fiberglass satellite dish filled with water, all of which were in a dark room. The swivel arm was connected to a computer so that the direction of swimming turtles could be recorded. The dish was also surrounded by a magnetic coil system that could control the direction of the magnetic field. The turtles were exposed to a dim light directed from the east for one hour. The light was then turned off, and during the darkness the swimming directions of the turtles were determined. A significant number swam toward the east, and when the field was reversed by the magnetic coil, the turtles reversed their direction and swam toward the west (which was still east for them).

In a significant experiment the Lohmanns discovered that the hatchlings could detect the angle of the magnetic field relative to the Earth's surface, which would allow them to detect how far north or south they were. When a 57° angle was employed, the turtles continued swimming toward the east, but when the angle reached 60°, the turtles swam in a southerly direction.

On the basis of these and previous experiments, the scientists developed the

following sequence of events for turtles hatching on the eastern coast of Florida. The newly hatched turtles emerge from their nest and travel toward the light coming off the ocean. In the water the magnetic orientation takes over. The scientists further determined that turtles leaving the Florida beaches are exposed to a 57° magnetic inclination. The 60° magnetic inclination occurs near the Azores, where the turtles turn south toward the Sargasso Sea. Failure to turn south would send them to a chilly death in the colder waters surrounding England.

Flying reptiles

The pterosaurs, flying reptiles during the Jurassic and Cretaceous periods of the Mesozoic Era (245 million to 66.4 million years ago), were true fliers. The traditional view is that they raced along the ground in a bipedal fashion and became airborne. To aid in the liftoff and flight were wing membranes that were joined to the animal's body from the arms to above the legs.

This traditional view has been updated by David M. Unwin and Natasha N. Bakhurina of the department of geology at the University of Bristol, England, in their examination of a crow-size pterosaur fossil *Sordes pilosus* from the Upper Jurassic Karabastau formation in Kazakhstan. This species possessed a wing membrane differing from that of the traditional pterosaur and more similar to the flight apparatus of a bat. In *S. pilosus* the wing extended from the forearm fingers to the ankles. In addition, a significant structure of *S. pilosus* was a membrane called the uropatagium, which stretched between the hind legs and was controlled by the toes. This apparatus would allow the creature to fly more slowly and to be more maneuverable than its contemporaries.

The scientists concluded that this creature crawled around like a bat and launched itself from above the ground. Once in the air, *S. pilosus* could skim over large bodies of water to seize prey. The uropatagium and the extension of the wing membrane to the ankle would impede the traditional bipedal locomotion.

Snakes and forked tongues

Recent research has led Kurt Schwenk of the University of Connecticut to conclude that snakes and their relatives possess forked tongues as detectors to follow pheromone trails of prey or mates. (Pheromones are substances that animals secrete into the air to influence the behavior, often sexual, of other animals of the same species.) The flicking of the forked tongue involves a sampling phase (protrusion, oscillation, and chemical pickup) and a delivery phase, the release of a chemical in the oral cavity for monitoring by the two vomeronasal organs (VNO), also called Jacobson's organs.

In the sampling phase the tip of each fork of the tongue separates from the other to a distance that may be twice the width of the snake's head and then contacts the ground or various substrates in order to absorb chemicals; the tongue is then retracted. The chemicals are passed into the VNOs, which are located on different sides of the oral cavity. The information from each VNO is then relayed to the snake's brain.

The distance between the prongs of the forked tongue allows the animal to detect a chemical gradient or detect the edge of a pheromone trail. By flicking continuously the snake can follow the trail. Even the direction in which the prey or mate traveled may be deduced through variations in the concentrations of pheromones on the vegetation or rocks that the prey or mate passed.

The forked tongue has evolved in snakes and those lizards that forage for their food. This evolutionary pattern is particularly fascinating to examine since it includes the combination of

Kenneth J. Lohmann and Catherine M.F. Lohmann

A loggerhead turtle hatchling is placed in a harness in an experiment to determine how such hatchlings migrate great distances across the ocean and then return several years later.

tongue anatomy, tongue function, sensory anatomy, neuroanatomy, behavior, and ecology.

Birds, seed storage, and memory

In the fall in North American temperate forests, the black-capped chickadee *Parus atricapillus* forages for seeds and then stores them in many different locations. During the following months, when food becomes less abundant, these storage areas are revisited and the contents consumed. How the bird remembers the location of the seeds is believed to be a function of the hippocampal complex, a portion of the forebrain associated with spatial learning.

Testing the hypothesis that the chickadees would form new neurons (neurogenesis) to become memory cells and replace old neurons during this period of time, Anat Barnea of Tel Aviv University, Ramat-Aviv, Israel, and Fernando Nottebohm at the Rockefeller University, New York City, examined hippocampi removed from wild chickadees at different times of the year. First, birds were caught over a two-year period and injected with 3H-thymidine, a compound that is incorporated into new DNA. The birds were released at various times and then recaptured six weeks later. This gave them time to carry on their normal activities. Each bird was then killed and its hippocampus examined for new neurons. The results showed that the birds collected and examined in October had more new neurons than those studied at any other times and that they had twice as many as birds that were kept in the lab and fed a continuous supply of seeds.

The implication is that birds form new neurons during a critical phase of their survival, replacing old neurons that have memories no longer needed. Understanding the mechanisms controlling neurogenesis in the bird's brain could possibly provide information on how to establish similar mechanisms (which are presently lacking) in the human brain.

—George G. Brown

See also Feature Articles: BIODIVERSITY IN THE OCEANS: A WORLD AT RISK; THE MOTHERS OF AGGRESSION; A TIME TO DIE.

MATHEMATICS

The most significant mathematical development in 1994 occurred near the end of the year, when Andrew Wiles of Princeton University presented a revised proof of Fermat's last theorem, a year and a half after his first announcement of a proof and almost a year after he admitted that the first proof contained a gap. Other mathematical developments and discoveries included further progress on another problem in number theory, the Goldbach conjecture; the revelation that the Intel Pentium computer chip makes numerical errors; the factoring of a 129-digit integer that had been set as a challenge problem; the first example of "molecular computing" to solve a mathematical problem; and an argument over whether a sphere-packing conjecture has been proved. In an unprecedented achievement, each of the six members of the U.S. team of high-school students participating in the International Mathematical Olympiad earned a perfect score in the competition (*see* Year in Review: SCIENTISTS OF THE YEAR: *Honors and Awards*).

Fermat's last theorem

In June 1993, after seven years of secret work, Wiles made a surprise announcement that he had solved the most famous outstanding problem in pure mathematics, the proof of Fermat's last theorem. His announcement created the greatest popular excitement about mathematical research in decades.

Pierre de Fermat (1601–65) wrote that there are no solutions in positive integers to $a^n + b^n = c^n$ for $n > 2$. In other words, there is no cube that is the sum of two cubes, no fourth power that is

the sum of two other fourth powers, etc. Fermat claimed to have a proof of this conjecture, which became known as Fermat's last theorem, but no proof was found, and until now no one has been able to produce one.

Although the conjecture is about properties of whole numbers, Wiles's proof concerns elliptic curves. Elliptic curves are part of algebraic geometry, a branch of mathematics that applies algebraic methods to geometric objects, such as curves and surfaces. In this case, any counterexample to Fermat's last theorem—that is, *a, b, c,* and *n* that satisfy the equation—must have a companion elliptic curve. Ken Ribet of the University of California, Berkeley, proved in 1986 that such a companion curve cannot be modular; that is, it cannot be obtained as a particular kind of projection of the upper half plane. Associated to each elliptic curve is a positive integer, its conductor. If the conductor is square-free, that is, not divisible by the square of any integer larger than 1, then the elliptic curve is said to be semistable. Wiles showed that all semistable elliptic curves must be modular. Since there cannot be a curve that is both modular and not modular, there can be no counterexample to the theorem.

At the end of 1993, colleagues checking the 200-page proof by Wiles discovered a gap in one detail. Wiles's work did not justify an essential claim that he made for an upper bound on the size of one particular structure, known as a Selmer group. In late October 1994, Wiles announced a revised proof that he claimed bridges the gap. This was done with the help of former student Richard L. Tay-

lor of the University of Cambridge. The proof needs to be examined carefully by other mathematicians and its correctness confirmed—a process that may take six months to a year—before the matter can be regarded as settled and Wiles can be granted credit for the achievement.

Goldbach's conjecture

Further progress was made on the Goldbach conjecture, another famous unproven conjecture in number theory. Christian Goldbach (1690–1764) stated in 1742 in a letter to Leonhard Euler (1707–83) that every even integer is the sum of two primes and every odd integer is either a prime or the sum of at most three primes. (A prime, or prime number, is any positive integer greater than 1 that is not divisible without remainder by any other positive integers except 1 and the integer itself.) The second part was largely resolved in 1937, when I.M. Vinogradov (1891–1983) showed that it was true for all sufficiently large odd integers. The first part, which properly is known as Goldbach's conjecture, was shown in 1938 to be true for almost all even integers—that is, true except for a set of even integers of density zero. (The density of a set of integers is the limiting proportion, as n tends to infinity, of $1/n$ times the number of integers among 1, . . . , n that are in the set. For example, the set of even numbers has density one-half, while the set of powers of 10 has density zero.) Chen Jingrun showed in 1973 that every sufficiently large even integer is the sum of two primes or else the sum of a prime and a product of two primes. Hans I. Riesel and Robert C. Vaughan showed in 1983 that every sufficiently large integer is a sum of at most 19 primes.

"Sufficiently large" and "almost all" do not satisfy mathematicians, nor do numerical instances of the truth of the conjecture, no matter how many of them are produced. Still, using a substantial amount of computing, Matti K. Sinisalo of the University of Oulu, Fin., verified that the Goldbach conjecture is true for all even integers up to 400 billion. It had previously been verified for up to 20 billion.

Bug in a computer chip

Research in number theory also resulted in the discovery of a flaw in the Pen-tium computer chip manufactured by In-tel Corp. and installed in five million personal computers. Thomas Nicely of Lynchburg (Va.) College was trying to improve an estimate for the sum of the reciprocals of twin primes. (A reciprocal is either of a pair of numbers, as 11 and $\frac{1}{11}$, whose product is one.) Twin primes, such as 11 and 13 or 29 and 31, are primes that differ by 2; it is unknown whether there are infinitely many such pairs. Viggo Brun (1885–1978) had proved in 1919 that even if there are infinitely many twin primes, the sum in question, which begins $(\frac{1}{3} + \frac{1}{5}) + (\frac{1}{5} + \frac{1}{7}) + (\frac{1}{11} + \frac{1}{13}) + \ldots$, converges to a finite value as more terms are added. The sum is approxi-mately 1.90216054, which is the total us-ing all twin primes up to 100 billion.

Nicely was trying to improve the esti-mate by using all twin primes into the tril-lions. Comparing the results of different computations, he found that the Pentium gave reciprocals for 824,633,702,441 and 824,633,702,443 that were incorrect from the 10th significant digit on. Simpler test examples that give errors are 4,195,835/3,145,727, in which the Pentium is correct to only four digits, and the calculation $4,195,835 - [(1.3338204) \times 3,145,727]$, which should give 0 but for which the Pentium yields 256. Under intense pres-sure Intel agreed to provide a new cor-rect replacement chip free to users who

In an unprecedented achievement, each U.S. team member earned a perfect score in the International Mathematical Olympiad.

114, 381, 625, 757, 888, 867, 669, 235, 779, 976, 146,

612, 010, 218, 296, 721, 242, 362, 562, 561, 842, 935,

706, 935, 245, 733, 897, 830, 597, 123, 563, 958, 705,

058, 989, 075, 147, 599, 290, 026, 879, 543, 541 =

3, 490, 529, 510, 847, 650, 949, 147, 849, 619, 903, 898,

133, 417, 764, 638, 493, 387, 843, 990, 820, 577 x

32, 769, 132, 993, 266, 709, 549, 961, 988, 190, 834, 461,

413, 177, 642, 967, 992, 942, 539, 798, 288, 533

RSA-129, created in 1977 as a 129-digit secret password for a data-encryption system, was factored in 1994 by means of an international computing effort employing 1,600 computers.

request it. In April 1995 Intel agreed to pay claims by customers who had used the flawed chip plus $6 million for their lawyers' fees. (For additional information, *see* Year in Review: ELECTRONICS AND INFORMATION SCIENCES: *Computers and Computer Science.*)

Factoring success

Contemporary public-key cryptography depends for its security on the difficulty of factoring integers. For each user there are two keys. One, the public key, is published and can be used by anyone to encode a message. The other key is kept secret and is used by the receiver of the message to decode it. In practice the public key is an integer of several hundred digits that is the product of two primes, each at least 100 digits long. The private key is one of the two primes (from which the other can be determined easily by division). A person who knows both component primes can decode the message. The security of the message thus depends on how easy it is for someone with the public key but without the private key to factor an integer into its component primes.

In 1977 the inventors of one particular patented public-key cryptography system, called the RSA system, encoded a message by using a 129-digit public key, known as RSA-129. They proposed that with the computer hardware and algorithms (step-by-step mathematical procedures) available in 1977, it would take at least 40 quadrillion years to factor RSA-129. In April 1994, however, an international computing effort, distributed among 1,600 computers, succeeded in factoring RSA-129 and decoding the message after eight months.

Despite the use of hundreds of computers that are thousands of times as fast as 1977 computers, what made the factoring possible in so short a time was the great improvement in the factoring algorithm. The main method was the quadratic sieve, invented in 1981 by Carl Pomerance of the University of Georgia. Its basic idea is that if the integer n to be factored can be expressed as the difference of two squares, so that $n = x^2 - y^2$, then algebra gives a factorization of n as $(x + y)(x - y)$ unless x and y differ by only 1. More generally, if $(x^2 - y^2)$ is a multiple of n, then $(x - y)$ divides

it, so that the greatest common divisor of $(x - y)$ and n divides n itself. If this greatest common divisor is not 1, then a factor of n has been found. (For additional information, *see* ELECTRONICS AND INFORMATION SCIENCES: *Computers and Computer Science.*)

Molecular computing

During the past year Leonard Adleman of the University of Southern California conducted a laboratory experiment in which he solved an instance of the directed Hamiltonian path problem. The problem was to find a path connecting seven cities, passing through each exactly once, when routes exist between only some pairs of them.

In the experiment the cities were represented by short DNA sequences and the routes between them as oligonucleotides (strands of DNA), and the solution emerged as the presence of a particular DNA molecule. Adleman employed the inherent parallelism of the many molecules that were present to solve the problem. The parallelism consists of each of the approximately 10^{20} DNA sequences of each type independently combining with others to form virtually all possible molecules, including the one that corresponds to the solution of the problem. Adleman spent a year learning the necessary laboratory techniques of molecular biology. Since Adleman's success, fellow computer scientists have explored how to apply his techniques to other problems.

Packing spheres

Controversy persisted over whether Wu-Yi Hsiang of the University of California, Berkeley, has proved the Kepler conjecture. First enunciated by Johannes Kepler (1571–1630) in 1611, it states that the densest way to arrange same-size spheres in three-dimensional space is face-centered cubic packing, in which one layer of spheres arranged in horizontal rows nestles in the depressions of the similar rows above and below. This packing has density $\pi/\sqrt{18} = 0.74048....$

Hsiang announced a proof in 1990 and published it in 1993. A team of skeptical mathematicians then examined the proof closely and declared in 1994 that the paper did not offer enough support and details for its claims and could not be considered a proof; just as with the proof that Wiles originally offered for Fermat's last theorem, they concluded that there are gaps. Hsiang for his part responded to their specific mathematical objections and insisted that his critics have either not followed his ideas or else misunderstood them.

The situations of Wiles and Hsiang point out how difficult it can be to know for certain if a particular argument in fact proves what it claims. Occasionally, as with the proof of the Bieberbach conjecture in 1984 by Louis de Branges of Purdue University, West Lafayette, Ind., the matter is clinched by the subsequent development by others of simpler proofs based on the original ideas.

—Paul J. Campbell

MEDICAL SCIENCES

Isolation of the gene responsible for inherited breast cancer, a new blood test for heart attacks, proof of the effectiveness of a surgical procedure in reducing the risk of stroke, and a new vaccine for genital herpes were among the major advances in the medical sciences during the past year. A newly developed diagnostic test rapidly detected influenza in horses, and oral biologists identified the location of a gene that plays a major role in the hardening of dentin in teeth.

GENERAL MEDICINE

When the year began, most of the U.S. medical world, from caregivers to basic researchers, thought that 1994 would be remembered as the year of health care reform. But as it became clear that federal efforts to overhaul the health care system would not be successful, medical sciences in general—and genetics in particular—seized center stage, making 1994 the year when medical science finally began to get a firm grip on the molecular roots of some of the most common killers and disablers of humankind, including breast cancer, heart disease, osteoporosis, diabetes, and even obesity.

Cancer

Perhaps the most striking discovery of the year was announced in September when researchers from the University of Utah, the National Institute of Environmental Health Sciences, and Myriad Genetics Inc. revealed that they had won the four-year race to isolate the gene responsible for inherited breast cancer. Flawed versions of the gene, called BRCA1, are believed to cause 5% of all cases of breast cancer, a disease that strikes about one in nine women in the U.S. In the midst of the fanfare that greeted their report in the journal *Science,* researchers voiced hope that their discovery would lead to a new genetic screening test for breast cancer within two years. That optimism was dimmed by subsequent reports, however, that the unusually large gene can be flawed in at least 50 different ways, which makes it difficult to develop a reliable universal screening test.

Molecular biologists also added more key pieces to the genetic puzzle of another common killer—colorectal cancer. Following up on their discovery in December 1993 of the first gene for hereditary nonpolyposis colorectal cancer (HNPCC), an inherited form of colon cancer that affects as many as one in 200 people, researchers from the Dana-Farber Cancer Institute, Boston, and Johns Hopkins University, Baltimore, Md., in March reported the isolation of another gene that can also cause HNPCC. Both genes, in effect, act as genetic proofreaders, carrying instructions for proteins that help cells repair damage to their DNA. If these genes are defective, other repair mechanisms fail to spot and subsequently fix mistakes in a cell's DNA code and thus allow mistakes to accumulate in the cell's genetic material—errors that eventually can cause a cell to become malignant.

Scientists also began to explore the genetic underpinnings of melanoma, a deadly form of skin cancer that each year claims the lives of nearly 7,000 Americans. In September two separate studies implicated defects in a previously discovered "tumor suppression" gene, called p16, in some inherited cases of melanoma. The gene codes for a protein that helps regulate cell division.

Genetic research also yielded clues that may lead to better diagnosis, treatment, and even prevention of kidney cancer. In

May scientists from the National Cancer Institute identified the gene responsible for the most common type of kidney cancer, which is called sporadic clear cell carcinoma. The gene was found to be the same one that was pinpointed in 1993 as the cause of a rare inherited cancer syndrome called von Hippel-Lindau disease. Researchers said that their first goal for applying their newfound genetic knowledge was to develop a blood or urine test for early detection of kidney cancer. When a patient is diagnosed with the disease in its earliest stages, the survival rate is nearly 90%, compared with a survival rate of less than 20% for patients whose cancer is detected later.

For people at risk for a type of inherited thyroid cancer called multiple endocrine neoplasia type 2A (MEN-2A), 1994 marked the year that the dream of a genetic screening test became a reality. Researchers from Washington University, St. Louis, Mo., reported the development of a reliable test that can help physicians determine whether a child has inherited a defective MEN-2A gene. If a child has a flawed version of the gene, he or she almost always develops thyroid cancer just before puberty or during the teenage years. If the child has a normal MEN-2A gene, however, there is no cancer risk, as well as no risk of passing the genetic defect on to offspring. For those children who test positive for flawed MEN-2A genes, surgeons can remove their thyroids before puberty, which essentially "cures" such children of thyroid cancer before they develop the often fatal disease.

A more audacious attempt at genetic screening—a broad-based method aimed at detecting many types of cancer in their earliest, most treatable stages—was unveiled in October by researchers at Johns Hopkins University. The scientists said that the test screens for specific errors in DNA replication, called clonal markers, that act as a "red flag" for cancerous growth. In preliminary tests different body fluids were drawn for different cancer types, and the DNA from cells present in those fluids was then amplified by a technique called polymerase chain reaction to make the clonal markers easier to detect. For example, urine was tested for bladder cancer and sputum for lung cancer. Widespread human trials of the new screening test, estimated to cost about $50, were scheduled to begin in 1995.

Despite all the powerful ammunition that genetics can provide in the war against cancer, the past year also furnished strong evidence that genetics is not the total answer to combating the disease. In a paper published in *The Lancet* on August 13, National Cancer Institute researchers reported that their study of nearly 16,000 pairs of male twins found that heredity appears to play only a small role in the risk of developing lung cancer—the leading cancer killer in the United States. Leaders of the study said that cigarette smoking appeared to be the biggest risk factor for lung cancer, adding that it is probably a mistake for smokers to believe that they are protected from lung cancer just because they have close relatives who smoked for a long time and did not develop it. Smoking also was found to be a major culprit behind pancreatic cancer, one of the most lethal forms of cancer. Reporting in the *Journal of the National Cancer Institute,* epidemiologists said they found that longtime cigarette smokers were twice as likely to develop pancreatic cancer as nonsmokers. Only about 3% of patients with pancreatic cancer survive longer than five years after diagnosis.

Heart disease

Evidence that certain genetic makeups may offer protection against heart disease continued to mount in 1994. In September researchers from the Bowman Gray School of Medicine, Winston-Salem, N.C., presented data indicating that a common variant of a gene that encodes a fat-binding protein called Apolipoprotein A-IV may confer resistance to the artery-clogging effects of dietary cholesterol. The study of 11 people with one copy of the variant gene and one normal gene found that even a very high-cholesterol diet had little to no impact on their blood cholesterol levels. About one in seven Americans had at least one copy of the potentially protective gene variant, which possibly explains why some people can eat large amounts of eggs and other cholesterol-rich food and still have normal levels of cholesterol in their bloodstream.

A four-year study examining the blood cholesterol levels of nearly 1,000 people suggests that high blood cholesterol levels may pose less of a heart-disease risk to the elderly than they do to younger people. Researchers from Yale University found that among women over the age of 70 those with "high" cholesterol levels—above 240 mg per deciliter of blood—actually had better survival rates than those with lower readings.

In regard to the treatment of heart disease, the year produced mixed results. A team from Johns Hopkins University uncovered a possible explanation for why estrogen replacement therapy dramatically reduces the risk of heart attacks in women. In a study of postmenopausal women, researchers found that estrogen appears to prevent the constriction of arteries that occurs in response to cold-related stress. In many people at risk for heart attacks, the arteries around the heart respond to cold and other stressors by constricting.

Cardiologists at Baylor College of Medicine, Houston, Texas, reported the development of a new blood test that they claimed could help to determine quickly which patients with chest pains actually have suffered a heart attack. About five million people go to U.S. emergency rooms each year complaining of chest pain, but fewer than one-third have had a heart attack. The new test measures changes in the ratio between two forms of an enzyme released by the heart. Conclusive results are usually available within 1¼ hours, compared with the daylong wait using the previous method.

A drug commonly used to treat heart attacks was found in 1994 to have some potentially life-threatening side effects if not carefully administered. While conducting studies to compare the effectiveness of the standard clot-dissolving drug heparin with that of the experimental drug hirudin, two research teams discovered that increasing the dose of heparin as little as 20% could double a patient's risk of stroke. The trials were stopped, and physicians were warned not to exceed standard doses of heparin.

Stroke and neurological disorders

In September, in an unusual step, officials from the U.S. National Institutes of Health brought to an early conclusion a seven-year trial to evaluate the effectiveness of a surgical procedure in reducing the risk of stroke. The 1,700-patient trial was halted after researchers concluded that carotid endarterectomy, a procedure in which surgeons remove fatty deposits from the neck arteries that supply blood to the brain, cuts in half the five-year risk of stroke in patients with no outward sign of disease. Previously, surgery had not been recommended for patients with narrowing of the carotid arteries but with no strokelike symptoms. Blockage of the carotid artery is a major contributor to the nearly 150,000 stroke deaths that occur in the U.S. each year.

Sadly, 1994 will also be remembered as the year in which one of America's most prominent citizens, former president Ronald Reagan, disclosed that he has one of the most common—and most devastating—of neurological disorders, Alzheimer's disease. A statement from Reagan's physicians indicated that he was in the early stages of the disease, which is characterized by progressive confusion, memory loss, personality changes, dementia, and, eventually, death. As of 1995 there was no cure for Alzheimer's, which afflicts some four million Americans and is the fourth leading cause of death in the U.S., after heart disease, cancer, and strokes.

Experiments by molecular biologists and neuroscientists further strengthened the hypothesis, first proposed in 1992, that one variant of the gene coding for the cholesterol-carrying protein called Apolipoprotein E (ApoE) may play a key role in the development of Alzheimer's disease. First, a study in May revealed that a variant of ApoE called ApoE-IV stunts the branching of young nerve cells in laboratory dishes, while other variants of the protein stimulate healthy nerve-cell growth. Then, in November, other data suggested that ApoE-IV may also act in concert with another molecule, called ACT, to form the fibrous, neurotoxic plaques that riddle the brains of Alzheimer's victims.

Hopes for a simple, safe drug treatment for Alzheimer's were rekindled by an intriguing study by scientists at Duke University, Durham, N.C., that found a link between the use of common anti-inflammatory drugs and a delay or halt in the onset of the disease. In their study of 50 elderly pairs of twins of whom at least one twin had Alzheimer's disease, researchers found that unaffected twins were four times more likely to regularly use such anti-inflammatory drugs as steroids, ibuprofen, naproxen, or aspirin than were their affected siblings. Although scientists emphasized that their findings needed to be confirmed in larger studies, they concluded that the research underscores the possibility that inflammatory responses in the brain may be an integral part of the Alzheimer's disease process.

Perhaps the most immediately applicable advance related to Alzheimer's disease during the past year came in the diagnostic arena. In the past, doctors had no good way of detecting the disease, and patients often had to undergo a complex series of physical and psychological exams to make sure that their memory loss and other symptoms were not caused by other factors. An unusual method may provide a much simpler route to diagnosis, however. Following up on leads provided by ophthalmologists' observations, Harvard University neuroscientists studied 60 elderly people and found that subjects who had Alzheimer's were about four times more sensitive to tropicamide, a drug used to enlarge patients' pupils during routine eye examinations, than those without the disorder. The development of an easy diagnostic test for Alzheimer's disease not only could reduce the problem of misdiagnosing older people who actually suffer from treatable neurological or psychiatric problems but might also help researchers better select patients for trials of potential therapies for the disease.

Osteoporosis

To the surprise of many medical experts, a single gene was linked to a seemingly complicated scourge of elderly women, brittle bone disease, or osteoporosis. Australian biomedical researchers found that among 250 identical and fraternal twins, an increased risk of osteoporosis was associated with one variant of the gene that orchestrates the formation of the vitamin D receptor. That receptor is thought to play a pivotal role in regulating bone formation and disintegration.

If the Australian findings are confirmed in larger studies, it may be possible to develop a simple genetic screening test that could identify people at risk of developing the disease later in life, especially girls and young women. Osteoporosis-prone people could then avoid smoking, exercise more often, and in-

crease their dietary intake of calcium—factors all known to slow the thinning of bones.

Diabetes

A technical advance in surveying the human genome confirmed previous suspicions and yielded new insights on the genetic cause of insulin-dependent, or type 1, diabetes. Scientists from the University of Oxford combined computer and laser technology to quickly scan chromosomes, locating a small stretch of DNA that appears to contain a gene cluster responsible for the most severe form of diabetes. The cluster contains the HLA region, which codes for immune-system proteins and which was already implicated in diabetes, along with at least three other genes thought to influence the disease process. The exact function of the new genes remained to be determined.

Diabetes treatment also advanced in 1994. Researchers at the National Institute of Child Health and Human Development reported that in a small pilot study they had succeeded in reducing the insulin requirements of teenagers with diabetes by as much as 40% by giving them a new peptide hormone called insulin-like growth factor, or somatomedin C. Originally, it had been thought that the hormone acted only to mediate the effects of growth hormone on bone growth during adolescence. More recent research, however, indicated that the hormone also enhances sugar uptake into the musculoskeletal system throughout life.

Another common problem faced by people with diabetes is nerve damage in the lower limbs, which can lead to infection, ulcers, gangrene, and even ampu-

tation. In a study published in *The New England Journal of Medicine* in September, Pennsylvania State University physicians outlined a simple strategy to check if patients are losing nerve sensation in their feet. In the test a thin, hairlike nylon filament attached to a plastic handle is run across a patient's legs and feet. If patients cannot feel the fiber, researchers say they are at increased risk of developing limb-threatening infections and should be carefully educated and possibly prescribed special footwear.

Obesity and diet

For people who would rather blame their genes than their late-night snacks for their expanding waistlines, 1994 provided some scientific support in the form of some fat yellow mice from New York. In a much-publicized paper published in the December 1 issue of *Nature,* researchers at Rockefeller University, New York City, reported the discovery of the obese, or "ob," gene responsible for turning those laboratory mice into corpulent blobs weighing up to three times more than the average mouse. The scientists then went on to clone a human gene that closely resembles the mouse ob gene, which codes for a protein that is supposed to alert the brain that the body's fat cells are "full." Researchers suspect that in the fat mice the ob protein is defective, and the brain never receives the signal to stop eating. Despite the considerable attention paid to the ob gene and to the possibility of genetically engineered diet strategies, scientists cautioned that only the most severe cases of human obesity are likely to be caused by a single gene. Meanwhile, most over-

This overweight laboratory mouse (left) can blame its girth on a defect in an obese, or "ob," gene, discovered during the year by Rockefeller University researchers.

weight people probably have a complex array of genes as well as environmental factors that contribute to their girth, researchers said.

Obesity, as the ob mouse researchers noted, is the most common nutritional disorder in Western societies. In December an expert panel convened by the U.S. National Academy of Sciences concluded that 35% of U.S. women and 31% of U.S. men are obese despite the fact that Americans spend more than $33 billion a year on weight-loss diets and programs. That excess weight exacts a major health toll, with obesity contributing to deaths from diabetes, hypertension, heart disease, and other medical disorders.

A study of nearly 1,200 men by Johns Hopkins University researchers found that a 1.8-m (5-ft 11-in) man who weighed 86.2 kg (190 lb) during his 20s was nearly four times as likely to develop painful knee and hip osteoarthritis later in life as a man of similar height who weighed 66.2 kg (146 lb) in his 20s. Additional data indicated that obesity may even alter the immune system, possibly rendering overweight people vulnerable to certain diseases. In tests involving 40 obese

adolescents, researchers found that the teenagers' immune cells spontaneously secreted large amounts of a potentially toxic protein, called tumor necrosis factor, while the cells taken from normal-weight teenagers did not.

Reproduction

Researchers launched the first wide-scale study of the so-called French abortion pill, RU-486, in the U.S. More than 2,100 women at about a dozen centers nationwide were expected to receive the pregnancy-terminating drug in the controversial trial. RU-486, already approved for use in many European nations, works by blocking progesterone, a necessary hormone for pregnancy.

A U.S. government advisory panel in September recommended guidelines that would allow government funding for a wide range of human embryo research. The panel recommended against funding research involving the creation of clones, identical copies of a single cell or embryo, or chimeras, embryos made up of mixtures of human and nonhuman cells, but it did support the creation of embryos solely for research purposes. In De-

cember, however, U.S. Pres. Bill Clinton announced that the government would not support studies that used human embryos created specifically for research.

In November at the American Fertility Society meeting in San Antonio, Texas, reproductive biologists from Monash University, Clayton, Australia, reported that they had devised a better method of in vitro fertilization (IVF), the process used to make so-called test-tube babies. The alternate approach, which involves collecting immature eggs from the mother and "ripening" them outside the body prior to fertilization in a laboratory dish, is cheaper, simpler, and easier on the mother because it eliminates the need for fertility drugs and daily monitoring. As of early 1995, four babies had been produced worldwide by this "immature oocyte collection" method.

AIDS and infectious diseases

The 10th International Conference on AIDS, held in Yokohama, Japan, in August, served to bring into focus the tragic gulf between basic scientific knowledge and useful treatments that has troubled scientists and patients since the outset of the epidemic in the early 1980s. Even as intriguing findings were being presented on the basic machinery of the AIDS-causing HIV and its complex interactions with the human immune system, more than 10,000 people around the world were being newly infected with HIV each day, and there were no curative drugs or effective vaccines on the immediate horizon. As they had for the past several conferences, AIDS researchers hailed combination therapy as the best approach to attacking the deadly virus and emphasized the importance of new strategies to relieve HIV-related opportunistic infections and other symptoms, such as using a synthetic human growth hormone to increase body weight among people with HIV-associated wasting syndrome.

Perhaps the brightest ray of hope to emerge for HIV-infected people during the past year was increasing evidence that the retroviral infection may not always be fatal and that a small proportion of infected people go on to become long-term survivors. Lending support to a 1993 report of long-term survival among some HIV-exposed Kenyan prostitutes, U.S. immunologists at Johns Hopkins University detailed the case of an HIV-infected woman who has been healthy for 13 years and has only a trace of the virus within her body. The woman, who contracted HIV through a blood transfusion in 1981, may have been infected with replication-defective virus or may have powerful internal defenses against HIV, researchers said. Another ongoing study, conducted at the University of California, San Francisco, found that about 5% of people with HIV have no symptoms despite 12 or more years of infection.

Researchers hoped that studies of such long-term survivors may yield new information for AIDS drug development.

The outlook for an AIDS vaccine dimmed considerably in 1994. In June a U.S. AIDS advisory committee concluded that two AIDS vaccines being considered for wide-scale testing did not show enough promise to justify larger trials. In November, however, the World Health Organization (WHO) revealed that it would forge ahead with plans to begin large-scale tests of two other experimental AIDS vaccines in 1996 at sites yet to be determined.

Vaccines for some other infectious diseases met with more success. Researchers from the U.S. National Institute of Allergy and Infectious Diseases (NIAID) reported that an experimental vaccine reduced by one-third the number of genital herpes outbreaks in people who suffered from recurring bouts of the disease. More than 25 million Americans are infected with the sexually transmitted herpesvirus, which can cause repeated painful outbreaks of blisters on the genitals.

Another promising vaccine strategy targeted schistosomiasis, a disabling and potentially lethal parasitic worm infection affecting more than 200 million people throughout the Third World. Parasitologists from NIAID found that injections of a recently discovered immune system protein, interleukin 12, prevented organ damage in mice deliberately infected with eggs from worms that cause schistosomiasis.

The threat of antibiotic-resistant microbes and emerging infectious agents remained a major concern of both biomedical researchers and the public during

the year. The most publicized scare took place in the spring in Gloucestershire, England, where newspaper headlines blared sensational warnings about a new strain of "flesh-eating" bacteria that had suddenly stricken six people, killing three. Actually, the bacteria responsible for the outbreak, a virulent subtype of group A streptococcus, is not new and does not actually "eat" flesh. Nonetheless, the microbe, for yet-to-be-determined reasons, does appear to be more prevalent than in the past. It multiplies rapidly just below the surface of the skin, causing an often fatal condition called necrotizing fasciitis that destroys both skin and tissue as it spreads.

Perhaps a more grave threat than emerging infections was the problem of previously controllable infectious agents' developing resistance to standard drug therapies. In December WHO cautioned that misuse of antibiotics was fueling a resurgence of cholera, tuberculosis, and other diseases. WHO officials cited the example of the dysentery outbreak that afflicted Rwandan refugees in Zaire, saying that physicians were unable to treat the deathly ill patients until they finally located a drug to which the disease-causing microorganisms were not resistant.

Other treatment advances

Gene therapy pioneers made some significant strides and uncovered some potential pitfalls during the past year. In what was billed as the first report of successful human gene therapy to be published in a scientific journal, University of Pennsylvania researchers described in the April issue of *Nature Genetics* how they had used gene therapy to lower high blood cholesterol in a patient with familial hypercholesterolemia, an inherited disorder that often leads to fatal heart attacks and strokes early in life.

Scientists from the U.S. National Heart, Lung, and Blood Institute in September reported the first successful transfer of a healthy cystic fibrosis transmembrane-conductance regulator (CFTR) gene into the cells lining the lungs of cystic fibrosis (CF) patients. The new genes survived for less than two weeks, however, and so such genes would have to be given repeatedly for there to be any chance that gene therapy might improve a CF patient's long-term outlook. Meanwhile, results of a study of 900 CF patients indicated that an experimental drug can reduce respiratory infections and improve lung function in CF patients. Researchers found that CF patients receiving aerosolized doses of the genetically engineered drug dornase alpha (DNase) had up to one-third fewer respiratory problems requiring antibiotics than did untreated control subjects.

The field of transplantation also took some innovative steps during the year. Researchers from King's College Hospital in London reported that an artificial liver, which is used outside the body and is made of cloned human liver cells wrapped in synthetic material, was able to keep 9 of 12 patients alive until donor livers became available for transplant. An earlier version of the device had been tested in the U.S., but only one of 11 patients survived.

In a different approach toward filling the ever growing demand for transplant organs, scientists from Duke University and DNX Corp. reported in August that

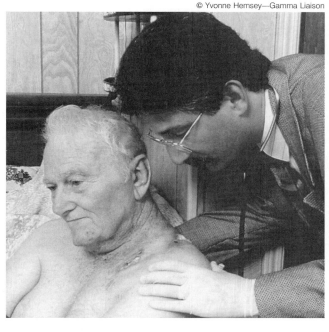

Suffering from a virulent form of group A streptococcus that can destroy skin and tissue as it spreads rapidly, a patient is saved by immediate treatment from a possibly quick and painful death.

gene transfer may make it possible to transfer organs across species. The researchers said that they had genetically engineered pigs so that the animals' hearts and other organs produced human proteins that guard against organ rejection. Hearts from the genetically altered pigs were than transplanted into four baboons, which have a genetic makeup similar to that of humans. Baboons receiving the genetically altered pig hearts survived 19 hours, compared with only about 40 minutes for baboons receiving regular pig hearts.

Doctors at Vanderbilt University, Nashville, Tenn., reported that they had repaired a common spinal defect, called spina bifida, in a 22-week-old fetus still in its mother's womb. The baby boy appeared healthy after delivery several months later, but physicians said that the child's long-term prognosis would not be

known for some time. Spina bifida is the most common birth defect in humans, occurring in about one in 1,000 births.

The treatment developments that had the biggest impact on the average person's life in 1994, however, did not involve genes or futuristic technology. In December two separate medical studies emphasized the importance of paying close attention to the warnings listed on drug labels, even for common over-the-counter painkillers. In their review of nearly 127,000 case records, University of Pittsburgh, Pa., researchers found that moderate overdoses of acetaminophen, defined as the equivalent of 8–20 extra-strength Tylenols taken within 24 hours, can lead to liver damage in patients who have been either drinking alcohol or eating very little. Another study of nonprescription painkillers found that heavy use of ibuprofen and acetaminophen may cause about 5,000 cases of kidney failure in the U.S. each year. Adults taking more than two tablets of ibuprofen a day for seven years had nine times the risk of kidney failure as those who took about two tablets a week, while those taking two tablets of acetaminophen a day for seven years faced a risk twice as high as that of less-frequent users.

Another major, but simple, shift in treatment strategies took place in December with the unveiling in the U.S. of federal treatment guidelines for acute low-back pain, a condition that strikes more than three-quarters of adults before age 50 and that costs the U.S. nearly $20 billion a year in direct medical expenses. Experts from the U.S. Agency for Health Care Policy and Research recommended against surgery, against X-rays and other expensive diagnostic tests, and also against prolonged bed rest. The panel concluded that low-stress exercise such as walking or swimming, aspirin, and spinal manipulation by chiropractors are usually the best remedies, noting that in 90% of cases, the back pain simply goes away by itself within a month.

—Rebecca Kolberg

DENTISTRY

While national health care reform in the U.S. appeared to be placed on the back burner during the past year, the dental profession intensified its already existing grass-roots efforts to provide care to indigent patients. From a reduced-fee dental care program in Massachusetts to a free dental clinic in California, dental societies and dental schools across the U.S. were doing their part to provide oral health care to people who other-

wise could not afford it, according to the American Dental Association (ADA).

Dentin-forming gene

Oral biologists at Northwestern University Dental School, Chicago, identified the location of a gene for a newly discovered protein believed to play a major role in the mineralization, or hardening, of dentin in teeth. The gene was named Dmp1 for "dentin matrix protein." The discovery marked the first time that a tooth-specific protein had been identified, cloned, and sequenced. Ann George, who directed the study, believed that a mutated form of the Dmp1 gene may also be responsible for a hereditary condition known as dentinogenesis imperfect type II (DI-II), which weakens tooth structure and causes teeth to turn a dull bluish brown. DI-II occurs in one in 10,000 people.

The Dpm1 gene was localized in mice on a chromosome that corresponds to a similar human chromosome, where, coincidentally, the gene for DI-II is located. Dentin, the major tissue of teeth, is formed by cells called odontoblasts, which secrete collagen, a protein that defines the shape of tissues. Further experiments showed that Dmp1 is found only in teeth and that the gene for Dmp1 is "turned on" only when odontoblasts are mature enough to play a role in the assembly of the mineralized dentin framework. The researchers found evidence of Dmp1 expression in animals beginning two days after birth.

Bone-measuring devices

By means of X-rays and two instruments developed by University of Buffalo, N.Y.,

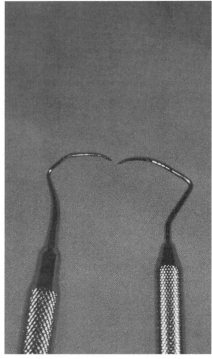

When used in conjunction with X-rays, these newly developed instruments can help oral surgeons accurately assess the degree of bone regeneration after periodontal surgery.

dental researchers, bone regeneration after periodontal surgery can be accurately assessed without additional surgery. Othman Shibley told the International Association for Dental Research (IADR) meeting in Seattle, Wash., that the handheld instruments can be used at the time the periodontal surgery is performed and after complete healing has taken place (six months to a year later).

It is important to assess the volume of bone density at the time of the surgery and afterward to determine if the surgery was successful in removing bacteria and unhealthy tissue. X-rays alone do not provide an accurate assessment of the volume achieved over time. Combined with X-rays, however, which provide a measurement of width, the new devices add measurements of height and depth, providing three-dimensional figures. When multiplied, these figures provide a measurement of the volume of bone density.

The first instrument designed by the Buffalo researchers is angled slightly at the tip so that it will catch under the roof of the furcation—the space between the roots of a multiroot tooth such as a molar that is filled with bone if not eroded by gum disease. This probe measures the distance from the roof to the free gingival margin (gum line). The second probe, which is curved horizontally with one-millimeter increments, measures the horizontal distance of the furcation.

In another report presented at the IADR meeting, researchers described a five-minute test designed for use in the dentist's office to determine the presence of antigens from three major bacteria found in localized juvenile periodontitis (LJP). Sara G. Grossi, assistant professor of oral biology at the University of Buffalo, said that the test also could be used to detect bacteria prevalent in the adult form of periodontal disease. Loss of attachments of tooth-supporting tissue also was measured, with losses of three millimeters or less rated as healthy and those of four millimeters or greater labeled diseased. The researchers found that the higher the numbers for the bacterial antigens, the greater the losses.

Cloned bone grafts

Genetically engineered and cloned bone grafts could soon lead to a breakthrough in the field of implant dentistry, according to A. Hari Reddi, professor and director of the Laboratory of Musculoskeletal Biology at Johns Hopkins University. Speaking at the annual meeting of the American Academy of Implant Dentistry, in New Orleans, La., he pointed out that these grafts would result in more successful oral implants.

There are two major categories of dental implants: endosseous implants that are inserted into the bone and subperiosteal implants that fit directly over the jawbone. The key ingredient that enables the implant to integrate more completely into the existing bony foundation is a molecular cell initiator consisting of a family of seven bone morphogenetic proteins (BMPs) related to the development of normal organic form, Reddi explained. "Considerable progress has been made very recently in the identification and cloning of these BMPs. The biomechanics of BMP-induced bone formation needs to be further investigated before they can be applied to implant dentistry and orthopedic surgery," he added. In addition to benefiting dental implants, the use of BMP-induced bone formation was expected to improve many medical treatments, including the nonunion of fractures, segmental defects, bone ingrowth into prostheses, spinal fusions, bone cysts, and perhaps limb lengthening. Reddi concluded that cloned bone grafts seem certain to be far more advantageous than conventional bone grafts not only because they would offer a better implant but also because they would not carry the risk posed by cadaver bone grafts, which may have been infected by disease.

Another speaker discussed ways to ensure that human donor bone grafts are disease-free and become integrated with existing bone in the patient's jaw. Paul A. Schnitman said that bone purified by means of strong levels of radiation presents a lesser risk of disease transmission, and that demineralized and sterilized bone has the least disease-transmission risk.

Other developments

An oil-and-water-based mouthwash currently sold in Israel could soon help Americans who suffer from severe bad breath. The only truly effective mouthwashes sold in the U.S. contain the drug chlorhexidine, an antiseptic that is available by prescription only. The oil-and-water mouthwash developed in Israel works because bacteria adhere to the oil and are washed away with water during rinsing.

The number of root canal procedures performed in the U.S. doubled from almost 7 million in 1979 to nearly 14 million in 1990. Although many associate root canals with pain, "millions of people who have had a root canal are telling their friends and relatives that the procedure is not the traumatic life experience it's been perceived to be," explained Stephen Cohen, a professor of dentistry at the University of the Pacific, Stockton, Calif. In reality, root canals can often offer dental patients a relatively pain-free, cost-effective alternative to tooth extraction, tooth implants, and dentures. In fact, root canals are often the best way to preserve a tooth that has been infected with bacteria owing to fracture or a deep cavity, according to Cohen.

Patients suffering from dry mouth, often the result of irradiation for head and neck cancer, might benefit from taking pilocarpine, a drug that stimulates saliva production, according to Jonas T. Johnson at the University of Pittsburgh School of Medicine and Philip C. Fox and Ingrid H. Valdez of the U.S. National Institute of Dental Research. Oral dryness is a frustrating and potentially serious side effect of radiation therapy, affecting 43,000 cancer patients annually. Also known as xerostomia, it can produce considerable oral discomfort and pain, tooth decay, and mouth infections or ulcerations; it also may make chewing, speaking, and swallowing difficult.

—Lou Joseph

VETERINARY MEDICINE

Computer technology was rapidly finding its way into veterinary practices, and by 1995 more than 66% of them were using computers for business management, accounting, and medical records. During the past year the American Veterinary Medical Association (AVMA) established the Network of Animal Health (NOAH) as a component of the CompuServe on-line network. NOAH had five forums: clinical medicine, which addressed medical issues by species such as cattle or aquatic animals; specialty medicine, which addressed issues by specialties such as ophthalmology or surgery; professional issues, which addressed nonmedical topics such as veterinary medical law or practice management; organizations, which had an AVMA membership list; and industry, which provided current information on groups such as the pharmaceutical industry.

In one example of its usefulness, while traveling to a farm to treat a stallion, an equine clinician at the Purdue University School of Veterinary Medicine, West Lafayette, Ind., accessed NOAH's drug formulary through a laptop computer with a data-passage interface connected to the cellular phone in the veterinary vehicle. Information derived from the formulary provided a valuable learning experience for the veterinary students accompanying the clinician and enabled prompt treatment of the stallion upon arrival at the farm.

Veterinary legislation

On Oct. 14, 1994, both houses of the U.S. Congress voted unanimously to pass the Animal Medicinal Drug Use Clarification Act of 1994. Pres. Bill Clinton signed the bill into law a week later. Passage of this act represented the culmination of two years of intensive effort on the part of the AVMA, pharmaceutical manufacturers, agricultural organizations, animal owners, and humane organizations. The act amended the Federal Food, Drug, and Cosmetic Act and provided veterinarians with a degree of legal protection when, in their best professional judgment, the use of a legally available drug not labeled for that specific use (extralabel use) was selected for treatment of an animal disease. A major problem in veterinary medicine, especially in food-animal medicine, had been the limited availability of drugs approved for several important disease problems, making extralabel use essential. In addition, small-animal veterinarians could not legally use human drugs even when a comparable veterinary drug was not available.

With input from the veterinary profession, the U.S. Food and Drug Administration (FDA) planned to develop special guidelines for extralabel drug use. Important considerations would include existence of a veterinarian-client-patient relationship prior to extralabel use and a listing of drugs that could not be used in food-producing animals under any circumstances.

Equine medicine

Concern about the effect of climate on the health of horses that would be competing in the Olympic Games in Atlanta, Ga., in July 1996 prompted the initiation of studies in at least five countries planning to compete. During the Olympic equestrian events in Barcelona, Spain, in 1992, several horses collapsed from heat exhaustion. During these events the summer daytime temperature was 30° C (86° F) and humidity was 40%. Atlanta summer temperatures are similar, but the humidity may reach 80%.

Using horses trained to exercise on a treadmill, scientists at the Animal Health Trust Laboratory in Newmarket, England, were able to evaluate the effects of Atlanta's climate on equine health. Some of the horses were unable to complete the exercise regimen under conditions simulating those expected in Atlanta. Humidity appeared to be a greater problem than temperature because in conditions of high humidity the time required for a horse to cool down is much longer than the time previously allowed between the Olympic equestrian events. Results of the studies would be considered in recommending changes in the rules governing the event in Atlanta.

Diagnostic tests and disease treatments

A University of Florida veterinary scientist developed a rapid test (10 minutes) to detect AIDS-like diseases in cats. These diseases include feline leukemia and feline immunodeficiency disease. The test was similar to a saliva-based HIV test previously developed by that scientist but differed by using blood as the test material.

Researchers at Cornell University's Baker Institute for Animal Health, Ithaca, N.Y., developed a new DNA blood test that could identify the genetic defect causing progressive retinal atrophy (PRA) in Irish setters. The test could be applied at an early age and could distinguish between dogs that would become blind from PRA, were disease-free carriers of the genetic defect, or were free of the defect.

The incidence of equine influenza virus, the most important cause of acute respiratory disease in horses, was increasing worldwide. Collaborative research by scientists in Lexington, Ky., and Hong Kong led to the application of a human influenza diagnostic test to achieve rapid detection of influenza in horses. The test was able to detect the presence of equine-2 influenza virus in nasopharyngeal fluids within about 15 minutes. The traditional equine influenza serological diagnostic test required two weeks and the assistance of highly skilled technical personnel. In 1989 vaccinated as well as unvaccinated horses were susceptible to an equine influenza outbreak in the U.K. Explanations for the lack of protection by the vaccine included a change in the wild virus compared with the virus used

Proteins in the malignant catarrhal fever (MCF) virus are analyzed by means of electrophoresis, as scientists during the past year succeeded in developing the first reliable diagnostic test for MCF, a disease of cattle in which outbreaks vary in lethality.

in preparation of the vaccine and a short-lived antibody response to the vaccine. A new approach to the preparation of an equine influenza vaccine proved successful in early trials that involved the strain that caused the 1989 epidemic. Protection by the new vaccine lasted at least 15 months.

A collaborative effort between the U.S. Department of Agriculture and Washington State University scientists led to the development of the first reliable diagnostic test for bovine malignant catarrhal fever (MCF). Lethality associated with the MCF virus in cattle was quite variable from one outbreak to another. Cattle that survived an infection became carriers of the virus. U.S. cattle appeared to contract the disease from infected sheep, but infected sheep were only carriers, as they showed no clinical signs of MCF. Factors contributing to the disease-free carrier state in MCF and other diseases having carrier states were of great interest to medical scientists.

Many racetrack injuries to thoroughbred horses were found to result from weakened leg bone structure. The structural changes were subtle, rarely associated with readily observable clinical signs and not revealed by standard radiographic techniques. These changes could, however, be detected with scintigraphy, a technique usually limited to human medicine because of the cost of the equipment. An equine nuclear scintigraphy diagnostic service was established by a group of Long Island, N.Y., veterinarians. Application of this technique involved injection of an isotopic tracer that had a high affinity for growing and healing bone. Weakened areas of bone when not apparent could be identified by traditional radiographic examination; bone healing could be monitored; and altered blood flow in small bones of hooves could be evaluated.

Zoonotic diseases

Cat-scratch disease was first recognized more than 60 years ago, but only within the past few years had definitive information been obtained on the cause and incidence of this zoonotic disease (a human disease acquired from or transmitted to a vertebrate). While the disease had previously been attributed to a variety of infectious organisms, including viruses, the rickettsial organism *Rochalimaea henselae* was identified as its principal cause. In several surveys of cat populations, the incidence of antibodies against the organism was 30% to 60%. Signs of *R. henselae* infection in cats were rarely detectable, and more than 90% of humans who contracted it recovered without the need for hospitalization. More serious cases, however, occurred in people whose immune systems had been suppressed. Care in avoiding cat scratches and bites and washing hands after handling cats minimized the potential for disease transmission. Since fleas may be involved in transmission, a good flea-control program was also important.

Rabies was ranked as one of the top zoonotic diseases in the world. Human deaths were rare in countries with strong control programs and access to new postexposure vaccines, but in Third World nations the lack of control programs and of the human vaccine resulted in nearly 50,000 human deaths each year. Successes with the oral recombinant rabies vaccine, administered to animals in a special bait, led to expansion of the vaccine's applications. WHO announced plans for the world's first controlled field trials for vaccination of stray dogs. Oral immunization of foxes in Europe and Canada and raccoons in the U.S. had been successful. During the past year Tufts University School of Veterinary Medicine in North Grafton, Mass., participated in the distribution of 16,000 vaccine baits for raccoons along the Cape Cod Canal. Within seven days 97% of the baits had been consumed. Examination of feeding sites revealed the presence of raccoon tracks at 75% of the sites. Most of the small number of human rabies cases in the U.S. resulted from contact with rabid bats. As of 1995, oral immunization programs for bats had not been developed.

Since first diagnosed in the U.S. in 1975, Lyme disease has been identified in the U.K., continental Europe, and Japan in animals and people. Studies by Japanese veterinary scientists suggested that strain differences in the causative organism, *Borrelia burgdorferi*, might account for the differences in clinical signs reported for infected animals. The disease is transmitted by bites from infected ticks. A U.S. research team examined the question of whether infected dogs could serve as a source of infection for immature ticks. Results indicated that 78% of the ticks feeding on such dogs became infected. Thus, infected dogs could serve as reservoirs for the Lyme disease organism and could expand the infected tick population, which would increase the likelihood of human infection.

Tuberculosis was a reemerging disease of cattle just as it was of people, although the *Mycobacterium* species causing the disease in cattle and people were usually different. Importation of cattle from Mexico into the U.S. was thought to be one source of this disease in U.S. cattle. Since a high percentage of Mexican dairy cattle were infected, only steers and spayed heifers were imported. A skin test for tuberculosis in cattle was valuable in tuberculosis-eradication programs, but it did not identify every infected animal. A combination of the skin test with a new blood test was expected to improve the accuracy of test results. Cats were reported to be susceptible to both human and bovine tuberculosis. It appeared more likely that a cat would gain the infection from a human than the reverse.

—John M. Bowen

OPTICAL ENGINEERING

The recovering international economy ensured that the past year was a reasonably good one for optical engineering. Reduction of military spending was balanced by a growth in commercial optoelectronic developments, and more reliable solid-state lasers began to push the traditional gas and dye lasers out of the market. The production of traditional optical instruments did not grow significantly, but optics integrated with electronic systems and devices continued to take over the market.

Data storage

Optical data storage finally reached significant market penetration. By the end of 1994 the majority of personal computers (PCs) sold contained a CD-ROM (compact disc read-only memory) drive, and many predicted that by the end of 1995 all PCs sold would be equipped with a CD-ROM drive; this would make optical storage the medium of choice for the distribution and use of software and databases. A number of rewritable optical-disk devices were on the market, but they had not achieved the cost and performance status of traditional magnetic media for high-speed internal storage of data and programs. New magneto-optical drives offered rewritable gigabytes (billion bytes) of storage on disks that were 3.5 or 5.25 in in diameter. The time required for obtaining data from storage was significantly longer than on magnetic disks, however. Even higher information density achieved by the use of clever recording tricks was announced, and a disk holding up to five gigabytes of data was developed.

The heavy use of CD-ROM suggested that a market was developing of a write-once, read-many storage medium. One suggested high-volume CD-ROM type of storage contained 10 layers of data physically stacked in one disk.

Imaging applications

Traditional imaging optics appeared to be healthy when combined with electronics. The number of small video cameras continued to increase, with one innovation in 1994 being the use of a large-area liquid crystal display in the camera for display and pointing. The accepted standard for photography remained the 35-mm camera, with more than a dozen new or updated automated point-and-shoot cameras entering the market during the year.

During the past year color ink-jet printers for personal computers became the fastest-selling new computer output device. Some of these printers can produce photographic images with quality quite acceptable for consumer purposes, and CD storage of images may become more widespread among consumers in the near future.

The development of large high-quality two-dimensional arrays of charge-coupled device detectors permitted almost photographic quality to be achieved entirely electronically, and some professional and technical photographers began to use them. (A charge-coupled device is a semi-conductor device that stores charge and transfers it sequentially to an amplifier and detector.) The fully electronic photographic camera still seemed several years away from general consumer use but was becoming more widely used in the news and graphic arts field. Direct electro-optical methods of generating printed images did advance; scanners were used with ultraviolet lasers to write directly onto printing plates, bypassing the traditional making of expensive separation negatives.

Infrared imagery was made increasingly practical by the availability of lower-cost, uncooled, thermal imagers. Two-dimensional detectors such as a ferroelectric temperature-sensitive array at the focal plane do not require an active scanner, as with traditional infrared imagers, and are compatible with current television standards. The availability of such detectors permits their widespread use in thermal nondestructive testing, in nighttime surveillance, and, of course, for military purposes.

Other imaging applications that were realized during 1994 included high-resolution, multispectral Earth resources sensing. This was achieved by high-resolution imaging spectrometers, which can be flown in an aircraft to provide detailed information on the spectral reflection of light from the ground in the visible and near-infrared region. Massive quantities of data are obtained with a high-resolution spectral scan of each small region of interest on the ground. Such data can be used to gain considerable information about the condition of plants and minerals on the ground. Experimental data were being generated by the Advanced Visual and Infrared Imaging Spectrometer (AVIRIS) program at the Jet Propulsion Laboratory in Pasadena, Calif., soon to be supplemented by a new high-resolution instrument, Hyperspectral Demonstration Imagery Collection Experiment (HYDICE), principally funded by the U.S. Naval Research Laboratory.

Remote sensing

Several new applications for probing the environment involved active sensors. Remote sensing systems were being used to determine the concentration of molecular species at very high altitudes in the atmosphere, to detect early stages of diseases in plants, and to sense contaminants in soils. Dye lasers are scanned over a reasonably wide wavelength range, and their light is projected onto a region of interest. Scattering of photons by certain materials causes a rapid change in reflectivity as the laser is scanned through a particular wavelength. Thus, remote sensing of the amount of particular chemicals in an object can be achieved by collection of the light scattered off the target.

In the recent applications solid-state lasers pumped by laser diodes are replacing traditional dye lasers. In devices called optical parametric oscillators, a nonlinear crystal (one that produces a response that is not proportional to the influence) is irradiated by a diode-pumped solid-state laser, with variable wavelengths of output obtained by alteration of the crystal orientation. Outputs of better than a half watt with a tuning range including the visible and near infrared were demonstrated. Using high-power, solid-state tunable lasers permits construction of a less complicated device.

Artist's drawing reveals the segmented mirror of the Hobby-Eberly Telescope of the University of Texas at the McDonald Observatory in Texas. Scheduled for completion in mid-1996, the 11-meter-wide primary mirror will consist of 91 hexagonal segments and will be the first major instrument dedicated to spectroscopy.

Courtesy of McDonald
Observatory

Telescopes

The number of large astronomical telescope programs remained constant. By 1995 there were so many large-aperture telescopes in operation or construction that serious consideration was being given to closing down several smaller-aperture ones. The second Keck 10-m-aperture telescope was completed. Progress continued on the Japanese 8.31-m telescope with the delivery of the mirror blank from Corning, N.Y., to the polishing facility near Pittsburgh, Pa. Work continued on the European Southern Ob-

servatory (ESO) 8-m telescope project, with the mirrors being polished at a facility near Paris and construction continuing on a mountain in Chile. Twin 8-m-aperture Gemini telescopes to be located in Hawaii and Chile were being built by the U.S. National Optical Astronomy Observatory. The project continued with detailed design and construction. The first mirror blank was completed at Corning, N.Y., and was to be sent to Paris for polishing along with the ESO mirrors. The University of Arizona's large-mirror program continued, with the 6-m-diameter blank for the Multiple Mirror Telescope primary mirror replacement in the early stages of polishing.

Progress on the University of Texas segmented mirror telescope continued. This instrument would contain 91 spherical-surfaced mirror segments and a reflective aspheric corrector for the aberration produced by the primary mirror assembly. The telescope was expected to provide large-aperture spectroscopic capability over most of the sky at a modest cost. A program to build a very-high-resolution array using a few widely spaced one-meter-aperture telescopes was initiated by Georgia State University. This array had the theoretical capability to far exceed the resolution of the Hubble Space Telescope if all systems worked properly.

Early indications were that the repair of the Hubble Space Telescope in late 1993 was successful. There were renewed plans to install a new near-infrared imaging system during a maintenance mission in 1997 and some improved wide-field, high-resolution cameras during a mission in about 1999.

Other developments

Optical fiber applications for communications continued to grow. Most notable during the past year was the development of a number of new products for coupling, splicing, and splitting data in fiber-optic systems. These developments are important in providing the flexibility necessary for the widespread installation of optical fibers in individual residences. This use of fibers would permit access to a wide bandwidth range for individual users and was expected to smooth out some of the bumps on the information highway.

Fully optical computers did not come any closer to practical realization, though there were some minor developments in components for such devices. One major area of activity was in photorefractive materials. These materials exhibit temporary changes in the index of refraction (the ratio of the phase velocity of light in a vacuum to that in a specified medium) induced by light of a specific wavelength. This stored refractive index change produces a stored image that can be read out as required.

The development of automated fabrication machinery for conventional optical components moved forward, with several companies initiating the use of numerically controlled generators developed by the Center for Optical Manufacturing. Lens prototypes completed within less than a week were demonstrated, coming a bit closer to the idea of an optical foundry that would be similar to a semiconductor-chip prototyping system.

One interesting application announced during 1994 was the availability of laser-selective paints. These materials have a very high reflectivity at certain laser wavelengths. Such paints can be used to tag items for identification and were proposed for use on aircraft in order to help locate a downed plane from the air.

Very high-power diode-pumped lasers with 2.5–6 kw of peak power were demonstrated during the year. These lasers have many applications in machining and industrial processes. The reliability of fully solid-state lasers for these applications ensures continuing penetration into traditional machining applications. A major Technology Reinvestment Program was directing high-energy laser resources previously devoted to military purposes to the development of these devices.

Military applications continued to be highly funded even as overall defense expenditures decreased. Political changes in the U.S. produced a renewed call for implementation of the Strategic Defense Initiative, popularly known as Star Wars. The goals were generally more modest than in past years, with concentration on tactical weapons defense. Optics plays a basic role in such systems for guidance and control. The use of high-energy lasers as direct weapons was still being considered but as a secondary application.

Diffractive optics reached maturity and was expected to provide a growing part of the optics market in the coming years. Major growth was taking place in hybrid lenses, which are combinations of conventional refractive lenses and diffractive surfaces. Providing an additional capability of being able to correct chromatic aberration (a lens defect causing color fringes) in a single element, these components are suited for many applications, including many video and photographic cameras. The production of high-quality injection-molded plastic hybrid diffractive lenses was demonstrated during the year by several manufacturers and promised to become an important business. It was likely that such components would replace some standard imaging systems.

Another interesting application of diffractive optics is in placing binary encoded phase masks into ordinary images or documents, such as credit cards. A binary phase mask consists of a two-dimensional array of many adjacent steps of different heights that impresses a phase distribution into the light reflected from the mask. The effect is similar to the encoding of information on a compact disc. The arrangement of the steps can contain information that can be read by using another matching mask that filters the identification information from the mask associated with the document. The size of the steps can be sufficiently small that they are not readable by ordinary means. There are some practical limitations in such applications, but the development of inexpensive binary optical components makes the technique economical for high-value documents.

The developments in diffractive optics and variable-wavelength solid-state lasers along with the economically efficient production of conventional optics components provide a base for continuous growth in commercial optical and optoelectronic areas. In the longer term the introduction of new light-switching devices, such as those using photorefractive materials, greatly expands the possibility of integrating optical systems and computing technology.

—Robert R. Shannon

PHYSICS

A major event in physics during the past year was the announcement of persuasive evidence for the long-sought fundamental particle known as the top quark. Researchers also unveiled several new types of lasers, trapped short-lived radioactive atoms for the first time, and observed DNA molecules "reptating," or moving in a snakelike fashion, in a concentrated polymer solution. The fabrication of bright, blue light-emitting diodes (LEDs) was seen as a significant step toward improved flat-panel video displays and other optoelectronic applications.

GENERAL DEVELOPMENTS

Physicists in 1994 demonstrated several new concepts for lasers and measured the masses of atoms to new levels of accuracy. They also produced stationary uranium ions stripped of all of their electrons in order to verify modern atomic theory and tested the mechanical properties of DNA against theories that describe polymeric molecules.

New laser designs

The year 1994 was significant for laser researchers, who demonstrated several types of lasers that were fundamentally different in concept from earlier ones. Michael Feld and his colleagues of the Massachusetts Institute of Technology (MIT) announced the construction of a single-atom laser, which produces laser light by using one atom at a time. Lasers usually require billions of light-emitting molecules, atoms, or subatomic particles confined in a resonator, a structure (usually a cavity bounded by a pair of partially reflecting mirrors) that recirculates some of the light to sustain the laser process

while simultaneously producing an output beam.

The MIT researchers designed a resonator consisting of two highly reflecting mirrors spaced a millimeter (about 0.04 in) apart. They then passed a beam of energetically excited barium-138 atoms between the mirrors such that one atom at most was inside the resonator at any one time. As each excited atom entered the resonator, it was stimulated to emit a photon (quantum packet) of light energy via interaction with a photon that had been deposited in the resonator by a previous atom. Eventually enough photons built up in the resonator to emerge as a detectable laser beam. The device produced laser light in the near-infrared range, at a wavelength of 791 nm (nanometers; billionths of a meter). The single-atom laser is expected to be useful for precision measurements in atomic physics, particularly in investigations of the way that individual atoms interact with light.

Federico Capasso and his colleagues of AT&T Bell Laboratories, Murray Hill, N.J., devised a quantum-cascade laser, a design that is expected to allow traditional semiconductor laser materials to produce colors heretofore unachievable with that medium. In the quantum-cascade design, electrons climb and descend "energy staircases" to produce light. The staircases are actually ultrathin structures called quantum wells; the thickness of a well, typically measured in nanometers, dictates the allowed energy states for an electron. The AT&T researchers created a 500-layer semiconductor material containing quantum wells made of aluminum indium arsenide separated by barriers of

gallium indium arsenide. The material is divided into 25 groups of 10 wells and 10 barriers. As electrons pass through a series of wells, they first assume high-energy states; they then enter wells in which only lower-energy levels are allowed, which causes them to release photons whose energy is equal to the energy difference between the wells. The process then repeats as the electrons enter successive series of wells and barriers.

The AT&T device produced light in the mid-infrared range, specifically at a wavelength of 4.26 μm (micrometers; millionths of a meter)—traditionally a difficult range to obtain. By adjusting the quantum-well thicknesses, researchers should be able to fabricate variations that produce light in the range of 2–100 μm (the mid- to far-infrared range). Current versions of the laser operate only at very cold temperatures and produce light in pulses, not as a continuous beam. Once the design has been developed and refined, however, its potential wavelength range may make it suitable for use in automobile collision-detection systems and devices for measuring levels of atmospheric pollution.

Perhaps the most unusual laser of the past year was reported by Nabil Lawandy and his co-workers of Brown University, Providence, R.I., who demonstrated laser action in a device that lacks a proper resonator. The active ingredient in Lawandy's design is titanium dioxide, a compound familiar to people as a white pigment in paint. Lawandy's team first prepared a solution of a dye known as rhodamine 640 perchlorate dissolved in methanol. Shining green light through the dye produced a faint glow of orange light. However, adding titanium dioxide at a concentration of 10 billion particles per cubic centimeter to the dye greatly amplified the orange light. The result was surprising and left the researchers unsure as to the way that photons of light ricocheting off the randomly distributed titanium dioxide particles (in the form of crystals averaging 250 nm in size) could trigger a laser process. Although the design does not generate a conventional pencillike laser beam, it does produce the intense, essentially single-color light that characterizes lasers. Possible future applications include custom-designed "laser creams" that dermatologists could apply to the skin and then stimulate with a light source to remove unwanted marks or stains. It may also find use in special "laser-paint" pixels that could be used, for instance, in ultrathin television and computer displays.

Measuring atomic masses

MIT physicist David Pritchard and his colleagues during the year published mass values of greatly improved accuracy for nine isotopes (involving seven elements on the periodic table), plus the neutron, paving the way for redefining the kilogram and opening possibilities for the most stringent test yet of Einstein's equation $E=mc^2$. The kilogram remains the only basic scientific unit of measurement not defined in terms of fundamental physical constants. For instance, the standard for length, the meter, is defined as the distance that light travels in a vacuum in 1/299,792,458 second. The second is defined as the time required for a cesium-133 atom to undergo 9,192,631,-770 vibrations. The kilogram, in contrast,

is a platinum-iridium cylinder stored in Sèvres, France.

The new MIT mass table includes such important atoms as hydrogen, oxygen-16, and silicon-28. The atomic mass values, some of which are 1,000 times more accurate than previous measurements, have uncertainties in the range of 100 parts per trillion. The new values complemented those obtained by Robert Van Dyck and his colleagues of the University of Washington, who measured the mass for several other atoms, such as tritium (hydrogen-3) and helium-3, to comparable levels of accuracy.

To obtain such precise mass values, scientists use a device, known as a Penning trap, that catches and holds ions (electrically charged atoms or molecules) in electric and magnetic fields. Once the ion has been trapped, the researchers expose it to a radio-frequency field and tune the field until they detect the ion's cyclotron frequency, the rate at which the ion completes a circular orbit in the magnetic confines of the trap. The cyclotron frequency is directly proportional to an ion's ratio of electric charge to mass. Since the amount of charge on the ion is easily measured, the researchers can determine the mass of the ion. The trapped ions used for the measurements, in general, are not individual atoms but charged molecules containing the atoms of interest. From their measurements the researchers can extract values for individual atoms, which are expressed in terms of the mass of carbon-12.

How might these mass measurements result in a more fundamental definition for the kilogram? One way would be to begin with the new mass measurement

for ^{28}Si, one of the most-studied materials in the world because of its importance to the microelectronics industry. Its mass, as determined by the MIT group, is accurate to 70 parts per trillion, better than 10 times the accuracy of the physical kilogram mass in France. To redefine the kilogram in terms of ^{28}Si, however, scientists must make comparably accurate measurements of two other quantities: the density of an ultrapure ^{28}Si crystal and its lattice spacing, the distances between neighboring atoms in a crystal. Knowing the spacing would allow calculation of the number of atoms in a given volume.

As of early 1995 these two measurements were at best only $\frac{1}{10}$ as accurate as the ^{28}Si mass measurement but were in the process of being improved. Once all three quantities are known to sufficient accuracy, scientists can then calculate a precise new value of a constant called Avogadro's number—the number of atoms (or molecules) in a quantity of a substance equal to its atomic (or molecular) mass in grams. Since Avogadro's number is the same for all substances, it applies equally well to carbon as to silicon. A gram would then be defined as $\frac{1}{12}$ of Avogadro's number of carbon atoms (whose mass is defined as 12 atomic mass units). A kilogram is 1,000 grams.

The MIT team also plans to participate in a precise new test of $E=mc^2$, Einstein's famous equation that describes the interchangeability of energy and mass. Although the precision of the equation as a description of physical reality has stood firm for more than half a century, researchers are always testing it to make sure that it does not fail at increasingly fine levels of measurement. To conduct the test, the MIT team plans to use its mass values for nitrogen-14, nitrogen-15, and the neutron. When a ^{14}N atom and a neutron combine, the resulting ^{15}N atom is less massive than the sum of its parts because some of the mass is converted into energy and released as a pair of gamma rays. In another experiment being planned at Grenoble, France, physicists plan to test the E side of the equation by making highly accurate measurements of the energies of these gamma rays.

Bare uranium ions

While some researchers in 1994 succeeded in creating very heavy artificial elements in the laboratory (*see* Year in Review: CHEMISTRY: *Inorganic and Physical Chemistry;* and *Nuclear Physics,* below), others performed new tricks with the heaviest natural element—uranium. Best known for its association with nuclear fission, uranium can also provide great insights into several fundamental theories of physics. Einstein's special theory of relativity and the modern theory of the atom, known as quantum electrodynamics (QED), both predict a number of effects in atoms that are ordinarily very subtle and hard to detect. One avenue into this realm is provided by the uranium nucleus; its 92 positively charged protons produce an intense electromagnetic field that leads to pronounced QED and relativistic effects. Unfortunately, in its neutral form the uranium atom also possesses 92 electrons that orbit the nucleus. Their interactions add a staggering degree of complexity that easily obscures relativistic and QED effects.

In 1994 Ross Marrs and colleagues of Lawrence Livermore National Labo-ratory, Livermore, Calif., not only succeeded in stripping uranium atoms of all 92 electrons but also managed to hold the resulting ions (U^{92+}) stationary for precision measurements. Their accomplishment depended on a device called an electron-beam ion trap (EBIT). The device employs a beam of electrons, which is negatively charged, to attract a sample of uranium atoms previously stripped of one to four electrons each. The beam knocks off the remaining electrons while holding the ions with its electric field.

Using EBIT, the researchers performed several tests of theory. They made measurements on a series of uranium ions carrying 3 to 10 electrons and thus having the same electron configuration as the elements lithium through neon. Whereas QED theory accurately predicted the results for lithium-like uranium, it did not fare as well for uranium ions carrying more than three remaining electrons, which suggests that improved calculations are needed. Other EBIT experiments found that the probability of removing the final electron from U^{91+} with an electron beam at a particular beam energy (an energy at which the electrons are moving at near-light, or relativistic, speed) was 50% larger than theoretical predictions, which shows a need for improved treatment of relativistic interactions in present theories.

Manipulating DNA

One usually thinks of DNA as the molecule that stores genetic information in living cells, not as a molecule like those that make up plastics, rubber, and adhesives. Nevertheless, both DNA and the other materials belong to a class known as polymers—long chainlike structures comprising simple molecular units. In 1994 researchers used the laser equivalent of tweezers to manipulate single DNA molecules and test directly the predictions of polymer theory.

Scientists have tried for decades to learn the rules of polymer behavior. Making it difficult is the fact that polymers traditionally have been measured en masse—as billions of molecules in solution whose behavior has been averaged out. To measure single DNA molecules, Steven Chu and his co-workers of Stanford University isolated single molecular strands of DNA and attached fluorescent molecules to them to make them easier to image. They also attached a microscopic latex bead to one end of each strand. Using a pair of laser beams trained on the bead, the researchers were able to move it and thereby could stretch and contort the attached DNA molecule to order. The movement of the glowing DNA strand was picked up with a sensitive video camera.

When polymer molecules become crowded together in solution, they exhibit distinctive properties. In the early 1970s French physicist Pierre-Gilles de Gennes introduced the theory of reptation, which predicts that polymer molecules in a concentrated solution are restricted to moving in a snakelike fashion—they can move along their length but not sideways. To test the prediction, the Stanford experimenters pulled strands of DNA up to 100 μm long through contorted paths in a concentrated solution of 16-μm-long bits of DNA. In viewing subsequent movies of the motion, they found that the DNA indeed "reptated"—it moved

Thomas T. Perkins, Douglas E. Smith, and Steven Chu; Stanford University

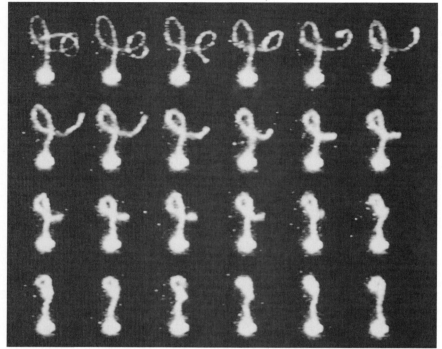

A stretched strand of DNA in a polymer solution "reptates" as it relaxes, following a contorted path drawn with optical tweezers by manipulation of a latex bead attached to one end of the strand. The sequence of images, made at 1.5-second intervals, reads from left to right, top to bottom.

in a restricted, lengthwise fashion even while highly stretched and with water molecules bombarding it from all sides.

The second law of thermodynamics states that everything in nature maintains or increases its amount of disorder—measured in a quantity called entropy. Polymers are no different; they spontaneously settle into a twisted, tangled, disordered shape. The Stanford researchers measured the rate at which polymers relax from a highly stretched shape, finding that a DNA strand's relaxation time was proportional to its length raised to the power of 1.66 ± 0.10. This value was closer to that predicted by one polymer model (the Zimm model) than another model (the Rouse model). Interestingly, the Zimm model takes into account an effect called hydrodynamic coupling,

in which forces between the individual chains within polymers are transmitted indirectly through the fluid in which they are dissolved. The better agreement of the Zimm model with experiment suggests that hydrodynamic coupling may be an important aspect of the behavior of polymers in solution.

—Ben P. Stein

ELEMENTARY-PARTICLE PHYSICS

Elementary-particle physics is often called high-energy physics, as a large part of the studies and discoveries in the field have been made with the use of particles accelerated to much higher energies than are typical in other fields of science. Many important discoveries, however, have also been made at rather low

energies, and energy in itself is not the only determining factor in the relevance of a particular experiment. In fact, the objectives of elementary-particle physics are to understand the constituents of nature at their most fundamental level as well as the forces, or interactions, that govern their behavior. The great majority of the elementary particles that are presently known are heavy and unstable and decay spontaneously to a few stable, lighter particles. To produce these heavier particles, physicists must create collisions at high energy, as the energy required to create a mass is equal to that mass multiplied by the velocity of light squared ($E = mc^2$). Often the heavy particles can be created only as pairs (a particle-antiparticle pair), and in many situations the available energy must be much greater that the energy equivalent to the mass of the produced particle for the probability of production to be great enough to be of use. Hence, there is a strong motivation to achieve collisions at ever higher energies, through the construction of ever more powerful particle accelerators, in order to discover predicted and unexpected new particles.

Nevertheless, much remains to be learned about the nature of the elementary particles already discovered, and many of the relevant studies can be done at lower energies, with either existing accelerators or new, specially designed accelerator systems. Nor are laboratory studies the only avenue to significant discoveries in particle physics. Scientists are taking increasing advantage of the strong link that exists between particle physics and astrophysics. Studies of particles from space—from the Sun and from within our Galaxy and beyond—are relevant to the solution of basic problems in particle physics. Developments during the past year provided examples of advances both at the high-energy frontier and at much lower energies.

The top quark

The recent achievements in elementary-particle physics must be viewed from the perspective of the standard model, the highly successful theoretical framework for organizing and understanding all known particles and forces as well as the more complex objects made from these particles. The fundamental particles are of two classes: quarks and leptons. Protons, neutrons, mesons, and other particles that experience the strong interaction are made of quarks, antiquarks, or both. Quarks have an electric charge of $+\frac{2}{3}$ or $-\frac{1}{3}$ (in units of the magnitude of the charge on an electron); antiquarks, the antimatter counterparts of quarks, have the opposite electric charge. Leptons, which do not experience the strong interaction, have an electric charge of -1 or 0. There are three generations of quarks and of leptons, giving 12 species of fundamental particles (plus 12 corresponding antiparticles). The neutral leptons, the neutrinos, are massless or nearly so. The negatively charged leptons and the quarks have masses (expressed as their equivalent energies) ranging from 0.511 MeV (million electron volts) for the electron to 176 GeV (billion electron volts) for the top quark. All of these particles have an intrinsic spin of $\frac{1}{2}$.

In addition to these particles, each of the four fundamental interactions between particles is propagated by a field quantum (field particle or gauge boson) with an intrinsic spin of 1 or 2. The strong interaction is mediated by the gluon, the weak interaction by the $W^{\pm}$ and Z^0 intermediate vector bosons, and the electromagnetic interaction by the photon.

Ordinary stable matter is made of only three elementary particles: the up and down quarks and the electron. Protons and neutrons, the nucleons of all stable nuclear matter, are composed of up and down quarks, the lightest of the quarks; the heavier quarks decay into them through the weak interaction. Correspondingly, the tau and mu leptons decay to electrons.

Until recently the most massive quark known was the bottom (b) quark, with a mass of 4.1–4.5 GeV. The top (t) quark was known to be more than 130 GeV in mass but had not yet been observed. The availability of 1,800 GeV of energy at the center of mass of proton-antiproton collisions in the Tevatron colliding-beam accelerator at the Fermi National Accelerator Laboratory (Fermilab) near Chicago made possible a serious search for the t quark. Two major collaborations, called CDF and D0, assembled large detectors at the Tevatron that were engineered to be sensitive to the existence of the t quark. In April 1995 both collaborations published persuasive evidence for the particle. CDF reported 56 events with signatures consistent with the production of pairs of t quarks, compared with a background of about 20 such events expected from other, "conventional" processes. This group deduced a mass for the t quark of 176 GeV with about a 7% uncertainty. The D0 group reported 17 events, compared with an expected 4 background events. Their reported mass was somewhat higher than

THE STANDARD MODEL				
particles[1]				
	quarks		leptons	
electric charge[2]	$+\frac{2}{3}$	$-\frac{1}{3}$	-1	0
generation				
1	up (u)	down (d)	electron (e)	electron neutrino (υ_e)
2	charm (c)	strange (s)	muon (μ)	muon neutrino (υ_μ)
3	top (t)	bottom (b)	tau (τ)	tau neutrino (υ_τ)
field quanta[3]				
force	field quantum		electric charge[2]	spin[4]
strong interaction	gluon (g)		0	1
electromagnetism	photon (γ)		0	1
weak interaction	{ intermediate vector bosons }	($W^{\pm}$) (Z^0)	+1 or −1 / 0	1 / 1
gravity	graviton (G)		0	2

[1] Particles have intrinsic spin of $\hbar/2$, or about 3.3×10^{-22} MeV-seconds.
[2] Electric charge in units of the magnitude of charge on an electron; 1.6×10^{-19} coulomb.
[3] Field quanta have intrinsic spin of 1 or 2 units of $\hbar$.
[4] Spin in units of $\hbar$ (Planck's constant/2π), or about 6.6×10^{-22} MeV-seconds.

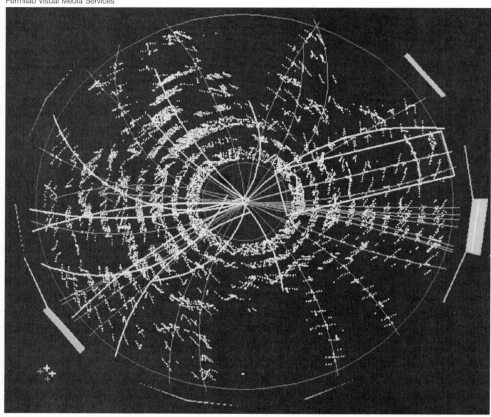

A computer-generated image shows data gathered from a proton-antiproton collision in the form of tracks of particles emerging from the center of the collision. Billions of such collisions at Fermilab's Tevatron were examined to find particle signatures consistent with the decay of a top quark.

CDF's but also less certain. The masses reported by the two groups are consistent within their quoted errors. Once produced, the t quark decays promptly into a b quark and a W boson; they, in turn, decay into quarks, leptons, or both. It is on the analysis of these rather complex final states that the discovery of the t quark is based; hence, the evidence for it is less direct and more difficult to extract than had been the case for the lighter elementary particles found previously. The mass of the t quark, essentially that of the nucleus of a gold atom, is surprisingly large for an "elementary" particle. Now that its existence is established, an extensive program to understand its decay and other properties will begin.

Neutrino masses and oscillations

Neutrinos indeed may be massless (as had long been thought), but no physical laws or constraints of the standard model require that they be so. The best measurements reported to date set upper limits of 4.5 eV (electron volts) on the electron-neutrino mass, 160 KeV (thousand electron volts) on the muon-neutrino mass, and 29 MeV on the tau-neutrino mass. According to theory, if their masses are not zero, a significant effect might follow—specifically, one type of neutrino may be able to transform, or oscillate, into another type. For example, some nuclear reactions produce electron neutrinos, which can be detected with suitable equipment. If neutrinos can change identities, then a collection of particles that emerge from a source of nuclear reactions can arrive at a detector as a mixture of electron neutrinos and muon neutrinos. Consequently, the flux of observed electron neutrinos coming from the reaction source will be less than that calculated from simple geometric considerations. Observations of two puzzling phenomena, one involving the Sun and the other involving cosmic rays, have stimulated physicists to consider neutrino oscillations as a possible explanation.

The nuclear reactions that occur inside the Sun are believed to be reasonably well understood, and from known nuclear physics the flux of solar electron neutrinos that reach Earth can be calculated. For more than 20 years, Raymond Davis of the University of Pennsylvania has monitored solar neutrinos by using large tanks filled with chlorine-containing molecules as detector material. His results have consistently yielded neutrino fluxes that are less than half of the calculated values. More recently, two other kinds of solar neutrino observations have been carried out—in Japan at the Kamiokande detector, which looks for neutrino reactions in a large volume of water, and in Russia and Italy, where two groups have observed neutrino reactions in a large quantity of the element gallium. The chlorine, gallium, and water detectors each observe a different energy range of neutrinos. In each case the observed flux of neutrinos has been below that predicted, although the discrepancy is smaller in the gallium data. Three possibilities for the discrepancy exist: the experiments are in error, scientists do not understand the Sun as well as they think they do, or neutrino oscillations are transforming electron neutrinos into muon neutrinos and reducing their flux.

In other experiments with the Kamiokande detector, neutrinos created from cosmic-ray interactions with matter in the atmosphere have been observed. High-energy protons (and other nuclei) interact with atomic nuclei in the air to produce a cascade of pi mesons. A fraction of these mesons decay in flight into a muon and a muon neutrino. Each muon, in turn, decays into an electron, an electron neutrino, and a muon neutrino. Thus, one expects to find approximately two muon neutrinos for each electron neutrino. The Kamiokande detector as well as a water detector previously in operation near Cleveland, Ohio, can distinguish between different kinds of neutrinos. Both detectors have seen only about 60% as many muon neutrinos as expected. The results have been qualitatively confirmed by another detector in the Soudan iron mine in Minnesota. Again, neutrino oscillations are a candidate explanation for the discrepancy.

A strong stimulus for endowing neutrinos with mass is the prospect for solving the cosmological dark matter problem. Astrophysicists and cosmologists argue, on the basis of the observed expansion of the universe, the rotation of galaxies, and the motions of galaxies bound by gravity into clusters, that more than 90% of the mass of the universe must be invisible; i.e., not incorporated in the observed galaxies, visible stars, gas clouds, and other luminous matter. Although some of this dark matter may be ordinary matter incorporated in objects resembling very dim stars or large planets, it is argued that the majority of it must be some kind of weakly interacting particles. The only known particles that can fill this role are tau neutrinos. If the mass of the tau neutrino was even as small as 30 eV, collectively the particles could supply all the mass necessary.

At each of the large proton accelerators, physicists have sought evidence for neutrino oscillation—so far with generally negative results. A new, more ambitious round of such neutrino experiments is being mounted at Fermilab, Brookhaven National Laboratory, Upton, N.Y., and the Super Proton Synchrotron at CERN (European Laboratory for Particle Physics), near Geneva. A recent experiment at the Los Alamos (N.M.) National Laboratory produced evidence for muon neutrinos oscillating into electron neutrinos, and confirmation of these preliminary results is eagerly awaited. In addition, the Kamiokande cosmic-ray neutrino measurements appear to show an energy dependence on the muon-to electron-neutrino ratio, which, if confirmed, would also support the idea of oscillations. (See also Feature Article: THE ELUSIVE NEUTRINO: A WINDOW ON THE UNIVERSE.)

Future research and facilities

Although the standard model has proved successful and although it is now certain that there are only three generations of quarks and leptons, major problems remain. The standard model gives no hint of why the known particles have the masses that they do; it would still work perfectly well if all particles were massless. The Scottish physicist Peter Higgs proposed a mechanism that would give the particles and field quanta their observed masses. The mechanism, however, requires a new, massive particle, the Higgs boson, which has not yet been observed. Finding the Higgs boson is one of the next challenges facing elementary-particle physicists when accelerators of higher energy become available.

A second challenge is the search for supersymmetric particles, particles analogous to quarks and leptons but with

A prototype bending magnet 10 m (33 ft) long is similar to the magnets to be used for CERN's Large Hadron Collider (LHC). Approved in December 1994, the LHC will be installed in the tunnel of the existing Large Electron Positron (LEP) facility.

integer spins (spins expressed as whole numbers), and for corresponding field quanta with half-integer spins. Theoretically, these particles can exist, and some theorists argue strongly that they must exist. To date, experimental evidence for them is lacking, but the search will continue at higher energies.

The particle-physics community was greatly disappointed by the cancellation of the Superconducting Super Collider (SSC) in the U.S. in late 1993. The project had the goal of achieving 40 TeV (trillion electron volts) in the center-of-mass collision between two protons and would have comfortably encompassed the energies required for producing the most massive new elementary particles conjectured. In December 1994, however, CERN received the go-ahead to build the Large Hadron Collider (LHC), wherein proton-proton collisions as energetic as 14 TeV will be achieved. The new machine, to be built in stages, may not be completed until 2008. Meanwhile, the Large Electron Positron (LEP) accelerator-collider facility at CERN will be upgraded to twice its current energy in

1996, which will make possible the production of pairs of W bosons. At Stanford, Calif., and Tsukuba, Japan, new electron-positron colliders are being built specifically to study the B-meson system. (B mesons each comprise a pair of quarks, one of which is a b quark or antiquark.) In several laboratories around the world (Stanford, Tsukuba, CERN, and Hamburg, Germany), groups are studying the design of electron-positron colliding-beam linear accelerators that could achieve greater energies than the upgraded LEP. Finally, a novel concept for achieving greater energies in lepton collisions than is practical with electrons would make use of muon-muon collisions. This technological tour de force, proposed by Robert Palmer of Brookhaven, is being seriously studied.

—Lawrence W. Jones

NUCLEAR PHYSICS

The inexorable march toward superheavy atomic nuclei continued during the past year with the discovery of elements 110 and 111; *i.e.,* elements whose nuclei have 110 and 111 protons, respectively. Knowl-

edge of the limits of stability of neutron-deficient nuclei was advanced with the first-ever observation of the "doubly magic" nucleus tin-100, with 50 protons and 50 neutrons. This achievement has important implications in astrophysics (nuclear burning processes in stars) and studies of nuclear structure. Although the technology for trapping atoms has been under development for several decades, for the first time it proved possible to trap short-lived radioactive atoms, a feat accomplished with an ingenious system of lasers. Through studies of their decays, the trapped atoms can be used to explore unknown aspects of nuclear structure and test the validity of the standard model of elementary particles. Another area of rapid growth, radioactive-nuclear-beam research, promised to alter profoundly the study of nuclear structure and nuclear astrophysics in the near future.

The tin-100 nucleus

The classic theoretical tool for interpreting the energy levels observed in nuclei is the nuclear shell model. In the shell model the neutrons and protons of the nucleus are pictured as being arranged in orbits of different angular momentum, much like the orbits of the electrons around an atom. Certain configurations of nuclear protons or neutrons, referred to as magic numbers, correspond to particularly stable nuclei. Examples of magic numbers for heavier nuclei are 50 and 82 protons or neutrons. Thus, among isotopes of the tin nucleus, which has 50 protons, tin-100 (^{100}Sn, with 50 protons and 50 neutrons) and tin-132 (^{132}Sn, with 50 protons and 82 neutrons) are doubly magic isotopes. Evidence for ^{132}Sn was found some 20 years ago, but until recently ^{100}Sn had eluded detection.

The sum of the protons and neutrons of a nucleus is known as its mass number. Neutron-deficient isotopes that have mass numbers near that of the ^{100}Sn nucleus are of fundamental interest because they provide information about the interaction between neutrons and protons occupying identical shell-model orbits. Whereas most lighter (low-mass-number) nuclei that have the same number of neutrons as protons are stable, the heavier ones are not. The ^{100}Sn nucleus is about 18 neutrons short of the mean atomic mass of the stable isotopes of tin; it is expected to be the heaviest nucleus with identical numbers of neutrons and protons that is stable against decay by the emission of a proton (a phenomenon nuclear physicists call proton drip). Determining which of those nuclei with mass numbers in the vicinity of ^{100}Sn are stable against proton drip and which are not (i.e., mapping the proton-drip line) also has importance for astrophysics since the properties of the neutron-deficient nuclei dictate the pathway of the rapid proton-capture process in hot, dense stars—one of the processes that determine the abundance of heavy elements in stars.

During the past year, in experiments at the GSI facility, Darmstadt, Germany, and at the GANIL accelerator, Caen, France, ^{100}Sn was produced and observed for the first time. At SIS, GSI's heavy-ion synchrotron, a beam of xenon-124 nuclei having an energy of 1 GeV (billion electron volts) per nucleon (proton or neutron) bombarded a beryllium target, which led to production of ^{100}Sn and other isotopes as beam fragments. At GANIL's

heavy-ion accelerator, the ^{100}Sn nuclei resulted from the encounter of a tin-112 beam at 63 MeV (million electron volts) per nucleon with a nickel target. In addition to ^{100}Sn, many other new isotopes at or beyond the anticipated proton-drip line were identified for the first time. In the recent first-generation experiments, only a small number of ^{100}Sn nuclei were seen. Both GSI and GANIL are pursuing second-generation experiments, with the goal of studying the properties of ^{100}Sn in greater detail.

New very heavy nuclei

For decades physicists have worked to synthesize and study ever heavier nuclei—possibly even nuclei of unusual stability in the so-called superheavy island, a cluster of relatively long-lived isotopes with proton numbers beyond about 110 that have been predicted to exist among the highly unstable nuclei. Producing such nuclei is both a technological challenge and a critical test of modern theories of nuclear structure and stability.

After much early progress, efforts in this direction slowed until the past year, when technological advances in accelerators, targets, and detectors broke a nearly decade-old impasse. Four new artificial nuclei, heavier than any others yet observed, were synthesized in experiments at GSI and by a collaboration of Russian and U.S. groups from the Joint Institute for Nuclear Research, Dubna, and the Lawrence Livermore National Laboratory, Livermore, Calif. The GSI experiments identified the nuclei of two isotopes of element 110 (with 159 and 161 neutrons) and one of element 111 (with 161 neutrons), which confirmed

predictions of relatively long lifetimes for nuclei having close to 162 neutrons. This work used "cold" nuclear reactions such as the fusion of lead-208 with nickel-62, followed by the emission of one neutron to give the 159-neutron isotope of element 110 (^{269}110). The Russian-U.S. team created ^{273}110 (with 163 neutrons) by exploiting a "hotter" reaction in which sulfur-34 fuses with plutonium-244 and forms a nucleus with 278 nucleons. Emission of five neutrons leads to ^{273}110.

The results are an experimental tour de force in themselves since the probabilities of producing the heavy nuclei are a millionth or less of those of typical nuclear reactions. They also support recent theoretical calculations and increase the likelihood that even heavier nuclei can be made. (For further information on artificial elements, see Year in Review: CHEMISTRY: Inorganic and Physical Chemistry.)

Trapping radioactive atoms

In recent years the trapping of small numbers of atoms in a suspended state in a tiny region of space has been an area of intense activity motivated by promising applications in both basic physics and technology. The most common trap for electrically neutral atoms is the magneto-optical trap. Such traps use the radiation pressure of light from lasers arrayed in three dimensions around the confinement region to confine, levitate, and cool (slow down) the atoms.

For years stable atoms such as cesium and sodium have been trapped by these techniques for study and manipulation. Recently, important progress in the more difficult task of trapping short-lived radioactive atoms was made by groups at the State University of New York at Stony Brook and the Lawrence Berkeley Laboratory (LBL), Berkeley, Calif. The Stony Brook group succeeded in producing radioactive ruthenium-79 ions by means of a nuclear reaction in which a vanadium-51 target was bombarded with a phosphorus-31 beam from the Stony Brook tandem Van de Graaff generator. The ^{79}Ru atoms have a half-life of 22.8 minutes. After neutralizing the ions, the researchers sent some of the atoms through a port in a glass cell and into a magneto-optical trapping region at the center of the cell; in equilibrium, about 80 atoms of ^{79}Ru were confined in this way. The LBL group produced a radioactive isotope of sodium—^{21}Na, with a half-life of 22.5 seconds—by a different technique. They bombarded magnesium chips that were contained in an atomic-beam-producing oven with 25-MeV protons. The ^{21}Na beam that exited from the oven was focused with laser light and then brought to a stop at the center of a magneto-optical trap by means of a clever magnetic-field technique; about 4,000 atoms of ^{21}Na were trapped.

The trapping techniques are of interest not only in their own right but also for the study of basic aspects of particle and nuclear physics. For instance, the decay of ^{21}Na via weak interactions, the so-called beta-decay process in which an electron and a neutrino are emitted from the nucleus, will be used by the LBL group to test the predictions of the standard model of the known particles and interactions, which unifies the electromagnetic and weak interactions. In this case they will study the pattern of emission of the electron and the neutrino by measuring the recoil energy of the nucleus. For the future a number of groups, including those at LBL and Stony Brook, hope to trap isotopes of the radioactive heavy nucleus francium (87 protons), whose large nuclear charge offers opportunities to carry out even more-stringent tests of the standard model.

Radioactive beams

Developments in the technology of ion sources and particle accelerators have opened up a new era in nuclear physics in the past few years and are rapidly revolutionizing the fields of low-energy nuclear structure, nuclear reactions, and much of nuclear astrophysics. Traditionally, much nuclear physics research has depended on experiments in which target nuclei are bombarded with accelerated beams of other, stable nuclei. The limitation of using stable projectiles has been a natural one since most unstable nuclei do not live long enough to be prepared and formed into beams. Extensive data gathered from the use of stable nuclei have led to a number of models, such as the shell model, to describe them, and these models have become the standard vehicles through which scientists understand and interpret the structure and interactions of atomic nuclei in general.

There is reason to believe, however, that nuclear structure may be entirely different in as-yet-undiscovered nuclei that have excessive numbers of either protons or neutrons (and thus are highly unstable). For example, one can conceive of a nucleus in which there are so many more neutrons than protons that the outermost neutrons orbit the nuclear "core" like planets at very large distances from their parent star. In such a neutron-rich nucleus the outer reaches would constitute essentially a new form of matter consisting of diffuse, weakly bound neutrons. (The protons orbit at distances much closer to the center.) In this environment nuclear structure would be very different from anything yet encountered; the density of neutrons in the outer regions would be thousands of times less than in normal nuclei. These differences might cause current concepts of the nuclear surface and the nuclear shape to lose their meaning and even force scientists to invent a new vocabulary for nuclear structure.

Recent technological advances are making it possible, for the first time, to study such exotic nuclei with accelerated beams of radioactive nuclei. A number of first-generation radioactive-nuclear-beam (RNB) facilities already exist, such as those at Michigan State University, RIKEN in Japan, and GSI in Germany. Others, including the HRIB facility at Oak Ridge (Tenn.) National Laboratory and GANIL's Spiral project in France, are under construction. There are plans to upgrade existing facilities and to build the next, much more powerful generation of RNB machines in the near future. In recent RNB research diffuse neutron "halos" like that described above have been observed in the lithium-11 nucleus, which has three protons and eight neutrons (normal stable lithium-7 has only four neutrons). Other "halo nuclei" such as boron-14 (5 protons, 9 neutrons) and carbon-19 (6 protons, 13 neutrons) also have been discovered.

—Carl B. Dover

CONDENSED-MATTER PHYSICS

The application of condensed-matter physics to optics and the more recent field of optoelectronics—the use of electronic devices to generate and manipulate light—continued its rapid advance during the past year. A major driving force is the perception that communications using light may be the only way to satisfy the demands of a society for increasingly more information at its fingertips—preferably in the form of imagery in full color, at high resolution, and in three dimensions. These demands require that an enormous amount of data be processed and sent speeding through communications networks from one end of the globe to the other. Research in optoelectronics is helping to pave this future information superhighway in its efforts to develop materials for all-optical computing; lasers that are more efficient, less costly, and able to generate wavelengths of light not currently attainable; new technologies for full-color flat-panel video displays; and methods to better integrate optics with electronics.

Blue light from semiconductors

The light-emitting diodes (LEDs) that dot the control panels of modern electronic equipment in the home and office may be red or green, but to date they have not been blue. Commercially practical blue LEDs have been difficult to make, and the reason is related to the fact that the color, or wavelength, of the light emitted by an LED is determined by the electronic band gap of the semiconductor material of which it is made. The band gap is a forbidden region in the levels of energy that can be occu-

pied by the electrons in a semiconductor. At low temperature all the possible energy states below the band gap, called the valence band, are occupied by electrons, while the energy states above the gap are empty. At higher temperatures the electrons can be energetically excited such that they occupy some of the energy states above the gap, in the so-called conduction band.

The electrons in a partially filled conduction band are free to move about the semiconductor crystal and thus conduct electricity. At the same time, the electron vacancies, or "holes," that are left behind in the valence band can also move about as the remaining electrons jump from hole to hole. The free-moving electrons and holes are both carriers of electric current. Semiconductors become truly useful for electronic devices, however, only if they are doped. Doping is the introduction of a controlled amount of an impurity substance that has energy levels in the semiconductor's band gap close to the band edges. Through doping, one controls the amount of carriers of a given kind, electrons or holes, in the semiconductor material.

An LED is made of a semiconductor doped to have regions with excess electrons (termed n-type material) and regions with excess holes (p-type material). When a voltage is applied to the LED, the excess electrons move to the region with excess holes (or vice versa), where they recombine. The energy that is released in the recombination process is emitted as light having a wavelength related to the size of the gap—specifically, $\lambda = hc/E_g$, in which λ is the wavelength, h is Planck's constant, c is the velocity

of light, and E_g is the energy difference across the band gap.

The semiconductor material of red LEDs is an alloy of aluminum gallium arsenide (AlGaAs), which has a band gap E_g of about 1.9 eV (electron volts) and thus emits light with a wavelength of 650–660 nm (nanometers; billionths of a meter). Green light with a wavelength of 555 nm is usually obtained from gallium phosphide (GaP) with a band gap of 2.2 eV. The wavelength of the emitted light is inversely proportional to the size of the band gap of the semiconductor. Generating light with shorter wavelengths, in the blue-to-violet region of the spectrum, requires a semiconductor material with a larger band gap. One such material is gallium nitride (GaN). Its band gap of 3.4 eV at room temperature actually corresponds to ultraviolet light, but when GaN is doped with magnesium (Mg), it emits intense blue light as a result of the smaller energy difference between the conduction band and the energy level in the gap provided by the magnesium.

Although getting blue light from GaN has been experimentally possible since the 1970s, commercial development has taken decades and has depended on a series of technical breakthroughs in growing and doping the material and fine-tuning its output wavelength. The first successful p-type doping of GaN with magnesium was achieved in 1989 by Isamu Akasaki and co-workers of Nagoya University in Japan. In the past year Nichia Chemical Industries in Tokushima, Japan, on the basis of research led by Shuji Nakamura, announced the fabrication of blue and blue-green LEDs based on GaN (technically indium gallium nitride/

aluminum gallium nitride [InGaN/Al-GaN] heterostructures) that have wavelengths of 450 nm and 500 nm and a brightness exceeding one candela (cd). This brightness approaches that achievable by red AlGaAs LEDs (as high as 1.8 cd) and is high enough for consideration in large-scale applications such as outdoor displays, traffic signals, and even direct lighting.

The availability of bright blue LEDs brings great versatility to the use of LEDs because arrays of mixed, green, and blue devices can be used to produce any color of light desired, including white. The conventional color picture tubes used in televisions and computers, whose screens are coated with arrays of blue, red, and green phosphor dots, operate on the same principle, but they are bulky because they must accommodate the electron beams that stimulate the phosphors. Tricolor LED arrays have the potential to provide a much simpler and flatter video display. Current flat-panel displays used, for example, in palm-sized televisions and laptop computers are based on liquid crystals. LEDs, however, promise brighter, higher-resolution, wider-angle, faster-responding, and less-power-hungry displays.

The GaN material as presently fabricated still has a significant amount of performance-degrading defects in its crystalline structure. In fact, a major puzzle for researchers is how the devices work at all, given the amount of dislocations visible in them under the electron microscope. Optimists see this as a sign that there is much room for improvement in the material's performance. Looking further to the future, researchers are

hopeful that intense full-color light emission can be achieved with GaN's cousin materials indium nitride (InN) and aluminum nitride (AlN). In principle, the aluminum, indium, and gallium content can be mixed in any desired proportion in alloys to make LEDs that emit over a continuous range of wavelengths from orange to ultraviolet.

The next immediate challenge for GaN research is to make a semiconductor laser with the material. The stimulated light emission characteristic of lasers has already been demonstrated in GaN, but only when it is pumped, or excited, with an external light source. A semiconductor laser is powered directly by electrical energy. It works by the creation of a population inversion, in which a great number of electrons are excited from the valence band to the conduction band. The emitted light is confined in a so-called cavity between mirrorlike crystalline planes of the semiconductor. There the light bounces back and forth, creating more excited electrons and holes, which in turn generate more light, and so on. When this feedback loop is sufficiently effective, coherent laser light emerges from the material. The challenge is to further increase the efficiency of conversion of electrical energy into light, currently at 4.5%, so that a GaN device can boost itself into laser action without an external light source.

While other kinds of lasers that emit at short wavelengths can be made, a semiconductor laser yielding light in the blue-to-ultraviolet range will be a significant development simply because it is such a compact device. Today's compact-disc (CD) drives for audio systems and

computers read the stored information on the disc with a semiconductor laser that emits in the infrared region. Changing from an infrared device to a blue or an ultraviolet one for such applications will increase the amount of data that can be written to, and read from, an optical disc, raising the storage capacity as much as fourfold. (For discussion of another new kind of semiconductor laser, the quantum-cascade laser, see *General Developments,* above.)

Optical computing with polymers

Novel materials can be used not only to generate light but also to manipulate it in such complex ways as to constitute actual mathematical computations. This possibility is based on the nonlinear optical (NLO) properties possessed by certain materials. Nonlinear interaction of light with matter means that the amount of light coming out of a material is not merely proportional to the amount of light going in but depends on the intensity of the light itself.

Rather complex phenomena can occur as the result of the interaction of such a material with beams of light. For example, when two intense light beams, typically laser beams, are directed onto a material with strong NLO properties, their interference sets up a pattern of standing waves that vary periodically in intensity. The standing wave pattern, in turn, causes local changes in the material's refractive index—its ability to bend light passing through it—and, in effect, turns the material into a diffraction grating, which can be used to modify another light beam. Such a technique—using beams of light and an NLO mate-

C. Halvorson, A. Hays, B. Kraabel, R. Wu, F. Wudl, and A.J. Heeger; University of California, Santa Barbara

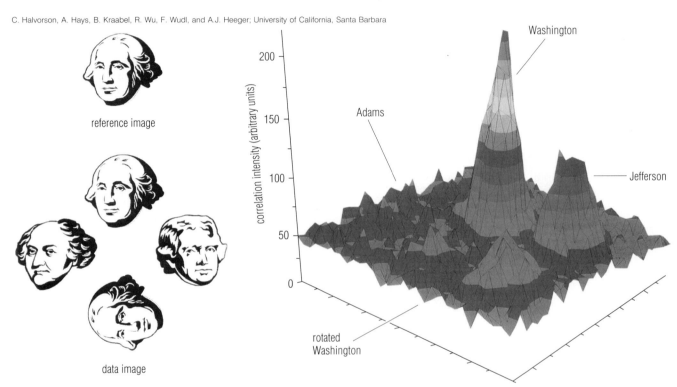

reference image

data image

Optical correlation between a reference image of George Washington (top left) and a four-part test image (bottom left) is shown as a graph that plots the coordinates of the test image against correlation intensity (right). Correlation between the two upright images of Washington generated the highest peak.

rial to manipulate another light beam—constitutes an all-optical method for light modification. One of the major advantages of the technique is that it can be extremely fast.

In some cases such modifications of a light beam can be equivalent to an actual computation. This possibility was demonstrated dramatically during the past year by Alan J. Heeger and co-workers of the University of California, Santa Barbara. The device that they set up for their experiment is known technically as a four-wave mixing optical correlator and is based essentially on the procedure described above. The function of the device is to calculate the correlation

between two images; that is, it compares a test image with a reference image and picks out those regions in the images that most resemble one another. In their experiment, which used simple drawings of U.S. presidents for the images, the optical correlator was able to pick out the image of George Washington from those of two other presidents and a rotated image of Washington. Each image comparison took less than 160 femtoseconds (quadrillionths of a second; 10^{-15} second).

The core element of the optical correlator is a film made of poly(1,6-heptadiester) (PHDE), an organic polymer having strong NLO properties. In

the experiment the polymer film served to combine a light beam containing a test image and a beam containing the reference image with a third beam so as to produce an output beam that was the correlation of the first two. The significance of the achievement is that a simple device was able to carry out an operation that is equivalent to a complex computation performed on a digital computer. In fact, the researchers determined the "computational speed" of their device to be equivalent to 30 quadrillion (3×10^{16}) operations per second, more than a million times faster than the fastest supercomputer available.

—Walter R.L. Lambrecht

PSYCHOLOGY

Encouraging news for prospective psychology graduate students was reported during the past year in the U.S. Labor Department's *Occupational Outlook Handbook*. The projected career growth to 2005 included an anticipated 48% increase for psychologists who gained doctoral degrees, putting that category in sixth place in such growth among all occupations. A major factor in this projection was the increasing prevalence of problems requiring professional intervention, most notably alcohol and drug abuse, as well as marital difficulties and family violence.

Learning and performance

The third report of the special committee established by the U.S. National Research Council to evaluate "techniques in the enhancement of human performance" was published in 1994. The committee had been formed at the request of the U.S. Army to review the scientific status of a variety of such techniques that were being promoted by military and/or commercial interests but that the army did not feel qualified to evaluate.

In addition to confirming some of the earlier (1987, 1991) committee conclusions (*e.g.,* finding even less evidence for any important effects of "sleep learning"), their third report contained a number of new results. With respect to the role of specific or contextual factors in the acquisition of skill, some interesting conclusions were drawn. Contrary to the somewhat extreme claims of proponents of "situated learning," which emphasizes the crucial role of specific factors, both concrete experiences and abstract principles were found to be important in skill acquisition. It was also concluded that the role of innate factors (most generally identified as "aptitudes") in particular learning situations was typically overemphasized; the more crucial role of practice was said to be very often insufficiently appreciated, especially by some training organizations, such as those involving military service and industrial operations.

The committee reported that a significant role in performance is often played by task-specific confidence, which can be manipulated by supervisors so as to maximize performance. Moreover, the committee concluded that learners should be regularly informed of the extent to which they comprehend the materials being learned or can properly perform the required tasks; wide gaps between a learner's feelings of knowledge and his or her actual comprehension, with possibly detrimental effects on performance, were found to be all too common.

Finally, the committee pointed out that feelings of familiarity with a task are readily misinterpreted as indicative of competence. Competence, however, needs to be directly measured, outside the training situation, before it can be accurately assessed.

The fourth phase of the committee's work, the enhancement of organizational performance, was under way. A report in 1997 was anticipated.

An attack on "expert performance" was also published during the year by psychologists K. Anders Ericsson and Neil Charness of Florida State University. On the basis of a comprehensive, fine-grained analysis of people who had achieved the highest level of excellence in a given domain, Ericsson and Charness concluded that "elite performers" generally initiate practice in their disciplines at a very early age and maintain it on a more or less daily schedule for more than a decade. The effects of this kind of persistent and concentrated practice were shown to be much more significant than was commonly believed. Furthermore, such practice can circumvent what are often considered to be the limits of working memory and sequential information processing.

Thinking and decision making

Several provocative approaches to thinking and decision making appeared during the year. Psychologist Seymour Epstein of the University of Massachusetts at Amherst summarized his integration of the cognitive and the psychodynamic (Freudian) views of the unconscious. The basis of his "cognitive existential self-theory" was the assumption of two parallel but interacting lines of information processing: a rational mode and an emotionally driven experiential mode.

Epstein demonstrated the way in which the intuitions of the emotionally driven processing system can overcome strictly rational and conscious processing. For example, participants in one series of experiments were given the opportunity to earn prize money for drawing a red jelly bean from one of two bowls. A small bowl had one red bean in every 10 beans; a large bowl had 10 red beans in every 100. Participants were required to pay one dime for any trial in which they could select which of the two bowls was to be used; otherwise, the bowls were selected randomly. Most of the participants elected to choose from the larger bowl, even though they had to pay for that privilege. According to Epstein, several of the participants "spontaneously commented that they felt foolish paying for a choice between equal probabilities, but, although they knew better, they felt they had a better chance of drawing a red bean when there were more of them."

In later research Epstein found that even when the probabilities were altered to favor the drawing of a red bean from the smaller bowl, participants still preferred to draw from the larger bowl. This result occurred even when the chance of drawing a red bean from the larger bowl was only one-half that for the smaller bowl. Participants who chose the larger bowl again reported a conflict between the better odds and the larger number of red beans. The temptation to draw from the larger bowl was also mentioned by some of those who had been able to overcome it. Apparently there is a strong tendency to make decisions in accordance with the emotionally driven, intuitive processing system rather than with the rational system. This tendency, found in a variety of everyday-life situations, needs more experimental attention.

Another approach to nonconscious cognitive processing was reported by psychologist Pawel Lewicki and his associates at the University of Tulsa, Okla. In one experiment college students were first shown a videotape of persons engaged in simple activities (walking, lifting objects, throwing a Frisbee). The videotape actually showed only small strips of fluorescent tapes affixed to the hands and the limb joints. All other visual cues were absent; the actor photographed was dressed completely in black, and the background was black. Participants were briefed on the way in which relatively simple kinematic information had been shown to be useful in enabling observers to make correct inferences about such factors as gender and intentions. They were told that the experiment was designed to determine whether they could make simple personality judgments solely on the basis of the various movements seen in the videotape.

In the first learning phase of the experiment, there were slight differences in the distance between the white bands on the ankles and on the knees and slight differences in size of the white dots on the arms. Performers with short distances between leg bands had larger arm dots, and vice versa. In the second learning phase, performers with short distances between leg bands were described as "likable"; others were called "not likable." No arm dots were shown.

In the test phase additional episodes were shown, without the leg bands or any likability information but with the smaller or larger arm dots appearing. Participants were asked to use their intuition to make an estimate of likability. The prediction was that the combinations shown earlier of short leg distances and large arm dots (phase 1) and short leg distances and likability (phase 2) would lead participants to give higher likability estimates to those performers with large arm dots, even though large arm dots and likability had not themselves been directly linked. The predicted results did in fact occur. Moreover, postexperimental questionnaires revealed no recognition by the participants that their responses might have been manipulated, which was consistent with the earlier findings.

Health issues

Psychologists increasingly were becoming actively involved in a wide range of health-related activities. Possibly the most significant, and certainly the most pervasive, movement was the recent rapid expansion in the number of school-affiliated health clinics. Within the past decade these clinics in the U.S. had grown in number from nearly zero to approximately 500. Among health care professionals, nurses and social workers made up the majority of the staffs of these new clinics, but psychologists had been increasingly involved as well.

The school clinic in Memphis, Tenn., was especially active and was often cited as a model. Among its 161 staff members were 12 psychologists with doctorates and several others with master's degrees. Teams from the clinic rotated among the schools in the system, treating physical and mental disorders. A major value of this kind of clinic was that it reached children from poor families who otherwise had no access to health care.

Encouraging progress reports during the past year came from two studies designed to reduce the alarmingly high levels of alcohol and drug use among young people. Lorand Szalay, head of the Institute of Comparative Social and Cultural Studies in Washington, D.C., reported on his use of "associative group analysis." Subjects were asked to free-associate with "trigger words" (such as acid, booze, and divorce) in six areas—drugs, alcohol, social relationships, family relationships, values, and problems.

Computerized analyses of their responses produced "cognitive maps" that indicated which students did or did not use alcohol or drugs.

Results from tests on 20,000 students in 50 U.S. colleges consistently indicated that nonusers associate alcohol and drugs with negative consequences (personal harm, sickness, death); their responses also indicated tendencies to have high self-esteem and to relate positively to family ties and caring relationships. Heavy substance users, in contrast, associated drugs and alcohol with fun and entertainment and showed more concern with social alienation and emotional ambivalence.

The magnitude of the drinking problem among college students was strikingly shown by figures recently released by the Harvard University School of Public Health. In a survey of 140 college campuses, 44% of the students were classified as "bingers" (defined for men as having consumed five consecutive alcoholic drinks at least once during the two weeks prior to the survey and for women as having consumed four consecutive drinks). "Frequent bingers" had three or more such binges in the two-week period.

Frequent bingers were found to have a much higher incidence of personal problems compared with nonbingeing drinkers. For example, they were much more likely to have been physically injured (23% to 2%), to have damaged property (22% to 2%), and to have had unplanned sex (41% to 8%). Moreover, on campuses where heavy levels of bingeing occurred, 9 of 10 students reported having suffered as a consequence of someone else's drinking (property damage, unwanted sexual advance, interruption of sleep or study, or some form of insult or humiliation, not to mention having had to take care of a drunk).

Earlier studies had found that college-bound high-school students drank less than their non-college-bound peers. Thus, it seems reasonable to infer that there is something about the college campus that is responsible for the reversal of that trend; noncollege youths of corresponding ages were actually reducing their alcohol consumption.

Some hints about the factors that might be responsible for the maintenance of high alcohol consumption in colleges, and what could be done to alleviate the problem, were provided by a study at Northern Illinois University at DeKalb. Directed by Michael Haines, this study was based on earlier research and theories of Alan Berkowitz, a psychologist, and Wesley Perkins, a sociologist, at Hobart and William Smith Colleges, Geneva, N.Y. They showed that college students consistently overestimated both the number of students who drink heavily and the degree of acceptance of this kind of behavior by their peers. In 1988 Haines began to collect information on health-related issues, including the amount of alcohol that was consumed at college parties and the respondents' estimates of the amounts consumed. Large discrepancies between these two measures were found in annual assessments, with the students once again overestimating the amounts consumed.

In 1990 a campuswide public-information program was initiated to educate students about this discrepancy. Later Haines reported that there has been a consistent decline both in actual drinking and in students' perceptions of drinking. In 1989, for example, 69% of the students said that other students drank heavily, whereas in 1994 only 54% made such a statement. In terms of actual heavy drinking, 45% of the students were found to binge in 1989, compared with 33% in 1994.

A survey of 140 U.S. colleges found that 44% of the students had binged on alcoholic drinks at least once during the two weeks prior to the survey.

Psychotherapy

Telling one's problems to a therapist—the so-called talking cure—seems to be a factor in all of the major forms of psychotherapy. Initially emphasized by Sigmund Freud as a means of coping with emotional stress, it has persisted, in one form or another, for well over a century.

Why talking works so well was the question considered by an international group of researchers assembled during the past year at a conference on the Taos, N.M., campus of Southern Methodist University. The difference between sharing emotions and merely sharing objective facts was highlighted in research reported by Bernard Rime of the Catholic University of Louvain, Belgium. In one experiment two groups of women were interviewed the day after giving birth. One group was asked detailed questions about their emotions during delivery, while a second group was asked more routine questions about their daily lives. Those who had discussed their emotions were reported to have recovered better and to have had fewer unpleasant memories of delivery.

Another set of results was reported by Keith Petrie of the University of Auckland (N.Z.) Medical School. In one study subjects in an experimental group were asked to write about their most traumatic experiences and to reveal emotional reactions that they had until then kept to themselves. Control-group subjects were asked simply to write about their everyday activities. Four such daily writing sessions, each 20 minutes long, preceded the giving of a hepatitis B vaccine to all subjects. The first group showed significantly higher antibody levels, indicating a stronger immune reaction.

Other research reported at the conference suggested that unless there is a receptive listener, the disclosure of emotional experiences may be counterproductive. Roxanne Silver of the University of California, Irvine, interviewed more than 1,000 Vietnam War veterans and found that greater disclosure of their wartime experiences was correlated with reduced subsequent distress. The veterans who described their listeners as unsympathetic, however, reported that they had suffered increased distress and more intrusive thoughts. Similar results were reported for other subject groups, such as Californians who had lost their homes to fire and parents who had lost an infant to sudden infant death syndrome.

Social problems: research synthesis

A promising new approach to policy making on social problems was discussed during the past year at a meeting of members of the U.S. Congress and 50 senior officers from 30 U.S. government agencies. The National Conference on Research Synthesis, organized in part by the American Psychological Association and sponsored by the Russell Sage Foundation, was held in Washington, D.C.

Research synthesis is a blanket description of attacks upon a single problem from a number of resources for which quantitative data are available. The best-known technique is meta-analysis, in which conclusions about the effects of variables are drawn from the results of several studies rather than from just one.

Four case studies presented at the conference illuminated both the need for better research synthesis and the social benefits it has the potential to provide. They dealt with the questions of (1) whether additional funding improves education (it does, contrary to earlier conclusions, which were said to have been based upon inadequate analysis of data); (2) whether job training can effectively replace welfare (yes, especially when the rate of participation is high and clients are carefully matched with particular programs); (3) whether thorough preparation of surgical cases can simplify recovery and reduce the length of postsurgery hospital stays (it can, as was shown by a total of 191 studies reviewed, even for such simple interventions as informing patients what to expect during recovery and first ascertaining and then relieving each patient's specific anxieties); and (4) whether programs for juvenile delinquents are effective (contrary to some earlier reviews, they were said to be so, especially when behavior modification or other structured training techniques were used).

—Melvin H. Marx

International developments

Under the former communist regime in Russia, certain theories including the unconscious were typically regarded as taboo and were suppressed. It was possible in Soviet psychology to study topics such as the proper upbringing of children, and some outstanding scientific research in this area was carried out. By 1994, however, under a new government, there was a desire not just to study children and family life but also to help families and children with difficulties. This reawakened concern for the well-being of the individual resulted in an increase in the number of Russian psychologists seeking to enter clinical practice. Salaries, however, were often insufficient, forcing psychologists to find other ways of making money. In Russia as of early 1995, there were no standards for professional accreditation or codes of ethics.

Another country in which social changes had had an influence on psychology was Vietnam. Economic restructuring in Vietnam following a shift toward a market economy in 1986, coupled with the loss of influence and support from Soviet-bloc countries after 1989, resulted in a demand for expertise in increasing productivity, in marketing, and in management, all of which are the concerns of organizational psychology. The staff at the Institute of Psychology, founded in Hanoi in 1988, wrote a text on management psychology and conducted seminars on the Vietnamese consumer. With the decline of Soviet influence, psychology opened up to encompass practices such as psychometric testing for clinical and educational purposes. Vietnamese psychologists were called in to help in a variety of settings.

Likewise, in South Africa the ending of the apartheid regime was accompanied by major changes in the organization and orientation of psychology. The former Psychological Association of South Africa was dissolved, and a new Psychological Society of South Africa was formed with, as its primary goals, the advancement of psychology as a science, as a profession, and as a means of promoting human welfare by actively striving for social justice. The inaugural congress of the transformed society concentrated on real-life concerns within South Africa—AIDS, the psychology of oppression, in-

terracial marriage, homelessness, the victims of violence, and the provision of psychological services in a multiethnic context. It was recognized that the legacy of past policies, under which only 10% of the country's registered psychologists were black, would have to be overcome if the profession was to reflect the needs of multiracial South Africa.

In Europe a Danish law concerned with the protection of the title and the licensing of psychologists took effect on Jan. 1, 1994. Likewise in Sweden, from the same date, the title of "psychologist" became protected by law in the field of health care. In Belgium legislation was being introduced to protect the title "psychologist." Published in the United Kingdom was the first *Directory of Chartered Psychologists,* in which psychologists registered with the British Psychological Society could give details of the professional services they offered. In Malta the first conference of the Malta Union of Professional Psychologists was held. The union was founded in 1992 and joined the European Federation of Professional Psychologists Associations in 1993.

The major international conference in 1994 was the quadrennial meeting of the International Association of Applied Psychology, held in Madrid. The scientific program consisted of 40 major addresses and more then 250 symposia and new "problem-solving" sessions. In the latter the Scientific Committee selected four or five "problems" arising in the global society, and at a round-table session expert discussants were asked to develop practical "solutions" to these from a psychological point of view.

—Colin V. Newman

SPACE EXPLORATION

Seven U.S. space shuttle voyages during 1994 carried out missions ranging from processing materials in the weightlessness of space to detecting landforms buried beneath the Earth's surface. Operations continued aboard Russia's *Mir 1* space station, and the design of the new International Space Station *Alpha* was completed. Unmanned probes explored Venus and the Moon, and Voyagers 1 and 2 transmitted data from the edge of the solar system.

MANNED FLIGHT

The United States and Russia combined forces to develop a single International Space Station *Alpha* and planned a series of U.S. space shuttle missions to Russia's *Mir 1* space station. The U.S. also initiated a program to replace the shuttle with a new reusable launch vehicle.

U.S. space shuttle

Only seven space shuttle missions were flown during the year. Two carried the same Space Radar Laboratory (SRL) to survey the Earth at different times of the year. Three missions studied materials and life sciences in space. Two continued detailed observations of the Earth's atmosphere.

On Jan. 13, 1994, the National Aeronautics and Space Administration (NASA) confirmed that the late-1993 repairs to the Hubble Space Telescope had been successful and that the observatory's optics were working as planned. Before-and-after pictures showed a marked increase in the sharpness of images taken by the Wide Field Planetary Camera, which received an upgrade during repairs.

The first mission of the year, STS-60

With the Earth in the background, astronaut Mark C. Lee floats freely in space as he tests a miniature backpack designed to rescue astronauts who have drifted far from their space stations.

(*Discovery,* February 3–11), carried the Wake Shield Facility and Spacehab-02. The Wake Shield Facility, a satellite designed to be released by the shuttle and retrieved a few days later, was to orbit on its own, its wake creating a near-perfect vacuum in which high-quality semiconductor films could be grown. A problem with the facility's own guidance system, however, prevented the astronauts from releasing the satellite. Six metal balls, 5 to 15 cm (2 to 6 in) in diameter, were released for use as calibration targets by ground-based radar. And Sergey K. Krikalev became the first Russian to be launched aboard a U.S. spacecraft as the two nations initiated their joint space station program.

Materials sciences were advanced with the STS-62 (*Columbia,* March 4–18), which carried the U.S. Microgravity Payload (USMP-1). The USMP-1 comprised several automated devices for processing materials in the weightlessness of space. In one a furnace processed samples of mercury cadmium telluride, an alloy that was valued as an infrared detector but suffered from defects in ground-based growth. Another device observed the growth of dendrites—branchlike structures—in transparent crystalline materials. *Columbia* also carried a Shuttle Solar Backscatter Ultraviolet instrument to measure ozone in the upper atmosphere by determining the amount of solar ultraviolet radiation that is reflected into space. Inside *Columbia* the crew assembled scale models of solar array supports to measure vibration and stress.

The Earth was given a close examination by a special mapping radar flown twice by *Endeavour,* on April 9–20 and September 30–October 11. The SRL uses a synthetic-aperture radar, which mathematically combines a series of radar echoes to generate an image that otherwise would require a single, larger antenna. Predecessors had been flown on the shuttle on STS-2 (1981) and STS-41G (1984). The SRL was the first space radar to use three frequency bands—C, L, and X—at once to obtain more detailed images. Elements of the radar were provided by Germany and Italy. At some frequencies the radar penetrated the ground and revealed structures such as ancient streambeds.

A laser probed the atmosphere on STS-64 (*Discovery,* September 9–20) with the Laser In-Flight Technology Experiment (LITE). LITE focused lasers on the Earth's atmosphere through a 1.5-m-diameter reflector telescope and then measured the return signal. This allowed scientists to measure the speed of aerosols and dust in clear air and even in tropical storm Debby. *Discovery* also deployed and retrieved the Spartan 201-II satellite, which observed the Sun's corona. During a planned space walk, astronauts Mark C. Lee and Carl J. Meade tested a miniature backpack designed to rescue astronauts should they drift so far away from the space station that it could not be maneuvered to retrieve them. This was the first untethered space walk since before the *Challenger* accident in 1986.

The second International Microgravity Laboratory (IML-2; STS-65, *Columbia,* July 8–23) carried a suite of life and materials sciences experiments provided by Japan's National Space Development Agency and the German Space Agency. In addition to tests on the crew, the life sciences experiments included observations of the hatching of newts and the behavior of goldfish and carp, some with their balance organs removed. Materials experiments included the cooling of samples of molten metal alloys to below freezing while they were suspended in an electromagnetic field. Such experiments are sharply limited on Earth.

Earth was surveyed yet again when STS-66 (*Atlantis,* November 3–14) carried the third Atmospheric Laboratory for Applications and Science (ATLAS-3). Instruments on ATLAS-3 observed the Sun as a source of energy for Earth's atmosphere and as a light source whose changes betray the presence of certain chemicals in the atmosphere.

Shuttle missions planned for 1995 were to carry the Astro cluster of ultraviolet telescopes on a new survey of the universe (STS-67, January), rendezvous with the *Mir 1* space station (STS-63, February) and then dock with the station (STS-71, June), recarry the Wake Shield Facility and launch a special Space Free-Flier Unit (STS-69, October), launch the seventh Tracking and Data Relay Satellite (STS-70, June), carry the second U.S. Microgravity Laboratory (STS-73,

September), and retrieve the Free-Flier Unit (STS-72, September). STS-63 would also have NASA's first woman pilot, Eileen M. Collins, on a shuttle mission. The microgravity laboratory mission was planned to last a record 16 days.

NASA started plans to replace the shuttles' 1970s "green screen" electronic displays and 1960s electromechanical displays with high-resolution, full-color liquid crystal displays (LCDs). Such "glass cockpits" would allow information to be displayed with much greater flexibility and detail. Replacement work was expected to be completed in 1998. The shuttle had used four 23-cm (9-in) displays, three on the forward flight deck and one on the aft flight deck. The multifunction electronics display system (MEDS) would be driven by four microcomputers based on the Intel 80386 processor plus a 300-megabyte hard drive. These would drive nine 17-cm (6.7-in)-square LCDs with a resolution of 6,633 × 6,633 pixels (44 times as much detail as most high-end computer monitors

used in publishing work). One small set of electromechanical displays would be retained as a backup.

Demonstrations began in the new Consolidated Control Center outfitted with new workstations based on the high-speed Alpha processor built by Digital Equipment Corp. Replacing the current Mission Control Center, it would allow flight directors to control a variety of spacecraft by switching programs. NASA would also equip shuttle crews with IBM Thinkpad 755C laptop computers that would hold details of planned operations, including pictures.

Mir 1 space station

Launched on Jan. 8, 1994, TM-18 carried Viktor Afanasyev, Yury Usacho, and Valery Polyakov to *Mir 1.* Polyakov was scheduled to stay in space for a record 460 days and return to the Earth on April 14, 1995. Soyuz TM-17 departed from *Mir* on January 14, returning with Vasily Tsibiliyev and Aleksandr Serebrov. On July 1 Soyuz TM-19 took Yury Malenchenko and Talgat Muabyev to *Mir* and returned with Afanasyev and Usacho. On October 4 German astronaut Ulf Merbold (who had flown twice on the space shuttle) was launched aboard Soyuz TM-20 to spend 30 days aboard *Mir* as part of the EuroMir program. A second European astronaut was to make a 135-day stay starting in August 1995. U.S. astronaut Norman Thagard and two Russians were to be launched to *Mir* on Soyuz TM-21 on March 14. Thagard would stay aboard for four months, the longest orbital stay by a U.S. astronaut since Skylab in 1973–74.

Operations aboard *Mir* were difficult.

Chiaki Mukai, a Japanese physician, demonstrates bean sprouts growing in a cassette case, part of the International Microgravity Laboratory mission aboard the space shuttle *Columbia*.

NASA

A computer-generated scene shows the space shuttle *Atlantis* docked to the International Space Station *Alpha*. The station is to be assembled during a five-year period beginning in 1997. Most of its design was based on the work done for the canceled U.S. *Freedom* program.

There were serious problems with on-board equipment, including breakdowns in radio communications and a broken materials furnace that was not fixed in time for Merbold to use it.

International Space Station *Alpha*

NASA completed the redesign of its space station program by including the Russian Space Agency as a partner equal with the European Space Agency (ESA), the National Space Development Agency of Japan (NASDA), and the Canadian Space Agency. The new International Space Station *Alpha* was to be assembled during a five-year period starting in 1997. Most of its design was based on earlier work on the canceled U.S. *Freedom* program, which experienced severe cost overruns and congressional disapproval.

The program was scheduled to be developed in three phases, the first of which started with Krikalev's 1994 flight aboard the shuttle. Shuttle *Atlantis* was to rendezvous with *Mir* in May 1995 and then dock and exchange Russian and U.S. crew personnel in October 1995; nine more docking missions were planned through 1996. Phase 2 would assemble enough of *Alpha* during 1997–98 for a crew of three to operate aboard the station. Phase 3 would add more modules and round out the station's capabilities by June 2002.

The U.S. planned to buy from Russia the FGB tug ("functional supply block" in Russian), which would act as a docking, power, and propulsion unit during early operations with *Alpha*. Russia's *Mir 2* would be rebuilt and launched to serve as the service module attached to the FGB. Russia also planned to supply a solar power array to provide extra electricity for science, two Soyuz TM spacecraft as lifeboats, and several experiment

modules. Some elements were to be purchased by NASA under a $400 million contract with the Russian Space Agency to help support the Russian economy.

The U.S. planned to build habitation and laboratory modules, connecting nodes, and the main truss. In 1994 NASA selected the Boeing Co. as the single prime contractor for the program; in early 1995 the two signed a $5.6 billion contract that extended to 2003.

Alpha's major international partners, and their principal contributions, were: United States (NASA)—laboratory, habitat, and logistics modules, connecting nodes, support truss, major systems (environmental control, life support, computer, communications, and primary electrical power); ESA—Attached Payload Module; Japan (NASDA)—Japan Experiment Module; Canadian Space Agency—Mobile Servicing System, including robot

447

arms to assemble the station as modules are delivered; Russian Space Agency—FGM module, service module, station propulsion, tug, experiment modules, power modules, Progress resupply craft, Soyuz crew-transfer vehicles, and docking modules; and Italian Space Agency—pressurized logistics module.

When completed, *Alpha* is to have a wingspan of 108.4 m (355.6 ft) and a length of 74.1 m (243 ft). By comparison, the space shuttle orbiter is 37 m (121.4 ft) long.

Alpha was designed to be a complex amalgam of modules and support structure that might be considered in three major groups: the truss and solar arrays, the Western modules, and the Russian modules. The truss and solar arrays could be envisioned as stretching left to right. The Western modules (U.S., Japan, Europe) would be grouped under it to form the "nose" of the station. The Russian modules would form *Alpha*'s core during its initial assembly and would form the trailing section when assembly was complete.

Alpha crews would be launched by the U.S. space shuttle, Russian Soyuz, and perhaps a European spacecraft now under study. Supplies would be launched by the U.S. space shuttle, Russian Progress, ESA's Ariane, and perhaps Japan's H-2 rocket.

Alpha was scheduled to be launched into an orbit inclined 51.6° to the Equator so that it could be reached by Russian vehicles. This would take it as far north as lower Canada and most of Europe and as far south as the tips of Argentina and Australia, thereby covering about 95% of the world's population. Most shuttle launches headed due east into orbits inclined 28.5° to the Equator (the same as Cape Canaveral's latitude). Any launch into a higher or lower inclination reduced the payload that could be carried. Because the inclination would be 51.6°, NASA planned to develop a lightweight external tank, using lithium aluminum alloy, which would allow the shuttle to carry 11,407 kg (25,140 lb) into an orbit 353 km (253 mi) high. Russia's Proton launcher would be able to carry 18,150 kg (40,000 lb) to the same orbit.

Experiments in the life sciences and microgravity materials sciences were to be the focus of science activities. The original space station *Freedom* included an array of instruments for solar and stellar observations, but they were eliminated as the cost of the program rose. NASA now planned to add modest accommodations for instruments that would be mounted in three or four areas on the outside of *Alpha*.

One element lost in the redesign effort during the last three years was dedicated sleeping quarters for the crews. Earlier designs provided compartments in which they could sleep or have privacy. In the new design the astronauts would sleep in bags attached to the sides of equipment racks in the habitation module, which housed the galley, shower, and life-support system.

The crew would operate *Alpha* through a series of Space Station Multiplexer/Demultiplexer stations based on the Intel 80386SX processor, programmed in the Ada language and connected by Ethernet. Portable computers would be used and could be connected at locations throughout the station.

An increasing hazard that *Alpha*'s crew had to face was debris left by satellite launches, expended rocket stages that had ruptured, and even items that the station itself might lose. The greatest hazard would come not from ahead but from the sides as objects in other orbits crossed the plane of *Alpha*'s orbit. Collison speeds could be almost 50,000 km/h (31,000 mph).

SPACE PROBES

A low-budget expedition to the Moon, the end of a survey of Venus, and the start of two new planetary programs highlighted space probe activities during the past year.

Deep space

Ulysses, the international solar polar spacecraft developed by ESA, officially began its four-month polar science mission on June 26, 1994, when it passed latitude 70° S as it arced over the Sun's southern hemisphere. It reached a maximum solar latitude of 80.2° S at a distance from the Earth of 2.3 astronomical units (AU) in September. (One astronomical unit = 150 million km, or 93 million mi.)

Ulysses' instruments revealed new structures in the plasma and magnetic fields of the solar wind at high latitudes. Earlier it had recorded solar winds blowing at 2.9 million km/h (1.8 million mph) as it dipped beneath the current sheet that extends outward from the Sun's magnetic equator. Ulysses made its closest approach to the Sun, 200 million km (124 million mi), when it crossed the solar equator in March 1995; the probe then continued on a trajectory over the northern hemisphere.

Artist's drawing shows the space-based Solar Heliospheric Observatory, scheduled to be launched in July 1995. It will investigate the Sun's interior and corona.

Venus

NASA's Magellan spacecraft ended its survey of Venus in a blaze of glory when engineers ordered the spacecraft to lower its orbit into the upper reaches of the planet's atmosphere. Magellan, launched in May 1989 and orbiting Venus since August 1990, was failing slowly and running out of attitude-control propellant. Magellan orbited Venus 15,000 times and provided high-resolution radar images of 98% of the planet's surface and a high-resolution gravity map of 95%. Its final experiment provided scientists with information about the density of the upper reaches of the atmosphere.

On Oct. 11, 1994, Magellan fired its thrusters and lowered its orbit so that it passed through the upper reaches of Venus' atmosphere. Contact with the spacecraft was lost on October 12. Incineration in the lower atmosphere was believed to have occurred within two days.

Among recent finds was evidence that Venus is geologically active. Gravity data showed evidence of both "top loading," indicating a mountain or volcano pressing down on a crustal plate, and "bottom loading," indicating hot, less-dense material pressing up from the mantle.

Earth

NASA launched Wind, its first probe for the International Solar-Terrestrial Physics (ISTP) program. Five spacecraft were to study space from the Earth's upper atmosphere to the regions beyond lunar orbit and into the solar wind.

The ISTP spacecraft and their launch dates were Geotail (Japan's Institute for Space and Astronautical Sciences, July 1992), Wind (NASA, Nov. 1, 1994), the Solar Heliospheric Observatory (SOHO; ESA, July 1995), Polar (NASA, November 1995), and Cluster (ESA, late 1995). Geotail probed the magnetosphere deep into the cometlike tail formed by pressure from the solar wind. Wind was probing space just ahead of the bow shock on the "windward" side, where the solar wind compresses the magnetosphere. Eventually it would be positioned in the "L1" Lagrangian point, a balance point between the gravity of Earth and the Sun about 1.6 million km (one million miles) from the Earth. SOHO also would be positioned at L1 to monitor the solar wind continuously and observe the Sun with several telescopes. Polar was scheduled to arc from 11,000 to 57,000 km (6,840 to 35,420 mi) above the cusps of the magnetic poles, where solar wind particles and cosmic rays are funneled into the atmosphere, forming the auroras. Cluster would involve four spacecraft flying in formation to study the fine-scale structure of the magnetosphere.

The Dante robot, rebuilt by NASA and Carnegie Mellon University, Pittsburgh, Pa., and renamed Dante II, took a stroll July 29–Aug. 5, 1994, into Mt. Spurr, an active volcano 128 km (79 mi) west of Anchorage, Alaska. The 770-kg (1,700-

Carrying several television cameras, the robot Dante II explores the crater of Mt. Spurr, an active volcano in Alaska. The robot succeeded in moving several hundred meters down a steep slope into the crater before it stumbled and fell.

NASA; photo, Bill Ingalls

Rydberg Crater, 50 km (30 mi) wide, dominates a region of the Moon's far side in an image obtained by the space probe Clementine.

Naval Research Laboratory

lb), 3-m (9.8-ft)-tall robot had eight legs that moved in groups of four. It carried several TV cameras to let scientists view from above and around the robot as it explored the volcano's crater. As Dante, the robot had stalled at the start of a 1993 expedition in Antarctica. As Dante II, it moved several hundred meters into the caldera before it stumbled and fell. A rock climber had to attach a harness for a helicopter to retrieve the robot. NASA officials said that they were pleased with the results, however, and would continue development work.

Moon

Almost 25 years after the Apollo 11 landing, the U.S. returned to the Moon with a modest probe originally built to test missile-tracking sensors. The Clementine spacecraft was built by the U.S. Ballistic Missile Defense Organization (BMDO) to carry an array of ultrasmall, lightweight missile-tracking sensors. Reduced budgets and potential arms treaty restrictions prompted the BMDO to test the sensors by observing the Moon rather than flying a special target vehicle. Clementine was launched Jan. 25, 1994, and, after some swingby maneuvers, arrived in lunar orbit on February 19. By the time it left lunar orbit on May 3, it had returned some 1.8 million images of the Earth and the Moon in infrared, visible, and near-ultraviolet light at the rate of 5,000 images every five-hour orbit. It mapped the Moon's polar regions and found a crater that is in perpetual darkness, an encouraging sign that water may be locked in the soil. It also discovered on the Moon the largest known impact basin in the solar system, 2,560 km (1,590 mi) wide and

12 km (7.5 mi) deep. Even though spacecraft in the 1960s had photographed the Moon's far side, the south pole-Aitken Basin region had been seen obliquely and had never before been measured directly. A laser altimeter scanned the Moon's surface and found it to be far rougher than anyone had suspected. The surface is also about 25% brighter than earlier measurements had indicated.

Clementine was to rendezvous with asteroid 1620 Geographos, but a computer failure later burned most of its propellant and reduced the ground directors' ability to control the spacecraft. Nevertheless, the mission was considered to have been a resounding success because of its low cost as well as the data it obtained.

Mars

Following the loss of the Mars Observer spacecraft in August 1993, NASA planned an ambitious program to explore Mars with a series of landers and orbiters. The Mars Surveyor program would comprise a series of small, low-cost craft launched by medium-cost Delta II rockets. The first, the Mars Global Surveyor, was to be launched in November 1996. It would carry copies of many of Mars Observer's instruments and thus achieve many of the scientific goals of that mission. Mars Global Surveyor would use the planet's atmosphere as a brake to slow it on arrival, thus reducing the size and cost of rockets needed to insert it into a polar orbit that would cover all of the planet during one Martian year. The spacecraft was also to serve as a relay station for landers to be launched in 1998, 2001, 2003, and 2005. Future Mars Global Surveyors, to be launched in 1998 and 2003, were scheduled to carry additional instruments.

The first Mars landing since the Viking landers of 1976 was to be made by the Mars Pathfinder, a small lander and miniature rover to be launched in December 1996. Mars Pathfinder was part of the Discovery program intended to blend low-cost management and current and advanced technologies. (*See* Feature Article: DISCOVERY: A NEW JOURNEY INTO SPACE.)

Outer planets

NASA's Galileo spacecraft was scheduled to go into orbit around Jupiter on Dec. 7, 1995, thus ending a six-year odyssey that started with its launch from the Earth in October 1989 and involved one flyby of Venus and two of Earth to reshape its trajectory and swing it outward to Jupiter. About a week before its insertion into orbit, Galileo was to release a probe that would plunge into Jupiter's atmosphere and relay data about the planet's structure and chemistry. This would be the first on-site measurements of the largest planet in the solar system. The probe was expected to function until it was crushed in the atmosphere at a depth equivalent to 10–20 times sea-level pressure on Earth. Galileo would be only the fifth man-made craft to visit Jupiter and the first to orbit it.

Galileo's science mission was hampered, however, by the refusal of its high-gain antenna to deploy. As a result, images had to be relayed at extremely slow speeds—40 bits per second—through the low-gain antenna. Nevertheless, the data returned by Galileo continued to be of high quality. Galileo observed the colli-

sion of Comet Shoemaker-Levy 9 with Jupiter in July 1994.

ESA started final development work on the Huygens probe, which was to be released by NASA's Cassini spacecraft to land on Titan, the methane-covered moon of Saturn. Cassini was to be launched on Oct. 6, 1997, and arrive at Saturn on June 25, 2004. The trajectory would involve two flybys of Venus, one of the Earth, and one of Jupiter to accelerate and direct the spacecraft toward Saturn. The Huygens probe was scheduled to be released on Nov. 6, 2004, and enter Titan's atmosphere on November 27.

Voyagers 1 and 2 continued to send data on the solar wind, cosmic rays, and other phenomena at the edge of the solar system. By early 1995 Voyager 1 was more than 8.7 billion km (5.4 billion mi) and Voyager 2 more than 6.7 billion km (4.1 billion mi) from the Earth. As the two spacecraft recede into the galaxy, the strength of their signals will fade until they can no longer be heard.

Small bodies

Galileo discovered a tiny moon orbiting asteroid 243 Ida, the first confirmation of a phenomenon that had been suggested in many asteroid observations. Galileo flew past Ida in August 1993, but the discovery did not become known until early 1994 because of Galileo's slow transmission rate.

NASA initiated its first dedicated small-body mission, the Near Earth Asteroid Rendezvous (NEAR). It was to be launched in February 1996 and make its closest approach to 433 Eros in February 1999.

ESA asked scientists to propose experiments for the Rosetta mission to fly past one or two asteroids and then orbit a comet and place a small science package on its surface. If implemented, Rosetta would be launched in 2003 or 2004. ESA's original plan was to have Rosetta return with samples for analysis on Earth, but rising costs forced the agency to redesign the mission.

—Dave Dooling

See also Feature Article: ASTEROIDS: SECRETS LOCKED IN STONE; Year in Review: ASTRONOMY.

TRANSPORTATION

The pace of change in transportation and logistics management had never been faster than in the past year. The challenges of new and emerging business concepts and technologies, fast and influential shifts in domestic and international trading patterns, and the growing trend of transportation deregulation and privatization supported innovative transportation services and a faster response to customer demands. The four major transportation modes—air, highway, rail, and water—experienced single- and, in some cases, double-digit growth in terms of volume and revenues for both passenger and cargo service. The pipeline industry remained relatively stable.

Air transport

The aviation industry, which during the past few years probably had felt the sting of the U.S. and worldwide recession more severely than any other form of transportation, in 1994 enjoyed an increase of 7% above 1993 levels for combined U.S.

The wide-body jetliner family of the Boeing Co. includes (left to right) the 747–400, the 777, and the 767–300. The 777 is expected to be placed in commercial operation within two years.

and international passenger, freight, and mail traffic. The world's airlines combined to operate profitably in 1994 after registering more than $11.5 billion in losses during the preceding three years— a sum greater than all the profits made since international scheduled service began. Total passenger traffic increased 4% in 1994 to 1,180,000,000 passengers on international services. Elimination of unprofitable routes, reduction of payrolls, and deferment of deliveries of new airplanes all contributed to a leaner, more efficient industry. Capacity increases for both domestic and international traffic were kept in check, and the overall passenger-load factor (the number of seats occupied as a percentage of the total) rose significantly for the first time since 1988, reaching 67%, which was often near or at the break-even point for profitability for most carrier operations.

Safety became a significant concern for the airlines in 1994 as they suffered their worst year in terms of accidents since 1988. More than 1,000 people were killed in crashes throughout the world. In response, U.S. Secretary of Transportation Federico Peña called a two-day emergency conference on Jan. 9–10, 1995, in Washington, D.C. Attended by some 950 industry experts, the conference concluded with 70 recommendations for

wide-ranging changes in equipment and training. Especially emphasized was the installation of new technologies, including deicing equipment and radar for preventing runway collisions.

Because of severe financial constraints, the industry was reluctant to introduce new and innovative equipment. Nevertheless, the Boeing Co., the world's largest manufacturer of commercial planes, continued to make progress with its new twin-engine 777 and expected to place it in commercial operation within the next two years.

U.S. airlines continued to develop innovative business concepts, including code-sharing alliances with foreign airlines in order to expand international operations. Code-sharing involved a carrier's placing its numerical code, as it appeared on a travel agent's computer reservation system, on another carrier's flight. Thus, the same flight would appear two or more times in the agent's computer, although all carriers would market the flight as if it were their own. Airlines then would decide among themselves what share of the revenues would go to the actual operator of the flight and what share would go to the seller of the ticket. Critics of the plan pointed out that customers might be forced to fly on planes of a carrier that they would prefer not to use.

The campaign to eliminate smoking on foreign flights to and from the U.S. appeared to have gathered fresh support. It seemed reasonable to project that all smoking would be banned on most international short-to-medium-distance flights within the next few years.

Highway transport

According to the International Bridge, Tunnel, and Turnpike Association, some 45,000 km (1 km = 0.62 mi) of toll roads were being planned throughout the world during the past year. Mexico alone scheduled more than 6,000 km.

In 1994 Mother Nature continued to remind the trucking industry that it still had a long way to go in terms of service reliability under severe circumstances. This was demonstrated by earthquakes that destroyed bridges and damaged highways in the Los Angeles area and in Kobe, Japan. Severe snow and ice conditions in the northern U.S. and floods that ravaged the South placed added strains on equipment and schedules.

Meanwhile, truckers continued to encourage the use of wider and longer truck units to improve transportation efficiency. With the increased acceptance of the 14.5-m (48-ft)-long trailer as the standard for U.S. highway transportation for goods, truckers were also considering increasing the width of some types of trailers from the traditional 245 cm (96 in) to 260 cm (102 in). A U.S. General Accounting Office study found that the use of longer vehicles would cut transportation costs and reduce highway and bridge wear.

Truckers in the U.S. faced a continuing shortage of qualified drivers, largely because of federally mandated drug- and alcohol-testing requirements. This was especially true for long-distance routes. By some estimates the annual turnover of drivers for many companies was as much as 100%. As a result, many carriers were forced to raise pay and search for better ways of recruiting and retaining drivers.

The trucking industry also was being forced to recognize and deal differently with the other modes of transportation. Until recently, deep animosity and mistrust of the other modes were the prevailing moods of the industry. The need to streamline operations in order to become more cost-efficient, however, caused some truckers, especially a few of the larger national carriers such as J.B. Hunt Transport Services, Inc., and Schneider National, Inc., to enter into partnerships with rail operators in order to take advantage of what each partner did best. In this case the trucker handled the trailer or container at both ends of the trip, and the rail carrier transported the units on long hauls. This concept was often used on trips that were 800–1,100 km or more in length. As of 1995 the results were encouraging, some trucking companies having cut their normal capital expenses by up to 50%.

The North American Free Trade Agreement (NAFTA), ratified in 1993, provided North American-based trucking companies with new opportunities, especially in trade to and from Mexico. Nevertheless, badly needed highway improvements in Mexico, along with non-compatible economic and operating regulations, restricted the operation of large and heavy trucks on Mexican roads.

In Europe and other parts of the world, the trucking industry continued to dominate in many nations because of their lack of substantial alternative systems such as railroads and inland waterways. Environmental issues and restrictions on financial support for highway infrastructure improvements were expected to place added pressure on the trucking industries of many countries, similar to the experiences of the U.S. in recent years.

Pipelines

New gas- and oil-pipeline development declined from the 1992 high of 25,-830 km to an estimated 23,650 km in 1994. The U.S. accounted for one-third of all new developments, although the gas-pipeline network expansion was held back pending clarification of federal and state regulatory procedures. Worldwide there was a new emphasis on long-term-storage facilities.

In Europe development centered on the $1.5 billion North Sea Europipe gas-line project. In the former U.S.S.R., after a number of years of underinvestment, the focus shifted to maintenance and rehabilitation, especially following the oil spill at Usinsk, Russia, in October, which was the third largest in history. The gas line connecting the China Sea Yacheng Field to Hong Kong was nearly complete, and the Maghreb-Europe line was begun. Major pipeline networks were under consideration in Oman, China, and South America.

Railroads

The U.S. railroad industry in 1994 experienced one of its best years in recent memory. Largely in response to an improved economic situation, rail traffic increased for grain, coal, automobiles, and finished steel. International and domestic shipments of cargo in containers and truck trailers (more than eight million units) continued to grow in double-digit numbers for most of the large carriers. Rail carriers that had direct access to the growing markets with Canada and Mexico also witnessed a considerable upturn in their operations, particularly since they were viewed as an alternative to the problems associated with the trucking industry in the same markets.

This good fortune, however, made more urgent the need to improve the utilization of equipment and to purchase new units that were larger and more durable. They also increased the need for new and more efficient locomotives with higher horsepower and for more efficient communications and traffic-control systems. After years of downsizing, some railroads, especially such long-haul carriers as Burlington Northern and Union Pacific, added new employees to meet the demand for increased services.

At the international level most of the rail carriers—passenger and cargo—were owned and/or controlled by governments. As a result, most of them, particularly in Europe, continued to be large drains on their national treasuries. As part of sweeping reforms brought about by government deregulation, including in some cases privatization, many of these railroads were being sold to the private sector, a process that, depending on the circumstances of each nation, could take several years. Members of the European Union (EU) made it a goal to privatize all of their national railroads during the next few years.

Despite the problems of the transition from government ownership, progress was made in several notable international rail operations. The newly constructed rail tunnel under the English Channel between England and France opened in 1994 for both passenger and freight operations. Despite early complications, it eventually would be possible to travel by train between London and Paris in about three hours, a saving of several hours from the conventional rail/ferry/rail service. By 1994 high-speed passenger trains linked Brussels, London, and Paris. China was planning a high-speed route to connect Beijing (Peking) and Shanghai.

Land-bridge services, which began in the U.S. during the 1980s, continued to gain market share from traditional all-water container shipments. With land-bridge, containers moved by rail over a large land mass such as the continental U.S., as well as by vessel at one or both ends of the trip. By 1995 land-bridge systems were beginning to be developed in Asia and Europe. Sea-Land Services, one of the world's largest and most-advanced intermodal carriers, is a partner in the development of a service that will link East Asian markets with Europe via the 9,650-km Trans-Siberian Railroad. Meanwhile, all-water carriers involved with that trade route were offering competitive services.

Development of urban mass-transit systems continued its rapid growth. More than 100 cities throughout the world were operating such systems and were planning to invest $13.8 billion in them during the year.

A new subway system opened in Brasília, Brazil, as did extensions to existing systems in Calcutta; Madrid; Munich, Germany; Nagoya, Japan; Paris; Pusan, South Korea; and Washington, D.C. Subway construction was under way in Hanover, Germany; Kao-hsiun, Taiwan; Pasadena, Calif.; Santiago, Chile; and Toronto. Subway extensions to airports were planned for Stockholm, Hong Kong, San Francisco, and Berlin.

Even more extensive growth took place in aboveground transit systems. New projects opened in Denver, Colo.; Guadalajara; Mexico; Rouen and Strasbourg, France; Sheffield, England; and Valencia, Spain. Extensions were made in many other cities, including the Docklands Light Railway in London. Construction was authorized in numerous cities, including Izmir, Turkey; Saarbrücken, Germany; and San Juan, P.R., with detailed studies and planning being undertaken for Brisbane, Australia; Copenhagen; Johannesburg, South Africa; and Salt Lake City, Utah.

Water transport

Advances in waterborne transportation industries continued to be made during the year as ship designs and sizes were made more cost-efficient for both passenger and cargo operations. Passenger service, mostly for cruises, was expanding to new markets such as Alaska and south of the Equator in both hemispheres. For cargo, a few containerships were ordered that would be capable of carrying enough containers to stretch the entire length of New York City's Manhattan Island if placed end to end.

The effort to increase the efficiency of international ocean-transportation containership services continued during the year. Carriers on the same routes shared vessels, cargo-handling equipment, terminals, and marketing in order to achieve a higher level of asset utilization and, it was hoped, larger profits. These partnerships, particularly on the heavily traveled North America–Europe–Far East containership

A car is loaded aboard a train for a trip through the Channel Tunnel, which links England and France. After almost nine years of work, the tunnel was completed and opened in 1994.

Jonathan Player—The New York Times

routes allowed carriers with expensive containerships—some of which had daily operating expenses as high as $50,000—to shift to routes where the market demand, as well as profit, was better.

Carriers also sought to introduce a more collective approach to vessel scheduling, service, and price stabilization to further reduce money-losing operations. This policy reduced the number of ships in service, particularly on the Far East–Europe and North America–Europe trade routes, and so met with strong shipper resistance. Shippers enlisted the help of such government agencies as the U.S. Federal Maritime Commission and the EU's competitive practices directorate to reverse what they considered unfair business practices. By 1995 it looked as if those differences of opinion would not be easily resolved.

On Sept. 28, 1994, the "roll-on, roll-off" ferry *Estonia* sank in the Baltic Sea after a loading door was apparently ripped off by pounding waves. The accident, in which more than 900 people died, raised questions about the safety of all such ferries.

Technology

For the most part, the greatest advances in technological development focused on the terminals through which passengers and cargo passed. Terminal operators continued to develop facilities that allowed faster transfer of cargo between the modes, especially containers. These "seamless" terminal operations were further enhanced by the increased use of electronic-based communications systems that permitted faster and more accurate flow of cargo and passengers.

Perhaps the greatest change by the transportation and logistics-management industry during the past year involved the transfer and handling of information. Increasingly, carriers were recognizing the need to develop and introduce electronic data-interchange (EDI) systems that provided real-time control of their operations. By using EDI, shippers could efficiently select, book, track, and adjust the transportation of their cargoes, thereby providing their customers with better service at often lower cost because of reduced transit times and lower inventory-handling costs. This form of improved EDI was central to the operations of such carriers as Sea-Land Services, American President Lines, United Parcel Services of America, and Federal Express.

Deregulation

Federal, state, and local governments and agencies in the U.S. continued during the year to make slow but persistent progress in meeting the requirements of the Intermodal Surface Transportation Efficiency Act of 1991 (ISTEA) and the Clean Air Act (CAA) Amendments of 1990. Both acts forced the public and private sector to work together to rethink how and why transportation services, both passenger and freight, could become better integrated to improve service and reduce the stress on financial resources and the environment.

New ISTEA- and CAA-related regulations and other clarifications issued in 1994 increased the emphasis on public participation in the planning process. One way this could be done was through a greater reliance on Metropolitan Planning Organizations and state de-

partments of transportation for the development of transportation systems of improved efficiency. The participation of the private sector (carriers, shippers, and other related services) in the decision-making process for infrastructure-investment proposals within a particular region would also be required.

Considerable progress was made during the year in deregulation, if not elimination, of some of the last bastions of economic transportation regulation in the U.S. Economic regulation of the transportation industry within a state's borders was removed on the basis of the apparent success of earlier interstate deregulation of similar services in the late 1970s and 1980s for all of the modes. Regulation of transportation-related safety issues remained untouched.

The Interstate Commerce Commission, which for more than a century was responsible for the economic regulation of surface transportation in the U.S., appeared on the verge of going out of business as part of the federal government's efforts to reduce the cost of government. The same fate could be in store for the Federal Maritime Commission, an agency responsible for regulating the economic activities of maritime services affecting international trade with the U.S. Issues and regulations related to safety would continue to be handled by the federal Department of Transportation.

For domestic and international waterborne transportation, including inland waterways, there was a slow but persistent move toward the deregulation of such services and the opening of them to a larger field of competitors, including operations under flags of other nations.

By the terms of the Jones Act, passengers and cargo moving between U.S. ports had to do so on vessels built and operated under the U.S. flag. This practice, it was suggested, increased the expense of operations because of the lack of potentially lower-cost carriers, especially foreign-flag operators. This issue continued to be debated in 1995.

International agreements such as NAFTA and, at the global level, the General Agreement on Tariffs and Trade (GATT) called for reduced restrictions on the flow of passengers and goods across international borders. These agreements were expected to open the door for U.S. carriers to participate in markets from which they previously had been restricted. To a large extent the benefits of such agreements had already been realized by the EU.

Trading patterns

Faster and more cost-efficient communications systems combined with quicker response times to market demands in 1994 accelerated the shift in markets for customers and suppliers of goods and services. There was an increasing need for the development of transportation systems that would provide the means to seek new and emerging markets that might not otherwise have been available. For example, until the 1990s most of the trade for finished and semifinished goods with the U.S. had been on a strong east-west axis involving the Far East, North America, and Europe. Largely because of the new markets opened by NAFTA and GATT, however, together with the need to respond faster to customer demands, many companies were shifting their man-ufacturing operations and markets for finished products to a trading pattern oriented along a more-pronounced north-south direction.

Transportation and logistics-management companies needed to respond to those changes within a relatively few years, if not months. Before deregulation, such a process of change in trading patterns and operations often took several decades to become fully developed.

Future prospects

As to the near future, it seemed reasonable to assume that transportation and logistics-management services would continue to expand throughout the world. The rate of growth would differ sharply on a regional basis, however. Advanced economies would grow at a faster pace than those that were still struggling to catch up after years of political and economic stagnation.

Transportation bottlenecks would continue to be drastically reduced. Passengers and cargo would move more efficiently and swiftly through ports and airports and between the modes. For cargo moving in standard-size containers, shippers would receive freight with precise and reliable schedules at competitive rates, and this would be accomplished in a safe and environmentally friendly way.

It was reasonable to assume that all of the participants in the transportation and logistics-management process would be closely tied together electronically. This could lead to the additional benefit of access to adequate capital and, consequently, to better profits.

More specifically, there would be a growing trend toward integration of the different modes to work more efficiently with one another to reduce duplication of services and costs. This would require the public and private sectors to form partnerships in developing transportation systems. Public and private companies and agencies would, as a result, continue to undergo restructuring.

A good example of such possibilities was Europe's current drive to deregulate railroads, highways, air transport, and inland waterways while continuing to address environmental concerns and the need for growth. In late 1994 EU leaders supported a priority list of 14 major projects, collectively known as Trans European Networks. These projects included high-speed rail routes radiating from France into Germany, Italy, and Spain; a new airport for Milan; a road and rail bridge linking Sweden and Denmark; and a superhighway crossing Spain and Portugal. All these, together with several other large-scale private advanced communications systems, were a key part of the EU's strategy to boost economic growth, create jobs, and improve competitiveness.

What was not so certain, however, was the degree to which the industry adjusted to the pressures placed on its human resources in terms of working conditions, education, and technological development. It could be said that the next revolution in transportation (the first three included technology, concepts, and communications systems) would be the way in which the industry identified, trained, and retained its personnel so that they could keep up with, manage, and anticipate future changes.

—Gerhardt Muller

U.S. SCIENCE POLICY

Pity the poor science policy analyst! First, after 12 years of Republican control of the White House, Democrat Bill Clinton became president, bringing with him a new set of priorities for science. Then, two years later, Republicans gained control of both the House of Representatives and Senate for the first time since 1954. Unlike the presidential campaign, where party platforms outlined at least a general direction for science and technology, these subjects were not major campaign themes in congressional races, and there was no mention of science in the Contract with America, the document Republicans embraced as their marching orders. People concerned about the future of U.S. science policy spent the days after the 1994 election trying to figure out just what changes a Republican-controlled Congress would mean for science. If analysts were certain of nothing else, they were certain of one thing: there would be changes.

Scientific misconduct

Some of the changes were easier to predict than others. For example, Rep. John Dingell, a Democrat from Michigan, won reelection to the 104th Congress, but he would no longer be chairman of the House Energy and Commerce Committee and its Oversight and Investigation Subcommittee. In 1994 the subcommittee was once again in the thick of a major investigation of scientific misconduct, this time involving University of Pittsburgh, Pa., cancer researcher Bernard Fisher. Fisher was chairman of the National Surgical Adjuvant Breast and Bowel Project (NSABP), one of the most successful multicenter clinical trial projects ever

launched. Under Fisher's leadership the NSABP was able to alter radically the treatment of women with breast cancer. NSABP studies showed that removing a small lump of cancerous tissue could frequently be as effective a treatment as removing the entire breast and that a woman's chance of surviving breast cancer improved substantially if surgery was followed by chemotherapy and hormone treatments.

In March 1994, however, the *Chicago Tribune* revealed that one of Fisher's collaborators, Roger Poisson at the St. Luc Hospital in Montreal, had been falsifying the records of patients he had enrolled in several NSABP studies of breast cancer. The falsifications included alterations of the dates when surgery was performed and admission of patients into the studies who did not meet the entry criteria. What alarmed many people and ultimately brought on an investigation by Dingell's subcommittee was that Fisher had known since 1990 that there were potential problems with Poisson's data but had failed to publicize those problems by alerting the journals where the studies containing the data had been published. Fisher argued that he had reanalyzed the studies and found that removing Poisson's data did not change the results.

Dingell was not satisfied with Fisher's answer. At a hearing in June he grilled Fisher about his reasons for not revealing the potential problems to the public. He was also highly critical of National Cancer Institute officials, who did not pressure Fisher to publish a note describing the reanalysis. NCI Director Samuel Broder promised that such errors would never happen again.

In the end Fisher was forced to step down as NSABP chairman, although he launched a lawsuit against the University of Pittsburgh on the grounds that he was wrongfully forced out. Also, Broder announced that he would be leaving the National Cancer Institute for the private sector. Rep. Joe Barton, a Texas Republican who replaced Dingell as committee chairman, has so far shown no enthusiasm for taking on such fights over misconduct.

Tobacco

Another issue the new Republican Congress seemed disinclined to address is tobacco. During 1994 Rep. Henry Waxman, a California Democrat, held a number of hearings seeking to prove that tobacco companies knowingly add nicotine to cigarettes in an attempt to induce addiction among cigarette smokers. At one memorable hearing in April 1994, Waxman assembled the top executives from seven of the leading tobacco companies to explain why they sold a product they knew was harmful. The executives argued that they were merely providing a product that the public demanded and that nicotine was naturally a part of that product.

The question of whether tobacco companies knowingly manipulate the nicotine content of cigarettes is an important one because proving that they do would open the door for the Food and Drug Administration to regulate tobacco products. FDA commissioner David Kessler said that his agency was exploring the possibility that it could have some jurisdiction over the tobacco industry. The new Congress is unlikely to allow Kessler

Executives from major U.S. tobacco companies testified before Congress that nicotine is a natural component of cigarettes and is not added to them to induce addiction among smokers.

to have that authority, however. The new chairman of the House Energy and Commerce Committee (renamed the Commerce Committee) is Thomas Bliley, Jr., a Republican from Virginia who staunchly defended the tobacco companies during the hearings.

If anything, the FDA's authority may be curtailed in the future. Conservative think tanks have argued that the agency takes an overprotective attitude to new drugs, denying products to people who may desperately need them and who are willing to accept the fact that they may not be as safe as the FDA now requires. That message seemed to resonate with the new Republican majority.

Embryo research

One controversial area of science that Republicans seem anxious to pursue is research on human embryos. In 1993 Congress passed a law that ended a de facto moratorium on federal support for research involving human embryos. Scientists have always been interested in studying the development of the normal human embryo, but that research took on an added urgency in 1978 when the first test-tube baby was born in the U.K. Since then the procedure, known as in vitro fertilization, has provided tens of thousands of babies to infertile couples. But the technique is expensive, and more often than not, couples who try it do not get a baby. Without federal support, research in the U.S. stagnated.

Scientists, therefore, were jubilant after the passage of the 1993 law. The National Institutes of Health, the federal agency that would ultimately supply the research funds, decided to move cautiously, however, into what was sure to be both ethical and political stormy waters. NIH director Harold Varmus created a Human Embryo Research panel to consider what types of research could ethically go forward. The panel met several times in 1994 and in September issued a report suggesting the kinds of research that were acceptable, those that were off limits, and those that needed additional ethical scrutiny.

The panel concluded, among other things, that research that was intended only to improve the outcome of in vitro fertilization could be funded, as could research on "spare" embryos that were not going to be transferred into a woman's uterus (provided the sperm and egg donors gave their consent). Deemed unacceptable was research on hybrid embryos created with a human egg and animal sperm with the intention of implanting such embryos into a woman. Further deliberation was needed on whether to permit researchers to continue to study a human embryo in the laboratory past the 14th day of development.

By far the most controversial of the panel's conclusions concerned creating embryos strictly for research purposes. Religious conservatives immediately labeled such research bizarre and appalling, and a group of congressmen led by Robert Dornan wrote Varmus and urged him to reject such research. Before Varmus could act, President Clinton weighed into the debate on Dornan's side and declared that no federal money would ever be spent to create embryos for research as long as he was president. For his part, Dornan declared that the president had not gone far enough, and he promised to introduce legislation that would ban all embryo research permanently.

The case in favor of embryo research was hardly helped by the revelation that an experiment on human embryos that had captured the national spotlight in 1993 had been performed without proper ethical approval. A research team at George Washington University, Washington, D.C., had shown that it was possible to divide an embryo into its component cells at the two-, four-, and eight-cell stage and then induce the individual cells to grow in the laboratory. In theory, each of the cells has the potential to mature into a complete human being, although in practice the embryonic cells that the researchers were studying had too many chromosomes and were, therefore, not viable. But according to university research rules, even research on nonviable embryos required prior approval of an ethics panel, something the researchers had failed to get. University president Stephen Trachtenberg ordered all the data from the experiment destroyed.

Space and defense research

If the message from Capitol Hill was "go slow" for embryo research, it was "step on it" for space research. The new speaker of the House, Newt Gingrich, has long been an active supporter of the U.S. space program, as has Robert Walker, the new chairman of the Science Committee. Not that things were looking so bad before the Republicans took over. After several years of titanic battles, the appropriation for NASA's permanently occupied space station sailed through both houses of Congress. The Clinton administration successfully argued that the space station served both scientific and strategic interests. Russian participation ensured a healthy cooperation between the two nations, the argument

went, and kept Russian engineers from turning their talents to less-peaceful uses for rockets and space technology.

After some well-publicized disasters, such as the failure of the Mars Observer spacecraft and the loss of the main antenna on the Galileo probe, NASA had its share of successes during the past year. The Hubble Space Telescope continued to provide dazzling pictures with its newly repaired optics. Perhaps most exciting was the ringside seat the telescope provided as about 21 chunks of Comet Shoemaker-Levy 9 pummeled Jupiter. Even more important from a scientific standpoint was a new measurement of distant stars that suggest the universe may be half the age astronomers originally thought.

One of the pleasant space surprises in 1994 was not a NASA spacecraft at all. Clementine, a tiny spacecraft costing only about $80 million, was built by the Department of Defense's Ballistic Missile Defense Organization, the agency formerly known as the Strategic Defense Initiative. The spacecraft spent several weeks orbiting the Moon, where its small but sophisticated instruments provided the first digital map of the surface. Scientists were overjoyed at the bounty of data, and the White House ordered NASA to start thinking small, because the days of the multibillion-dollar explorer probes was clearly over for the time being.

Defense, energy, and basic research

Clementine's success was a reminder to many that the Defense Department had done some sophisticated research during past years and that with the end

of the Cold War there was a need to decide what to do with the department's scientific infrastructure. In recent years the Pentagon has sought to make some military technology available for civilian applications. For example, the formerly top-secret underwater listening device built to detect enemy submarines is being used to track whales and detect underwater volcanoes. The navy also offered the system to oceanographers who wanted to measure the time it took low-frequency sound pulses to travel across the ocean. The speed of the pulse reflects the temperature of the water. Determining global ocean temperature would help researchers get a fix on how the oceans are responding to global warming trends. That experiment was put on hold, however, when some marine scientists argued that the sound pulses could be harmful to passing whales.

Despite these projects, it became clearer that the heyday of military research spending has passed. Universities that once relied heavily on defense contracts to support their research laboratories are now having to look elsewhere. The situation may improve slightly with a Republican Congress dedicated to strengthening the national defense, but money is more likely to go to the battlefield than to laboratory hardware.

Another federal agency struggling to redefine itself in the post-Cold War era was the Department of Energy (DOE). The cancellation in 1993 of the Superconducting Super Collider, a giant atom smasher already under construction outside Dallas, Texas, did not take the department completely out of the science business, but it did call into question its long-term commitment to science projects. By early 1995 the DOE appeared poised to pull the plug on two major fusion energy projects: the $500 million Tokamak Plasma Experiment and U.S. participation in the $10 billion International Thermonuclear Experimental Reactor.

Also uncertain was the future of the DOE's national laboratories, particularly Sandia (Albuquerque, N.M.), Lawrence Livermore (Livermore, Calif.), and Los Alamos (N.M.); all three are research facilities built to design nuclear weapons. The three have struggled to redefine themselves and their role in a world where such weapons are being dismantled rather than built. Even with a new defense-minded Congress, however, these and the other DOE labs will be hard-pressed to justify their budgets to increasingly cost-conscious legislators.

If the DOE faced continued pressure, the new Republican majority is likely to sharpen its pencils as it attacks the budgets of several federal agencies that enjoyed relative success during the first two years of the Clinton administration. The National Institute of Standards and Technology, an agency of the Department of Commerce, saw its budget grow dramatically as it was given the role of helping

to bring federally funded technology to the marketplace. The National Science Foundation, an independent agency that provides funds for scientific and engineering research, was also getting the message from a Democratic Congress that support for basic research was fine but that scientists should always be mindful of how their research might lead to products and services that would—in the words of President Clinton—grow the economy.

The good news for scientists is that in general the Republicans who will control the budgets of these agencies do not believe that it is the job of the federal government to develop products and services; that should be left to the private sector. The bad news for those same scientists is that the Republican say that they are willing to start cutting federal spending and that science budgets are definitely on the chopping block.

The NIH and health care

That could be true even for the National Institutes of Health. For several years the NIH has weathered the fiscal storms that have pounded other agencies. In addition to the controversy over the research on human embryos, however, there was renewed criticism about experiments in-

volving fetal tissue as a treatment for degenerative neurological disorders such as Parkinson's disease.

There was also criticism from clinical researchers that Varmus was ignoring clinical research as he set his priorities for the agency. Varmus, a Nobel Prize-winning biologist, believes that the government's first responsibility should be to sustain strong support for basic research. His own work was on obscure viruses that infect chickens, which does not leap out as a valuable expenditure of money, but it ultimately led to the realization that human genes infected by viruses may cause cancer. That understanding, Varmus would argue, will ultimately be more helpful in determining rational ways to combat cancer than will spending large sums of money testing a new chemotherapy.

Varmus also upset behavioral researchers by failing to move swiftly to establish a new office of behavioral research at the NIH, a project that Congress had mandated. He has, at times, been critical of behavioral research in general. At the same time, he won praise from many scientists for his attempts to overhaul the system by which the agency decides which science projects to fund, a system that had become clumsy and conservative in many people's opinion.

There were other success stories for the NIH. The Human Genome Project continued to thrive in 1994 under the leadership of geneticist Francis Collins. In September scientists from the University of Utah and the National Institute of Environmental Health Sciences announced they had found a long-sought gene that is responsible for at least some

© Robert Holmgren

A laser machine cuts metal at the Lawrence Livermore National Laboratory, Livermore, Calif. The future of this and other Department of Energy labs was uncertain in the post-Cold War era.

inherited forms of breast cancer. And researchers at Rockefeller University, New York City, pinned down what may turn out to be the holy grail of obesity research: a gene that appears to control appetite.

Unfortunately, there was little good news in the fight against AIDS. After a frustrating search, during which many prospective candidates declined to be considered for the job, immunologist William Paul was chosen to take over as head of the office of AIDS research at the NIH. The job, once just a second hat worn by Anthony Fauci, head of the National Institute of Allergy and Infectious Diseases, took on new importance because of a congressional decision to funnel all AIDS money through Paul's office. Despite significant funding—by 1995 AIDS research amounted to 12% of the NIH's $11.3 billion budget—there was little progress to report on new understanding of the virus or new ways to treat the disease.

As intractable a problem as AIDS appears to be, at times it seemed less intractable than reforming the nation's health care system. The Clinton administration spent an enormous amount of intellectual and political capital trying to devise a plan that would satisfy all parties in the health care community. In the end nothing changed, and the prospects for major reform now seem marginal at best.

"Science in the National Interest"

The focus on health care may in part explain why the administration's attempt to get a handle on national science policy never really seemed to succeed. On Jan. 31, 1994, the White House Office of Science and Technology Policy served as host to a meeting called the "Forum for Science in the National Interest." A parade of speakers described what they saw as the critical direction for the future of U.S. science policy. Scientists tended to emphasize the need for a renewed commitment to basic science, while politicians warned that science would face cuts and research would have to be tailored to meet national priorities.

On August 3 the administration released a document called *Science in the National Interest,* which set lofty goals such as maintaining scientific leadership in scientific disciplines and improving the public's scientific literacy. The mechanism for achieving those goals was hardly inspirational, however. The administration proposed utilizing the new National Science and Technology Council to coordinate federal science programs, a task at which the George Bush administration's Federal Coordinating Council for Science, Engineering and Technology had achieved only limited success. The President's Committee of Advisers on Science and Technology (not to be confused with the Bush administration's President's Council of Advisers on Science and Technology) invited outside advisers to help in the policy-setting exercise, but that body did not meet until October, nearly two years after the president was elected.

Environmental concerns

Environmentalists were also dismayed at Clinton's failure to do more to implement what they thought would be a proactive agenda on global environment issues. Secretary of the Interior Bruce Babbitt created a new National Biological Survey (NBS), an ambitious attempt to create an inventory of all plant and animal species in the U.S. But NBS never appealed very much to Congress even before the Republicans came in, and there was every likelihood that it would be abolished before it ever really got started. Babbitt's plans to impose grazing fees on Western ranchers in an attempt to protect grasslands also failed.

Other major environmental laws—the Clean Air Act, the Clean Water Act, and Superfund—were all due for reauthorization in Congress in 1994, but no final action was taken on any of them. Only the California Desert Protection Act, passed in the waning hours of the 103rd Congress, made it to the president's desk and became law.

The Environmental Protection Agency also faces a rocky future. Congress has never shown much enthusiasm for raising the EPA to the status of a Cabinet agency, although President Clinton has invited EPA administrator Carol Browner to participate in Cabinet meetings. In July Browner announced plans for a major expansion of her agency's support for basic science, aiming to increase spending on academic research from $20 million to $100 million during the next few years. Browner wants her agency to do more long-term research on the environment so that policy makers will have a better idea of the long-term consequences of their actions. But, like virtually any proposal for expanded federal spending, except perhaps the defense budget, Browner's plans are unlikely to receive a warm reception from Congress.

—Joseph Palca

HONORS AND AWARDS

The following article discusses recent awards and prizes in science and technology. In the first section the Nobel Prizes for 1994 are described in detail. The second section is a selective list of other honors.

NOBEL PRIZE FOR CHEMISTRY

For discovering how to extend the life span of an elusive family of compounds that appear and vanish in millionths of a second during the intermediary stages of chemical reactions, George A. Olah, an organic chemist from the University of Southern California (USC), won the 1994 Nobel Prize for Chemistry. The technique finally provided proof that these chemical intermediaries, termed carbocations, really do exist. It also allowed chemists to begin studying the structure of different carbocations and their role in organic reactions.

"Olah's discovery completely transformed the scientific study of the elusive carbocations," the Royal Swedish Academy of Sciences said in its citation. It led to a new understanding of how organic chemicals react together to produce new compounds (products) and suggested ways of manipulating reactions to make desired products. There have been many industrial applications of the discovery, including technology to synthesize unleaded gasoline that has a high octane content. Director of the Loker Hydrocarbon Research Institute at USC, Olah in 1995 was working on synthesizing gasoline additives in ways that would generate little pollution.

Olah became interested in carbocations while still in Hungary. He was born on May 22, 1927, in Budapest and received his Ph.D. degree in 1949 from the Technical University of Budapest. After holding various positions at the university, he served as head of the department of organic chemistry and associate director of the central research institute of the Hungarian Academy of Sciences. Olah fled Hungary after the 1956 Soviet invasion, resuming his research at a Dow Chemical Co. laboratory in Ontario, where he developed the techniques for stabilizing and isolating carbocations. After serving on the faculty of Case Western Reserve University, Cleveland, Ohio, from 1965 to 1977, he moved to USC in 1977 and became director of the Loker Hydrocarbon Research Institute in 1991.

Carbocations are positively charged fragments of hydrocarbon molecules whose properties and existence have been a source of great dispute among organic chemists since the 1920s and '30s. Chemists then had only a very poor understanding of how chemical reactions work. In a reaction two chemicals called the reactants interact to form products, new compounds with structures and properties that often are much different from those of the reactants. British and French chemists began the first studies of organic reactions in the 1920s and '30s. They soon realized that the final products in some reactions could not possibly form in a single step. Rather, intermediate products must form and disappear as a chemical reaction proceeds. There was no other way to explain the dramatic structural differences that existed between reactants and products. Chemists theorized that these intermediates would be positively charged hydrocarbon molecules, which came to be called carbocations.

University of Southern California News Service

George A. Olah, winner of the Nobel Prize for Chemistry.

Alfred G. Gilman,
cowinner of the Nobel
Prize for Physiology or
Medicine.

Bertram N. Brockhouse
(left) receives the Nobel
Prize for Physics from
Carl XVI Gustaf, king of
Sweden.

Martin Rodbell,
cowinner of the Nobel
Prize for Physiology or
Medicine.

Since most chemical reactions proceed quickly, it was obvious that carbocations must form and disappear in millionths or hundreds of millionths of a second. Chemists thus began to despair of ever being able to isolate them and study their structure and properties; carbocations would disappear long before any analytic technique could be started. Yet such studies were crucial for understanding organic reactions and searching for ways to modify the reactions to produce more desirable products.

During the following decades chemists invoked carbocations to explain different aspects of organic reactions, and yet nobody knew if carbocations existed. Frustration at ever being able to isolate them led to expressions of disbelief when Olah announced his results in 1962 at a chemistry symposium in Cold Spring Harbor, N.Y. Chemists recalled that a murmur of disbelief rippled through the audience, and several scientists told Olah outright that his findings must be a mistake.

Olah's technique for extending the life span of carbocations from millionths of a second to months was relatively simple. He prepared stable carbocations by dissolving hydrocarbon compounds in cold solutions of extremely powerful acids such as hydrogen fluoride–antimony pentafluoride. These acids, termed superacids, are trillions of times stronger than conventional acids such as the sulfuric acid found in automobile storage batteries. The technique produced large concentrations of stable carbocations that could be studied with conventional analytic techniques.

Some of the early analyses of carbocations, which were conducted by Olah's group, brought additional surprises. Olah's work punctured "the old dogma of the tetravalency of carbon," described for more than a century as "a cornerstone of structural organic chemistry." Ever since the work of the German chemist Friedrich August Kekule von Stradonitz in the 1860s, chemists believed in the tetrahedral carbon atom. They thought that carbon, with a "valence," or bonding power, of four, formed chemical bonds with four atoms. But with carbocations stabilized and available for study, researchers identified trivalent, pentavalent, and hexavalent carbocations, which are capable of forming three, five, and six bonds.

NOBEL PRIZE FOR PHYSICS
A U.S. and a Canadian scientist shared the 1994 Nobel Prize for Physics for having developed neutron scattering, a technique that uses nuclear radiation to probe the innermost structure and properties of matter. The Royal Swedish Academy of Sciences, which awards the prize, said that the pioneering studies conducted by Clifford G. Shull and Bertram N. Brockhouse were of major theoretical and practical importance. Neutron scattering finally allowed scientists to peer into the atomic structure of matter and begin to understand interactions that determine the properties of solid and liquid materials. Such understanding is important because scientists first must know the atomic makeup of a material before they can find ways of changing its structure to produce improved metals, plastics, catalysts, and other products.

Much of science's understanding of the properties of magnetic materials used in computer data storage devices came from neutron-scattering studies. Biologists use neutron scattering to study the structure of disease-causing viruses. Chemists have used the technique to develop better catalysts, including those used to remove air pollutants from automobile exhausts. Some of the most visible fruits of neutron research are extremely tough lightweight plastics. These include such common materials as the films used to package airline peanuts, material so strong it can be torn only at the precut notch. Other such materials developed with neutron research are widely used in automobiles, commercial and military aircraft, and synthetic fabrics. Neutron-scattering studies are proving critical in current efforts to make practical high-temperature superconductors. These materials would lose resistance to the flow of electric current without being cooled to the extreme low temperatures required for the present generation of superconductors.

Neutrons are electrically neutral subatomic particles that had been recognized as components of the nucleus of atoms long before the research of Brockhouse and Shull. In the 1930s Enrico Fermi and other physicists first suggested that neutrons could be used to study the atomic structure of materials. Physicists knew that neutrons, lacking an electric charge, would not interact with the atoms in a material. When neutrons strike a sample of matter, they collide with the nuclei of its atoms and diffract, or scatter, in characteristic patterns. The diffraction pattern depends on the structure of a material— how its atoms are arranged relative to one another—and thus provides detailed information about that structure.

Brockhouse and Shull conducted their research independently in the 1940s and '50s at the first nuclear reactors built in Canada and the U.S. Brockhouse, now retired from McMaster University in Hamilton, Ont., worked at the Chalk River research reactor in Ontario. Shull, retired from the Massachusetts Institute of Technology, worked at a research reactor at the Oak Ridge (Tenn.) National Laboratory. Both were relatively small and simple reactors. The work by Shull and Brockhouse led to the powerful, expensive reactors that are specially built today for neutron-scattering research.

In 1946 Shull joined at Oak Ridge a group of physicists headed by Ernest Wollan that was trying to use neutron-diffraction patterns to determine the three-dimensional position of atoms in solid materials. A similar technique, using X-rays, already was in use. X-ray diffraction, however, could not determine the location of hydrogen and other light atoms, which are an important component of many inorganic materials and all organic matter. Unlike neutrons, which deflect off the nucleus of an atom, X-rays deflect off the electrons. Thus, because hydrogen has just one electron, it is scarcely noticeable on X-ray-diffraction patterns. This property of neutrons proved especially important in transforming early plastics into today's light, almost-indestructible polymer. Researchers in the 1960s predicted that polymers could be given extraordinary strength if their molecules were aligned like the fibers in paper. X-ray diffraction was of little use in verifying the theory, since plastics are composed of such light atoms as hydrogen, carbon, and oxygen.

But neutron scattering allowed scientists to understand how the long, chainlike molecules in polymers pack together to produce plastics with different properties.

"Similar efforts were being made elsewhere," the Royal Swedish Academy of Sciences said of Shull's pioneering work in the 1940s. "But it was the Wollan-Shull group and later Shull in collaboration with other researchers that proceeded most purposively and achieved results with surprising rapidity." Nuclear reactors produce beams of neutrons that move at a variety of speeds. Researchers, in contrast, needed monochromatic beams of neutrons that travel at a single speed. (A monochromatic beam of neutrons is one whose energies are confined to an extremely narrow range of values.) Shull's group solved the problem by passing the mixed beams through crystals of sodium chloride and other materials. The crystals separated neutrons of different speeds into separate beams so that scientists could isolate and use one uniform beam. Using such beams, Shull's group then developed a neutron-scattering technique to probe the structure of magnetic materials, which had been impossible to do with X-ray diffraction. Unlike X-rays, neutrons interact with the magnetic structure of a crystalline material and thus can be used to study its properties. Without this technique much modern research on computer magnetic storage devices and other aspects of magnetism probably would be impossible.

Soon after Shull began his work, Brockhouse began studying a different kind of neutron-scattering process that led to development of neutron spectroscopy, the technique for which he received the Nobel Prize. "During a hectic period between 1955 and 1960 Brockhouse's pioneering work was without parallel within neutron spectroscopy," the Royal Swedish Academy said. Scientists already knew that atoms in the innermost structure of any material are in constant motion. Vibrations in one atom cause surrounding atoms to resonate, so that the entire crystal vibrates in a unique pattern determined by its atomic structure. Knowledge about a material's vibrational energy is extremely important because it helps to decide how well a material will conduct electricity or heat.

Brockhouse's neutron spectroscopy technique provided a way for scientists to measure vibrational energy and understand the properties of different materials. He devised an apparatus, similar to the one developed by Shull, to obtain monochromatic beams of neutrons and passed them through samples of material. When the neutrons collided with an atom, they lost energy and set up vibrations in the crystal structure of the material. He also developed the triple-axis spectrometer, an apparatus that measured the energy of neutrons after they were scattered. This measurement allowed calculation of how much energy the test material had absorbed. Brockhouse realized that the lost energy could be interpreted as energy absorbed by the sample in the creation of ponons, units of vibrational energy that proved to be of great value in studies of the properties of different materials. Brockhouse's basic technique remains in wide use in efforts to understand and manipulate the behavior of electrical superconductors and other materials.

Brockhouse was born on July 15, 1918, in Lethbridge, Alta. He received his Ph.D. degree in 1950 from the University of Toronto. Shull was born on Sept. 23, 1915, in Pittsburgh, Pa. He received a Ph.D. degree in 1941 from New York University.

NOBEL PRIZE FOR PHYSIOLOGY OR MEDICINE

Two U.S. scientists won the 1994 Nobel Prize for Physiology or Medicine for discovering G proteins, the missing link in a key cellular communications system. The system enables cells to respond to chemical signals arriving from elsewhere in the body and the outside world. Found within cells, G proteins are natural molecules that relay messages from hormones and other outside sources to the cell's interior. Cells then respond to the message in ways critical for normal body function.

The discovery of G proteins by Alfred G. Gilman and Martin Rodbell produced new understanding of how cells process signals from external sources, such as light and sound, and from internal sources, such as hormones and neurotransmitters. It opened up new fields of research into signal transduction, the process in which cells take information from the outside and react biochemically. These reactions are essential for specialized cells to function in ways that produce vision, smell, taste, and a host of other fundamental life functions. Disturbances in the function of G proteins and signal transduction can lead to disease.

Rodbell was born Dec. 1, 1925, in Baltimore, Md. He received his Ph.D. degree in 1954 from the University of Washington and then held positions in the U.S.

and Switzerland. From 1970 to 1985 he headed laboratories at the National Institutes of Health (NIH) in Bethesda, Md., the U.S. government agency that funds most biomedical research. In 1985 Rodbell joined the National Institute of Environmental Health Sciences, a division of the NIH located in Research Triangle Park, N.C. He retired in June 1994 as head of the institute's laboratory of signal transduction.

Gilman was born on July 1, 1941, in New Haven, Conn. He received M.D. and Ph.D. degrees in 1969 from Case Western Reserve University, Cleveland, Ohio. From 1971 to 1981 he served on the faculty of the University of Virginia School of Medicine. In 1981 Gilman moved to the University of Texas Southwestern Medical Center in Dallas, where he became professor and chairman of the department of pharmacology. He is coauthor of a well-known textbook on drug action, *The Pharmacological Basis of Therapeutics.*

Before Rodbell and Gilman began their work, conducted independently in separate laboratories in the 1960s and '70s, scientists knew that cells in organisms use chemical signals to communicate with one another. Human beings, for instance, are composed of more than 10 trillion cells that exist in about 1,000 different specialized forms. Heart, liver, nerve, and all other cells must work together in coordination for life to exist. Cells cooperate partly by using chemical signals to communicate with each other. Glands release hormones, for instance, and nerves release other chemical messenger molecules. When molecular signals from one cell reach their destination,

they attach to special receptor sites on that cell's outer surface.

A U.S. scientist, Earl W. Sutherland, Jr., received the 1971 Nobel Prize for Physiology or Medicine for discovering how hormones carry signals from one cell to another. Sutherland showed that hormones, which he called "first messengers," carry signals to the outer membrane that encloses each cell in an animal's body. Hormones bind to special receptor sites on the cell membrane. Binding triggers chemical events inside the membrane that convert the external signal into another molecular signal, the "second messenger," which acts inside the cell. These molecules, known as cyclic adenosine monophosphate (cAMP), move to other parts of the cell. cAMP serves as the final signal that converts the hormone's message into action and changes the cell's function. People respond to fright, for instance, by producing the hormone adrenaline, which orders heart cells to produce cAMP, which causes cells to beat faster and stronger. Other cells respond to other signals in their own characteristic ways. Very little, however, was known about the signal-processing mechanisms within cells. The research by Rodbell and Gilman identified these missing links.

In the late 1960s and early '70s, Rodbell and his associates, working at the NIH, showed that the communication process requires cooperation between three separate cellular components: a receptor or discriminator, a transducer that translates information from the receptor, and an amplifier that produces large quantities of a second messenger such as cAMP. The receptor discriminates between different kinds of hormones and other external chemical signals that constantly wash over the outer membrane of each body cell. It is a docking site that actually protrudes through the membrane to the interior of the cell. The exterior portion has a shape, or binding site, that will accommodate only those messenger molecules needed for the cell's function. Without this discriminating function, liver cells would respond to signals intended for kidney cells, and chaos would prevail in the body. Another component is the amplifier, which generates large quantities of cAMP. Rodbell was one of the first scientists to realize that the receptor and the amplifier are separate functions. His major contribution, however, was the discovery of a separate transducer function in cell communication. It provided the missing link between the receptor and the amplifier. Rodbell showed that the transducer works only in the presence of an energy-rich molecule called guanosine triphosphate. He also showed that there may be several transducers.

Gilman and his associates, working in the 1970s at the University of Virginia, set out to determine the chemical nature of Rodbell's mysterious transducer. They studied mutated leukemia cells. The cells had a normal receptor mechanism for accepting signals from a first messenger and a normal ability to generate cAMP as their second messenger. Yet when challenged with signals from the outside, nothing happened inside. Gilman showed that the mutated cells lacked a normal transducer mechanism. He further established that the missing component was a protein, found in normal cells, and showed that its transfer to defective cells restored normal signal transmission.

By 1980 Gilman's group had purified the protein so that its properties could be studied. Researchers found that the protein exists in an inactive form around receptor sites inside the cell membrane. When a signal binds to the receptor, however, the protein instantly changes into an active form by binding to the high-energy molecule guanosine triphosphate (GTP). This association with GTP led to the protein's name, the G protein. The activated G protein then shuttles from the receptor system to the amplifier system, stimulating the production of large amounts of cAMP. The events take only a few seconds, after which the G protein reverts to an inactive form, awaiting another activating signal.

The work of Rodbell and Gilman led to the identification of about 100 kinds of cell receptors that rely on G proteins for transducing signals and converting them into cellular action. G proteins in the rod and cone cells in the retinal cells of the eye, for instance, transduce the light signals that the brain interprets as images. Other G proteins work in olfactory cells and taste cells. G proteins also can regulate the total metabolic activity of cells and control the processes by which cells divide and become specialized.

"Many symptoms of disease are explained by an altered function of G-proteins," said the Nobel Assembly at the Karolinska Institute, a biomedical research center in Stockholm that selects winners of the prize. In humans abnormally active G proteins are associated with some forms of cancer and cause widespread illness and death during cholera epidemics. The toxin produced by cholera bacteria, *Vibrio cholerae,* prevents one G protein from reverting to an inactive form. Thus, stuck in the "on" position, it causes the severe loss of water and salts from the intestines of cholera victims.

Reduced activity of G proteins can lead to other health problems. The cells in patients with Albright's syndrome, for example, do not respond normally to signals from several different hormones. Victims of this hereditary condition suffer disorders of the bone, skin, and other parts of the body. Researchers have established that most patients with the syndrome have a 50% reduction in the activity of a G protein termed Gs. Evidence also suggests that abnormal activity of G proteins may also be involved in such health problems as diabetes and alcoholism.

—Michael Woods

■ ARCHITECTURE AND CIVIL ENGINEERING

Award	Winner	Affiliation
Academy of Arts and Letters Award	Hsin-ming Fung and Craig Hodgetts	Santa Monica, Calif.
Arnold W. Brunner Memorial Prize	Renzo Piano	Genoa, Italy
Gold Medal of the American Institute of Architects	Cesar Pelli	New Haven, Conn.
Lillian Gish Prize	Frank O. Gehry	Frank O. Gehry & Associates, Santa Monica, Calif.
National Medal of Science	Ray Clough (Retired)	University of California, Berkeley
Pritzker Architecture Prize	Christian de Portzamparc	Paris, France
Sadi Carnot Prize	Arthur H. Rosenfeld	University of California, Berkeley, and Lawrence Berkeley Laboratory
Toronto Society of Architects Fellowship Award	Irving Grossman	Toronto, Ont.
Toronto Society of Architects Fellowship Award	Jerome Markson	Toronto, Ont.

■ ASTRONOMY

Award	Winner	Affiliation
Beatrice M. Tinsley Prize	Raymond Davis	University of Pennsylvania, Philadelphia
Brouwer Award	Alar Toomre	Massachusetts Institute of Technology, Cambridge
Bruno Rossi Prize	Gerald J. Fishman	NASA
Dannie Heineman Prize for Astrophysics	John N. Bahcall	Institute for Advanced Study, Princeton, N.J.
Franklin Medal	Stirling A. Colgate	Los Alamos National Laboratory, N.M.
Gerald P. Kuiper Prize	James R. Arnold	University of California, San Diego
Harold C. Urey Prize	Roger V. Yelle	University of Arizona, Tucson
Henry Norris Russell Lecture	Vera Rubin	Carnegie Institution, Washington, D.C.
J. Lawrence Smith Medal	Donald E. Brownlee	University of Washington, Seattle
James Craig Watson Medal	Yasuo Tanaka	Institute of Space and Aeronautical Sciences, Kanagawa, Japan
John Price Wetherill Medal	Stirling A. Colgate	Los Alamos National Laboratory, N.M.
Nevada Medal	John N. Bahcall	Institute for Advanced Study, Princeton, N.J.

■ CHEMISTRY

Award	Winner	Affiliation
Alfred Bader Award	Stephen J. Benkovic	Pennsylvania State University, University Park
Alpha Chi Sigma Award	Julio M. Ottino	Northwestern University, Evanston, Ill.
American Chemical Society Award in Analytical Chemistry	Harry L. Pardue	Purdue University, West Lafayette, Ind.
Arthur C. Cope Scholar Award	Steven G. Boxer	Stanford University, Stanford, Calif.
Arthur C. Cope Scholar Award	Rick L. Danheiser	Massachusetts Institute of Technology, Cambridge
Arthur C. Cope Scholar Award	Michael E. Jung	University of California, Los Angeles
Arthur C. Cope Scholar Award	Thomas J. Katz	Columbia University, New York, N.Y.
Arthur C. Cope Scholar Award	Nelson J. Leonard (Emeritus)	University of Illinois, Urbana-Champaign
Arthur C. Cope Scholar Award	Kurt M. Mislow (Emeritus)	Princeton University, Princeton, N.J.
Arthur C. Cope Scholar Award	Alanna Schepartz	Yale University, New Haven, Conn.
Arthur C. Cope Scholar Award	Barry B. Snider	Brandeis University, Waltham, Mass.
Arthur C. Cope Scholar Award	Robert Waymouth	Stanford University, Stanford, Calif.
Arthur W. Adamson Award	Gabor A. Somorjai	University of California, Berkeley
Award for Creative Work in Synthetic Organic Chemistry	Larry E. Overman	University of California, Irvine
Carl S. Marvel Award	Krzysztof Matyjaszewski	Carnegie Mellon University, Pittsburgh, Pa.
Carl S. Marvel Award	Sukant K. Tripathy	University of Massachusetts, Lowell
Carl Wagner Award	Jacob Jorne	University of Rochester, N.Y.
Charles H. Stone Award	Darryl D. DesMarteau	Clemson University, Clemson, N.C.
Charles Lathrop Parsons Award	Alfred Bader	Aldrich Chemical Co., Milwaukee, Wis.

AWARD	WINNER	AFFILIATION
Clarence Gerhold Award	James R. Fair	University of Texas, Austin
Earle B. Barnes, Award	Leo E. Manzer	E.I. du Pont de Nemours & Co.
Edward W. Morley Award	Douglas C. Neckers	Bowling Green State University, Ohio
Francis P. Garvan-John M. Olin Medal	Angelica M. Stacy	University of California, Berkeley, and Lawrence Berkeley Laboratory
Gold Medal of the International Rubber Research & Development Board	Jean-Louis Jacob	Centre de Coopération Internationale en Recherche Agronomique pour de Développement, France
Harry & Carol Mosher Award	Peter Beak	University of Illinois, Urbana-Champaign
Henry H. Storch Award	Donald F. McMillen	Stanford Research Institute, Menlo Park, Calif.
Herman F. Mark Award	Harry R. Allcock	Pennsylvania State University, University Park
Inorganic Chemistry Award	Guido P. Pez	Air Products & Chemicals, Inc., Allentown, Pa.
Izaak Walton Killam Memorial Prize	Adrian Brook	University of Toronto, Ont.
James Flack Norris Award	William P. Jencks	Brandeis University, Waltham, Mass.
James Flack Norris Award	Samuel P. Massie	U.S. Naval Academy, Annapolis, Md.
James Flack Norris Award	George M. Whitesides	Harvard University, Cambridge, Mass.
Joel Henry Hildebrand Award	Robert W. Zwanzig	National Institutes of Health
Linus Pauling Award	James A. Ibers	Northwestern University, Evanston, Ill.
National Medal of Science	George S. Hammond	Bowling Green State University, Ohio
Nuclear Chemistry Award	Joseph B. Natowitz	Texas A&M University, College Station
Paracelsus Prize	F. Albert Cotton	Texas A&M University, College Station
Paul G. Gassman Award	Nelson J. Leonard (Emeritus)	University of Illinois, Urbana-Champaign
Pederson Award	Thomas L. Nelson (Retired)	E.I. du Pont de Nemours & Co.
Peter Debye Award	John C. Tully	AT&T Bell Laboratories
Priestley Medal	Derek H.R. Barton	Texas A&M University, College Station
Professional Progress Award	Matthew V. Tirrell	University of Minnesota, Minneapolis
R.H. Wilhelm Award	Milorad P. Dudukovic	Washington University, St. Louis, Mo.
Ralph F. Hirschmann Award	Shumpei Sakakibara	Protein Research Foundation, Osaka, Japan
Robert A. Welch Award	F. Albert Cotton	Texas A&M University, College Station
	Jack Halpern	University of Chicago, Ill.
Roger Adams Award	Barry M. Trost	Stanford University, Stanford, Calif.
Thomas Baron Award	Liang-shih Fan	Ohio State University, Columbus
William H. Nichols Medal	Peter B. Dervan	California Institute of Technology, Pasadena
Wolf Prize	Richard A. Lerner	Scripps Research Institute, La Jolla, San Diego, Calif.
	Peter G. Schultz	University of California, Berkeley, and Howard Hughes Medical Institute, Bethesda, Md.

■ EARTH SCIENCES

AWARD	WINNER	AFFILIATION
Blue Planet Prize	Eugen Seibold	University of Kiel, Germany
G.K. Warren Prize	Claudio Vito-Finzi	University College, London
Harry H. Hess Medal	Alfred E. Ringwood (Deceased)	Australian National University, Canberra
Henry Stommel Medal	John C. Swallow (Retired)	Institute of Oceanographic Sciences, Wormley, U.K.
International Meteorological Organization Prize	Verner E. Suomi (Retired)	University of Wisconsin, Madison
James B. Macelwane Medal	Jeremy Bloxham	Harvard University, Cambridge, Mass.
James B. Macelwane Medal	Margaret A. Tolbert	University of Colorado, Boulder
James B. Macelwane Medal	John E. Vidale	U.S. Geological Survey
John Adam Fleming Medal	John A. Jacobs	University College of Wales, Aberystwyth
Maurice Ewing Medal	Kirk Bryan (Retired)	National Oceanic and Atmospheric Administration
National Medal of Science	Frank Press	Carnegie Institution, Washington, D.C.
Robert E. Horton Medal	Mikhail I. Budyko	State Hydrological Institute, St. Petersburg, Russia

AWARD	WINNER	AFFILIATION
Silver Medal in Acoustical Oceanography	Clarence S. Clay (Emeritus)	University of Wisconsin, Madison
Vannevar Bush Award	Frank Press	Carnegie Institution, Washington, D.C.
Walter H. Bucher Medal	Aleksey N. Khramov	Oil Research and Geology Prospecting Institute, St. Petersburg, Russia
Will Allis Prize	Eldon E. Ferguson	National Oceanic and Atmospheric Administration
Willet G. Miller Medal	Frank C. Hawthorne	University of Manitoba, Winnipeg
William Bowie Medal	Peter S. Eagleson (Emeritus)	Massachusetts Institute of Technology, Cambridge
William Bowie Medal	Irwin I. Shapiro	Harvard University, Cambridge, Mass.

■ ELECTRONICS AND INFORMATION SCIENCES

Computers in Chemistry Award	Peter A. Kollman	University of California, San Francisco
Forefronts of Large-Scale Computation Award	Lynn Ten Eyck, Daniel Knighton, Janusz Sowadski, and Susan Taylor	University of California, San Diego, and San Diego Supercomputer Center
Izaak Walton Killam Memorial Prize	Andre Salama	University of Toronto, Ont.
Japan Prize	Nick Holonyak, Jr.	University of Illinois, Urbana-Champaign
National Medal of Science	John Cocke (Retired)	IBM Corp.
National Medal of Technology	Joel S. Engel	Ameritech Corp., Chicago, Ill.
National Medal of Technology	Irwin M. Jacobs	QUALCOMM Inc., San Diego, Calif.
National Medal of Technology	Richard H. Frenkiel	AT&T

■ ENERGY

Achievement Award	Marvin M. Johnson	Phillips Petroleum
Autoclave Engineer's Award	Jin Y. Park	University of Idaho, Moscow
Enrico Fermi Award	Freeman Dyson (Emeritus)	Institute for Advanced Study, Princeton, N.J.
Gold Medal of the American Petroleum Institute	George Keller (Retired)	Chevron Corp.

■ ENVIRONMENT

American Association of Zoological Parks and Aquariums Exhibit Award	Woodland Park Zoological Gardens	Seattle, Wash.
Australia Prize	Gene E. Likens	Institute of Ecosystems Studies, Millbrook, N.Y.
Award for International Scientific Cooperation	Thomas Malone	Research Triangle Park, N.C.
Blue Planet Prize	Lester Brown	Worldwatch Institute, Washington, D.C.
Goldman Environmental Prize	Matthew Coon Come	Nemeske, Que.
Goldman Environmental Prize	Tuenjai Deetes	Chiang Rai, Thailand
Goldman Environmental Prize	Laila Kamel	Cairo, Egypt
Goldman Environmental Prize	Luis Macas	Quito, Ecuador
Goldman Environmental Prize	Ildiko "Heffa" Schucking	Sassenberg, Germany
Goldman Environmental Prize	Andrew Simmons	Enhams, St. Vincent and the Grenadines
James B. Macelwane Medal	Daniel J. Jacob	Harvard University, Cambridge, Mass.
Roger Revelle Medal	F. Sherwood Rowland	University of California, Irvine
Sasakawa Environment Prize	Mostafa K. Tolba (Retired)	United Nations Environment Program
Tyler Prize for Environmental Achievement	F. Herbert Bormann and Gene E. Likens	Hubbard Brook Ecosystem Study, New Hampshire
Tyler Prize for Environmental Achievement	Arturo Gomez-Pompa	University of California, Riverside
	Peter Raven	Missouri Botanical Garden, St. Louis

■ FOOD AND AGRICULTURE

Award	Winner	Affiliation
Award for Creative Invention	Marinus Los	American Cyanamid Co.
Kenneth A. Spencer Award	Bruce D. Hammock	University of California, Davis
Technology Award	Cotswold Pig Development Co.	Lincolnshire, England

■ LIFE SCIENCES

Award	Winner	Affiliation
Alexander Humboldt Award	William Betz	University of Colorado, Boulder
Alexander Humboldt Award	John Dowling	Harvard University, Cambridge, Mass.
Alexander Humboldt Award	Richard Lerner	Scripps Research Institute, La Jolla, San Diego, Calif.
Alexander Humboldt Award	Thomas Taylor	Ohio State University, Columbus
Arthur C. Cope Scholar Award	Craig A. Townsend	Johns Hopkins University, Baltimore, Md.
Chemical Sciences Award	Koji Nakanishi	Columbia University, New York, N.Y.
Claude S. Hudson Award	Tomoya Ogawa	University of Tokyo, Japan
Distinguished Scientist Award	William L. Duax	Medical Foundation of Buffalo, N.Y.
Eli Lilly and Company Research Award	David Beach	Cold Spring Harbor Laboratory, N.Y.
Eli Lilly Award	Peter S. Kim	Massachusetts Institute of Technology, Cambridge
Enrico Fermi Award	Liane B. Russell	Oak Ridge National Laboratory, Tenn.
Franklin Medal	Marvin H. Caruthers	University of Colorado, Boulder
Gairdner Foundation International Award	Pamela Bjorkman	California Institute of Technology, Pasadena, and Howard Hughes Medical Institute, Bethesda, Md.
Gairdner Foundation International Award	Tony Hunter	Salk Institute for Biological Studies, San Diego, Calif.
Gairdner Foundation International Award	Anthony J. Pawson	Mount Sinai Hospital, Toronto, Ont.
Gairdner Foundation International Award	Don C. Wiley	Harvard University, Cambridge, Mass.
Gilbert Morgan Smith Medal	Elisabeth Gantt	University of Maryland, College Park
Gold Medal of the Acoustical Society of America	David M. Green	University of Florida, Gainesville
Golden Brain Award	Rudiger von der Heydt	Johns Hopkins University, Baltimore, Md.
Henry Shaw Medal	Edward O. Wilson	Harvard University, Cambridge, Mass.
Initiatives in Research Award	Joanne Chory	Salk Institute for Biological Studies, San Diego, Calif.
Japan Prize	Ernst Mayr (Emeritus)	Harvard University, Cambridge, Mass.
John D. and Catherine T. MacArthur Foundation Award	Peter E. Kenmore	UN Food and Agriculture Organization
Molecular Biology Award	Gerald F. Joyce	Scripps Research Institute, La Jolla, San Diego, Calif.
	Jack W. Szostak	Harvard Medical School, Boston, Mass.
National Medal of Science	Thomas Eisner	Cornell University, Ithaca, N.Y.
Neurosciences Gold Medal	Walle J.H. Nauta (Deceased)	Massachusetts Institute of Technology, Cambridge
Pfizer Award in Enzymology	Donald Hilvert	Scripps Research Institute, La Jolla, San Diego, Calif.
R. Bruce Lindsay Award	Robert P. Carlyon	University of Sussex, England
Repligen Award	Judith P. Klinman	University of California, Berkeley
Silver Medal in Psychological and Physiological Acoustics	Nathaniel I. Durlach	Massachusetts Institute of Technology, Cambridge
Troland Research Award	Donald D. Hoffman	University of California, Irvine
Troland Research Award	David D. Lavond	University of Southern California, Los Angeles
V.D. Mattia Award	James E. Rothman	Memorial Sloan-Kettering Cancer Center, New York, N.Y.
Weizman Women and Science Award	Joan Argetsinger Steitz	Yale University, New Haven, Conn.

■ MATERIALS SCIENCES

AWARD	WINNER	AFFILIATION
Charles M.A. Stine Award	Timothy J. Anderson	University of Florida, Gainesville
David Turnbull Lecture	Arthur S. Nowick	Columbia University, New York, N.Y.
George Kimball Burgess Memorial Award	David J. Michel	Naval Research Laboratory, Washington, D.C.
J.H. Hall Award	Cecil W. Schneider	Lockheed Aeronautical Systems Co., Marietta, Ga.
Medal of the Materials Research Society	Max G. Lagally	University of Wisconsin, Madison
Medal of the Materials Research Society	Kenneth S. Suslick	University of Illinois, Urbana-Champaign
Von Hippel Award	Alfred Y. Cho	AT&T Bell Laboratories

■ MATHEMATICS

AWARD	WINNER	AFFILIATION
Alan T. Waterman Award	Tian Gang	New York University, New York City
Fields Medal	Jean Bourgain	Institut des Hautes Études Scientifiques, Paris
Fields Medal	Pierre-Louis Lions	University of Paris
Fields Medal	Jean-Christophe Yoccoz	University of Paris
Fields Medal	Efim Isaakovich Zelmanov	University of Wisconsin, Madison
Franklin Medal	Harold J. Kushner	Brown University, Providence, R.I.
Frederic Esser Nemmers Prize	Yuri I. Manin	Max Planck Institute, Germany
John D. and Catherine T. MacArthur Foundation Award	Israel M. Gelfand	American Mathematics Correspondence School
John J. Carty Award	Marina Ratner	University of California, Berkeley
King Faisal International Prize	Dennis P. Sullivan	City University of New York and Institut des Hautes Études Scientifiques, Paris
Kyoto Prize	André Weil (Emeritus)	Institute for Advanced Study, Princeton, N.J.
Ostrowski Prize	Miklós Laczkovich	Loránd Eötvös University, Budapest, Hung.
Ostrowski Prize	Marina Ratner	University of California, Berkeley
Otto LaPorte Award	Philip G. Saffman	California Institute of Technology, Pasadena
Team Gold Medal in International Mathematical Olympiad	Jeremy Bem	Ithaca High School, Ithaca, N.Y.
	Aleksandr L. Khazanov	Stuyvesant High School, New York, N.Y.
	Jacob A. Lurie	Montgomery Blair High School, Silver Spring, Md.
	Noam M. Shazeer	Swampscott High School, Swampscott, Mass.
	Stephen S. Wang	Illinois Mathematics and Science Academy, Aurora
	Jonathan Weinstein	Lexington High School, Lexington, Mass.
Wolf Prize	Jurgen K. Moser	Swiss Federal Institute of Technology, Zürich

■ MEDICAL SCIENCES

AWARD	WINNER	AFFILIATION
Abbott Award	David M. Goldenberg	Garden State Cancer Center, Newark, N.J.
Abbott Award	Jean-Pierre Mach	Lausanne University, Switzerland
Albert Lasker Basic Medical Research Award	Stanley B. Prusiner	University of California, San Francisco
Albert Lasker Clinical Medical Research Award	John A. Clements	University of California, San Francisco
Albert Lasker Special Public Health Award	Maclyn McCarty (Emeritus)	Rockefeller University, New York, N.Y.
Alexander Humboldt Award	Jorge Crosa	Oregon Health Sciences University, Portland
Alton Ochsner Award	Hildegard Schüller	University of Tennessee, Knoxville
Award for Medical Research	Alison Goate	Washington University, St. Louis, Mo.
	John Hardy	University of South Florida, Tampa
	Robert W. Mahley	University of California, San Francisco
	Karl Weisgraber	University of California, San Francisco

AWARD	WINNER	AFFILIATION
Bristol-Myers Squibb Award	William D. Willis, Jr.	University of Texas Marine Biomedical Institute, Galveston
CIBA Award for Hypertension Research	Adolfo J. deBold	University of Ottawa, Ont.
	Ervin G. Erdös	University of Illinois, Chicago
Distinguished Scientist Award	Robert S. Langer	Massachusetts Institute of Technology, Cambridge
Franklin Medal	Barbara V. Howard	George Washington University, Washington, D.C.
Gairdner Foundation International Award	Donald Metcalf	Royal Melbourne Hospital, Victoria, Australia
Helmut Horten Research Award	Herbert W. Boyer	University of California, San Francisco
	Stanley N. Cohen	Stanford University, Stanford, Calif.
Izaak Walton Killam Memorial Prize	Endel Tulving	University of Toronto, Ont.
Jessie Stevenson Kovalenko Medal	Donald Metcalf	Walter and Eliza Hall Institute of Medical Research, Melbourne, Australia
John Scott Award	Beatrice Mintz	Fox Chase Cancer Center, Philadelphia, Pa.
Kyoto Prize	Paul C. Lauterbur	University of Illinois, Urbana-Champaign
Lifetime Achievement Award	Gerhard Levy	State University of New York, Buffalo
Louisa Gross Horwitz Prize	John W. Kappler	Howard Hughes Medical Institute, Bethesda, Md.
	Philippa Marrack	Howard Hughes Medical Institute, Bethesda, Md.
Medical Research Award	Blas Frangione	New York University, New York City
	Allen Roses	Duke University, Durham, N.C.
Mullard Award	Brad Amos	Medical Research Council, Cambridge, England
	Richard Durbin	Medical Research Council, Cambridge, England
	Michael Fordham	Medical Research Council, Cambridge, England
National Medal of Science	Elizabeth Neufeld	University of California, Los Angeles
National Medal of Technology	Amgen	Thousand Oaks, Calif.
Pacesetter Award	F. Ivy Carroll	Research Triangle Institute, Research Triangle Park, N.C.
Public Service Award	John Porter	U.S. House of Representatives
Scientific Achievement Award	Eva Engvall	La Jolla Cancer Research Foundation, San Diego, Calif.

■ OPTICAL ENGINEERING

AWARD	WINNER	AFFILIATION
Edwin H. Land Medal	William E. Humphrey	Humphrey Instruments
Engineering Excellence Award	Peter P. Clark	Polaroid Corp.
Engineering Excellence Award	John M. Guerra	Polaroid Corp.
Engineering Excellence Award	Jon Van Tassell	Polaroid Corp.
Franklin Medal	Joseph Braat	Philips Research Laboratories, Eindhoven, Neth.
National Medal of Technology	Corning, Inc.	Corning, N.Y.

■ PHYSICS

AWARD	WINNER	AFFILIATION
Aneesur Rahman Prize	John Dawson	University of California, Los Angeles
Arthur L. Schawlow Prize	Steven Chu	Stanford University, Stanford, Calif.
Arthur L. Schawlow Prize	John L. Hall	National Institute of Standards and Technology, Boulder, Colo.
Award for Excellence	Ronald Davidson	Princeton University, Princeton, N.J.
Benjamin Franklin Medal	Chen Ning Yang	State University of New York, Stony Brook
Bingham Medal	Andreas Acrivos	City University of New York
Bingham Medal	Daniel D. Joseph	University of Minnesota, Minneapolis
Dannie Heineman Award	Richard N. Zare	Stanford University, Stanford, Calif.

AWARD	WINNER	AFFILIATION
Davisson-Germer Prize	Carl E. Wieman	University of Colorado, Boulder
Dirac Medal	Frank Wilczek	Institute for Advanced Study, Princeton, N.J.
Distinguished Service Citations	J. Richard Christman	U.S. Coast Guard Academy, New London, Conn.
Edward Longstreth Medal	Joseph J. Braat	Philips Research Laboratories, Eindhoven, Neth.
European Accelerator Prize	Hakan Danared	Manne Siegbahn Laboratory, Stockholm, Sweden
	Igor Syrachev	Institute of Nuclear Physics, Protvino, Russia
Excellence in Plasma Physics Award	Yoshiaki Kato and Kunioki Mima	Osaka University, Japan
	Robert H. Lehmberg and Stephen P. Obenschain	Naval Research Laboratory, Washington, D.C.
	Stanley Skupsky and John M. Soures	University of Rochester, N.Y.
Excellence in Plasma Physics Research Award	Lang Lao	General Atomics, San Diego, Calif.
	Ronald Stambaugh	General Atomics, San Diego, Calif.
	Edward J. Strait	General Atomics, San Diego, Calif.
	Tony S. Taylor	General Atomics, San Diego, Calif.
Faraday Cup	Ralph Fiorito and Donald Rule	Naval Surface Warfare Center, Silver Spring, Md.
Fluid Dynamics Prize	Stephen H. Davis	Northwestern University, Evanston, Ill.
Fluid Dynamics Prize	Theodore Y.T. Wu	California Institute of Technology, Pasadena
Gertrude S. Goldhaber Prize	Fang Shu	State University of New York, Stony Brook
H. Dudley Wright Prize	Freeman J. Dyson	Institute for Advanced Study, Princeton, N.J.
Helen B. Warner Prize	David N. Spergel	Princeton University, Princeton, N.J.
Herzberg Medal	Jeff Young	University of British Columbia, Vancouver
High Energy and Particle Physics Prize	Martinus Veltman	University of Michigan, Ann Arbor
James Clerk Maxwell Prize	Roy W. Gould	California Institute of Technology, Pasadena
John D. and Catherine T. MacArthur Foundation Award	Jack Wisdom	Massachusetts Institute of Technology, Cambridge
Klopsteg Memorial Lecture	N. David Mermin	Cornell University, Ithaca, N.Y.
Maxwell Prize	Russell M. Kulsrud	Princeton University, Princeton, N.J.
Medal for Achievement in Physics	Gordon F. Drake	University of Windsor, Ont.
Mullard Award	John White	University of Wisconsin, Madison
National Medal of Science	Albert Overhauser	Purdue University, West Lafayette, Ind.
Oersted Medal	E. Leonard Jossem (Emeritus)	Ohio State University, Columbus
Otto LaPorte Award	Robert Kraichnan	Santa Fe, N.M.
Peter Mark Memorial Award	Robert J. Hamers	University of Wisconsin, Madison
Pioneers of Underwater Acoustics Medal	Homer P. Bucker	Naval Command Control and Ocean Surveillance Center, San Diego, Calif.
Richtmyer Memorial Lecture	Sheldon L. Glashow	Harvard University, Cambridge, Mass.
Robert A. Millikan Medal	Frederick Reif	Carnegie Mellon University, Pittsburgh, Pa.
Silver Medal in Physical and Engineering Acoustics	Steven L. Garrett	Naval Postgraduate School, Monterey, Calif.
Simon Ramo Award	Carey Forest	Princeton University, Princeton, N.J.
Simon Ramo Award	Michael E. Glinsky	Lawrence Livermore National Laboratory, Calif.
Tom W. Bonner Prize	Ernest K. Warburton	Brookhaven National Laboratory, Upton, N.Y.
Wolf Prize	Vitaly L. Ginzburg	Lebedev Physical Institute, Moscow
	Yoichiro Nambu (Emeritus)	University of Chicago, Ill.

■ SCIENCE WRITING

Allan P. Colburn Award	Joannis G. Kevrekidis	Princeton University, Princeton, N.J.
Andrew Gemant Award	Abraham Pais (Emeritus)	Rockefeller University, New York, N.Y.
Annenberg Foundation Award	Andrew Fraknoi	Foothill College, Los Altos Hills, Calif.
Award for Scientific Reviewing	Thomas Jessell	Columbia University, New York, N.Y.

AWARD	WINNER	AFFILIATION
George Polya Award	Charles W. Groetsch	University of Cincinnati, Ohio
Harold Masursky Award	Mildred Shapley Matthews	University of Arizona, Tucson
James T. Grady-James H. Stack Award	Ivan Amato	National Institute of Standards and Technology
John D. and Catherine T. MacArthur Foundation Award	Donella Meadows	Dartmouth College, Hanover, N.H.
Newcomb Cleveland Prize	Michael J. Mahan	University of California, Santa Barbara
Newcomb Cleveland Prize	John J. Mekalanos	Harvard Medical School, Boston, Mass.
Newcomb Cleveland Prize	James M. Slauch	University of Illinois, Urbana-Champaign
Phi Beta Kappa Award	Kip S. Thorne	California Institute of Technology, Pasadena
Publication Award	John M. Dealy	McGill University, Montreal
	Savvas G. Hatzikiriakos	University of British Columbia, Vancouver
Science Writing Award in Physics and Astronomy	Kip S. Thorne	California Institute of Technology, Pasadena
Walter Sullivan Award	Robert Kunzig	*Discover*
Westinghouse Science Journalism Award	Nancy Bazilchuk	*Burlington Free Press*
	John Horgan	*Scientific American*
	Dan Mushalko	Phonic Lab (Radio Broadcast)
	Boyce Rensberger	*The Washington Post*
William H. Walker Award	Daniel I.C. Wang	Massachusetts Institute of Technology, Cambridge

■ TRANSPORTATION

AWARD	WINNER	AFFILIATION
Aerospace Power Systems Award	Lowell D. Massie (Retired)	U.S. Air Force Wright Laboratory
Aircraft Operations Excellence Award	Herbert D. Kelleher	Southwest Airlines Co.
DeFlorez Training Award for Flight Simulation	R. Thomas Galloway	U.S. Naval Training Systems Center, Orlando, Fla.
Energy Systems Award	Geoffrey J. Sturgess	Pratt & Whitney, East Hartford, Conn.
Fluid Dynamics Award	Peter Bradshaw	Stanford University, Stanford, Calif.
Mechanics and Control of Flight Award	Nguyen X. Vinh	University of Michigan, Ann Arbor
Sir Adrian Swire Trophy	Richard Cheung Ka-fuk	Cathay Pacific Airways
Sir Alan Cobham Trophy	Wilson Tang Wai-yin	Cathay Pacific Airways
V.L. Larsen Award	Henry Lehrer	Embry-Riddle Aeronautical University, Daytona Beach, Fla.
Wyld Propulsion Award	Richard R. Weiss	U.S. Air Force Phillips Laboratory

■ OTHER AWARDS

AWARD	WINNER	AFFILIATION
Award for Engineering Professionalism	Robert H. Tanner	Naples, Fla.
Dwight Nicholson Award	Andrew H. Sessler	Lawrence Berkeley Laboratory, Calif.
Ethics Award	Fred Ordway	Instart Corp., Bethesda, Md.
Hilliard Roderick Prize	Frank von Hippel	U.S. Office of Science and Technology Policy
James Bryant Conant Award	Robert J. Lewis	Downers, Grove North High School, Ill.
Japan Prize	William H. Pickering (Emeritus)	California Institute of Technology, Pasadena
John D. and Catherine T. MacArthur Foundation Award	Faye D. Ginsburg	New York University, New York City
Leo Szilard Award	Herbert F. York (Emeritus)	University of California, San Diego
Mentor Award	Carol A. Gross	University of California, San Francisco
Mentor Award for Lifetime Achievement	Lewis P. Lipsitt	Brown University, Providence, R.I.
Mentor Award for Lifetime Achievement	John A. Watson	University of California, San Francisco
National Medal of Science	Robert K. Merton	Columbia University, New York, N.Y.
National Medal of Technology	H. Joseph Gerber	Gerber Scientific, South Windsor, Conn.
Philip Hauge Abelson Prize	Harvey Brooks	Harvard University, Cambridge, Mass.
Prize for Behavioral Science Research	Nalini Ambady	College of the Holy Cross, Worcester, Mass.
	Robert Rosenthal	Harvard University, Cambridge, Mass.

AWARD	WINNER	AFFILIATION
Public Welfare Medal	Carl E. Sagan	Cornell University, Ithaca, N.Y.
Scientific Freedom and Responsibility Award	Mathilde Krim	American Foundation for AIDS Research
	June Osborn	University of Michigan, Ann Arbor
Warren K. Lewis Award	J. Larry Duda	Pennsylvania State University, University Park
Westinghouse Science Talent Search	1. Irene A. Chen	La Jolla High School, San Diego, Calif.
	2. Tracy C. Phillips	Long Beach High School, Long Beach, N.Y.
	3. Martin T. Stiaszny	Shawnee Mission South High School, Shawnee Mission, Kan.
	4. Samit Dasgupta	Montgomery Blair High School, Silver Spring, Md.
	5. Deborah C. Yeh	Plano Senior High School, Plano, Texas
	6. Gina Petrocelli	Edward R. Murrow High School, New York, N.Y.
	7. Aleksandr L. Khazanov	Stuyvesant High School, New York, N.Y.
	8. Griffin M. Weber	Denbigh High School, Newport News, Va.
	9. Jordan M. Cummins	Livingston High School, Livingston, N.J.
	10. Franz E. Boas	La Jolla High School, San Diego, Calif.

OBITUARIES

Arnon, Daniel Israel
Nov. 14, 1910—Dec. 20, 1994

U.S. biochemist Daniel Arnon was awarded the 1973 U.S. National Medal of Science for "fundamental research into the mechanism of green plant utilization of light to produce chemical energy and oxygen and for contributions to our understanding of plant nutrition." Arnon also contributed to the understanding of how adenosine triphosphate (ATP), the "energy messenger" of the cell, is synthesized. (The formation of energy-rich ATP is highly important to photosynthesis, a process upon which almost all life on Earth is in some way dependent.) In demonstrating that ATP could be synthesized in the laboratory within chloroplasts isolated from spinach leaves, Arnon and his colleagues discovered a natural process for the formation of ATP called photophosphorylation. This process differed from those of ATP formation known from earlier research in fermentation and respiration in that no energy-rich chemical substrate was consumed; rather, the source of the energy was light. After emigrating from Poland to the U.S., Arnon settled in New York before earning a Ph.D. (1936) from the University of California, Berkeley. His earliest studies focused on plant nutrients and the role of such trace elements as vanadium and molybdenum in plant metabolism. Arnon joined the faculty of his alma mater upon graduating and remained there until his retirement in 1978. While serving (1943–46) as a major in the U.S. Army, he became a celebrity among the troops stationed at a barren western Pacific island when he successfully grew crops by using only gravel and nutrient-rich water. After World War II he was appointed a professor of cell physiology and a research biochemist at Berkeley, where he also served as founding chairperson of the department of cell physiology. Arnon was elected a member of such international academic societies as the French Agriculture Academy (1955), the U.S. National Academy of Sciences (1961), the Royal Swedish Academy of Sciences (1969), and the Spanish Biochemical Society (1975). He was also the recipient of the Newcomb Cleveland Prize of the American Association for the Advancement of Science (1940), the Charles F. Kettering Award for research in photosynthesis (1963), and the Stephen Hales Prize of the American Society of Plant Physiologists (1966).

Butenandt, Adolf Friedrich Johann
March 24, 1903—Jan. 18, 1995

German biochemist Adolf Butenandt was the co-winner (with Leopold Ruzicka) of the 1939 Nobel Prize for Chemistry for pioneering work (1929–34) on sex hormones, prominently the isolation of estrone (a hormone that influences development of the female reproductive tract), progesterone (a female hormone that primarily regulates the condition of the inner lining of the uterus), and the male hormone androsterone. Butenandt also synthesized testosterone, which stimulates the development of masculine characteristics. He isolated estrone about the time that biochemist Edward Doisy accomplished the same feat in the U.S. Butenandt, who was also the first to explain the role of these hormones, found that they were closely related to steroids. Forbidden by Germany's Nazi government to receive the Nobel Prize when it was awarded him, he accepted the gold medal and diploma in 1949. His discoveries about hormones influenced the large-scale production of cortisone and laid the groundwork for the development of birth control pills. Butenandt, the first to crystallize an insect hormone, ecdysone, also isolated the first pheromone, bombykol, the sex attractant of the female silk moth. After earning (1927) a Ph.D. from the University of Göttingen, he taught there and at the Danzig Institute of Technology (1933–36). He was director (1936–45) of the Kaiser Wilhelm Institute for Biochemistry, Berlin-Dahlem (later Tübingen), and professor of physiological chemistry there from 1945 to 1956. When the institute (after World War II renamed the Max Planck Institute for Biochemistry) moved to Munich in 1956, he retained those posts. Butenandt also served (1960–72) as president of the Max Planck Society for the Advancement of Science.

Durrell, Gerald Malcolm
Jan. 7, 1925—Jan. 30, 1995

British naturalist Gerald Durrell gained international stature among conservationists for his pioneering yet sometimes controversial role in preserving and breeding endangered species by housing them in zoos with the intent of eventually returning them to the wild. He was also a prolific author, producing more than 35 amusing and informative books about the animal kingdom and his adventures in pursuit of threatened species. Durrell's love of animals began when he was a boy living on the Greek island of Corfu. After his family returned to Britain, he became an assistant at the Whipsnade Zoo in Bedfordshire and was encouraged by his brother, novelist Lawrence, to write about his passion for nature. Durrell's first book, *The Overloaded Ark* (1953), was a best-seller and was followed by such popular successes as *Three Singles to Adventure* (1954), *My Family and Other Animals* (1956), *A Zoo in My Luggage* (1960), and *Birds, Beasts, and Relatives* (1969), the sales from which helped support his expeditions and conservation efforts. An inheritance and loan financed the founding, on the Channel Island of Jersey, of the Jersey Zoological Park in 1959 and the Jersey Wildlife Preservation Trust in 1964. Besides writing about his extensive travels to such locales as Argentina, Paraguay, Sierra Leone, Mexico, Australia, Mauritius, and Madagascar (where he captured a thought-to-be-extinct rare lemur, the aye-aye), Durrell produced a series of television programs,

among them "Two in the Bush" (1962), "The Amateur Naturalist" (1983), and "Ourselves and Other Animals" (1987). In 1976 he erected, adjacent to the Jersey Zoo, the International Training Centre, an educational facility that trained more than 700 scientists and field-workers from 80 countries. In 1983 Durrell was made an Officer of the Order of the British Empire in recognition of his wildlife-conservation work.

Erikson, Erik Homburger
June 15, 1902—May 12, 1994

German psychoanalyst Erik Erikson profoundly influenced the study of human development with the 1950 publication of *Childhood and Society,* in which he divided human development, from infancy to old age, into eight stages. Each of these stages in the life cycle, he theorized, presents a crisis resolution that is influenced by culture, society, and history

and contributes to the individual's ability to grow and change. Erikson also coined the term *identity crisis,* a personal psychosocial conflict that shapes a distinct aspect of personality. Though he was a disciple of Sigmund Freud, Erikson departed from Freud's theory that the ego is fixed in early childhood. Erikson's psychobiographies of Martin Luther, *Young Man Luther* (1958), and Mohandas K. Gandhi, *Gandhi's Truth on the Origins of Militant Nonviolence* (1969), interpreted their lives in terms of their psychological development. The latter book won Erikson a Pulitzer Prize and a National Book Award in 1970.

When he was 68, Erikson divulged the secret behind his own identity crisis: his birth was the result of his Danish Lutheran mother's extramarital affair. He never knew his father. From the age of three, however, he was raised in the faith of his stepfather, a German Jew, and was known at that time as Erik Homburger. This dual identity disturbed him emotionally. After graduating from high school, he traveled in Europe before settling in Vienna. He was 25 when Anna Freud became his psychoanalyst. He trained at the Vienna Psychoanalytic Institute and became a full member in 1933, the year he fled from Hitler's Europe to the U.S. There, with neither a medical nor a university degree, he practiced child psychoanalysis in Boston and served on the faculties of Harvard Medical School (1935–36), the Yale School of Medicine (1936–39), and the University of California, Berkeley (1939–50). His studies concentrated on those living on the fringes of society, and he was known especially for his observations of the Yurok tribe of

Gerald Malcolm Durrell wrote many books about animals and protecting endangered species.

Chris Harris—The Times Newspapers Ltd.

northern California. He repeatedly found that similar problems are approached in various ways by different societies. Erikson left Berkeley after refusing to sign a loyalty oath and joined the Austen Riggs Center in Stockbridge, Mass. In 1960 he returned to Harvard, and in 1970 he was made professor emeritus.

Hodgkin, Dorothy Mary Crowfoot
May 12, 1910—July 29, 1994

British chemist Dorothy Hodgkin won the 1964 Nobel Prize for Chemistry for her work in determining the atomic structure of vitamin B_{12} and other important biochemical compounds. Hodgkin studied chemistry at Somerville College, Oxford (B.A., 1931; B.Sc., 1932), and the University of Cambridge (Ph.D., 1937), but most of her research was in X-ray crystallography, which was more closely linked to physics than to chemistry. She returned to Somerville College as a tutor in 1935; she became a fellow the following year and remained there until 1977. Hodgkin then became fellow by special election (1977–82) at Oxford's Wolfson College. She remained active as chancellor (1970–88) and honorary fellow (from 1988) at the University of Bristol. In the 1930s and early '40s, Hodgkin began work on an X-ray analysis of the atomic structure of penicillin and of insulin (though it took nearly 35 years to complete the latter). From 1948 to 1956 she concentrated her crystallographic research on vitamin B_{12}, an enormously complex nonprotein compound crucial to the treatment of pernicious anemia. She also did research into other compounds, including cholesterol and vitamin D. Hodgkin was a founder (1957) of the Pugwash,

Dorothy Hodgkin, shown above in a painting by Maggi Hambling, won the 1964 Nobel Prize for Chemistry for her work on atomic structures.

Nova Scotia, Conference on Science and World Affairs, Wolfson research professor of the Royal Society (1960–77), a foreign associate of the U.S. National Academy of Sciences, a member of the Order of Merit (1965), and the winner of numerous international awards.

Jerne, Niels Kaj
Dec. 23, 1911—Oct. 7, 1994

British-Danish immunologist Niels Jerne was a corecipient—with César Milstein and Georges Köhler—of the 1984 Nobel Prize for Physiology or Medicine for his theories of immunology and the effect they had on research. These theories proposed that the body uses a preexisting, immensely diverse repertoire of antibodies to recognize invading organisms and other foreign substances and provided explanations for the way the immune system develops and for the system of interactions by which the immune system is activated when it is needed and then is inactivated. Jerne grew up in Denmark and was educated first in The Netherlands, studying physics at the University of Leiden, and later in Denmark at the University of Copenhagen, from which he received his medical degree (1951). From 1943 to 1956 he was a researcher at the Danish State Serum Institute, and he then spent six years (1956–62) as the chief medical officer of the World Health Organization. Jerne taught biophysics at the University of Geneva (1960–62), was chairman of the microbiology department at the University of Pittsburgh, Pa. (1962–66), and was professor of experimental therapy at J.W. Goethe University and director of the Paul Ehrlich Institute in Frankfurt am Main, Germany (1966–69). He then served (1969–80) as director of the Basel (Switz.) Institute for

Immunology, which he helped establish, and taught (1981–82) at the Pasteur Institute in Paris. Jerne was a member of the American Academy of Arts and Sciences and a foreign associate of the U.S. National Academy of Sciences.

Kildall, Gary A.
May 19, 1942—July 11, 1994

U.S. computer scientist and businessman Gary Kildall developed the first and most popular of the early operating systems for microcomputers, the Control Program/Monitor (CP/M), which controlled the way the central processing unit stored and retrieved information from a floppy disk. Kildall earned (1972) a Ph.D. in computer science from the University of Washington, and during the following year, while teaching at the U.S. Naval Postgraduate School, Monterey, Calif., he wrote CP/M. He continued to teach computer science there even after founding (1974) a company with his wife to market his software. Their firm, Intergalactic Digital Research (later shortened to Digital Research), increased its earnings from approximately $80,000 in 1976 to $5.4 million in 1981, when IBM introduced its first line of personal computers. IBM offered Kildall's CP/M-16 with a hefty price tag of $240 and Microsoft Corp.'s MS-DOS for $40; the latter, which many believed was initially a copycat version of Kildall's software, quickly became the industry standard. In 1991 Kildall sold his company for $80 million. He had founded another firm in 1985, KnowledgeSet, which produced a CD-ROM version of the *Grolier Encyclopedia,* one of the first consumer products in that format. In Austin, Texas, he

founded yet another firm, Prometheus Light and Sound. In 1994 Kildall published the book *Computer Connections,* in which he gave a historical account of the computer industry.

Lejeune, Jérôme-Jean-Louis-Marie
June 13, 1926—April 3, 1994

French geneticist Jérôme Lejeune identified (1959) the human chromosomal abnormality linked to Down syndrome, one of the most common forms of mental retardation and the first chromosomal disorder to be positively identified. Lejeune's discovery marked a turning point in the new science of cytogenetics (the scientific study of genetic variations at the chromosomal level). Lejeune attended the University of Paris (M.D., 1951; Ph.D., 1960). In the early 1950s he began research into inheritance patterns of Down syndrome in twins at the National Center for Scientific Research (CNRS) in Paris. In 1959, just three years after the correct number of human chromosomes (46; 23 pairs) had been discovered, he demonstrated that children with Down syndrome have an extra chromosome 21, making three where there would normally be a pair. The term *trisomy* was coined to describe this condition. He later identified several other chromosomal aberrations, notably the cause of the syndrome known as *cri du chat,* which is associated with severe mental retardation. He served as director of research at the CNRS from 1963 and held the post of professor of fundamental genetics at the Faculty of Medicine in Paris from 1964. A devout antiabortion activist, Lejeune was named to the Pontifical Academy of Sciences in 1974, and shortly before his death he was appointed

by Pope John Paul II to head the newly formed Pontifical Academy for Life.

Lwoff, André-Michel
May 8, 1902—Sept. 30, 1994

French scientist André-Michel Lwoff shared the 1965 Nobel Prize for Physiology or Medicine with François Jacob and Jacques Monod. Their research established how the genetic material of certain bacteria-infecting viruses that have become incorporated into the chromosome of their host cell can be passed along in a noninfective state to succeeding generations of bacteria and then reactivated to produce infective viral particles. Lwoff graduated from the University of Paris in 1921, the same year he joined the Pasteur Institute. He earned medical and science doctorates at Paris in 1927 and 1932, respectively. Lwoff was appointed head of a laboratory at the Pasteur Institute in 1929, and in 1938 he became the head of the microbiology and physiology department. During World War II he was an active member of the Resistance and was awarded the Grand Cross of the Legion of Honour and the Medal of the Resistance. From 1959 to 1968 he chaired the microbiology department at the Sorbonne. Lwoff's work on viral interactions with host cells greatly influenced cancer research and resulted in his appointment (1968) as director of the Cancer Research Institute at Villejuif, France, a position he held until his retirement in 1972. In later years Lwoff became involved in various social movements, ranging from family planning to the control and banning of chemical and biological weapons. His writings include *Biological Order* (1962).

U.S. astronomer William Wilson Morgan (right) discovered the spiral shape of the Milky Way Galaxy (artist's drawing above) after many years of observing and analyzing the distances and arrangements of stars.

May, Rollo Reece
April 21, 1909—Oct. 22, 1994

U.S. psychologist and author Rollo May was known as the father of existential psychotherapy. He was one of the first to abandon Freudian theories of human nature, and in his humanistic approach to therapy, he stressed that anxiety could be harnessed and used as a positive force and that people could use their inner resources in making the choices that guide the direction of their lives. May presented his views in a number of popular books, including *The Meaning of Anxiety* (1950), *Man's Search for Himself* (1953), *Love and Will* (1969), *Power and Innocence* (1972), and *The Courage to Create* (1975). He earned (1930) a bachelor's degree from Oberlin (Ohio) College and became a teacher of English at an American college in Greece. During holidays he attended psychoanalyst Alfred Adler's seminars in Vienna and was inspired to study theology. He returned (1933) to the U.S. and entered Union Theological Seminary, receiving a bachelor of divinity degree in 1938. After serving as a Congregationalist minister for two years, he resigned to study psychology at Columbia University, New York City. He contracted tuberculosis, however, and was given only a 50–50 chance of surviving. He realized that his personal struggle against death would do more than medical care would to determine whether he lived, and this solidified his existentialist views. He received his Ph.D. in 1949. May served on the faculty of the William Alanson White Institute of Psychiatry, Psychology, and Psychoanalysis and was a lecturer at the New School for Social Research, both in New York City. He also was a visiting professor at several universities.

Morgan, William Wilson
Jan. 3, 1906—June 21, 1994

U.S. astronomer William Morgan discovered the spiral shape of the Milky Way Galaxy after years of observing and analyzing the distances and arrangements of stars. Morgan's feat was complicated because our solar system lies within the Milky Way, and outside telescopic observation of its configuration is not possible. With Philip C. Keenan he had developed the MK (for Morgan Keenan) system for using observations of stars' spectra to determine their luminosity and, therefore, their distance from Earth, and in 1943 he published *An Atlas of Stellar Spectra,* a classification guide. Using the MK system, he estimated the distances of bright stars within the Milky Way. In 1951 at an American Astronomical Society meeting, Morgan received a standing ovation when he revealed that the structure of the Milky Way Galaxy includes two spiral arms and provided evidence for a third arm. After earning a Ph.D. (1931) from the University of Chicago, Morgan spent his entire career associated with his alma mater and its Yerkes Observatory, of which he was director from 1960 to 1963. As an astronomical morphologist he studied and classified stars and galaxies, and he also proved the existence of supergiant galaxies. Morgan, a member of the National Academy of Sciences, was awarded the Bruce Gold Medal of the Astronomical Society of the Pacific and the Herschel Medal of the Royal Astronomical Society of London.

Pauling, Linus Carl
Feb. 28, 1901—Aug. 19, 1994

U.S. chemist Linus Pauling was a towering figure in the scientific community and the only solo winner of two Nobel Prizes in different categories. He was awarded the 1954 Nobel Prize for Chemistry for discoveries on the nature of chemical bonding, work that was instrumental in describing the structure and shape of molecules, including the complex molecules of living tissues, and he received the 1962 Nobel Prize for Peace as a tireless crusader against the use of warfare, especially nuclear weapons, as a means of resolving international disputes. Pauling, the son of a pharmacist, shared his father's fascination with chemistry. After earning a B.S. (1922) in chemical engineering from Oregon State Agricultural College, he received a Ph.D. (1925) in physical chemistry from the California Institute of Technology, where he taught and conducted research until 1963. An insightful and brilliant scientist who had a knack for recognizing interrelation

Linus Pauling was the only solo winner of two Nobel Prizes in different categories.

ships, Pauling was the first to apply the principles of quantum mechanics to the structure of molecules; he used a variety of data to calculate the lengths and angles of the bonds that exist between the atoms in a molecule and ultimately to develop a theoretical framework for understanding the forces that hold atoms together. He put forth his findings in *The Nature of the Chemical Bond, and the Structure of Molecules and Crystals* (1939), undoubtedly the most influential chemistry textbook of the early to mid-20th century.

Pauling was also a leader in the movement against nuclear weapons testing in the 1950s and '60s. During the McCarthy era of communist witch-hunts, his passport was revoked for two years. He also submitted to the UN a petition opposing nuclear testing that was signed by more than 11,000 scientists, a move that was credited with helping to persuade the U.S., the U.K., and the U.S.S.R. to initial the 1963 Nuclear Test-Ban Treaty. His pacifist views were echoed in his denunciation of the war in Vietnam, a stand for which he was widely criticized. He aroused controversy during the 1970s with his zealous advocacy of vitamin C, taken in large doses, as a cure for a variety of conditions, ranging from the common cold to cancer. His bold experimentation and courage in pursuing unorthodox ideas led him to discoveries in molecular biology, notably the identification of the genetic defect in the hemoglobin molecule that is the cause of sickle-cell anemia. He was at the forefront of efforts to unravel the structure of DNA, a feat ultimately accomplished by James Watson and Francis Crick. During his remarkable career Pauling was a member of the Center for the Study of Democratic Institutions in Santa Barbara, Calif., a faculty member of Stanford University, and director of research at the Linus Pauling Institute of Science and Medicine in Palo Alto, Calif.

Rich, Benjamin R.
June 18, 1925—Jan. 5, 1995

U.S. engineer Benjamin Rich conducted top-secret research on advanced military aircraft while working under the alias Ben Dover at Lockheed Aircraft Corp. Rich helped develop more than 25 airplanes, notably the F-117A "Stealth" fighter-bomber, which eluded detection on enemy radar screens and was responsible for damaging 40% of the Iraqi targets during the 1991 Persian Gulf War while flying only 1% of the U.S.-led air-strike attacks; the SR71 Blackbird, a reconnaissance craft that cruised at three times the speed of sound; and the U-2, the spy plane that flew successful missions over the Soviet Union from 1956 to 1960. After earning a B.A. (1949) and M.A. (1950) from the University of California, Rich joined Lockheed at its Burbank, Calif., "Skunk Works," so named both because of its location near a malodorous plastics factory and because it was a secret installation, much like the moonshine still of similar name portrayed in the "Li'l Abner" comic strip. In his 1994 autobiography Rich recounted that the technology for his crowning achievement, the Stealth fighter-bomber, virtually "fell into my lap" after a Soviet scientist openly published (1975) an idea that led to the technology for the Stealth. Rich, who retired in 1991 as president of Lock

Benjamin Rich helped develop more than 25 airplanes, including the F-117A "Stealth" fighter-bomber (above).

heed Advanced Development Co., was a member of the National Academy of Engineering from 1981 and the 1994 recipient of the Distinguished Service Medal, the highest U.S. military honor for a civilian.

Schwinger, Julian Seymour
Feb. 12, 1918—July 16, 1994

U.S. physicist Julian Schwinger was a brilliant theoretician whose studies helped define the basic principles of quantum electrodynamics, a theoretical description of the interaction of electrically charged particles with electromagnetic radiation; he shared the 1965 Nobel Prize for Physics (with Richard P. Feynman of the U.S. and Tomonaga Shin'ichiro of Japan) for this important work. A prodigy, Schwinger received (1939) a Ph.D. from Columbia University, New York City, at the age of 21 and began conducting research in the newly emerging field of nuclear physics under J. Robert Oppenheimer at the University of California, Berkeley. During World War II he helped develop radar at the Radiation Laboratory of the Massachusetts Institute of Technology. In 1945 he joined the faculty of Harvard University, where he began his work on quantum electrodynamics. His superb teaching methods were distinguished by scintillating lectures, and his mentorship of students resulted in dozens of them earning their Ph.D.'s under his guidance. From 1972 to 1980 he served as professor of physics at the University of California, Los Angeles, and from 1980 until his death he was university professor there. Among his other honors were the first Albert Einstein Prize in 1951 (with Kurt Gödel) and the National Medal of Science in 1964.

Sperry, Roger Wolcott
Aug. 20, 1913—April 17, 1994

U.S. neurobiologist Roger Sperry conducted fundamental studies on the left and right cerebral hemispheres of the brain and shared the 1981 Nobel Prize for Physiology or Medicine with David Hunter Hubel and Torsten Nils Wiesel for this work. Sperry was honored for uncovering the function of the corpus callosum, a thick bundle of nerve fibers that passes information between the brain's hemispheres. He earned a B.A. in literature and an M.A. in psychology from Oberlin (Ohio) College and a Ph.D. (1941) in zoology from the University of Chicago before serving as an associate of Karl Lashley, first at Harvard University in Cambridge, Mass., and then at the Yerkes Laboratories of Primate Biology in Orange Park, Fla. He then joined the University of Chicago faculty before spending the remainder of his career (1954–84) at the California Institute of Technology in Pasadena. Beginning in the late 1940s, Sperry developed experimental and surgical techniques that dismantled previously held notions about the function of the brain and helped formulate a "map" that detailed various mental processes. During the latter part of his career, Sperry, who was hailed as a brilliant experimentalist, became fascinated with the mind and turned to psychology. He developed a controversial theory of consciousness and was in the process of formulating a new science based on ethical values. It was for this work that he wished to be remembered. He was honored with the National Medal of Science in 1989 and was a member of the National Academy of Sciences.

Stibitz, George Robert
April 30, 1904—Jan. 31, 1995

U.S. mathematician George Stibitz was regarded by many as the "father of the modern digital computer." While serving as a research mathematician at Bell Telephone Laboratories in New York City, Stibitz worked on relay switching equipment used in telephone networks. Because he and his colleagues were unable to quickly perform the complex mathematical calculations needed for this work, Stibitz began tinkering at home and devised a primitive binary adder comprising dry-cell batteries, metal strips from a tobacco can, and flashlight bulbs connected to two old telephone relays. Stibitz and co-worker Samuel Williams, an engineer, expanded this desktop electrical device into the closet-size Model I Complex Calculator, which became operational at Bell Labs on Jan. 8, 1940. The machine remained in use until 1949 and was considered a forerunner of the digital computer. A replica of Stibitz' first rudimentary adder later was housed in the Smithsonian Institution, Washington, D.C. In 1940 Stibitz also achieved what was believed to have been the first remote computer operation when he transmitted problems to be solved over a teletypewriter from Dartmouth College, Hanover, N.H., to a Bell Labs Model I computer in New York City and received the answers back in the same way. After earning (1930) a Ph.D. in mathematical physics from Cornell University, Ithaca, N.Y., Stibitz joined Bell Labs, where he remained until 1941. During World War II he served on the U.S. National Defense Research Committee and also conducted research on increasingly powerful binary computers for military use. He then worked as a private consultant until joining (1964) the faculty of Dartmouth Medical School as professor of physiology. There he pioneered computer applications in such biomedical areas as the movement of oxygen in the lungs, renal exchange, brain-cell anatomy, the diffusion of nutrients and drugs in the body, and capillary transport. In 1973 he became professor emeritus, but he continued to conduct research at Dartmouth into the 1980s. Stibitz, who held 38 patents, was inducted into the Inventors Hall of Fame in 1983 and was elected to the National Academy of Engineering in 1981.

Synge, Richard Laurence Millington
Oct. 28, 1914—Aug. 18, 1994

British biochemist Richard Synge shared the 1952 Nobel Prize for Chemistry with Archer J.P. Martin for their work in the development of partition chromatography, a sophisticated analytic technique by means of which samples of a mixture of closely related chemicals such as amino acids can be separated for identification and further study. In his most important individual research, Synge determined the sequence of amino acids that make up the antibiotic gramicidin S. Synge studied classics at Winchester College and then switched to the natural sciences at Trinity College, Cambridge, where he earned a Ph.D. in 1941. He spent his entire professional career as an active researcher, first with Martin under the auspices of the Wool Industries Research Association, Leeds (1941–43), and later on his own at the Lister Institute of Preventive Medicine, London (1943–48), the Rowett Research Institute, near Aberdeen, Scotland (1948–67), and the Food Research Institute, Norwich, England (1967–76). He was also an honorary professor at the University of East Anglia (1968–84). Synge was elected a fellow of the Royal Society in 1950.

Tax, Sol
Oct. 30, 1907—Jan. 4, 1995

U.S. anthropologist Sol Tax was instrumental in establishing anthropology as a global discipline, especially as the founding editor (1957–74) of *Current Anthropology*, an international journal devoted to the exchange of ideas and discussion of important issues in the field. He was also an expert on the cultures of North and Middle American Indians, especially the Fox (Mesquakie) and Sauk. From 1948 to 1962 he served as director of the Fox Indian Project in Tama, Iowa, and he was coordinator of the 1961 American Indian Chicago Conference, at which some 700 Native Americans from more than 80 tribes drafted a "Declaration of Indian Purpose." The document urged the government to respect native customs and to include Native Americans in economic and social development projects. Tax received a Ph.D. (1935) from the University of Chicago and was an ethnologist (1934–48) for the Carnegie Institution in Washington, D.C. At the University of Chicago he served as a research associate (1940–44), associate professor (1944–48), and professor of anthropology from 1948 until his retirement in 1974. He was also department chairman (1955–58) and dean (1963–68) of the University Extension. Tax conducted anthropological studies in Guatemala, Mexico (training a number of anthropologists there) and in the U.S., where he established "action anthropology." This approach was meant to incorporate the work of anthropologists and involve them in solving the problems identified by the people they were studying. Tax was president of the American Anthropological Association (1958–59) and was the recipient in 1962 of the Viking Fund Medal and Award for his outstanding anthropological achievements. His writings include *Heritage of Conquest: The Ethnology of Middle America* (1952; with others), *Penny Capitalism: A Guatemalan Indian Economy* (1953), and contributions for Encyclopædia Britannica's *Yearbook of Science and the Future.*

Turnbull, Colin Macmillan
Nov. 23, 1924—July 28, 1994

British-born anthropologist Colin Turnbull conducted extensive field studies in Africa among the Mbuti Pygmies in the Belgian Congo (now Zaire) and the Ik hunters of northern Uganda and recorded his experiences in two best-selling books, *The Forest People* (1961) and *The Mountain People* (1972). Turnbull earned a B.A. (1947) and an M.A. (1949) from Magdalen College, Oxford, and received degrees from Oxford in social anthropology (1956), literature (1957), and anthropology (D.Phil., 1964). During World War II he served in the Royal Navy. Turnbull was employed (1959–69) as a curator of African ethnology at the American Museum of Natural History, New York City, and then taught anthropology at Hofstra University, Hempstead, N.Y. (1969–72), Virginia Commonwealth University (1972–75), and George Washington University, Washington, D.C. (1976 until his retirement in 1983). His anthropological field studies provided grist for such works as *The Lonely African* (1962); *Wayward Servants* (1965), another look at the Mbuti; *Tibet* (1968; with Thubten Jigme Norbu); *Man in Africa* (1976); and *The Human Cycle* (1983), which explored childhood to old age among various cultures. His classics, *The Forest People,* an uplifting account of the resourceful Ituri Forest Pygmies, and *The Mountain People,* an exceedingly grisly portrayal of the seemingly brutal customs of the starving Ik, secured his reputation. Turnbull spent the latter years of his life in Hawaii, Samoa, and India, where he became a Buddhist monk and adopted the name Lobsang Rigdol.

Wiesner, Jerome Bert
May 30, 1915—Oct. 21, 1994

U.S. scientist Jerome Wiesner exerted a powerful influence on U.S. science policy while serving on the President's Science Advisory Committee (1958–68) and as a special assistant for science and technology (1961–64) to Presidents John F. Kennedy and Lyndon B. Johnson. Wiesner was strongly opposed to the nuclear arms race, and he did much of the preliminary work on the 1963 Nuclear Test-Ban Treaty, which was first signed by the U.S., the U.S.S.R., and the U.K. and banned all tests of nuclear weapons except those conducted underground. (Within a few months of the initial signing, more than 100 governments had added the names of their nations to the treaty.) Wiesner, who earned a Ph.D. (1950) from the University of Michigan, was an expert on microwave theory and served on the staff of the Massachusetts Institute of Technology radiation laboratory (1942–45) and the University of California's Los Alamos, N.M., laboratory (1945–46) before returning to MIT. His tenure there was interrupted by government service, but when he returned to MIT he became dean of the School of Science. He was university provost (1966–71) before serving as MIT's president (1971–80) and fostering the application of science and technology to such problem-plagued fields as housing, health care, mass transportation, and urban blight. He was a member of both the National Academy of Sciences and the National Academy of Engineering. Wiesner remained active in disarmament issues. He was an early participant in the Pugwash conferences and was a founding member, along with Soviet dissident Andrey Sakharov, of the International Foundation for the Survival and Development of Humanity, which sought to raise funds for the study of global problems. Wiesner set forth his views about cutting U.S. military procurement and expenditures in the 1993 booklet, *Beyond the Looking Glass: The United States Military in 2000 and Later.*

Wigglesworth, Sir Vincent Brian
April 17, 1899—Feb. 12, 1994

British entomologist Sir Vincent Wigglesworth pioneered in the study of insect physiology; he was particularly respected for his research into the role of hormones in insect growth, metamorphosis, and reproduction and for his insights into simple mechanisms, such as the one by which insects walk upside down. Wigglesworth was educated at Gonville and Caius College, Cambridge. He received his medical qualification at St. Thomas' Hospital in London, but a research project into cockroaches (and later into other medically important insects) led him to change careers. Wigglesworth was lecturer in medical entomology at the London School of Hygiene and Tropical Medicine (1926–45), reader in entomology (1945–52) and later Quick professor of biology (1952–66) at Cambridge, and founding director of the Agricultural Research Council Unit of Insect Physiology (1943–67). He published some 300 papers and half a dozen books, most notably *Insect Physiology* (1934), *The Principles of Insect Physiology* (1939), *The Physiology of Insect Metamorphosis* (1954), and *Insect Hormones* (1970). He was elected to the Royal Society in 1939 and as a foreign associate of the U.S. National Academy of Sciences in 1971, made Commander of the Order of the British Empire in 1951, and knighted in 1964.

Wigner, Eugene Paul
Nov. 17, 1902—Jan. 1, 1995

Hungarian-born U.S. physicist Eugene Wigner was the joint winner of the 1963 Nobel Prize for Physics (with Maria Goeppert Mayer and Johannes Hans Jensen) for his insight into quantum mechanics, especially the principles governing the interaction of protons and neutrons in the nucleus. Wigner determined that the nuclear force that binds neutrons and protons together was necessarily short-range and independent of any electric charge. In his work Wigner used the abstract mathematical concept of group theory to investigate problems of atomic structure. Using this approach, he gathered information by focusing on the symmetries, rather than the dynamics, among subatomic particles in a physical system such as an atomic nucleus. He detailed this work in the classic book *Gruppentheorie und ihre Anwendung auf die Quantenmechanik der Atomspektren* (1931; *Group Theory*, 1959). Wigner was initially trained as an engineer and earned a Ph.D. (1925) in that field from the Berlin Institute of Technology. He immigrated to the U.S. in 1930 and began working part-time at Princeton University. In 1937 he became a U.S. citizen and a permanent faculty member at Princeton, where he remained until his retirement in 1971. When he perceived in 1939 that German scientists might be on the brink of achieving a nuclear chain reaction and thus the capability of developing nuclear weapons,

Wigner and fellow Hungarians Leo Szilard and Edward Teller persuaded Albert Einstein to write to Pres. Franklin D. Roosevelt and outline the potential threat. Einstein's historic letter was instrumental in launching the U.S. into the nuclear age and prompted Wigner to interrupt his career at Princeton, beginning in 1942, to help Enrico Fermi at the University of Chicago with work on the top-secret atomic bomb. There they explored the technology needed for nuclear reactors to produce plutonium for the first atomic bomb. After the war Wigner briefly served as director of research and development at the Clinton Laboratories (later Oak Ridge [Tenn.] National Laboratory). He later became a supporter of the Atoms for Peace movement. Among Wigner's other publications are *Dispersion Relations and Their Connection with Causality* (1964) and *Symmetries and Reflections* (1967). A member of the National Academy of Sciences, he was the recipient of numerous awards, including the Atoms for Peace Award (1960), the Max Planck Medal (1961), the Einstein Award (1972), and the Order of Merit (1994), Hungary's highest award, for scientific achievement.

Yegorov, Boris Borisovich
Nov. 26, 1937—Sept. 12, 1994

Russian physician Boris Yegorov participated in the first nonsolo spaceflight and was the first practicing physician to orbit the Earth in space. His flight was also the first in which the crew members did not wear space suits. Yegorov graduated (1961) from the First Moscow Medical Institute, where he specialized in aviation and space medicine. He then

worked in medical research institutions, studying medical telemetry data from Soviet missions, before beginning (1964) training for his flight. On Oct. 12–13, 1964—crowded with two other cosmonauts aboard Voskhod 1, a craft designed for one—Yegorov performed a number of tests on himself and the others during their 16 orbits. The information gained on the effects of radiation, confinement, and weightlessness helped scientists make advances in human adaptation to long journeys in space. After his flight he earned (1965) a doctor of medicine degree from Humboldt University in East Berlin and went on to serve as head of several medical research institutions. Yegorov received a number of his country's highest awards, including the Order of Lenin.

Russian physician Boris Yegorov in 1964 became the first practicing physician to orbit the Earth in a spacecraft.

Itar—Tass/Sovfoto

CONTRIBUTORS TO THE SCIENCE YEAR IN REVIEW

Paul Bradley Addis

Food and agriculture: Nutrition. Professor of Nutrition and Dietetics, and Food Science and Technology, University of Minnesota, St. Paul.

Michael Allaby

Environment (in part). Writer and Lecturer; author of *Ecology Facts: A Guide to Gaia,* Cornwall, England.

Harold Borko

Electronics and information sciences: Information systems and services. Professor Emeritus, Graduate School of Education and Library Studies, University of California, Los Angeles.

John M. Bowen

Medical sciences: Veterinary medicine. Associate Dean for Research and Graduate Affairs and Professor of Pharmacology and Toxicology, College of Veterinary Medicine, University of Georgia, Athens.

George G. Brown

Life sciences: Zoology. Professor of Zoology and Genetics, Iowa State University, Ames.

Paul J. Campbell

Mathematics. Professor of Mathematics and Computer Science, Beloit College, Beloit, Wis.

Robert Campbell

Architecture and civil engineering (in part). Architect and Architecture Critic. Author of *Cityscapes of Boston,* Cambridge, Mass.

David B. Collum

Chemistry: Organic chemistry. Professor of Chemistry, Cornell University, Ithaca, N.Y.

Douglas E. Comer

Electronics and information sciences: Computers and computer science (in part). Professor of Computer Science, Purdue University, West Lafayette, Ind.

Dave Dooling

Space exploration. D² Associates, Freelance Science Writing and Aerospace Consulting, Huntsville, Ala.

Carl B. Dover

Physics: Nuclear physics. Senior Scientist, Brookhaven National Laboratory, Upton, N.Y.

F.C. Durant III

Electronics and information sciences: Satellite systems (in part). Aerospace Historian and Consultant, Chevy Chase, Md.

R. Cargill Hall

Electronics and information sciences: Satellite systems (in part). Aerospace Historian, Center for Air Force History, Bolling Air Force Base, Washington, D.C.

Robert Haselkorn

Life sciences: Molecular biology. F.L. Pritzker Distinguished Service Professor, Department of Molecular Genetics and Cell Biology, University of Chicago.

Lawrence W. Jones

Physics: Elementary-particle physics. Professor of Physics, University of Michigan, Ann Arbor.

John Patrick Jordan

Food and agriculture: Agriculture (in part). Administrator, Cooperative State Research Service, U.S. Department of Agriculture, Washington, D.C.

Lou Joseph

Medical sciences: Dentistry. Science Writer, Des Plaines, Ill.

Ronald H. Kaitchuck

Astronomy. Associate Professor of Physics and Astronomy, Ball State University, Muncie, Ind.

George B. Kauffman

Chemistry: Applied chemistry. Professor of Chemistry, California State University, Fresno.

David B. Kitts

Earth sciences: Geology and geochemistry. Professor Emeritus of the History of Science, University of Oklahoma, Norman.

Stephen A. Kliment

Architecture and civil engineering (in part). Editor-in-Chief, *Architectural Record,* New York, N.Y.

Rebecca Kolberg

Medical sciences: General medicine. Managing Editor, *The NIH Catalyst,* Bethesda, Md.

Walter R.L. Lambrecht

Physics: Condensed-matter physics. Principal Researcher, Department of Physics, Case Western Reserve University, Cleveland, Ohio.

Patricia Brazeel Lewis

Food and agriculture: Agriculture (in part). Public Relations Consultant, New Jersey Agricultural Experiment Station, Rutgers University, New Brunswick, N.J.

Melvin H. Marx

Psychology (in part). Professor of Psychology, Western Carolina University, Cullowhee, N.C., and Professor Emeritus of Psychology, University of Missouri, Columbia.

Richard Monastersky
Earth sciences: Oceanography. Earth Science Editor, *Science News,* Washington, D.C.

Franz J. Monssen
Electronics and information sciences: Electronics. Instructor, Department of Electronic and Computer Engineering Technology, Queensborough Community College, New York, N.Y.

Charles S. Mueller
Earth sciences: Geophysics. Geophysicist, U.S. Geological Survey, Menlo Park, Calif.

Gerhardt Muller
Transportation. Manager, Freight Planning, Port Authority of New York and New Jersey, New York, N.Y.

Larry L. Naylor
Anthropology. Institute of Anthropology, University of North Texas, Denton.

Colin V. Newman
Psychology (in part). Executive Secretary, British Psychological Society, Leicester, England.

Joseph Palca
U.S. science policy. Science Correspondent, National Public Radio, Washington, D.C.

Roger A. Pielke
Earth sciences: Atmospheric sciences. Professor of Atmospheric Science, Colorado State University, Fort Collins.

John Rhea
Defense research. Freelance Science Writer, Woodstock, Va.

Robin K. Roy
Energy. Project Director, Office of Technology Assessment, Congress of the United States, Washington, D.C.

Frank B. Salisbury
Life sciences: Botany. Professor of Plant Physiology, Utah State University, Logan.

Robert R. Shannon
Optical engineering. Professor Emeritus and Past Director, Optical Sciences Center, University of Arizona, Tucson.

Melinda C. Shepherd
Electronics and information sciences: Computers and computer science (in part). Associate Editor, Encyclopædia Britannica Yearbooks, Chicago, Ill.

Lawrence J. Shimkets
Life sciences: Microbiology. Professor of Microbiology, University of Georgia, Athens.

Leslie Smith
Earth sciences: Hydrology. Professor of Geological Sciences, University of British Columbia, Vancouver.

Ben P. Stein
Physics: General developments. Science Writer, American Institute of Physics, College Park. Md.

Robert E. Stoffels
Electronics and information sciences: Communications systems. Telecommunications Consultant, Glen Ellyn, Ill.

Edward S. Warner
Electronics and information sciences: Computers and computer science (in part). Editor, *FCC Report,* Telecom Publishing Group, Washington, D.C.

Philip R. Watson
Chemistry: Inorganic and physical chemistry (in part). Professor of Chemistry, Oregon State University, Corvallis.

Kenneth E.F. Watt
Environment (in part). Professor of Ecology and Evolution, University of California, Davis.

James D. Wilde
Archaeology. Director, Office of Public Archaeology, Brigham Young University, Provo, Utah.

Michael Woods
Chemistry: Inorganic and physical chemistry (in part) and *Scientists of the Year: Nobel Prizes.* Science Editor, The *Toledo Blade,* Toledo, Ohio.

CONTRIBUTORS TO THE ENCYCLOPÆDIA BRITANNICA SCIENCE UPDATE

P.W. Atkins
Chemical Bonding. Fellow of Lincoln College, Oxford, and Lecturer in Physical Chemistry, University of Oxford, England.

H.C. Casey, Jr.
Electronics (in part). Professor and Chairman, Department of Electrical Engineering, Duke University, Durham, N.C.

Terry J. Scheffer
Electronics (in part). Chief Scientist, Motif Inc., Wilsonville, Ore.

INDEX

This is a three-year cumulative index. Index entries for review articles in this and previous editions of the *Yearbook of Science and the Future* are set in boldface type, *e.g.,* **Astronomy**. Feature articles appear under the article title and are identified as such. Entries to other subjects are set in lightface type, *e.g.,* radiation. Additional information on any of these subjects is identified with a subheading and indented under the entry heading. Subheadings in quotes refer to feature articles on that topic. The numbers following headings and subheadings indicate the year (boldface) of the edition and the page number (lightface) on which the information appears. The abbreviation "*il.*" indicates an illustration.

Astronomy 96–322; **95**–293; **94**–293
asteroids **96**–77
Big Science **94**–14
Max Planck Institute **96**–271

All entry headings are alphabetized word by word. Hyphenated words and words separated by dashes or slashes are treated as two words. When one word differs from another only by the presence of additional characters at the end, the shorter precedes the longer. In inverted names, the words following the comma are considered only after the preceding part of the name has been alphabetized. Names beginning with "Mc" and "Mac" are alphabetized as "Mac"; "St." is alphabetized as "Saint." Examples:

Lake
Lake, Simon
Lake Placid
Lakeland

A

A4 chip (microchip) **95**–484, *il.* 481
AAAS: *see* American Association for the Advancement of Science
ab initio quantum mechanical calculation: *see* first-principles quantum mechanical calculation
Abbe, Ernst **94**–106
ABE: *see* Autonomous Benthic Explorer
Aborigine (people)
anthropology **96**–312
abortion
fetal tissue transplantation **94**–429
genetic research **94**–387
RU-486 pill **96**–415
abscisic acid
botany **94**–394
absorption bands
asteroids **96**–82
abstraction
biomimetics **95**–182
AC: *see* alternating current
AC 114
extragalactic astronomy **94**–297, *il.* 298
AC induction motor, *or* AC asynchronous motor: *see* permanent magnet DC brushless motor
Acanthodactylus dumerili: *see* desert lizard
accident and safety
electric vehicles **95**–164
lecture guidelines **95**–235
transportation **96**–452
see also disaster
accretion disk
astronomy **94**–296
accumulator ring
antimatter **94**–38
ACE: *see* Advanced Computing Environment
ACE inhibitor: *see* angiotensin converting enzyme inhibitor
acetaminophen
warning labels **96**–417
acetic acid
wine **96**–187
acetogenesis **94**–364
Acheulean technology
anthropology **96**–311
acid deposition **95**–345
acid rain **96**–385
Acinonyx jubatus: *see* cheetah
acoustic cycle **94**–142
acoustic impedance
aerogels **96**–158
acoustics: *see* sound
acquired immune deficiency syndrome: *see* AIDS
actin **94**–364
active galaxy **95**–61
active-matrix liquid crystal display, *or* active-matrix LCD **94**–314
active oxygen species, *or* AOS
nutrition **95**–358

acute respiratory distress syndrome, *or* Four Corners disease **95**–387
ADA: *see* American Dental Association
ADAMHA (U.S.): *see* Alcohol, Drug Abuse, and Mental Health Administration
adenine
DNA repair **96**–399
adenosine triphosphate, *or* ATP
molecular biology **96**–402
Adleman, Leonard **96**–410
adobe
earthquake damage **94**–322
Adriano, Domy **94**–478
ADSL, *or* asymmetrical digital subscriber line (commu.) **95**–330
Advanced Communications Technology Satellite **94**–343
Advanced Electronics System, *or* ARES
automatic train control **94**–425
Advanced Mobile Phone Service, *or* AMPS **96**–361
Advanced Networks and Services, *or* ANS **94**–336
Advanced Research Projects Agency, *or* ARPA
defense research **96**–342; **95**–312
Internet **96**–34
Advanced Satellite for Cosmology and Astrophysics, *or* ASCA **95**–295
Advanced Technology Program, *or* ATP **94**–313
Advanced Traffic Management Systems **94**–180, *il.* 181
advanced train control system, *or* ATCS
railroad transport **95**–424
Advanced Traveler Information Systems **94**–183
Advanced Turbine Technology Applications Project, *or* ATTAP **94**–375
Advanced Vehicle Control Systems **94**–187
Advanced Weather Interactive Processing System **95**–315
AEC: *see* Atomic Energy Commission
Aedes albopictus: *see* Asian tiger mosquito
AEI: *see* Automatic Equipment-Identification System
aerogel **94**–310
"Aerogels: The Lightest Solids" **96**–146
aerosol **94**–316
Jupiter-comet collision **96**–98, *il.* 99
aerospace industry
defense research **94**–315
navigation satellites **94**–345
Africa
AIDS and tuberculosis **94**–383
cats **94**–167
El Niño effects **96**–358
environmental factors **94**–350
human origin **96**–310; **95**–283; **94**–284, *il.* 285
"Indigenous Science: A Star in Africa's Future?" **96**–160
molecular archaeology **94**–134
silver ants **94**–372
aftershock (geophys.) **95**–322; **94**–323

AFTI: *see* Automated Tariff Filing and Information System
aggregate (oceanography) **94**–329
aggression **94**–355
beauty-behavior study **96**–51
environment **95**–351
female masculinization **96**–228
aging **96**–103
glutathione treatment **95**–357
agriculture: *see* Food and agriculture
Agriculture, U.S. Department of, *or* USDA
food and agriculture **95**–355; **94**–358
veterinary medicine **95**–393
AIDS, *or* acquired immune deficiency syndrome
computer-aided drug design **94**–98, *il.*
cubanes **96**–331
dementia **95**–92
dentistry **95**–390
environment **94**–355
information systems **96**–370
medical microbiology **95**–365
medical research **96**–415; **95**–383; **94**–384
organic chemistry **95**–304
U.S. science policy **96**–461; **95**–427; **94**–429
AIDSLINE **96**–370
air pollution: *see* pollution
air pump **95**–223
air-traffic control: *see* aviation
air transport: *see* aviation
Airbus Industrie of France **94**–422
aircraft: *see* aviation
airport **94**–422
architecture **94**–292, *il.*
Airy disk **94**–113
Akashi Kaikyo (bridge, Japan) **96**–321
Akers, Thomas D. **95**–412; **94**–414
Alan Guttmacher Institute
AIDS research **94**–355
Alaska (state, U.S.)
botany **96**–394
oil spill **96**–380
Alcock, Charles **95**–296
alcogel
metal oxide aerogels **96**–150
alcohol
abuse
depression **95**–388
psychology **96**–441
manufacturing
aerogels **96**–149
wine production **96**–180
Alcohol, Drug Abuse, and Mental Health Administration, *or* ADAMHA (U.S.) **94**–429
ALERT, *or* Automated Local Evaluation in Real Time
flood forecasting **96**–356
algae **94**–363
coral degradation **96**–29, 403, *il.* 29
eukaryote discovery **96**–397
farm-raised catfish **95**–357
Lake Baikal **94**–217
see also individual genera and species by name
algal bloom, *or* water bloom **94**–363
Ali-Scout
traveler information system *il.* **94**–186
alien
"Imagining Aliens" **94**–68, *ils.* 69–85
"Alien" (motion picture) **94**–68
all-trans-retinoic acid **94**–368
allele
animal genome mapping **96**–387
allergy **94**–387
air pollution **96**–386
alloy **94**–379
Allseas Marine Services **94**–424
Almaz SAR **94**–344
"Alpha" (space station) **96**–447, *il.*
Alpha chip **94**–337
computers **96**–364; **94**–334
alpha/proton/X-ray spectrometer, *or* APX
Mars Pathfinder **96**–141
ALS: *see* amyotrophic lateral sclerosis
alternating current, *or* AC
locomotive traction **95**–424; **94**–426
aluminum
batteries **95**–309
corrosion resistance **95**–378
aluminum gallium arsenide **94**–408
aluminum nitride
light-emitting diodes **96**–438
Alvarex, Luis **96**–90
"Alvin" (submersible) **95**–11, *il.*; **94**–330
deep-sea research **96**–26
Alyea, Hubert Newcombe **95**–232, *il.*
Alzheimer's disease **96**–413; **95**–384; **94**–386
aging **96**–106
amalgam tooth filling
mercury contamination **95**–364
AMANDA, *or* Antarctic Muon and Neutrino Detector Array **96**–123, *il.* 120
Amazon River region (S.Am.)
indigenous peoples **94**–284

amber
DNA preservation **96**–396; **95**–360; **94**–370
Ambulocetus
whale evolution **96**–351
Ambystoma tigrinum neblosum: *see* tiger salamander
American Anthropological Association **96**–312; **94**–283
"American Anthropologist" (Am. journ.) **96**–312
archaeology **94**–286
American Association for the Advancement of Science, *or* AAAS
molecule of the year **94**–299
psychology **94**–411
American Bureau of Shipping
computerized standards **95**–425
American cactus: *see* prickly pear
American Center (Paris, Fr.)
architecture **96**–317, *il.*
American Chemical Society **96**–327; **95**–235; **94**–312
American chestnut, *or* Castanea dentata **95**–214; **94**–362
American College of Veterinary Behaviorists **95**–392
American Dental Association, *or* ADA **95**–389; **94**–389
American Flywheel Systems Inc. (Am. co.)
electronics **95**–338
American Heritage Center (Laramie, Wy., U.S.) **96**–319, *il.*
American Indian, *or* Native American
anthropology **96**–311; **95**–285
archaeology **94**–286
molecular archaeology **94**–126, 131
American Institute of Architects **94**–291
American literature
information systems and services **95**–341
American Mobile Satellite Corp. (Am. co.)
communications satellites **95**–342
American President Companies (Am. co.)
automatic equipment identification **95**–425
American Psychoanalytic Association **94**–413
American Psychological Association, *or* APA **95**–411; **94**–410
information systems and services **95**–340
American Railroads, Association of **94**–424
"American Scientist" (journ.) **94**–309
American Society of Civil Engineers **94**–293
American Telephone & Telegraph Company, *or* AT&T (Am. co.) **94**–331
high-definition television **94**–337
Magic Link **96**–363
satellites **96**–374
voice encryption **95**–336
see also AT&T Bell Laboratories
American Veterinary Medical Association, *or* AVMA **96**–420; **95**–392; **94**–392
American Veterinary Medical Law Association **95**–392
amino acid **95**–126, 366; **94**–89
bacterial prey attraction **96**–397
botany **96**–392
combinatorial synthesis **96**–333
protein synthesis **96**–340
ammonium ion
microbiology **96**–397
ammonium salts
applied chemistry **96**–337
amnesia **94**–413
Amonix Inc.
solar energy **96**–369
amorphous iron **94**–153
amorphous metal
sonochemistry **94**–153
AMP: *see* cyclic adenosine monophosphate
amphibian
decline **96**–355
Savannah River Ecology Laboratory **94**–483
amphioxus
vertebrate evolution **96**–405
amphipod
Lake Baikal **94**–218, *il.* 221
AMPS: *see* Advanced Mobile Phone Service
AMR Corp. (Am. co.)
automated shipping **94**–421
Amtrak **96**–320; **95**–423; **94**–425
rail subsidies **96**–383, *il.*
amyotrophic lateral sclerosis, *or* ALS **95**–384
analog microscope **94**–111
analog transmission, *or* analog scheme **94**–332
Anatomist
CD-ROM data bases **94**–340
anatomy **95**–224
female spotted hyena **96**–226, *il.* 231
"Anatomy Lesson of Dr. Nicolaes Tulp, The" (Rembrandt) **95**–224, *il.*
anchored instruction **95**–410
Andersen Bjornstad Kane Jacobs **94**–293
Anderson, Carl David **94**–33, *il.*
Andrew, Hurricane: *see* hurricane

ACKNOWLEDGMENTS

6
(Top) © Robert Frerck—Tony Stone Images; (center, left) © Norbert Wu; (center, right) © Lennart Nilsson; (bottom) © Don Dixon

7
(Top) Charles O'Rear—Westlight; (center, right) PAS/Y.Yoshii; (bottom, left) Thomas Eisner; (bottom, right) Wolfgang Filser

53
(Far right) Warner Bros./First National

58–59
From "Composite faces that represent six different composite sets," J.H. Langlois and L.A. Roggman, *Psychological Science*, vol. 1 (1990), pp. 117–121; reprinted with permission of Cambridge University Press

74
(Top) adapted from "The ins and outs of programmed cell death during *C. elegans* development," M.O. Hengartner and H.R. Horvitz, *Philosophical Transactions of the Royal Society of London Series B*, vol. 345 (1994), pp. 243–246, © The Royal Society; (bottom) photos from "*Caenorhabditis elegans* gene ced-9 protects cells from programmed cell death," M.O. Hengartner, R.E. Ellis, and H.R. Horvitz, reprinted by permission of *Nature*, vol. 6369, no. 356, pp. 494–499, April 9, 1992, © Macmillan Magazines Ltd.

94–95
Reprinted with permission from "Shape of Asteroid 4769 Castalia (1989PB) from Inversion of Radar Images," R.S. Hudson and S.J. Ostro, *Science*, vol. 263, no. 5149, pp. 940–943, February 18, 1994, ©AAAS

133
Adapted from information obtained from NASA

180
(Top) original tempera facsimile painting by Nina M. Davies; photo, Jean M. Grant

188
Wine aroma wheel adapted from A.C. Noble *et al.*, *The American Journal of Enology and Viticulture*, vol. 38 (1987), pp. 143–146, reprinted by permission

304
(Top) illustration by Mick Ellison (trans. no. K17089), courtesy Department Library Services, American Museum of Natural History, N.Y.

318
(Bottom) courtesy of the Cartier Foundation, Paris

332
(Top) photos from "Fullerenes in an impact crater on the LDEF spacecraft," F. Radicati di Brozolo, T.E. Bunch, R.H. Fleming, and J. Macklin, reprinted by permission of *Nature*, vol. 369, no. 6475, pp. 37–40, May 5, 1994, © Macmillan Magazines Ltd.

359
From "Importance of iron for plankton blooms and carbon dioxide drawdown in the Southern Ocean," H.H.W. de Baar, J.T.M. de Jong, D.C.E. Bakker, B.M. Loscher, C. Veth, U. Bathmann, and V. Smetacek, reprinted by permission of *Nature*, vol. 373, no. 6513, pp. 412–415, February 2, 1995, © Macmillan Magazines Ltd.

402
Adapted from "The crystal structure of the bacterial chaperonin GroEL at 2.8Å," K. Braig, Z. Otwinowski, R. Hegde, D.C. Boisvert, A. Joachimiak, A. Horwich, and P. Sigler, reprinted by permission of *Nature*, vol. 371, no. 6498, pp. 578–586, October 13, 1994, © Macmillan Magazines Ltd.

403
Reprinted with permission from "Catastrophes, Phase Shifts, and Large–Scale Degradation of a Caribbean Coral Reef," T.P. Hughes, *Science*, vol. 265, no. 5178, pp. 1547–1551, September 9, 1994, ©AAAS

424–425
By courtesy of the University of Texas at Austin, Pennsylvania State University, Stanford University, Ludwig Maximilian University, Munich, and Georg–August University, Göttingen

430
Reprinted with permission from "Relaxation of a Single DNA Molecule Observed by Optical Microscopy," T.T. Perkins, S.R. Quake, D.E. Smith, and S. Chu, *Science*, vol. 264, no. 5160, pp. 822–826, May 6, 1994, ©AAAS

439
Reprinted with permission from "A 160–Femtosecond Optical Image Processor Based on a Conjugated Polymer," C. Halvorson, A. Hays, B. Kraabel, R. Wu, F. Wudl, A.J. Heeger, *Science*, vol. 265, no. 5176, pp. 1215–1216, August 26, 1994, ©AAAS